PERIODIC TABLE OF THE ELEMENTS

1A	2A	3B	4B	5B	6B	7B	8B	8B	8B	1B	2B	3A	4A	5A	6A	7A	8A
1	2	3	4	5	6	7	8	9	10	11	12	13	14	15	16	17	18
1 H 1.008																	2 He 4.003
3 Li 6.941	4 Be 9.012											5 B 10.81	6 C 12.01	7 N 14.01	8 O 16.00	9 F 19.00	10 Ne 20.18
11 Na 22.99	12 Mg 24.31											13 Al 26.98	14 Si 28.09	15 P 30.97	16 S 32.07	17 Cl 35.45	18 Ar 39.95
19 K 39.10	20 Ca 40.08	21 Sc 44.96	22 Ti 47.87	23 V 50.94	24 Cr 52.00	25 Mn 54.94	26 Fe 55.85	27 Co 58.93	28 Ni 58.69	29 Cu 63.55	30 Zn 65.39	31 Ga 69.72	32 Ge 72.61	33 As 74.92	34 Se 78.96	35 Br 79.90	36 Kr 83.80
37 Rb 85.47	38 Sr 87.62	39 Y 88.91	40 Zr 91.22	41 Nb 92.91	42 Mo 95.94	43 Tc (98)	44 Ru 101.07	45 Rh 102.91	46 Pd 106.42	47 Ag 107.87	48 Cd 112.41	49 In 114.82	50 Sn 118.71	51 Sb 121.76	52 Te 127.60	53 I 126.90	54 Xe 131.29
55 Cs 132.91	56 Ba 137.33	57 La 138.91	72 Hf 178.49	73 Ta 180.95	74 W 183.84	75 Re 186.21	76 Os 190.23	77 Ir 192.22	78 Pt 195.08	79 Au 196.97	80 Hg 200.59	81 Tl 204.38	82 Pb 207.19	83 Bi 208.98	84 Po (209)	85 At (210)	86 Rn (222)
87 Fr (22)	88 Ra (2)	89 Ac (27)	104 Rf (267)	105 Db (268)	106 Sg (271)	107 Bh (270)	108 Hs (277)	109 Mt (278)	110 Ds (281)	111 Rg (281)	112 Cn (285)	113 Aug 2003 (286)	114 Dec 1998 (289)	115 Feb 2004 (289)	116 Jun 1999 (293)	117 Apr 2010 (294)	118 Oct 2006 (294)

58 Ce 140.12	59 Pr 140.91	60 Nd 144.24	61 Pm (145)	62 Sm 150.36	63 Eu 151.96	64 Gd 157.25	65 Tb 158.93	66 Dy 162.50	67 Ho 164.93	68 Er 167.26	69 Tm 168.93	70 Yb 173.04	71 Lu 174.97
90 Th 232.04	91 Pa 231.04	92 U 238.03	93 Np (237)	94 Pu (244)	95 Am (243)	96 Cm (247)	97 Bk (247)	98 Cf (251)	99 Es (252)	100 Fm (257)	101 Md (258)	102 No (259)	103 Lr (262)

For e
those
in par
numbe
mass)
the onl

Alphabetical List of the Elements

Element	Symbol	Atomic number	Atomic mass	Element	Symbol	Atomic number	Atomic mass
Actinium	Ac	89	(227)	Meitnerium	Mt	109	(278)
Aluminum	Al	13	26.982	Mendelevium	Md	101	(258)
Americium	Am	95	(243)	Mercury	Hg	80	200.592
Antimony	Sb	51	121.760	Molybdenum	Mo	42	95.942
Argon	Ar	18	39.948	Neodymium	Nd	60	144.242
Arsenic	As	33	74.922	Neon	Ne	10	20.180
Astatine	At	85	(210)	Neptunium	Np	93	(237)
Barium	Ba	56	137.327	Nickel	Ni	28	58.693
Berkelium	Bk	97	(247)	Niobium	Nb	41	92.906
Beryllium	Be	4	9.012	Nitrogen	N	7	14.007
Bismuth	Bi	83	208.980	Nobelium	No	102	(259)
Bohrium	Bh	107	(270)	Osmium	Os	76	190.233
Boron	B	5	10.811	Oxygen	O	8	15.999
Bromine	Br	35	79.904	Palladium	Pd	46	106.421
Cadmium	Cd	48	112.411	Phosphorus	P	15	30.974
Calcium	Ca	20	40.078	Platinum	Pt	78	195.078
Californium	Cf	98	(251)	Plutonium	Pu	94	(244)
Carbon	C	6	12.011	Polonium	Po	84	(209)
Cerium	Ce	58	140.116	Potassium	K	19	39.098
Cesium	Cs	55	132.905	Praseodymium	Pr	59	140.908
Chlorine	Cl	17	35.453	Promethium	Pm	61	(145)
Chromium	Cr	24	51.996	Protactinium	Pa	91	231.036
Cobalt	Co	27	58.933	Radium	Ra	88	(226)
Copernicium	Cn	112	(285)	Radon	Rn	86	(222)
Copper	Cu	29	63.546	Rhenium	Re	75	186.207
Curium	Cm	96	(247)	Rhodium	Rh	45	102.906
Darmstadtium	Ds	110	(281)	Roentgenium	Rg	111	(281)
Dubnium	Db	105	(268)	Rubidium	Rb	37	85.468
Dysprosium	Dy	66	162.500	Ruthenium	Ru	44	101.072
Einsteinium	Es	99	(252)	Rutherfordium	Rf	104	(267)
Erbium	Er	68	167.269	Samarium	Sm	62	150.362
Europium	Eu	63	151.964	Scandium	Sc	21	44.956
Fermium	Fm	100	(257)	Seaborgium	Sg	106	(271)
Fluorine	F	9	18.998	Selenium	Se	34	78.963
Francium	Fr	87	(223)	Silicon	Si	14	28.086
Gadolinium	Gd	64	157.253	Silver	Ag	47	107.868
Gallium	Ga	31	69.723	Sodium	Na	11	22.990
Germanium	Ge	32	72.641	Strontium	Sr	38	87.621
Gold	Au	79	196.967	Sulfur	S	16	32.065
Hafnium	Hf	72	178.492	Tantalum	Ta	73	180.948
Hassium	Hs	108	(277)	Technetium	Tc	43	(98)
Helium	He	2	4.003	Tellurium	Te	52	127.603
Holmium	Ho	67	164.930	Terbium	Tb	65	158.925
Hydrogen	H	1	1.008	Thallium	Tl	81	204.383
Indium	In	49	114.818	Thorium	Th	90	232.038
Iodine	I	53	126.904	Thulium	Tm	69	168.934
Iridium	Ir	77	192.217	Tin	Sn	50	118.710
Iron	Fe	26	55.845	Titanium	Ti	22	47.867
Krypton	Kr	36	83.798	Tungsten	W	74	183.841
Lanthanum	La	57	138.906	Uranium	U	92	238.029
Lawrencium	Lr	103	(262)	Vanadium	V	23	50.942
Lead	Pb	82	207.19	Xenon	Xe	54	131.293
Lithium	Li	3	6.941	Ytterbium	Yb	70	173.043
Lutetium	Lu	71	174.967	Yttrium	Y	39	88.906
Magnesium	Mg	12	24.305	Zinc	Zn	30	65.409
Manganese	Mn	25	54.938	Zirconium	Zr	40	91.224

CHEMISTRY

VOLUME II

PAUL W. W. HUNTER & AMY M. POLLOCK

BOSTON   BURR RIDGE, IL   DUBUQUE, IA   NEW YORK   SAN FRANCISCO   ST. LOUIS
BANGKOK   BOGOTÁ   CARACAS   LISBON   LONDON   MADRID
MEXICO CITY   MILAN   NEW DELHI   SEOUL   SINGAPORE   SYDNEY   TAIPEI   TORONTO

CHEMISTRY
Volume II

6 7 8 9 10 11   QVS/QVS   22 21 20 19 18

ISBN-13: 978-0-07-804230-0
ISBN-10: 0-07-804230-5

Learning Solutions Consultant: Christy Rybak
Production Editor: Lynn Nagel
Printer/Binder: Quad/Graphics
Cover Photo Credits: Flourite © 2012 JupiterImages Corporation
Inside Covers: Periodic Table and List of Elements © Paul Hunter

Interior Photo Credits
Figure 51.10: © The McGraw-Hill Companies, Inc. /Stephen Frisch, photographer; 53.3: © Gary Retherford / Photo Researchers, Inc.; 53.4: © The McGraw-Hill Companies, Inc. / Steven Frisch, photographer; 54.5: © David A. Tietz/Editorial Image, LLC ; 54.8: © The McGraw-Hill Companies, Inc./Charles D. Winters, photographer; 54.20: © The McGraw-Hill Companies, Inc./Bob Coyle, photographer ; 54.23: © John Cancalosi / Peter Arnold / Getty Images; 56.1: © The McGraw-Hill Companies, Inc. / Doug Sherman, photographer; 56.4: © The McGraw-Hill Companies, Inc. / Steven Frisch, photographer; 56.8: © The McGraw-Hill Companies, Inc. / Ken Karp, photographer; 57.9: Courtesy of NASA Headquarters - GReatest Images of NASA (NASA-HQ-GRIN); 57.11: Neil Bartlett, 1962; 57.12: © Ed Degginger/Color-Pic; 58.1: © Peter Ryan/Photo Researchers; 58.5i: © RF Company/Alamy; 58.11: © Nick Koudis/Stockbyte; 59.1: © McGraw-Hill Higher Education Inc./Ken Karp, Photographer; 59.14: © Richard Megna /Fundamental Photographs; 59.17: © Jackie George, Beverly Sinclair/photo by Janice Haney Carr; 61.5: © Steve Allen/Brand X Pictures; 61.6: © Business Wire / Handout / Getty Images; 61.7: © Pascal Boegli / Getty Images; 62.5: Photo courtesy of National Nuclear Security Administration/Nevada Site Office/DOE; 62.6: © Royalty-Free/CORBIS; 62.8: © Monty Rakusen / Getty Images; 62.10: © Dr. Robert Friedland/SPL/Photo Researchers Inc.; 65.13: © McGraw-Hill Companies, Inc. / Charles D. Winters, photographer; 65.27: © Tracy Montana/PhotoLink/Getty Images

CONTENTS

Chemistry of the Main Group Elements

Chemistry of the Tranisition Elements

Nuclear Chemistry

Organic Chemistry and Biochemistry

How Fast Do Reactions Go?

36.1 How Fast Do Reactions Go?

When light enters the eye, a reaction occurs in the retina that is extremely fast. The rods and cones of the retina contain a light-sensitive molecule called rhodopsin. Rhodopsin is a compound of *cis*-retinal and a protein called opsin (Figure 36.1). The retinal is anchored to the opsin through the aldehyde (–CHO) group at the end of the molecule. When a photon hits the rhodopsin, the retinal changes from the *cis*-isomer to the *trans*-isomer—a structural change called isomerization. This makes the compound unstable and the rhodopsin breaks down. This chemical change causes electrical impulses that travel through the optic nerve to the brain where, with all the other impulses received, it is interpreted as an image. As you know from experience, the entire process is almost instantaneous.

As described above, some reactions occur almost instantaneously. Acid–base titrations that you have done in the laboratory also occur extremely rapidly. In an acid-base reaction, the hydronium ions of the acid and the hydroxide ions of the base react to form water as soon as the solutions are mixed.

Other reactions take place much more slowly. The biodegradation of a discarded plastic container takes years to accomplish. Some reactions take place so slowly that the rate of the reaction is imperceptible. The transformation of diamond into graphite is spontaneous but the process is so slow that diamonds really do last forever.

The conditions under which a reaction takes place have an effect upon the rate of the reaction. For example, the oxidation of iron in a dry environment takes a long time but in a warm humid environment the reaction occurs quite rapidly. Hydrogen and oxygen can exist together indefinitely at room temperature but provide a spark or a flame and the reaction to form water occurs at an explosive rate.

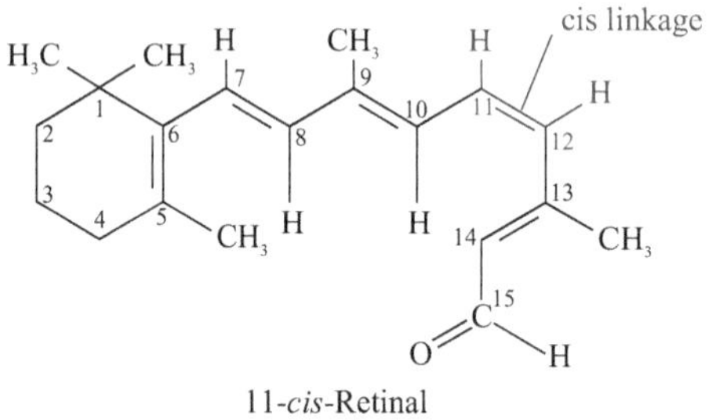

The rhodopsin in the rods are sensitive to all light, including dim light. In the cones the opsin proteins are slightly different and the wavelength of the light absorbed is different. The cones can therefore distinguish the different colors red, blue and green, but only in reasonably bright light. You may have noticed that your eyes cannot distinguish colors in dim light.

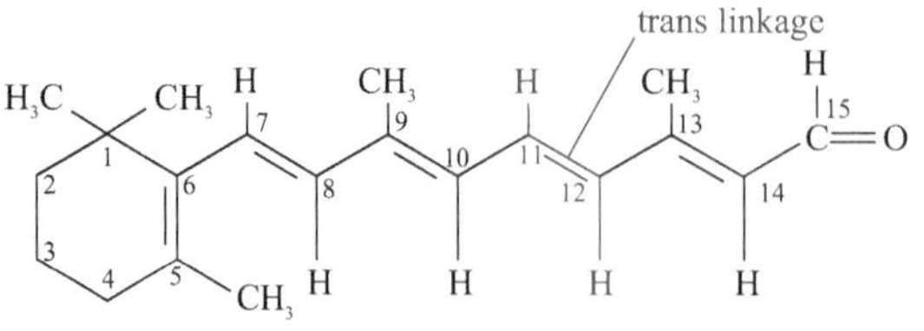

FIGURE 36.1 The structures of 11-*cis*-retinal and 11-*trans*-retinal.
When light hits rhodopsin, the *cis*- isomer is converted into the *trans*- isomer. The *trans*-isomer then breaks away from the opsin protein and is slowly converted back to the *cis*-isomer. It then reattaches to the opsin protein. The regeneration of the rhodopsin complex is relatively slow and causes temporary blindness when a bright light is shone into the eyes. The bright light exhausts all the available rhodopsin.

The rates of some reactions are greatly influenced by the presence of a **catalyst**. This is particularly significant in biological reactions where catalysts are called **enzymes**. Enzymes are large protein molecules with a structure specifically suited for a particular reaction, many of which could not otherwise take place effectively. It is often the task of an industrial research chemist to find a suitable catalyst for a reaction so that the desired product can be made more rapidly under less extreme and energy-intensive conditions.

In this unit, we will revisit the subject of chemical kinetics—the rates and mechanisms of chemical reactions. We have already learned in Unit 34 some of the reasons why the rates of chemical reactions differ. We'll now investigate the subject in more detail.

36.2 The Rates of Reactions

The rate of a chemical reaction can be affected by several factors, including:

- The concentrations of the reactant molecules.
- The temperature at which the reaction occurs.
- The presence of a catalyst.
- The extent to which the reactant molecules are in contact.

In this unit we will examine the dependence of the reaction rate upon the concentrations of the reactants. In Unit 37 we will examine the effect of temperature and investigate the mechanisms of reactions—how a reaction actually takes place.

The rate, or speed, of a reaction is the rate at which the product is formed or the rate at which the reactant is used up. The relationship between the two is defined by the stoichiometry of the reaction. Consider, for example, the reaction of nitrous oxide with oxygen to form nitrogen dioxide:

$$2\,N_2O + 3\,O_2 \rightarrow 4\,NO_2$$

The rate of the reaction could be expressed as the change in the concentration of the product, NO_2, per unit of time:

$$\text{Rate} = \frac{\Delta[NO_2]}{\Delta t} \qquad \text{where the } \Delta \text{ symbol represents the change.}$$

Recall that the square brackets indicate concentration. For example, $[NO_2]$ represents the concentration of NO_2.

The rate, however, could equally well be expressed as the rate of change in the concentration of the reactant N_2O:

$$\text{Rate} = -\frac{\Delta[N_2O]}{\Delta t} \qquad \text{where the negative sign ensures that the rate is expressed as a positive number because as the reaction happens, the } [N_2O] \text{ will decrease.}$$

The rate can also be expressed as the rate of change in the concentration of the reactant O_2:

$$\text{Rate} = -\frac{\Delta[O_2]}{\Delta t}$$

Are these rates equal? No, the O_2 is used at a rate 1.5 times faster than the N_2O—three moles of O_2 are used for every two moles of N_2O. The rate at which the NO_2 is formed is twice the rate at which the N_2O is used—four moles of NO_2 are formed for every two moles of N_2O used. These relationships are evident in the stoichiometry of the reaction illustrated in the equation above. Because these rates differ, it is common practice to express the rate of the reaction as a **normalized rate**, in which case the rates are all equal and the rate of the reaction is unambiguous—the result is the same regardless of which reaction component is chosen. The normalized rate is obtained by dividing each rate by the corresponding coefficient in the equation:

$$\text{Rate of reaction} = -(1/2)\Delta[N_2O]/\Delta t = -(1/3)\Delta[NO_2]/\Delta t = (1/4)\Delta[NO_2]/\Delta t$$

The rate of the reaction can now be expressed equally in terms of any reactant or product and the rate is always positive.

EXAMPLE 36.1   RELATIVE CHANGES IN THE CONCENTRATIONS OF REACTANTS AND PRODUCTS

Determine the relationships between the rate of formation of the products and the rate of disappearance of the reactants in the following reactions and express the rate of the reaction as a normalized rate.

a. $N_2 + 3H_2 \rightarrow 2NH_3$

b. $2NOCl \rightarrow 2NO + Cl_2$

UNDERSTAND THE QUESTION

The relative rates at which the reactants are used and the products are formed is determined by the stoichiometry of the reaction. This is indicated by the coefficients in the balanced equation for the reaction. The normalized rate is obtained by dividing the rate by the corresponding stoichiometric coefficient.

PLAN THE SOLUTION

Examine the stoichiometric ratios indicated in the balanced equation and therefore determine the relative rates at which the concentrations change.

SOLVE THE PROBLEM

a. Hydrogen H_2 is used at a rate three times that of nitrogen N_2—the stoichiometric ratio is 3:1. The ammonia is formed at a rate twice the rate at which the nitrogen is used.

The reaction rate = $-\Delta[N_2]/\Delta t = -(1/3)\Delta[H_2]/\Delta t = (1/2)\Delta[NH_3]/\Delta t$

b. Nitrosyl chloride NOCl is used at a rate equal to the rate at which nitric oxide NO is formed—the stoichiometric coefficients are the same. This rate is twice the rate at which chlorine Cl_2 is formed.

The reaction rate = $-(1/2)\Delta[NOCl]/\Delta t = (1/2)\Delta[NO]/\Delta t = \Delta[Cl_2]/\Delta t$

PROBLEM 36.1A

Determine the relationships between the rate of formation of the products and the rate of disappearance of the reactants in the following reaction. Determine the (normalized) rate of the reaction.

$$3SCl_2 + 4NaF \rightarrow SF_4 + S_2Cl_2 + 4NaCl$$

If, at one point in the reaction, the rate of appearance of NaCl is 6.0 M min^{-1}, what is the rate at which SCl_2 is used and what is the rate of the reaction at this point?

PROBLEM 36.1B

Determine the relationships between the rate of formation of the products and the rate of disappearance of the reactants in the following reactions. Determine the (normalized) rate of the reaction.

$$2 \text{ Ir} + 5 \text{ XeF}_2 \rightarrow 2 \text{ IrF}_5 + 5 \text{ Xe}$$

As we learned in Unit 34, the rate of the reaction may change as time progresses because the reactants are used up in the reaction and their concentrations decrease. The changes in the concentrations of the reactants and products in the reaction described earlier can be plotted on a diagram such as that illustrated in Figure 36.2.

The rate of the change in the concentration of any reactant or product at any stage in the reaction can be obtained by calculating the slope of the tangent to the curve at that point. This rate is called the **instantaneous rate** of the reaction at that point. In Figure 36.2, the slopes of the tangents at time t are in the ratio 4:3:2 as expected from the stoichiometry of the reaction. The instantaneous rate at the beginning of a reaction is called the **initial rate** of the reaction.

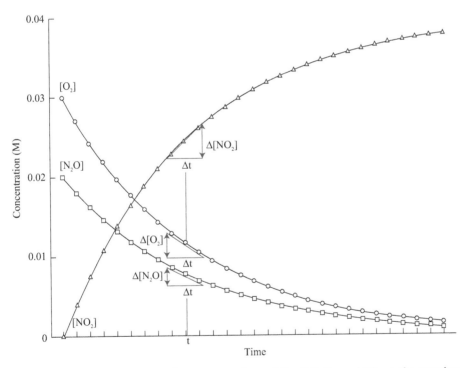

FIGURE 36.2   The changes in the concentrations of the N_2O, O_2, and NO_2 as the reaction proceeds.
The reaction starts with a 2:3 mole ratio of nitrous oxide and oxygen. As the reaction proceeds, the concentration of the product NO_2 increases at twice the rate at which the concentration of the reactant N_2O decreases. The concentrations of the two reactants decrease at rates proportional to their stoichiometric coefficients in the balanced equation.

36.3 The Rate Law

As a system reaches equilibrium, the rate of the reaction in the reverse direction becomes equal to the rate of the reaction in the forward direction. At equilibrium there is no net change in the composition of the reaction mixture. In other words, the net rate of the reaction is zero.

At equilibrium: Rate in forward direction = rate in reverse direction

Net rate of reaction = zero

In order to determine experimentally the dependence of the forward rate upon the concentrations of the reactant molecules, it is useful to measure the dependence at the beginning of the reaction, where appreciable products have not yet been formed and the rate of the reverse reaction is negligible.

The dependence of the rate of reaction in the forward direction (the net rate at the beginning of the reaction) upon the concentrations of the reactants is expressed by a **rate law** (often called the **rate equation**):

Rate = $k[A]^m[B]^n$...   where k is the **rate constant** and A and B are the reactants

The exponents m and n in the rate law are called the **reaction orders**. The exponent m is called the reaction order with respect to A and the exponent n is called the reaction order with respect to B. The sum of the exponents m and n is called the **overall order** of the reaction.

> Note that the rate 'constant' does depend upon the temperature—we'll examine this dependence in the next unit.
>
> Usually the reaction orders are whole numbers (0, 1, 2, etc.) but they can be negative or fractional.

It is important to note that the reaction orders bear no relation to the coefficients in the balanced chemical equation for the reaction. This is because the rate of a reaction is determined by the mechanism of the reaction and this is often a series of individual steps. The chemical equation merely summarizes the overall process. The rate law must be determined experimentally and cannot be derived from the chemical equation. The experimental determination of the rate law is often the first step in deducing the mechanism for the reaction—the series of steps that makes up the reaction process. We will investigate this process further in the next unit.

The determination of the dependence of the rate of a reaction on the concentrations of the reactants at the beginning of a reaction is referred to as the **method of initial rates**. Let's look at an example using this method.

EXAMPLE 36.2   METHOD OF INITIAL RATES

At high temperatures, hydrogen iodide decomposes to hydrogen and iodine according to the equation:

$$2\,HI(g) \rightarrow H_2(g) + I_2(g)$$

The initial rate of the reaction was determined using different initial concentrations of HI(g) and the results were as follows:

Experiment	Initial [HI(g)] (M)	Rate of disappearance of HI (M s^{-1})
1	0.0040	6.0×10^{-4}
2	0.0080	2.4×10^{-3}
3	0.0240	2.2×10^{-2}

a. Determine the order of the reaction with respect to HI.

b. Write the rate law.

c. What is the value of the rate constant k?

d. What would the initial rate be if the initial concentration of HI(g) was 0.0160 M?

UNDERSTAND THE QUESTION

The rate of a reaction usually depends upon the concentration of a reactant. A comparison of the rates of a reaction at two different initial concentrations of a reactant, all other variables being the same, allows us to determine the dependence of the rate upon that reactant.

PLAN THE SOLUTION

Choose any two experiments. It makes sense to choose two for which there is an obvious relationship. For example in Experiments 1 and 2, the concentration of HI doubles. Then examine the difference in the rate of the reaction for these two experiments. If the change in the rate is not equally obvious, write rate equations for the two experiments:

$$\text{Rate}_1 = k[HI]_1^n$$

$$\text{Rate}_2 = k[HI]_2^n$$

The task is to determine the exponent n—the order of reaction with respect to HI. Substitute the data in the two rate equations and divide one by the other.

$$\text{Rate}_2/\text{Rate}_1 = [HI]_2^n/[HI]_1^n = ([HI]_2/[HI]_1)^n$$ —the rate constant k cancels.

The procedure can sometimes be made easier by taking the logarithm of both sides:

$$\log(\text{Rate}_2/\text{Rate}_1) = n \log([HI]_2/[HI]_1)$$

Logarithms to the base 10 or natural logarithms can be used, but be consistent. Recall that $\log(x^n) = n(\log x)$.

Now n can be determined.

The value of the rate constant k can be determined by substituting the data for any one of the experiments into the rate equation. Once k is known the rate for any initial concentration of HI can be calculated.

SOLVE THE PROBLEM

a. For Experiments 1 and 2:

$$6.0 \times 10^{-4} = k(0.0040)$$

$$2.4 \times 10^{-3} = k(0.0080)$$

The rate increases four times when the concentration of HI doubles. In other words:

$$\text{Rate} = [HI]^n$$

$$4 = 2^n$$

In this case n must equal 2 (since $2^2 = 4$).

Use of the logarithmic relationship is unnecessary in this case. However, sometimes the relationship between the change in the rate and the change in the concentration is not so obvious (for example, the order may be fractional) and the logarithmic relationship is useful. The calculation proceeds as follows:

$$\log(2.4 \times 10^{-3}/6.0 \times 10^{-4}) = n \log(0.0080/0.0040)$$

$$\log 4 = n \log 2$$

$$n = \log 4 / \log 2 = 0.60/0.30 = 2$$

This reaction is second order with respect to HI and second order overall.

b. The rate equation is Rate = $k[HI]^2$

This rate equation can be confirmed by repeating the calculation for another pair of experiments.

c. The value of the rate constant k is determined by substituting the data for any one of the experiments into the rate equation. For example, using the data for Experiment 1:

Rate = $k[HI]^2$

6.0×10^{-4} M s^{-1} = k × $(0.0040$ M$)^2$

k = $6.0 \times 10^{-4}/(0.0040)^2$ M^{-1}s^{-1} = 37.5 M^{-1}s^{-1}

d. Now the rate for an initial concentration [HI] = 0.0160 M can be calculated:

Rate = $k[HI]^2$

Rate = 37.5 M^{-1}s^{-1} × $(0.0160$ M$)^2$ = 9.6×10^{-3} M s^{-1}

We expect the rate to be between the rates for Experiments 2 and 3 because the initial concentration of HI falls between the initial concentrations for Experiments 2 and 3.

PROBLEM 36.2A

The reaction of nitrogen dioxide and carbon monoxide at high temperatures and pressures produces nitric oxide and carbon dioxide according to the equation:

$$NO_2(g) + CO(g) \rightarrow NO(g) + CO_2(g)$$

The initial rate of the reaction was determined using different initial concentrations of the reactants and the results were:

Experiment	Initial $[NO_2(g)]$ (mol L^{-1})	Initial $[CO(g)]$ (mol L^{-1})	Rate of appearance of $CO_2(g)$ (mol L^{-1}s^{-1})
1	0.30	0.20	0.020
2	0.90	0.20	0.180
3	0.60	0.30	0.080

a. Determine the order of the reaction with respect to each reactant and the overall order of the reaction.

b. Write the rate law.

c. What is the value of the rate constant k?

PROBLEM 36.2B

In 1828, Friedrich Wohler heated ammonium cyanate NH_4CNO and produced urea NH_2CONH_2. The urea was identical to the urea from the urine of animals—a fact that helped to destroy the idea of 'vitalism' (*cf.* Unit 4). The decomposition of ammonium cyanate in warm water was investigated using two different initial concentrations of ammonium cyanate:

Experiment	Initial $[NH_4CNO(aq)]$ (M)	Rate of appearance of $NH_2CONH_2(aq)$ (M s^{-1})
1	0.250	0.162
2	0.500	0.651

a. Determine the order of the reaction with respect to ammonium cyanate.

b. Write the rate law.

c. What is the value of the rate constant k?

d. What would the rate be if the initial concentration of $NH_4CNO(aq)$ was 1.00 M?

36.4   Concentration and Time

The rate law describes the relationship between the rate of a reaction and the concentrations of the reactants. As we have seen, the rate usually decreases as the concentrations of the reactants decrease. It would be useful to be able to determine how the concentrations of the reactants and products change as the reaction proceeds. How can we determine how much reactant is left after a certain time, or how can we determine how long it takes for a certain amount of product to form? We can modify the rate equation for a reaction to answer these questions. The relationship between *time* and concentration, rather than *rate* and concentration, is described by the **integrated rate laws**, or **integrated rate equations**.

First Order Reactions

The rate equation for a first order reaction is:

Rate = k[R]—where R is the reactant and the exponent n = 1 (first order)

However, we determined earlier that the rate also $= -\dfrac{d[R]}{dt}$

These two equations can be combined:

$$\text{Rate} = k[R] = -\frac{d[R]}{dt}$$

and rearranged:

$$\frac{1}{[R]}\, d[R] = -k\, dt$$

Integration over time: $\displaystyle\int_{[R]_0}^{[R]_t} \frac{1}{[R]}\, d[R] = -k\int_0^t dt$

yields the integrated rate equation:

$$\ln\frac{[R]_t}{[R]_0} = -kt$$

Taking the antilogarithm of both sides of this equation:

$$[R]_t = [R]_0\, e^{-kt}$$

This equation illustrates that the concentration of the reactant R in a first order reaction decreases exponentially as the reaction proceeds. The rate of the decrease is determined by the magnitude of the rate constant k (Figure 36.3). We will meet this exponential decrease in the concentration of a reactant again when we examine radioactive decay. The decrease in concentration is often referred to as **exponential decay**.

The integrated rate equation for a first order reaction can also be written in the form:

$$\ln[R]_t = -kt + \ln[R]_0$$

This equation has the same form as an equation for a straight line (y = mx + b). If $\ln[R]_t$ is plotted against t, the line has a slope –k and a y intercept $\ln[R]_0$ (Figure 36.4). This can be used qualitatively as a test to determine if a reaction is first order. If the plot of $\ln[R]_t$ *vs.* t is a straight line, then the reaction is first order. The plot can also be used

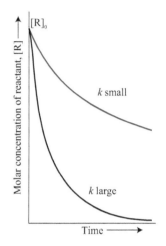

FIGURE 36.3   The exponential decrease in the concentration of the reactant in a first order reaction. The rate of the decrease is determined by the magnitude of the rate constant k.

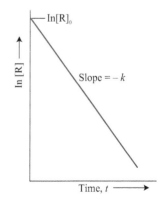

FIGURE 36.4   For a first order reaction, a plot of $\ln[R]t$ *vs.* t produces a straight line with a slope equal to –k.

to determine the value of the rate constant k. The slope of the line is equal to –k. In fact the value of the rate constant is often determined graphically in this way. Note that these graphs assume that no appreciable reaction in the reverse direction is occurring to increase the value of [R], in other words, the system is some distance from equilibrium.

Graphing the change in the concentration of a reactant *vs.* time during a reaction is a useful way to determine the order of the reaction with respect to that reactant. In reactions involving more than one reactant, the initial concentration of the reactant being investigated is made much smaller than the concentrations of other reactants. This ensures that the concentrations of the other reactants do not change appreciably as the reaction proceeds; that is, the rate depends only upon the reactant of interest.

EXAMPLE 36.3   CONFIRMATION OF THE ORDER OF REACTION

Dinitrogen pentoxide decomposes to produce nitrogen dioxide and oxygen according to the equation:

$$2\ N_2O_5(g) \rightarrow 4\ NO_2(g) + O_2(g)$$

The decrease in the concentration of the dinitrogen pentoxide was monitored and the following results obtained:

Time (s)	$[N_2O_5(g)]$ (M)
initial	0.0492
30	0.0348
60	0.0246
90	0.0173
120	0.0123
150	0.0087

a. Verify that the order of the reaction with respect to N_2O_5 is first order.

b. Plot $\ln[N_2O_5]$ *vs.* t, calculate the slope of the line, and determine the rate constant k.

c. How much N_2O_5 remains after 100 seconds, after 240 seconds?

UNDERSTAND THE QUESTION

If $\ln[N_2O_5]$ is plotted against t, the line will be straight if the reaction order is one. The slope of the line equals –k, the rate constant. Once the rate constant is known, the concentration at any time t can be calculated.

PLAN THE SOLUTION

Calculate $\ln[N_2O_5]$ for each time interval and plot $\ln[N_2O_5]$ *vs.* t. Determine the rate constant from the slope of the line. Then calculate the concentrations at 100 and 240 seconds using the first order integrated rate equation.

SOLVE THE PROBLEM

The data and graph are:

Time	$[N_2O_5(g)]$	$\ln[N_2O_5]$
initial	0.0492	–3.01
30	0.0348	–3.36
60	0.0246	–3.71
90	0.0173	–4.06
120	0.0123	–4.40
150	0.0087	–4.74

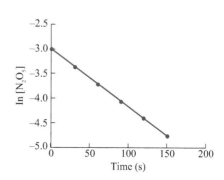

a. The plot is a straight line, confirming that the reaction is first order with respect to N_2O_5.

b. The slope of the line is determined by dividing the rise (a change on the y axis) by the run (the corresponding change on the x axis) and equals -1.15×10^{-2} s^{-1}.

Therefore k, the rate constant $= 1.15 \times 10^{-2}$ s^{-1}.

c. $[R]_t = [R]_0 \, e^{-kt}$

At 100 s, $[R]_{100} = (0.0492) \, e^{-(1.15 \times 10^{-2}) \times 100} = 0.0492 \times 0.317 = 0.0156$ M—between the value of [R] at 90 sec (0.0173 M) and the value of [R] at 120 sec (0.0123 M) as expected.

At 240 s, $[R]_{240} = (0.0492) \, e^{-(1.15 \times 10^{-2}) \times 240} = 0.0492 \times 0.063 = 0.0031$ M

PROBLEM 36.3A

The isomerization of methyl isonitrile to acetonitrile was investigated and the following data were collected:

$$CH_3NC(g) \rightarrow CH_3CN(g)$$

Time (min)	$[CH_3NC(g)]$ (M)
initial	1.022
30	0.723
60	0.511
90	0.362
120	0.256

a. Verify that the order of the reaction with respect to CH_3NC is first order.

b. Plot $\ln[CH_3NC]$ vs. t, calculate the slope of the line, and determine the rate constant k at the temperature of this experiment.

c. Calculate the concentration of methyl isonitrile CH_3NC after 5.0 hours.

PROBLEM 36.3B

At high temperatures chloroethane C_2H_5Cl decomposes to ethylene C_2H_4 and hydrogen chloride HCl. At 750°C the following data were collected:

Time (s)	$[C_2H_5Cl(g)]$ (M)
initial	0.0110
75	0.0078
150	0.0055
225	0.0039
300	0.0028

a. Verify that the order of the reaction with respect to C_2H_5Cl is first order.

b. Plot $\ln[C_2H_5Cl]$ vs. t, calculate the slope of the line, and determine the rate constant k at 750°C.

c. Calculate how much chloroethane remains after 500 seconds.

Half-Life

You may have noticed in the preceding Example 36.3 that the concentration of the reactant N_2O_5 decreased to one-half of its initial value in 60 seconds, and then to one-half again in the next 60 seconds. This decrease in the concentration to 50% in a consistent time period is a feature of all first order reactions—the time period is called

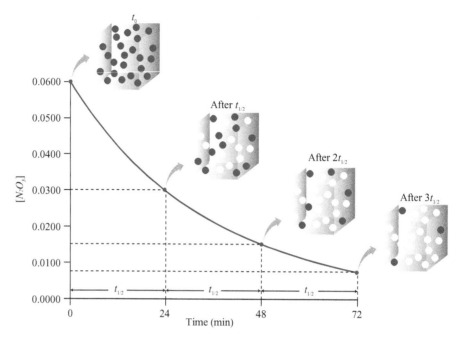

FIGURE 36.5 The constant half-life $t_{1/2}$ of a reactant in a first order reaction.
For each half-life that passes, the concentration of the reactant decreases to one-half of the initial concentration. There is an exponential decrease in the concentration of the reactant in a first order reaction. The rate of the decrease is determined by the magnitude of the rate constant k.

the **half-life $t_{1/2}$**. The half-life of a reactant is the time taken for a reactant to decrease to one-half of its initial concentration (Figure 36.5).

If the initial concentration of the reactant is $[R]_0$

then the concentration $[R]_t$ after one half-life is $\frac{1}{2}[R]_0$

Substituting these concentrations in the rate equation for a first order reaction,

$$\ln\frac{\frac{1}{2}[R]_0}{[R]_0} = -kt_{1/2}$$
$$\ln(\tfrac{1}{2}) = -kt_{1/2}$$
$$t_{1/2} = -\ln(\tfrac{1}{2})/k = 0.693/k$$

The half-life of the reactant in a first order reaction is independent of the initial concentration and depends only upon the rate constant k. Whatever the initial concentration, it is reduced to one-half in one half-life. This is true throughout the reaction—the concentration of the reactant decreases by one-half for every half-life that passes. Notice that the half-life $t_{1/2}$ and the rate constant k are inversely proportional—the two multiplied together always equals 0.693. A larger value for k means a faster reaction and a shorter half-life.

The half-life is a term often applied in describing radioactive decay where it is the time taken for the radioactivity to decrease to one-half of its original value. Radioactive decay is a first order process—it depends only upon the concentration of the radioactive isotope.

EXAMPLE 36.4 CALCULATIONS OF THE HALF-LIFE OF A FIRST-ORDER REACTION

In the first order isomerization of cyclopropane to propene at a relatively low temperature, the rate constant k is equal to 0.116 s^{-1}.

a. Calculate the half-life of cyclopropane at this temperature.

b. Estimate the fraction of cyclopropane that remains after 18 seconds.

c. Use the integrated rate law to calculate the fraction of cyclopropane that remains after 18 seconds.

The cyclopropane molecule is cyclic, with bond angles equal to 60°. The normal C–C–C bond angle in the cycloalkanes is near the tetrahedral angle of 109.5°. The cyclopropane molecule is strained and readily isomerizes to the less strained propene molecule:

1 Cyclopropane, C_3H_6

2 Propene, C_3H_6

UNDERSTAND THE QUESTION

For a first order reaction, the rate constant k and the half-life $t_{1/2}$ are related by the equation: $kt_{1/2} = 0.693$. If one is known, then the other can be calculated. Because the concentration of the reactant halves every half-life, an estimate of the concentration after some time has passed can often be made by dividing the time into a number of half-lives. The concentration at any time t can be calculated more precisely using the integrated rate equation—as in the previous example.

PLAN THE SOLUTION

Calculate $t_{1/2}$ from the expression $kt_{1/2} = 0.693$. Then estimate the relative concentration after 18 seconds from the number of half-lives. Check the result by using the integrated rate equation for a first order reaction to calculate the concentration of cyclopropane more precisely.

SOLVE THE PROBLEM

a. $t_{1/2} = 0.693/k = 0.693/0.116 = 5.97 \text{ s}$.

b. 18 seconds is almost exactly 3 half-lives.

In three half-lives, the concentration will decrease to $\frac{1}{2} \times \frac{1}{2} \times \frac{1}{2} = 1/8$ of its original concentration.

Using the integrated rate equation:

$[R]_t = [R]_0 \, e^{-kt}$

At 18 s, $[R]_{18}/[R]_0 = e^{-0.116 \times 18} = 0.124$—very near 1/8 as we estimated.

PROBLEM 36.4A

The hydrocarbon ethane CH_3CH_3 breaks up into two CH_3 fragments at high temperatures in a first order reaction. At one temperature the rate constant k equals 0.029 min^{-1}.

a. Calculate the half-life of ethane at this temperature.

b. Estimate what fraction of the original ethane remains after 2 hours.

PROBLEM 36.4B

The decomposition of dinitrogen pentoxide is first order in N_2O_5 (*cf.* Example 36.3). If k, the rate constant $= 1.15 \times 10^{-2}$,

a. calculate the half-life of dinitrogen pentoxide under the same conditions.

b. how long does it take for the concentration of dinitrogen pentoxide to decrease to 1/32nd of its original concentration?

Second Order Reactions

An integrated rate equation can be derived for a second order reaction following the same procedure as for the first order reaction. The simplest second order rate equation is:

$$Rate = k[R]^2$$

As before, the rate also $= -\dfrac{d[R]}{dt}$

These two equations can be combined:

$$Rate = k[R]^2 = -\dfrac{d[R]}{dt}$$

and rearranged:

$$\dfrac{1}{[R]^2}\, d[R] = -k\, dt$$

Integration over time yields the integrated rate equation:

$$\dfrac{1}{[R]_t} - \dfrac{1}{[R]_0} = kt$$

Alternatively, the equation can be written:

$$[R]_t = \dfrac{[R]_0}{1 + [R]_0\, kt}$$

The difference in the change of the reaction rate during a second order reaction ($Rate = k[R]^2$), compared to the change during a first order reaction ($Rate = k[R]$), is shown in Figure 36.6. The decrease in the rate for the second order reaction is slower. The curve is the square of the curve for the first order reaction.

It's interesting to examine how long it takes the initial concentration of the reactant to decrease to one-half in a second order reaction. It takes longer because the curve is shallower. The half-life also depends upon the initial concentration of the reactant:

If the initial concentration of the reactant is $[R]_0$

then the concentration $[R]_t$ after one half-life is $\tfrac{1}{2}[R]_0$

Substituting these concentrations in the rate equation for a second order reaction,

$$\dfrac{1}{\tfrac{1}{2}[R]_0} - \dfrac{1}{[R]_0} = kt_{1/2}$$

$$\dfrac{1}{[R]_0} = kt_{1/2}$$

$$\text{or } t_{1/2} = \dfrac{1}{k[R]_0}$$

The half-life of the reactant in a second order reaction depends upon the initial concentration of the reactant. In fact, since the concentration of the reactant [R] halves every half-life, the half-life doubles each time. This is illustrated in Figure 36.7.

A second order reaction can be recognized graphically just as a first order reaction can. The integrated rate equation for the second order reaction can be rearranged to:

$$\dfrac{1}{[R]_t} = kt + \dfrac{1}{[R]_0}$$

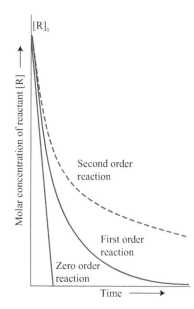

FIGURE 36.6   The difference in the rates at which the reactant is used in a zero order, first order, and second order reactions.
The initial rates are the same for all three reactions. Note that the slope for the second order reaction is shallower than for the first order reaction—the reactant is used more slowly.

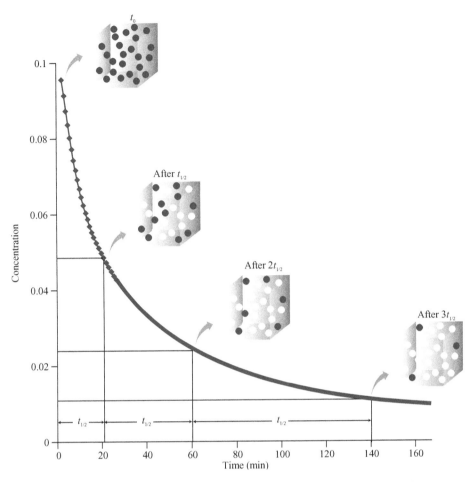

FIGURE 36.7   The increasing half-life $t_{1/2}$ of a reactant in a second order reaction. Each successive half-life is double the previous half-life. The first half-life = 20 s – 0 s = 20 sec; the second half-life = 60 s – 20 s = 40 sec; etc.

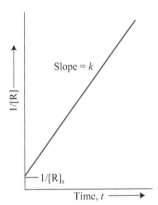

FIGURE 36.8   For a second order reaction, a plot of $1/[R]_t$ *vs.* t produces a straight line with a slope equal to k.

A plot of $1/[R]_t$ *vs.* t yields a straight line with a slope equal to k if , and only if, the reaction is second order (Figure 36.8).

EXAMPLE 36.5   SECOND ORDER REACTIONS

The gas-phase decomposition of nitrogen dioxide to nitric oxide and oxygen is a second order reaction. At about 600 K, the rate constant for the reaction, $k = 0.600$ M^{-1} s^{-1}.

$$NO_2(g) \rightarrow NO(g) + \tfrac{1}{2}\,O_2(g)$$

If the initial concentration of nitrogen dioxide is 0.0200 M,

a. Calculate the time taken for the concentration to decrease to 0.0100 M.

b. How long does it take for the concentration to decrease to one-half of this, to 0.0050 M ?

c. Calculate the concentration of nitrogen dioxide after 5 minutes.

d. What is the concentration of nitric oxide NO at this point?

UNDERSTAND THE QUESTION

For a second order reaction, the rate constant k and the half-life $t_{1/2}$ are related by the equation: $t_{1/2} = 1/k\,[R]_0$. The half-life depends upon the concentration $[R]_0$. The concentration of the reactant after an integral number of half-lives can be determined because the half-life increases by a factor of 2 (doubles) for every half-life that passes.

The concentration of the reactant can be calculated for any time t using the integrated rate equation for a second order process.

PLAN THE SOLUTION

Calculate the first half-life using the relation $t_{1/2} = 1/k\,[R]_0$. Then determine the number of half-lives that need to pass to reach a concentration of 0.0050 M. The concentration after 5 minutes can be estimated using a similar procedure and is calculated using the integrated equation. The initial estimation is a useful check of the result.

SOLVE THE PROBLEM

a. The decrease to 0.0100 M is a reduction to one-half of the original concentration.
$$t_{1/2} = 1/k\,[R]_0 = 1/(0.600\ M^{-1}s^{-1} \times 0.0200\ M) = 83\ \text{seconds}$$

b. The next decrease to 0.0050 M takes another half-life. But the half-life is twice as long because the initial concentration is half as great. In other words,
$$t_{1/2} = 1/k\,[R] = 1/(0.600\ M^{-1}s^{-1} \times 0.0100\ M) = 167\ \text{seconds}$$
The time taken to reach this concentration of 0.0050 M from the start of the reaction is $83 + 167\ s = 250\ s$.

c. 250 s is a little over 4 minutes. The concentration at the five minute mark is estimated to be a little less than 0.0050 M. Convert the time to seconds to keep the units consistent with the units of k. Five minutes = 300 s.
$$[R]_{300} = \frac{[R]_0}{1 + [R]_0\,kt} = 0.0200\ M/(1 + 0.0200\ M \times 0.600\ M^{-1}s^{-1} \times 300\ s\ ) = 0.0044\ M$$
The result is a little less than 0.0050 M as predicted.

d. The concentration of NO equals the decrease in the concentration of the NO_2. The stoichiometry of the reaction indicates that one NO molecule is formed for every NO_2 molecule that decomposes.

Initial concentration of NO_2 = 0.0200 M

Concentration of NO_2 at 5 minutes = 0.0044 M

Decrease in the concentration of NO_2 = 0.0200 M – 0.0040 M = 0.0156 M

The concentration of NO at this point is the same = 0.0156 M

PROBLEM 36.5A

The dimerization of the fluorinated ethylene molecule C_2F_4 to produce octafluoro-cyclobutane C_4F_8 is a second order process with respect to the reactant (and a second order process overall). At 175°C, the rate constant k equals $0.0440\ M^{-1}s^{-1}$.

a. If the initial concentration of C_2F_4 is 0.240 M, what is the first half-life of the reaction? In other words, how long does it take for the concentration of the reactant to decrease to 0.120 M?

b. How long does it take for the concentration of C_2F_4 to decrease to 0.030 M?

PROBLEM 36.5B

Acetaldehyde CH_3CHO decomposes in a second order reaction with a rate constant at 500°C equal to 0.330 $M^{-1}s^{-1}$. If the initial concentration of acetaldehyde is 0.0160 M,

a. calculate the length of time taken for the concentration to decrease to 0.0080 M.

b. estimate, and then calculate, the length of time taken for the concentration to decrease to 0.0018 M.

A reaction that is second order overall may be first order in two reactants. In other words, the rate equation may have the form:

Rate = k[A][B]

In this case, a plot of 1/[A] *vs.* t will not produce a straight line because the reaction is not second order with respect to A. Nor, however, will a plot of ln[A] *vs.* t produce a straight line because, although the reaction is first order with respect to [A], the rate also depends upon the concentration of B. The situation is more complicated than the second order rate equation Rate = $k[A]^2$.

In cases like these, a common approach is to make one of the concentrations, either [A] or [B], so large that there is no effective change in the concentration as the reaction proceeds. The rate then depends only upon the other reactant and is first order with respect to that reactant. The reaction is now described as **pseudo-first-order**.

For example, if [B] is large and effectively constant,

Rate = k[A][B]

and Rate = k'[A]—pseudo-first-order in A where k' = k[B].

If [B] is known then k can be calculated.

Complex reactions can be studied using this approach. The concentration of each reactant in turn is made much smaller than the concentrations of other reactants. The dependence of the rate of the reaction upon that reactant is then measured.

Zero Order Reactions

Although it may appear strange, some reactions occur at a rate that is independent of the concentration of any reactant. The overall order of such a reaction is zero and the rate simply depends upon k, the rate constant. The rate is constant until the reactants are used up.

$$\text{Rate} = k\,[R]_0 = k$$

Zero order reactions occur when something other than the reactant concentration limits the rate of the reaction. This limiting factor may be the amount of catalyst or enzyme present. The difference in the change of the reaction rate for a zero order reaction, compared to a first and second order reaction, is shown in Figure 36.6.

The integrated rate equation for a zero order reaction is simply:

$$[R]_t = [R]_0 - kt$$

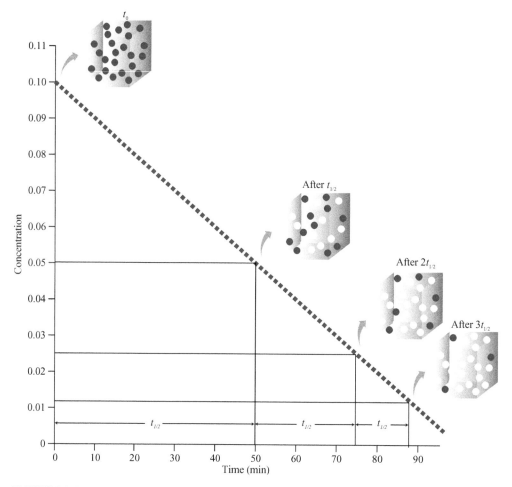

FIGURE 36.9 **The decreasing half-life t$_{1/2}$ of a reactant in a zero order reaction.**
Each half-life is half the previous half-life. For a zero order reaction, a straight line is produced when the concentration is plotted against time; the slope is –k and the intercept is [R]$_0$.

A graph of [R]$_t$ *vs.* t is a straight line with a slope equal to –k and an intercept equal to [R]$_0$. The half-life of a zero order reaction depends upon how much reactant is initially present [R]$_0$ and the value of k. The greater the amount of reactant initially present, the longer the half-life—it takes longer to use more reactant. The expression for the half-life is:

$$t_{1/2} = \frac{[R]_0}{2k}$$

For example, if the first half-life is 200 s, then the second half-life will be 100 s, the third half-life will be 50 s, and so on as the amount of reactant decreases (Figure 36.9). This behavior is the opposite of that for a second order reaction, for which the half-life doubles each successive period:

Zero order reaction: t$_{1/2}$ halves each successive half-life

First order reaction: t$_{1/2}$ constant

Second order reaction: t$_{1/2}$ doubles each successive half-life

Review Questions

1. Describe the ways in which the rate of a chemical reaction can be affected.

2. How is the rate of a chemical reaction defined? How is the rate at which a reactant is used up related to the rate at which a product is formed in a reaction?

3. What is the instantaneous rate? How is it determined?

4. What is meant by the term reaction order. What does the reaction order signify?

5. Describe the method of initial rates for determining the order of reaction with respect to each reactant involved in a reaction.

6. What is the difference between a rate equation and an integrated rate equation?

7. Explain how the value of the rate constant k can be obtained graphically using the integrated rate equation for a first order reaction. What graph would be used for a second order reaction?

8. What is meant by the half-life of a reactant? Why is the half-life a more useful concept for a first order reaction compared to the half-life for a zero order or second order reaction?

9. Construct a table summarizing the rate law, the integrated rate law, the half-life, and the linear plot for a zero-order, first-order, and second-order reaction.

Solutions to Problems

PROBLEM 36.1A

The stoichiometric coefficients indicate the relative rates of appearance of products and disappearance of reactants:

$$3 \, SCl_2 + 4 \, NaF \rightarrow SF_4 + S_2Cl_2 + 4 \, NaCl$$

Relative to the rate of production of SF_4,

the rate of production of S_2Cl_2 is the same,

the rate of production of NaCl is four times faster,

the rate at which SCl_2 is used is three times faster,

and the rate at which NaF is used is four times faster.

$$6 \, M \, min^{-1} \, NaCl \times \frac{3 \, mol \, SCl}{4 \, mol \, NaCl} = 4.5 \, M \, min^{-1} \, SCl_2$$

PROBLEM 36.2A

a. Compare Experiments 1 and 2, for which [CO(g)] is constant.

Multiplying [NO₂(g)] by 3 causes the rate to increase 9 times, from $0.020 \, mol \, L^{-1}s^{-1}$ to $0.180 \, mol \, L^{-1}s^{-1}$.

9 is the square of 3, and therefore the order with respect to NO_2 is 2.

There is no set of experiments for which [NO₂(g)] is constant, so choose for example Experiments 1 and 3.

The rate increases by four, from $0.020 \, mol \, L^{-1}s^{-1}$ to $0.080 \, mol \, L^{-1}s^{-1}$. This would be expected if the [NO₂(g)] increased by a factor of 2, which it does (from $0.30 \, mol \, L^{-1}$ to $0.60 \, mol \, L^{-1}$). The concentration of carbon monoxide has no effect—the order with respect to CO is zero. The reaction is second order overall.

b. The rate law is Rate = k [NO₂]².

c. Using the data from Experiment 1,
$0.020 \, mol \, L^{-1}s^{-1} = k \times (0.30 \, mol \, L^{-1})^2$
$k = 0.020/(0.30)^2 \, M^{-1}s^{-1} = 0.067 \, M^{-1}s^{-1}$.

PROBLEM 36.3A

The data and graph are:

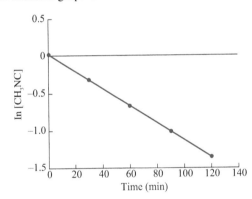

Time	[CH₃NC(g)]	ln[CH₃NC(g)]
initial	1.022	0.0218
30	0.723	–0.324
60	0.511	–0.671
90	0.362	–1.016
120	0.256	–1.363

a. The plot is a straight line, confirming that the reaction is first order with respect to CH₃NC.

b. The slope of the line = $1.15 \times 10^{-2} \, min^{-1} = 1.92 \times 10^{-4} s^{-1}$ and therefore k, the rate constant = $1.92 \times 10^{-4} s^{-1}$.

c. 5 hours = 18,000 s

$$[R]_t = [R]_0 e^{-kt}$$

At 18,000 s, $[R]_{18,000} = (1.022) \, e^{-(1.92 \times 10-4) \times 18,000} = 1.022 \times 0.0318 = 0.0324 \text{ mol L}^{-1}$.

PROBLEM 36.4A

a. $t^{1/2} = 0.693/k = 0.693/0.029 = 23.9$ min.

b. 2 hours is almost exactly 5 half-lives (5×23.9 min = 119.5 min).

In five half-lives, the concentration will decrease to $\frac{1}{2} \times \frac{1}{2} \times \frac{1}{2} \times \frac{1}{2} \times \frac{1}{2} = 1/32$ of its original concentration.

PROBLEM 36.5A

At 175°C, the rate constant k equals 0.0440 $M^{-1}s^{-1}$.

a. $t_{1/2} = 1/k \, [R]_0 = 1/(0.0440 \, M^{-1}s^{-1} \times 0.240 \, M) = 95$ seconds

b. A decrease to 0.030 M takes 3 half-lives:

0.240 to 0.120 M, 95 s

0.120 to 0.060 M, twice as long: 190 s

and 0.060 to 0.030 M, twice as long again: 380 s

The total time taken = 95 s + 190 s + 380 s = 665 s.

Alternatively, use the integrated rate equation:

$$\frac{1}{[R]_t} - \frac{1}{[R]_0} = kt$$

$(1/0.030) \, M^{-1} - (1/0.240) \, M^{-1} = 0.0440 \, M^{-1}s^{-1} \times t$

$t = 29.2 / 0.0440 \text{ s} = 663$ s.

Answers to Review Questions

1. The rate of a chemical reaction can be affected by several factors, including the concentrations of the reactant molecules, the temperature at which the reaction occurs, the presence of a catalyst, and the extent to which the reactant molecules are in contact.

2. The rate of a chemical reaction is the rate at which the concentration of a reactant or product changes per unit time. The relative rates of appearance of products and disappearance of reactants depend upon the stoichiometry of the reaction.

3. The instantaneous rate of a reaction is the rate at any particular time during the reaction. It is the slope of the tangent to the curve of reaction rate *vs.* time at that particular time.

4. The rate law expresses the dependence of the rate upon the concentrations of the reactants. The concentration terms in the rate law are each raised to some power. The exponent of a concentration term is called the order of reaction with respect to that particular reactant. If the order is one, then the rate is directly proportional to that concentration. If the order is 2, then the rate is proportional to the square of the concentration. Although reaction orders are usually whole numbers, they may be fractional or negative.

5. In the method of initial rates the rate of the reaction is determined at the beginning of the reaction. At this stage the concentrations of the products, and the rate of the reverse reaction, are assumed to be negligible. The initial concentrations are varied in a systematic way in order to determine the effect on the rate of the reaction.

6. The rate equation relates the rate and the concentrations of the reactants. The integrated rate equation relates the time and the concentrations of the reactants.

7. The integrated rate equation for a first order reaction is:

$$\ln \frac{[R]_t}{[R]_0} = -kt \quad \text{which rearranges to}$$
$$\ln[R]_t = \ln[R]_0 - kt$$

Plotting $\ln[R]_t$ *vs.* t yields a straight line with a slope equal to $-k$.

For a second order reaction, the reciprocal of the concentration $1/[R]_t$ is plotted against t. This yields a straight line with a slope equal to k.

8. A half-life is the time taken for the reactant in a reaction to reduce to one-half its initial concentration. For a first order reaction, $t_{1/2} = 0.693/k$. In other words, the half-life is independent of the concentration of the reactant and remains the same throughout the reaction. For zero order and second order reactions, the half-life depends upon the concentration of the reactant.

9. A typical table is illustrated below.

Order	Rate Law	Integrated Rate Law	Half-Life	Linear Plot	
Zero	Rate = k	$[R]_0 - [R]_t = kt$	$t_{\frac{1}{2}} = \dfrac{[R]_0}{2k}$	plot $[R]_t$ vs. t	slope = −k
First	Rate = k[R]	$\ln\left(\dfrac{[R]_t}{[R]_0}\right) = -kt$	$t_{\frac{1}{2}} = \dfrac{0.693}{k}$	plot $\ln[R]_t$ vs. t	slope = −k
Second	Rate = k[R]²	$\dfrac{1}{[R]_t} - \dfrac{1}{[R]_0} = kt$	$t_{\frac{1}{2}} = \dfrac{1}{k[R]_0}$	plot $\dfrac{1}{[R]_t}$ vs. t	slope = +k

End-of-Unit Problems

1. Determine the relationships between the rate of formation of the products and the rate of disappearance of the reactants in the following reactions.

   a. $H_2 + I_2 \rightarrow 2\,HI$

   b. $4\,NH_3 + 7\,O_2 \rightarrow 4\,NO_2 + 6\,H_2O$

2. Determine the relationships between the rate of formation of the products and the rate of disappearance of the reactants in the following reactions. Express the rates of the reactions as normalized rates.

   a. $P_4O_{10} + 6\,H_2O \rightarrow 4\,H_3PO_4$

   b. $2\,NOBr \rightarrow 2\,NO + Br_2$

3. In the first step of the Ostwald process for the synthesis of nitric acid, ammonia is converted to nitric oxide at high temperature by the reaction:

   $$4\,NH_3(g) + 5\,O_2(g) \rightarrow 4\,NO(g) + 6\,H_2O(g)$$

   In one particular experiment, equal molar amounts of the reactants were mixed and the concentrations of the reactants and products were plotted as time progressed.

   The graph shown below was obtained.

   Identify the components A, B, C, and D.

   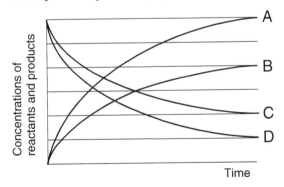

4. The oxidation of bromide ion Br^- by bromate ion BrO_3^- in acidic solution is represented by the equation below. At one stage in this reaction, bromine is produced at a rate of 60 M min⁻¹.

   $$5\,Br^- + BrO_3^- + 6\,H^+ \rightarrow 3\,Br_2 + 3\,H_2O$$

   a. At what rate is bromide ion Br^- used at this stage?

   b. At what rate is bromate ion BrO_3^- used at this stage?

5. Consider the oxidation of ammonia to nitrogen dioxide and water:

   $$4\,NH_3 + 7\,O_2 \rightarrow 4\,NO_2 + 6\,H_2O$$

   If, at some stage in the reaction, water is formed at a rate of 42 mol L⁻¹ min⁻¹,

   a. at what rate is the nitrogen dioxide formed?

   b. at what rate is oxygen used?

   c. at what rate is ammonia used?

6. Consider the oxidation of nitrous oxide to nitrogen dioxide:

   $$2\,N_2O + 3\,O_2 \rightarrow 4\,NO_2$$

   If initial rate of formation of nitrogen dioxide is 24 M s⁻¹,

   a. at what rate is the nitrous oxide used?

   b. at what rate is oxygen used?

7. At one stage in the reaction of ammonia and oxygen at a high temperature in the gas phase, water is produced at a rate of 30 M min⁻¹.

   $$4\,NH_3 + 5\,O_2 \rightarrow 4\,NO + 6\,H_2O$$

   a. At what rate is oxygen used at this stage?

   b. At what rate is ammonia used at this stage?

8. Sulfur dioxide reacts with disulfur dichloride and chlorine to form thionyl chloride according to the equation:

   $$2\,SO_2 + S_2Cl_2 + 3\,Cl_2 \rightarrow 4\,SOCl_2$$

   At one stage in this reaction, thionyl chloride is produced at a rate of 48 mol L⁻¹ m⁻¹.

   a. At what rate is chlorine used at this stage?

   b. At what rate is disulfur dichloride used at this stage?

9. Carbon monoxide reacts with oxygen:

$$CO(g) + \frac{1}{2} O_2(g) \rightarrow CO_2(g)$$

The rate law for this reaction is Rate = k $[CO]^m[O_2]^n$

Information for the reaction is given in the following table:

	[CO] (M)	[O_2] (M)	Initial Rate (M min^{-1})
Experiment 1	0.02	0.02	3.68×10^{-5}
Experiment 2	0.04	0.02	1.47×10^{-4}
Experiment 3	0.02	0.04	7.36×10^{-5}

a. What are the values of the exponents m and n?

b. What is the overall reaction order?

c. What is the value of k for the reaction?

10. The initial rate of the reaction:

$$S_2O_8^{2-} + 2 I^- \rightarrow 2 SO_4^{2-} + I_2$$

was determined in three experiments, each experiment using different initial concentrations of the reactants.

The data recorded were:

	Initial [$S_2O_8^{2-}$] M	Initial [I^-] M	Initial rate of reaction M s^{-1}
1	1×10^{-4}	1×10^{-2}	6.5×10^{-7}
2	2×10^{-4}	1×10^{-2}	1.3×10^{-6}
3	2×10^{-4}	5×10^{-3}	6.5×10^{-7}

a. What is the rate equation for the reaction?

b. What is the overall order of the reaction?

11. The initial rate of the reaction:

$$NH_4^+(aq) + NO_2^-(aq) \rightarrow 2 H_2O(l) + N_2(g)$$

was determined in three experiments, each experiment using different initial concentrations of the reactants.

The data recorded were:

	Initial [NH_4^+] M	Initial [NO_2^-] M	Initial rate of reaction M s^{-1}
1	0.24	0.10	7.2×10^{-6}
2	0.12	0.10	3.6×10^{-6}
3	0.12	0.15	5.4×10^{-6}

a. What is the rate equation for the reaction?

b. What is the overall order of the reaction?

12. Carbon monoxide reacts with chlorine to produce the highly toxic gas phosgene:

$$CO(g) + Cl_2(g) \rightarrow COCl_2(g)$$

The initial rate of the reaction was determined using different initial concentrations of carbon monoxide and chlorine and the results were as follows:

	Initial [CO(g)] (M)	Initial [Cl_2(g)] (M)	Rate of formation of COCl$_2$(g) (M hr^{-1})
1	1.00	0.500	2.3×10^{-25}
2	0.500	0.500	1.2×10^{-25}
3	0.500	1.00	2.4×10^{-25}

a. Determine the order of the reaction with respect to CO(g).

b. Determine the order of the reaction with respect to $Cl_2(g)$.

c. Determine the overall order of the reaction.

d. Write the rate law.

e. What is the value of the rate constant k?

13. The reaction of t-butyl-bromide $(CH_3)_3CBr$ with water is represented by the equation:

$$(CH_3)_3CBr + H_2O \rightarrow (CH_3)_3COH + HBr$$

The initial rate of the reaction was determined using different initial concentrations of the reactants and the following results were obtained:

	Initial [$(CH_3)_3CBr$] (M)	Initial [H_2O] (M)	Initial rate of reaction (M min–1)
1	4.0×10^{-2}	5.0×10^{-2}	2.0×10^{-6}
2	4.0×10^{-2}	2.0×10^{-3}	2.0×10^{-6}
3	1.2×10^{-1}	4.0×10^{-2}	6.0×10^{-6}

a. What is the order with respect to $(CH_3)_3CBr$?

b. What is the order with respect to H_2O?

c. What is the overall order of the reaction?

d. Write the rate equation.

e. Calculate the rate constant k for the reaction.

14. Initial rate data at 25°C are listed for the reaction. What is the overall reaction order?

$$NH_4^+(aq) + NO_2^-(aq) \rightarrow N_2(g) + 2 H_2O(l)$$

	Initial [NH_4^+]	Initial [NO_2^-]	Rate of formation of N$_2$
1	0.24 M	0.10 M	7.2×10^{-6} M s^{-1}
2	0.12 M	0.10 M	3.6×10^{-6} M s^{-1}
3	0.12 M	0.15 M	5.4×10^{-6} M s^{-1}

15. The rate law for the reaction of nitric oxide NO with oxygen O_2 to form nitrogen dioxide is
Rate = $k[NO]^2[O_2]$

What would happen to the initial rate of the reaction if

a. the concentration of NO is doubled?

b. the concentration of O_2 is halved?

c. the concentration of NO is halved and the concentration of O_2 is tripled?

16. The rate law for the reaction of nitrogen dioxide NO_2 with ozone O_3:

$$2\,NO_2 + O_3 \rightarrow N_2O_5 + O_2$$

is Rate = $k[NO_2][O_3]$

What would happen to the initial rate of this reaction if

a. the concentration of NO_2 is doubled?

b. the concentration of O_3 is reduced to one quarter?

c. the concentration of NO_2 is halved and the concentration of O_3 is doubled?

17. For the reduction of nitric oxide with hydrogen

$$NO(g) + H_2(g) \rightarrow N_2(g) + 2\,H_2O(g)$$

the order of reaction with respect to nitric oxide is 2 and with respect to hydrogen is 1.

a. Write the rate equation.

b. If the rate constant at 750°C is $5.0 \times 10^4\ M^{-2}s^{-1}$, what is the rate of the reaction when the initial concentrations are [NO] = 0.100 M and [H_2] = 0.0500 M.

c. What would the rate of the reaction be if the initial concentration of NO is doubled and the initial concentration of H_2 is halved?

18. For the reaction of iodide ion with hypochlorite ion in basic solution

$$I^-(aq) + ClO^-(aq) \rightarrow IO^-(aq) + Cl^-(aq)$$

the order of reaction with respect to iodide is 1, the order of reaction with respect to hypochlorite is 1, and the order of reaction with respect to hydroxide ion is −1,

a. Write the rate equation.

b. What would happen to the rate of the reaction if the initial concentration of $I^-(aq)$ is doubled, the initial concentration of $ClO^-(aq)$ is tripled, and the hydroxide ion concentration is halved?

19. In the reaction of ozone with nitrogen dioxide to produce nitrogen trioxide and oxygen, it was determined that doubling the initial concentration of ozone doubled the initial rate of the reaction. Doubling the initial concentration of nitrogen dioxide also doubled the initial rate of the reaction.

$$NO_2(g) + O_3(g) \rightarrow NO_3(g) + O_2(g)$$

a. What is the order of reaction with respect to each reactant?

b. Write the rate equation for the reaction.

20. In the reaction of iodine monochloride with hydrogen to produce iodine and hydrogen chloride, it was determined that doubling the initial concentration of ICl doubled the initial rate of the reaction. When the initial concentration of ICl was doubled and the initial concentration of hydrogen was halved, the initial rate of reaction remained unchanged.

$$2\,ICl(g) + H_2(g) \rightarrow I_2(g) + 2\,HCl(g)$$

a. What is the order of reaction with respect to each reactant?

b. Write the rate equation for the reaction.

21. The units of the rate constant k vary with the overall order of the reaction. Determine the orders of the reactions that have units for k equal to

a. hr^{-1}

b. $M^{-1}\ min^{-1}$

c. $M\ s^{-1}$

22. The units of the rate constant k vary with the overall order of the reaction. Determine the units of k for reactions that have orders equal to

a. 1

b. 3

c. 2

23. An initial concentration of a reactant (0.010 M) was found to drop to one-half of this value (0.0050 M) in 300 seconds in a second-order reaction. That is, $t_{1/2}$ = 300 seconds. How much longer does the reaction take for the concentration of this reactant to drop by another one-half to 0.0025 M?

24. In a reaction, a reactant A forms a product B. In an experiment in which the initial concentration of A was 0.10 M, the successive half-lives for the reaction were observed to be 10.0 minutes, 20.0 minutes and 40.0 minutes.

a. What is the overall order of the reaction?

b. What is the concentration of the reactant A after 150.0 minutes?

c. What is the concentration of the reactant A after 50.0 minutes?

25. Consider the first order reaction A → B in which A molecules (shaded circles) are converted to B molecules (clear circles). The first diagram illustrates the initial state of the system (pure A). The second diagram illustrates the situation after one minute. What is the half-life for this reaction?

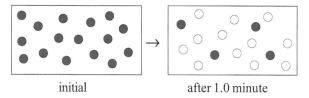

initial   after 1.0 minute

26. In a first-order reaction, a reactant A forms a product B. In an experiment in which the initial concentration of A was 0.10 M, the half-life for the reaction was observed to be 5.0 minutes.

    a. What is the value of the rate constant?

    b. How long does it take for the concentration to decrease to 3.1×10^{-3} M?

27. The rearrangement of methyl isocyanide CH_3NC to acetonitrile CH_3NC is a first order reaction and has a rate constant of 5.11×10^{-5} s^{-1} at 470 K. How many minutes does it take for the concentration of methyl isocyanide to fall from 0.0340 M to 0.0300 M?

28. Hydrogen iodide decomposes slowly to H_2 and I_2 at 600K. The reaction is second order in HI and the rate constant is 9.7×10^{-6} M^{-1}s^{-1}. If the initial concentration of HI is 0.100 M, what is the molarity after exactly 6 days?

29. The following pictures represent the progress of a reaction in which two molecules of a substance X combine together to form a dimer X_2 (a molecule in which two of the X molecules are bonded together).

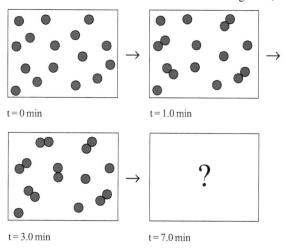

t = 0 min   t = 1.0 min

t = 3.0 min   t = 7.0 min

    a. What is the reaction order with respect to X?

    b. What is the rate law?

    c. How many molecules of the dimer X_2 will be present at time t = 7.0 minutes?

30. Hydrogen peroxide decays into water and oxygen in a first-order process.

$$H_2O_2(aq) \rightarrow H_2O(l) + 1/2O_2(g)_+$$

    At 20.0°C, the half-life for the reaction is 3.92×10^4 s.

    a. What is the rate constant k for this reaction?

    b. If the initial concentration of hydrogen peroxide is 1.5 M, what is the concentration after 7 days?

The Mechanisms of Chemical Reactions

37.1   Reaction Mechanisms

We learned earlier that a chemical reaction is a rearrangement of atoms. Molecules collide, bonds are broken, and new bonds are formed. The way in which this rearrangement takes place is called the **mechanism** of the reaction.

A chemical equation for a reaction represents the overall process. It indicates the reactants and the products of the reaction and the stoichiometric relationships between them. However, more often than not it provides no hint as to how the reaction happens. Consider, for example, the reaction between nitrogen dioxide and carbon monoxide described in Problem 36.2A:

$$NO_2(g) + CO(g) \rightarrow NO(g) + CO_2(g)$$

The experimental rate law for this reaction at low temperature has been determined to be Rate = $k[NO_2]^2$. Clearly the mechanism of the reaction is not a simple collision between an NO_2 molecule and a CO molecule. If this were the case, the rate would depend upon both the NO_2 concentration and the CO concentration and the rate law would be Rate = $k[NO_2][CO]$. The chemical equation provides no information about how the reaction between the NO_2 and CO actually happens. Even if the rate law matched the stoichiometry of the chemical equation, we cannot be certain of the mechanism.

In this unit we will investigate the ways in which the possible mechanisms for a reaction can be determined. We will also examine the effect of temperature upon the rate of a reaction and the ways in which catalysts influence the mechanism.

37.2   Reaction Steps

Many reactions are a series of individual steps. Each reaction step in the sequence is called an **elementary step**. An elementary step may involve one, two, or even three molecules. If only one molecule is involved, the elementary step is called **unimolecular**:

A $\rightarrow$ product   Rate = $k[A]$ first order

An elementary step that involves two molecules is more common. In this case the elementary step is **bimolecular**. The two molecules may be the same or they may be different:

A + A $\rightarrow$ product   Rate = $k[A]^2$ second order

A + B $\rightarrow$ product   Rate = $k[A][B]$ second order

Termolecular reaction steps, involving the simultaneous collision of three molecules, are less likely to occur:

3 A $\rightarrow$ product   Rate = $k[A]^3$ third order

2 A + B $\rightarrow$ product   Rate = $k[A]^2[B]$ third order

A + B + C $\rightarrow$ product   Rate = $k[A][B][C]$ third order

Note that a rate equation *can* be written for an elementary step and that the order of the rate equation for an elementary step matches the molecularity of the step. For example, a bimolecular reaction step is always second order, etc.

A sequence of elementary steps makes up the overall chemical reaction. During the progress through this sequence of elementary steps, intermediate chemical species are often formed. These **reaction intermediates** are produced in one step and then used in a subsequent step and therefore do not appear in the overall chemical equation for the reaction. For example, let's return to the reaction between nitrogen dioxide and carbon monoxide. The proposed mechanism for this reaction at low temperatures involves two elementary steps:

$$\text{Step I: } NO_2(g) + NO_2(g) \rightarrow NO(g) + NO_3(g)$$
$$\underline{\text{Step II: } NO_3(g) + CO(g) \rightarrow NO_2(g) + CO_2(g)}$$
$$\text{Overall: } NO_2(g) + CO(g) \rightarrow NO(g) + CO_2(g)$$

The NO_3 molecule is a reaction intermediate. When the two elementary steps are added, the NO_3 cancels from each side. The determination of the mechanism for a reaction often involves a search for, and identification of, reaction intermediates such as NO_3.

In a sequence of two elementary steps such as this, invariably one step occurs more slowly than the other. The entire sequence cannot progress any faster than the slower step. For example, if the first step is slower than the second, then the second step cannot occur until the NO_3 is produced in the first step. If the second step is slower, then it doesn't matter how fast the NO_3 is made in the first step. The slowest elementary step in a sequence is called the **rate-determining step**.

Suppose that in this example the first step is relatively slow and that the second step occurs quite quickly. The NO_3 is used in the second step as soon as it is formed in the first step. The rate of the reaction equals the rate of the slower step:

$$\text{Rate} = k_1[NO_2]^2$$

Note that this rate equation matches the observed rate equation for the reaction. This means that the suggested mechanism is possible. When the rate law for a proposed mechanism matches the observed rate law, the mechanism *may* be correct but is *not* necessarily so. On the other hand, when the rate law for a proposed mechanism does *not* match the observed rate law, the proposed mechanism *cannot* be correct.

The two requirements of a possible mechanism are that the sum of the elementary steps yields the overall chemical equation for the reaction and that the rate equation of the proposed mechanism matches the experimentally observed rate equation.

> An analogy for the rate determining step in a sequence of steps is a bottleneck in a water pipe. The water cannot pass through the pipe any faster than it passes through the bottleneck.
>
> Another analogy is a construction zone on a freeway where three lanes are reduced to just one. The flow of cars along the freeway is determined by the rate at which they pass the construction zone.

> The subscript on the k indicates the elementary step. In this case k_1 is the rate constant for step 1.

EXAMPLE 37.1 REACTION MECHANISMS

The following mechanism has been proposed for the decomposition of dinitrogen pentoxide to nitrogen dioxide and oxygen. The overall reaction is:

$2 N_2O_5 \rightarrow 4 NO_2 + O_2$

The elementary steps are:

$N_2O_5 \rightarrow NO_2 + NO_3$	slow
$NO_2 + NO_3 \rightarrow NO + NO_2 + O_2$	fast
$NO_3 + NO \rightarrow 2 NO_2$	fast

a. What is the molecularity of each step?

b. Which species are reaction intermediates?

c. Do the elementary steps add up to the correct balanced equation for the reaction?

d. If the first step is the rate-determining step, what is the rate law for the mechanism?

UNDERSTAND THE QUESTION

The molecularity of an elementary step is the number of reactant molecules involved in that step. Intermediates are neither reactants nor products; they are formed and then used *en route*; they do not appear in the overall chemical equation. The rate of the overall process equals the rate of the slowest step.

PLAN THE SOLUTION

Examine each step in turn and assign the molecularity. To recognize reaction intermediates, pick out any species that are not reactants or products—they will appear on both sides in the sequence of elementary steps. Add the elementary steps to produce the overall balanced equation. Note that sometimes an equation for an elementary step must be multiplied by a whole number before the summation.

SOLVE THE PROBLEM

a. $N_2O_5 \rightarrow NO_2 + NO_3$ unimolecular

   $NO_2 + NO_3 \rightarrow NO + NO_2 + O_2$ bimolecular

   $NO_3 + NO \rightarrow 2\, NO_2$ bimolecular

b. NO and NO_3 are both intermediates.

c. The first equation must be multiplied by two, so that the NO and the two NO_3 cancel from both sides when the equations are added.

$$2\, N_2O_5 \rightarrow 2\, NO_2 + 2\, NO_3$$
$$NO_2 + NO_3 \rightarrow NO + NO_2 + O_2$$
$$\underline{NO_3 + NO \rightarrow 2\, NO_2}$$
$$2\, N_2O_5 \rightarrow 4\, NO_2 + O_2$$

d. The rate equation is the rate equation for the rate-determining step (the first step):

Rate = k_1 [N_2O_5]

PROBLEM 37.1A

The following mechanism has been proposed for the reaction of hydrogen and iodine to produce hydrogen iodide:

$$H_2(g) + I_2(g) \rightarrow 2\, HI(g)$$

$I_2 \rightleftharpoons 2\, I$

$H_2 + I \rightleftharpoons H_2I$

$H_2I + I \rightarrow 2\, HI$

a. What is the molecularity of each step?

b. Which species are reaction intermediates?

c. Do the elementary steps add up to the correct balanced equation for the reaction?

PROBLEM 37.1B

The following mechanism has been proposed for the reaction of nitric oxide and chlorine to produce nitrosyl chloride:

$$2\,NO(g) + Cl(g) \rightarrow 2\,NOCl(g)$$

$2\,NO \rightleftharpoons N_2O_2$

$N_2O_2 + Cl_2 \rightarrow 2\,NOCl$

a. What is the molecularity of each step?

b. Which species are reaction intermediates?

c. Do the elementary steps add up to the correct balanced equation for the reaction?

In Example 37.1 the rate equation for the reaction is derived easily because the first step is the rate-determining step. The rate equation for the overall reaction equals the rate equation for the first step. Only reactant concentrations occur in this rate equation.

The process becomes interesting if the rate-determining step occurs later in the sequence of steps making up the reaction mechanism. For example, let's look at the three steps that make up the mechanism for the reaction described in Problem 37.1A. The reaction is:

$$H_2(g) + I_2(g) \rightarrow 2\,HI(g)$$

and the experimentally observed rate law is Rate = $k[H_2][I_2]$.

The proposed mechanism is:

$I_2 \rightleftharpoons 2\,I$	fast
$H_2 + I \rightleftharpoons H_2I$	fast
$H_2I + I \rightarrow 2\,HI$	slow

In the first step, iodine molecules dissociate to produce a small concentration of iodine atoms. The reaction is written as an equilibrium because the iodine atoms recombine to form iodine molecules at almost the same rate as the iodine molecules break up to form iodine atoms. The equilibrium is quickly established. Some of the iodine atoms react with hydrogen molecules to produce the dihydrogen iodide molecules H_2I. This is another equilibrium that is quickly established. The slow step in the sequence is the reaction of some H_2I molecules with iodine atoms to produce hydrogen iodide molecules HI.

The rate of the overall process equals the rate of the slowest step:

$$\text{Rate} = k_3[H_2I][I]$$

However, this rate equation is of limited use because it is expressed in terms of the concentrations of intermediates in the mechanism. The concentrations [H_2I] and [I] must be written in terms of the concentrations of the reactants. We can do this by making use of the fact that the first and second steps are equilibria. Write the equilibrium constant expression and then rearrange to solve for the concentration of the intermediate:

$$K_1 = \frac{[I]^2}{[I_2]} \qquad [I]^2 = K_1[I_2]$$

$$K_2 = \frac{[H_2I]}{[H_2][I]} \qquad [H_2I] = K_2[H_2][I]$$

The rate equation usually contains reactant concentrations. It sometimes contains the concentrations of the products of the reaction. It may contain the concentration of a catalyst used in the reaction and if, for example, the reaction is run under basic conditions, it may contain the concentration of hydroxide ion [OH^-], etc.

Substituting first for $[H_2I]$ and then $[I]^2$ in the rate equation:

$$\text{Rate} = k_3K_2[H_2][I][I] = k_3K_2[H_2][I]^2$$
$$\text{Rate} = k_3K_2K_1[H_2][I_2] = k[H_2][I_2]$$

The three constants $k_3K_2K_1$ are combined in a new constant k. This rate equation is the same as the experimentally observed rate equation and indicates that the proposed mechanism is feasible.

37.3   The Steady State Approximation

The derivation of the rate law for the reaction between hydrogen and iodine that we have just examined is a simplification of what is called the **steady state approximation**. The idea behind this approximation is that the concentration of an intermediate in a mechanism remains constant, or steady, as the reaction proceeds. The intermediate is quickly replenished by a relatively fast reaction as it is used in a slow rate-determining step.

Let's look at the two-step mechanism for the reduction of nitric oxide NO by hydrogen H_2 to produce nitrous oxide N_2O and water. The reaction is:

$$2\,NO(g) + H_2(g) \rightarrow N_2O(g) + H_2O(g)$$

The proposed mechanism is:

$$2\,NO \rightleftharpoons N_2O_2 \qquad \text{fast}$$
$$N_2O_2 + H_2 \rightarrow N_2O + H_2O \qquad \text{slow}$$

The simple approach to developing the rate equation is to write the rate law for the slow second step and then substitute for the concentration of the intermediate N_2O_2:

$$\text{Rate} = k_2[N_2O_2][H_2]$$

but the first step is an equilibrium and $K_1 = [N_2O_2]/[NO]^2$

rearranging, $[N_2O_2] = K_1[NO]^2$

and substituting in the rate equation,

$\text{Rate} = k_2K_1[NO]^2[H_2] = k[NO]^2[H_2]$ which is the experimentally observed law.

A more rigorous treatment of the steady state approximation, where the relative rates of the two steps might not be known, is:

Step 1: An equilibrium between NO and N_2O_2:

$$NO + NO \rightleftharpoons N_2O_2$$

Rate of formation of $N_2O_2 = k_1[NO]^2$

Rate of use of $N_2O_2 = k_{-1}[N_2O_2]$

Step 2: A bimolecular reaction of N_2O_2 with H_2:

$$N_2O_2 + H_2 \rightarrow N_2O + H_2O$$

Rate of use of $N_2O_2 = k_2[N_2O_2][H_2]$

The steady state condition means that the rate of formation of N_2O_2 and the rate of use of N_2O_2 are equal:

$$k_1[NO]^2 = k_{-1}[N_2O_2] + k_2[N_2O_2][H_2]$$

The -1 of the k_{-1} indicates the rate constant for the reverse of Step 1.

Rearranging this to obtain an expression for $[N_2O_2]$:

$$[N_2O_2] = \frac{k_1[NO]^2}{k_{-1} + k_2[H_2]}$$

If the rate of the reaction is defined as the rate of the rate-determining step (the second step), then

$$\text{Rate} = k_2[N_2O_2][H_2]$$

This rate law contains the concentration of the intermediate N_2O_2 and we must substitute this with the expression for $[N_2O_2]$ from above:

$$\text{Rate} = k_2 \frac{k_1[NO]^2}{k_{-1} + k_2[H_2]}[H_2] = \frac{k_1 k_2[NO]^2[H_2]}{k_{-1} + k_2[H_2]}$$

This rate law does not look very much like the experimentally determined rate law. However, if k_{-1} is considerably larger than $k_2[H_2]$, in other words, the first equilibrium step is much faster than the second (rate-determining) step and the concentration of H_2 is small, then the denominator reduces to k_{-1} and the rate law becomes:

$$\text{Rate} = \frac{k_1 k_2[NO]^2[H_2]}{k_{-1} + \cancel{k_2[H_2]}} = (k_1 k_2/k_{-1})[NO]^2[H_2] = k_2 K_1[NO]^2[H_2]$$

$K_1 = k_1/k_{-1}$

which is exactly what we have already derived in our simple approach.

If the concentration of H_2 is much larger than the concentration of NO, the reaction might be expected to be pseudo-second order in NO—since the concentration of H_2 will not change significantly during the reaction. In this case $k_2[H_2]$ will be greater than k_{-1} and, as predicted, the rate equation will reduce to:

$$\text{Rate} = k_1[NO]^2$$

The rate of the reaction will now depend upon how quickly the first step of the reaction occurs.

In general we will use the simple approach outlined earlier and assume that an initial equilibrium is quickly established—significantly more quickly than the rate of the second step that will determine the rate of the reaction.

EXAMPLE 37.2   MECHANISMS INVOLVING THE STEADY STATE APPROXIMATION

The proposed mechanism for the decomposition of ozone to oxygen is:

$$O_3(g) \rightleftharpoons O_2(g) + O(g) \qquad \text{fast}$$
$$O(g) + O_3(g) \rightarrow 2\,O_2(g) \qquad \text{slow}$$

a. Derive the overall equation for the reaction.

b. Identify any reaction intermediates.

c. Derive the rate law from this proposed mechanism.

UNDERSTAND THE QUESTION

The overall balanced equation is the sum of the elementary steps. Reaction intermediates are formed in one step and then used in a subsequent step. They are neither reactants nor products. Use the steady state approximation to derive the rate law.

PLAN THE SOLUTION

Add the elementary steps and cancel any intermediate from both sides. To recognize the intermediates, pick out any species that are not reactants (ozone) or products (oxygen O_2)—they will appear on both sides in the sequence of elementary steps. Write the rate law for the slower step and then substitute for the concentrations of any intermediate.

SOLVE THE PROBLEM

a. $O_3(g) \rightleftharpoons O_2(g) + \cancel{O}(g)$

$$\frac{\cancel{O}(g) + O_3(g) \rightarrow 2\,O_2(g)}{2\,O_3(g) \rightarrow 3\,O_2(g)}$$

b. The reaction intermediate is $O(g)$.

c. The rate law for the slow second step is:

$$\text{Rate} = k_2[O_3][O]$$

The first step is an equilibrium and $K_1 = [O_2][O]/[O_3]$

therefore $[O] = K_1[O_3]/[O_2]$

and $\text{Rate} = k_2 K_1[O_3]^2/[O_2] = k[O_3]^2/[O_2]$

which is the experimentally observed law.

PROBLEM 37.2A

A proposed mechanism for the oxidation of nitric oxide to nitrogen dioxide is:

$$NO(g) + O_2(g) \rightleftharpoons NO_3(g) \qquad \text{fast}$$
$$NO(g) + NO_3(g) \rightarrow 2\,NO_2(g) \qquad \text{slow}$$

Show that this mechanism is consistent with the overall equation for the reaction and the observed rate law: $\text{Rate} = k[NO_2]^2[O_2]$. Identify any reaction intermediate.

PROBLEM 37.2B

Another mechanism suggested for the reaction described in Problem 37.2A is:

$$NO(g) + NO(g) \rightleftharpoons N_2O_2(g) \qquad \text{fast}$$
$$N_2O_2(g) + O_2(g) \rightarrow 2\,NO_2(g) \qquad \text{slow}$$

Show that this mechanism is also consistent with the overall equation for the reaction and the observed rate law: $\text{Rate} = k\,[NO_2]^2[O_2]$. How would you attempt to determine which mechanism is correct?

37.4   Chain Reactions

In a **chain reaction**, a highly reactive intermediate reacts with another reactant molecule to produce another highly reactive intermediate. This intermediate reacts with another reactant molecule to produce another intermediate, and so the reaction continues. Very often the intermediate is a **radical**, an atom or molecular fragment with an unpaired electron. An example is the reaction of hydrogen and chlorine. The first step in the mechanism, called the **initiation step**, is the generation of the radical by the dissociation of the chlorine molecule:

Initiation: $Cl_2 \rightarrow 2\,Cl\cdot$

The generation of the Cl· radical may be initiated by addition of a catalyst or by the action of light for example.

The symbol for the radical includes the · to emphasize the presence of the unpaired electron. The next step in the mechanism is the reaction of the radical with a hydrogen molecule producing another radical. The step is called a **propagation step**:

Propagation: $Cl· + H_2 → HCl + H·$

Propagation: $H· + Cl_2 → HCl + Cl·$

These steps continue while there are reactant molecules available. The chain of steps finishes when two radicals combine. This step is called a **termination step**.

Termination: $H· + Cl· → HCl$

Chain reactions typically occur at high rates, sometimes explosively fast, because of the high reactivity of the reaction intermediates. Occasionally branching occurs which accelerates the rate—a **branching step** is a step in which more radicals are produced than are used. The concentration of reaction intermediates increases exponentially and the reaction quickly accelerates.

37.5   Collision Theory

The rate of a reaction usually increases if the concentrations of the reactants are increased. This is understandable if the rate of the reaction depends upon the rate at which the molecules collide. The more concentrated the reactants, the greater the frequency of collisions between the molecules, and the greater the reaction rate.

Imagine, for example, a bimolecular reaction between A and B in a system consisting of just one molecule of A and two molecules of B. Only two collisions between A and B are possible (Figure 37.1). Now consider a system of two molecules of A and two molecules of B. Four collisions between A and B are possible—each A molecule can collide with each B molecule. If one more B molecule is added, then the number of possible collisions increases to six—both A molecules can collide with three B molecules. It is the product of the concentrations of A and B that determines the rate. If there are three molecules of A and three molecules of B, the number of possible collisions increases to nine.

In most collisions, the molecules collide without any reaction. The molecules simply rebound from one another. As we learned in Unit 34, for a collision to be effective, two criteria must be satisfied:

- There must be sufficient energy in the collision.
- The molecules must collide with the correct orientation with respect to one another.

Svante Arrhenius believed that molecules had to become activated in order to react—the molecules had to possess a certain minimum amount of energy. This energy is called the **activation energy** and is given the symbol E_A.

37.6   The Effect of Temperature on Reaction Rate

In the great majority of cases, an increase in the temperature at which a reaction is run increases the rate of the reaction. For typical reactions, an increase of only 10°C doubles the rate of the reaction—the increase is exponential. We learned in Unit 34

One molecule of A and two molecules of B
Only two collisions possible:

Two molecules of A and two molecules of B
Four collisions possible:

Two molecules of A and three molecules of B
Six collisions possible:

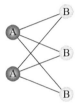

Three molecules of A and three molecules of B
Nine collisions possible:

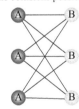

FIGURE 37.1   The increase in the number of possible collisions leading to a possible reaction as the number of molecules increases.

You might like to refer back to Figure 34.1.

that the increase in the rate of the reaction is due to an increase in the energy available at higher temperatures—a greater fraction of the molecules have sufficient energy to react (*cf.* Figure 34.3). This relationship was discovered by Svante Arrhenius and Jacobus van't Hoff and is described by the **Arrhenius equation**:

The factor A can be regarded as the value the rate constant would have if all the collisions resulted in a successful reaction.

$$k = A e^{-\frac{E_A}{RT}}$$

where A is the **frequency factor**—it depends upon the collision frequency and the orientation criterion.

R is the gas constant = 8.314 J K^{-1} mol^{-1}

E_A is the activation energy.

and T is the temperature of K.

Remember: Rate = k[reactants]

All these factors are incorporated in the rate constant k for the reaction. In particular, the temperature is in the denominator of a negative exponent, so an increase in T leads to an increase in k, and therefore an increase in the rate of the reaction.

One of the more useful results of determining the rate of a reaction at different temperatures is that it allows the energy E_A to be calculated. The logarithmic form of the Arrhenius equation is:

$$\ln k = \ln A - \frac{E_A}{RT}$$

Plotting ln k *vs.* 1/T produces a straight line with a slope equal to $-E_A/R$.

Or, for just two different temperatures T_1 and T_2,

$$\ln k_1 = \ln A - \frac{E_A}{RT_1}$$

$$\ln k_2 = \ln A - \frac{E_A}{RT_2}$$

Subtracting the first from the second:

$$\ln k_2 - \ln k_1 = \ln (k_2/k_1) = \ln A - \ln A - \frac{E_A}{RT_2} + \frac{E_A}{RT_1} = -\frac{E_A}{R}\left(\frac{1}{T_2} - \frac{1}{T_1}\right)$$

Both the graphical method and the comparison of two temperatures can be used to determine the value of E_A.

Energy is released when a bond is formed.

Is it possible that an increase in temperature would decrease the rate of a reaction? If the mechanism is a multistep sequence then it is possible. For example, consider the reaction described in Problem 37.2B. The first step is a rapidly established equilibrium that is exothermic in the forward direction. According to LeChatelier's principle, an increase in temperature drives this equilibrium to the left, decreasing the equilibrium concentration of the intermediate N_2O_2. This in turn decreases the rate of the second step (the rate-determining step).

In terms of the rate law for the reaction,

$$\text{Rate} = k_2K_1[NO_2]^2[O_2]$$

when the temperature is increased the rate constant k_2 increases according to the Arrhenius equation but the equilibrium constant K_1 decreases according to LeChatelier's principle. The overall effect depends upon the relative magnitude of the two changes.

EXAMPLE 37.3   DETERMINATION OF THE ACTIVATION ENERGY E_A

In the reaction of hydrogen and iodine to form hydrogen iodide described in Problem 37.1A, the value of the rate constant k was determined to be 1.0×10^{-8} L mol^{-1} s^{-1} at 225°C and 1.0×10^{-5} L mol^{-1} s^{-1} at 325°C. Calculate the activation energy E_A for the reaction.

UNDERSTAND THE QUESTION

The Arrhenius equation can be used to determine the value of E_A. The values of the rate constant at at least two different temperatures are required.

PLAN THE SOLUTION

Use the logarithmic version of the Arrhenius equation. Be sure that the units are consistent. For example, temperatures in K should be used. Also be careful not to lose precision when subtracting the reciprocals of large numbers.

SOLVE THE PROBLEM

A useful method for calculating the difference between the reciprocals of two large numbers is:

$$(1/T_1 - 1/T_2) = (T_2 - T_1)/T_1T_2$$

$$\ln (k_2/k_1) = -\frac{E_A}{R}\left(\frac{1}{T_2} - \frac{1}{T_1}\right)$$

$$\ln (1.0 \times 10^{-5}/1.0 \times 10^{-8}) = -E_A/R\,(1/598 - 1/498)$$

$$= (E_A/8.314\ \text{J K}^{-1}\text{mol}^{-1}) \times 100\ \text{K}/(598\ \text{K} \times 498\ \text{K})$$

$$6.91 = E_A \times 4.04 \times 10^{-5}\ \text{mol J}^{-1}$$

$$E_A = 1.7 \times 10^{5}\ \text{J mol}^{-1}$$

$$= 170\ \text{kJ mol}^{-1}$$

PROBLEM 37.3A

In the decomposition of dinitrogen pentoxide described in Example 37.1, the value of the rate constant k was determined to be 2.0×10^{-5} s^{-1} at 20°C and 3.0×10^{-3} s^{-1} at 60°C. Calculate the activation energy E_A for the reaction.

PROBLEM 37.3B

The activation energy for the isomerization of methyl isonitrile to acetonitrile is 160 kJ mol^{-1} (*cf.* Problem 36.3A). At 460 K the rate constant for the reaction is 2.50×10^{-5} s^{-1}. What is the rate constant at 500 K?

37.7   Transition State Theory

Collision theory provides a useful image of reactions. In order to react, molecules must collide. In order to break the bonds that need to be broken, a certain minimum energy must be available. And, in order to produce the desired rearrangement, the orientation of the collision must be appropriate.

Transition state theory takes the imagery a step further. The **transition state**, or **activated complex**, is the arrangement of atoms at the point of highest potential energy between the reactants and the products. The transition state is neither reactant nor product but a point in between.

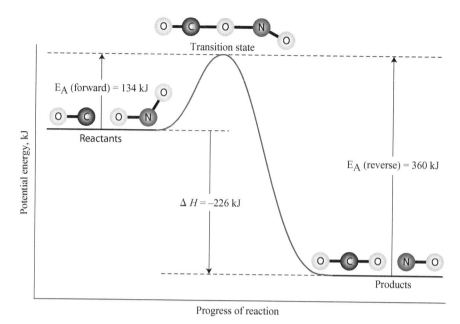

FIGURE 37.2 **The reaction profile for the bimolecular reaction between NO$_2$ and CO.** The transition state, or activated complex, is the configuration of atoms through which the molecular system must pass in order to form the products from the reactants.

The mechanism discussed at the beginning of the chapter was different—the temperature was lower.

At high temperatures the reaction between nitrogen dioxide and carbon monoxide occurs in a single elementary bimolecular collision between the two molecules:

$$NO_2(g) + CO(g) \rightarrow NO(g) + CO_2(g)$$

If the orientation in the collision is correct, so that the carbon atom of the CO collides with an oxygen atom of the NO$_2$, and if there is enough energy in the collision to weaken the N—O bond of the NO$_2$ molecule, how does the rearrangement of atoms take place? The transition state in the reaction is illustrated in Figure 37.2. The oxygen atom is halfway between the O—N fragment and the C—O fragment—on its way from the NO$_2$ molecule to the CO molecule. Of course, having reached the transition state, there is no guarantee that the NO and CO$_2$ molecules will be formed. The transition state could equally well break up to reform the reactant molecules.

The transition state does not exist as a molecular species as a reaction intermediate does; it merely represents the configuration of atoms through which the molecular system (the cluster of atoms) must pass in order to form the products from the reactants.

It is reasonable to assume that the rate of a reaction depends upon the concentration of the activated complex. If the concentration is high, then the products are easily formed and the rate of reaction is high. If, on the other hand, the concentration is low (or zero), then the rate at which the products can be formed is low (or zero).

We'll denote the equilibrium constant as K$^{\#}$. Usually K represents the equilibrium between the reactants and *products* of a reaction, which is *not* the case here.

In transition state theory, the activated complex is considered to be in equilibrium with the reactants. The activated complex is formed continuously from the reactants and it is continuously breaking up to reform the reactants:

$$K^{\#} = \frac{[\text{complex}]}{[\text{reactants}]}$$

Or, [complex] = $K^\#$ [reactants]

Since the rate depends upon the concentration of the complex,

$$\text{Rate} = K^\# \text{ [reactants]}$$

Compare this with the rate equation:

$$\text{Rate} = k \text{ [reactants]}$$

The significance is that the rate constant k is represented by $K^\#$, the equilibrium constant for the equilibrium between the reactants and the activated complex. And K is a thermodynamic function that equals $e^{-\frac{\Delta G^\#}{RT}}$.

We know that $\Delta G^\# = \Delta H^\# - T\Delta S^\#$, and therefore

$$K = e^{-\frac{\Delta G^\#}{RT}}$$

$$= e^{\frac{\Delta S^\#}{R}} \times e^{-\frac{\Delta H^\#}{RT}}$$

Compare this with the Arrhenius equation:

$$k = A \times e^{-\frac{E_A}{RT}}$$

The activation energy E_A can be identified as the enthalpy of activation $\Delta H^\#$. The frequency factor A can be identified as $e^{\frac{\Delta S^\#}{R}}$. Recall that the factor A incorporates the steric requirements of the collision. If the orientation requirements are more strict, this implies a more complicated activated complex and a larger decrease in entropy in its formation. That is, $\Delta S^\#$ is more negative and $e^{\frac{\Delta S^\#}{R}}$ is smaller. The rate of reaction is therefore lower.

37.8 Catalysis

Many reactions occur quite slowly under ordinary conditions. The rate can be increased by increasing the temperature but very often this makes alternative reaction mechanisms accessible leading to undesirable products. An alternative is to use a **catalyst**. A catalyst is a substance that provides an alternate route between the reactants and products—a route that has a lower activation energy and therefore a rate that is faster. The catalyst itself enters into the chemical reaction—it is involved in the reaction mechanism—but is left chemically unchanged after the reaction. For this reason, often only small quantities of a catalyst are required. The catalyst is used over and over again as the reaction proceeds.

A catalyst may change physically and deteriorate over time.

Great effort is devoted to developing catalysts in the chemical industry. Billions of dollars are spent each year to replace catalysts and to develop new ones. Without catalysts, some chemical processes would be prohibitively expensive.

Catalysts are kinetic agents—they cannot affect the thermodynamics of a reaction. For example, no catalyst can make a nonspontaneous reaction spontaneous and no catalyst can make an endothermic reaction exothermic. The reactants and products,

You can imagine that if the reaction was speeded up in just one direction, the equilibrium position would be changed, that is, K would be different. K is a thermodynamic quantity and cannot be changed by a catalyst.

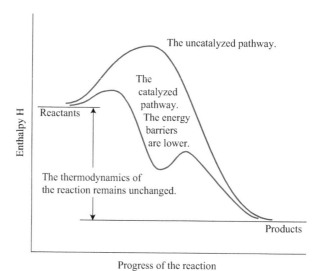

FIGURE 37.3   A catalyst provides an alternate route to the products.
The catalyzed reaction is faster because the activation energy is reduced.

and the difference between them are unaffected by catalysts—it is the route between the reactants and products that is changed (Figure 37.3).

As we now know, all systems are driven spontaneously toward equilibrium and catalysts do not affect the equilibrium reached by the system. They simply allow the equilibrium to be reached more quickly. Another feature of catalysts is that they catalyze reactions in both directions, forward and reverse. If it's easier to overcome the activation energy in the forward direction it must also be easier to overcome the same barrier in the reverse direction. No catalyst exists that catalyzes a reaction in just one direction.

Catalysts are classified as homogeneous or heterogeneous. A **homogeneous catalyst** is in the same phase as the reactants. A **heterogeneous catalyst** exists in a different phase. More often than not the catalyst in this case is a solid and the reactants are either gases, liquids, or in solution.

Homogeneous Catalysis

CCl_2F_2 is a common CFC called Freon-12.

A significant example of homogeneous catalysis occurs in the destruction of ozone in the upper atmosphere by chlorofluorocarbons (CFCs). CFCs are inert, nontoxic compounds used as refrigerants, in air-conditioning, and once used on a large scale in aerosol sprays and in manufacturing styrofoam insulation and similar products. Once allowed to escape into the atmosphere, the CFCs diffuse slowly up to the stratosphere where they break down under the influence of UV radiation. This produces chlorine atoms:

$$CCl_2F_2 \xrightarrow{h\nu} CClF_2 + Cl$$

The chlorine atoms react with ozone molecules to produce oxygen molecules and chlorine monoxide ClO.

$$Cl + O_3 \rightarrow ClO + O_2$$

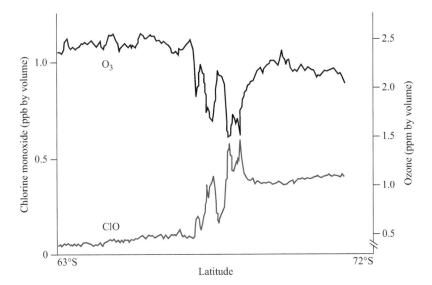

FIGURE 37.4 The correlation between the concentration of ClO in the atmosphere and the depletion of ozone.

The chlorine monoxide is the active agent in the destruction of the ozone layer. There is a direct correlation between the concentration of ClO in the atmosphere and the depletion of ozone (Figure 37.4).

The ClO, in a series of reactions, regenerates the chlorine atoms and produces oxygen molecules. We can summarize the process as:

$$2 \, ClO \rightarrow 2 \, Cl + O_2$$

The chlorine atoms then go on to destroy more ozone molecules. Doubling the first equation and adding the second produces the equation for the overall reaction:

$$2 \, O_3 \rightarrow 3 \, O_2$$

The chlorine atoms are a catalyst for the reaction. They participate in the reaction but are not used up. The chlorine atoms are used in the first step and regenerated in the second step and it is estimated that each chlorine atom catalyzes the destruction of about 100,000 ozone molecules before it is removed in a different reaction.

Heterogeneous Catalysis

A common example of a heterogeneous catalyst is the catalytic convertor in the emission systems of all modern automobiles. Untreated exhaust from an internal combustion engine contains many undesirable compounds that contribute to the toxic pollution of the atmosphere. This pollution is evident as the smog that hangs like a blanket over cities such as Los Angeles and Mexico City. The smog contains nitrogen oxides, unburned hydrocarbons, as well as ozone and other molecules formed by the action of sunlight on this mixture.

Under normal conditions, nitrogen does not react with oxygen but under the high pressures and temperatures of an internal combustion engine, some nitrogen oxides are produced. These nitrogen oxides, carbon monoxide, and unburned

The Montreal Protocol of 1987, and the amendments of 1992, set a program for phasing out the use of CFCs by 1996. Even if the use of CFCs stopped immediately, there is so much already free in the lower atmosphere, and it takes so long for the molecules to diffuse to the stratosphere, that the depletion of the ozone layer will continue for many years. Replacements for the CFCs include the HCFCs (hydrochlorofluorocarbons) which decay much more rapidly in the troposphere (before they reach the stratosphere), and the HFCs (hydrofluorocarbons) which do not catalyze the breakdown of ozone molecules like the CFCs.

The catalyst is not efficient until it becomes hot. Most pollution occurs in the first few minutes after the engine is started because the catalyst is not hot enough. Current designs incorporate a preheater for the catalyst to prevent this 'cold-start' pollution.

FIGURE 37.5 The internal structure of a catalytic converter.
The catalyst is deposited as a thin layer on an inert honeycomb ceramic matrix. The catalysts are expensive noble metals and the matrix maximizes the surface area while the thin layer minimizes the amount of catalyst required.

hydrocarbons are converted to nitrogen, carbon dioxide, and oxygen as they pass through the catalytic convertor:

$$2\,NO \xrightarrow{catalyst} N_2 + O_2 \qquad \text{reduction (of nitrogen)}$$

$$2\,CO + O_2 \xrightarrow{catalyst} 2\,CO_2 \qquad \text{oxidation (of carbon)}$$

$$C_xH_y + O_2 \xrightarrow{catalyst} CO_2 + H_2O \qquad \text{oxidation (of carbon)}$$

In this way the components responsible for the formation of smog are removed from the exhaust. The different reactions (oxidation and reduction) require different catalysts and several are found in a catalytic converter. Most converters are constructed of an inert honeycomb matrix covered in a thin layer of platinum, palladium, or rhodium metals and transition metal oxides such as copper(II) oxide or chromium(III) oxide. The construction is designed to maximize the contact between the catalysts and the exhaust gases (Figure 37.5).

Heterogeneous catalysis requires the transfer of the reactants from one phase to another. The basic steps of the reaction are

* Absorption of the reactants on the solid catalyst surface. This is a chemical interaction—chemical bonds are formed between the reactant molecules and the solid surface. The process is called **chemisorption**. Bonds within the reactant molecules are either weakened or broken as the bonds to the solid surface are formed.

* The reaction occurs on the surface of the catalyst. Molecules move about to some extent; bonds are broken, new bonds are formed.

* The product molecules leave the surface. This process is called **desorption**.

The process in Figure 37.6 illustrates the conversion of NO to N_2 and O_2 on a rhodium surface.

FIGURE 37.6 A representation of the catalyzed conversion of nitric oxide NO to nitrogren N_2 and oxygen O_2 on rhodium metal.

37.9 Enzymes

Many biological processes would be essentially impossible without appropriate catalysts called **enzymes**. The ability of enzymes to provide a pathway to complex biological molecules is truly impressive. A typical enzyme is a large protein molecule with a molar mass in the tens of thousands. The molecule has an active site, a location on the protein that can accept a reactant molecule called the **substrate**. The active site is substrate-specific—only certain molecules will fit. Very often the enzyme structure alters slightly when the substrate is attached—the enzyme is slightly distorted.

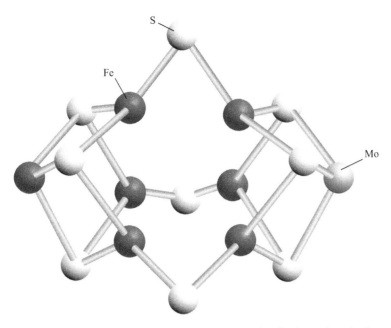

FIGURE 37.7   The cofactor of the enzyme nitrogenase that is the active site in reducing nitrogen to ammonia.
The mechanism of the reduction is not known but it is thought that the dinitrogen molecule bonds to the molybdenum atom.

When a substrate is attached to the enzyme, the required reaction is facilitated. Bonds that need to be broken are weakened by the interaction between the enzyme and substrate. Bonds that need to be made are more easily accomplished because the substrate is attached to the enzyme in such a way that two atoms that are required to bond are brought together. The substrate bound to the enzyme is in a more energetic state, poised to undergo the desired reaction. In this way, the enzyme directs the reaction in a very specific way—it provides a low energy pathway between the substrate and the product (that is, it reduces the activation energy E_A) and it orients the substrate, or substrates, appropriately (it increases the value of the pre-exponential factor A). The rearrangement takes place, the new substrate structure is no longer held so tightly, and the product is released.

An example is the **fixation** of nitrogen. Plants need nitrogen in order to grow but nitrogen itself is an unreactive molecule due in large part to the strength of the triple bond between the two nitrogen atoms. The nitrogen must be converted to compounds such as ammonia to be of use—this is the process called **nitrogen-fixation**. There is a remarkable enzyme that exists in the bacteria that live in the nodules of legumes called nitrogenase. This enzyme catalyzes the fixation of nitrogen at ordinary temperatures and atmospheric pressure and is responsible for the majority of fixed nitrogen present on this planet. The active site of the nitrogenase enzyme is a **cofactor** constructed from iron, molybdenum, and sulfur atoms illustrated in Figure 37.7 The mechanism of the reduction is not known but it is thought that the dinitrogen molecule bonds to the molybdenum atom. The conversion of nitrogen into ammonia requires a reduction in the oxidation number of the nitrogen from 0 to −3 and transition metals have variable oxidation states that are effective in oxidation-reduction reactions.

The suffix –ase is used to denote an enzyme.

A cofactor is a component of an enzyme, other than the protein, necessary for the proper function of the enzyme.

The Haber process is also discussed in Unit 35.

The Haber-Bosch process, developed in 1912, was the first successful industrial fixation of nitrogen. In this process, nitrogen and hydrogen are combined at a pressure of several hundred atmospheres at a temperature of several hundred degrees in the presence of an iron catalyst to produce ammonia. The Haber-Bosch process is a brute-force conversion of nitrogen and hydrogen into ammonia. The high pressures and temperatures are necessary to shift the equilibrium to the product side and to achieve a reasonable reaction rate and about 40 billion pounds of ammonia are manufactured each year in the United States using the Haber-Bosch process.

Elucidation of the mechanism of this reduction catalyzed by the enzyme nitrogenase would perhaps lead to the production of an industrial catalyst that would mimic the action of the enzyme. Such a catalyst would allow a far more efficient production of ammonia from nitrogen.

Review Questions

1. What is an elementary step and what is the molecularity of an elementary step?

2. How is the order of an elementary step related to its molecularity?

3. What is the rate-determining step of a reaction mechanism?

4. What is a reaction intermediate?

5. What are the two requirements of a proposed mechanism for a reaction? If the experimental rate equation can be derived from a proposed mechanism, does that mean the mechanism is correct?

6. Describe the steady-state approximation.

7. Describe the characteristic elementary steps in a chain reaction. What makes a chain reaction explosive?

8. List two requirements for a successful collision between molecules.

9. Describe the effect of temperature on the rate of an elementary step.

10. What is the Arrhenius equation and what does it describe?

11. What is a transition state?

12. Describe three ways to speed up a reaction and why the reaction does speed up when these three things are done.

13. What does a catalyst do? What is the difference between a homogeneous catalyst and a heterogeneous catalyst?

Solutions to Problems

PROBLEM 37.1A

a. $I_2 \rightleftharpoons 2\,I$ unimolecular

   $H_2 + I \rightleftharpoons H_2I$ bimolecular

   $H_2I + I \rightarrow 2\,HI$ bimolecular

b. I and H_2I are reaction intermediates.

c. $I_2 \rightleftharpoons 2\,I$

   $H_2 + I \rightleftharpoons H_2I$

   $\underline{H_2I + I \rightarrow 2\,HI}$

   $H_2 + I_2 \rightarrow 2\,HI$

PROBLEM 37.2A

$NO(g) + O_2(g) \rightleftharpoons NO_3(g)$ fast

$NO(g) + NO_3(g) \rightarrow 2\,NO_2(g)$ slow

Step 1: a rapidly established equilibrium:

$$K_1 = \frac{[NO_3]}{[NO][O_2]} \quad \text{and} \quad [NO_3] = K_1[NO][O_2]$$

Step 2: the rate-determining step:

$$\text{Rate} = k_2[NO][NO_3]$$

Substituting for $[NO_3]$, the reaction intermediate:

$$\text{Rate} = K_1 k_2[NO][NO][O_2] = k[NO]^2[O_2]$$

PROBLEM 37.3A

$$k_1 = 2.0 \times 10^{-5} \text{ s}^{-1} \text{ at } 20°\text{C (293 K)}$$

$$k_2 = 3.0 \times 10^{-3} \text{ s}^{-1} \text{ at } 60°\text{C (333 K)}$$

$$\ln(k_2/k_1) = -\frac{E_A}{R}\left(\frac{1}{T_2} - \frac{1}{T_1}\right)$$

$$\ln(3.0 \times 10^{-3}/2.0 \times 10^{-5}) = -E_A/R \,(1/333 - 1/293)$$

$$= (E_A/8.314 \text{ J K}^{-1}\text{mol}^{-1}) \times 40 \text{ K}/(333 \text{ K} \times 293 \text{ K})$$

$$5.01 = E_A \times 4.93 \times 10^{-5} \text{ mol J}^{-1}$$

$$E_A = 1.0 \times 10^{5} \text{ J mol}^{-1}$$

$$= 100 \text{ kJ mol}^{-1}$$

Answers to Review Questions

1. An elementary step of a reaction mechanism is a single step in a sequence of steps making up the chemical reaction. The molecularity of an elementary step is the number of reactant molecules involved in that step. The molecularity of an elementary step is the number of molecules or reacting species that come together in the reaction step. There are three types of elementary steps: unimolecular (one molecule involved), bimolecular (two molecules involved), and termolecular (three molecules involved).

2. The order of an elementary step equals the molecularity of the step. For example, the order of a bimolecular step is always two.

3. The rate-determining step in a sequence of elementary steps making up a chemical reaction is the slowest step. It is the step that determines the overall rate. The reaction cannot go more quickly than the slowest step.

4. A reaction intermediate is a species formed in one elementary step during a reaction and subsequently used in another elementary step. It does not appear in the overall chemical equation.

5. The sum of the elementary steps must yield the overall equation for the reaction and the mechanism must yield a rate law that matches the experimentally observed rate law. If the observed rate equation can be derived from a proposed mechanism, the mechanism may be correct, but is not necessarily correct.

6. The steady-state approximation is the assumption that the concentration of an intermediate in a reaction mechanism remains constant, or steady, as the reaction proceeds.

7. A chain reaction is a series of elementary steps all involving a highly reactive intermediate. The first step is the initiation of the intermediates. Following propagation steps use and generate the intermediates. A branching propagation step produces more intermediates than it uses—this accelerates the reaction. A termination step produces no intermediates and quenches the reaction. The branching steps cause an exponential increase in rate and lead to an explosive reaction.

8. The molecules must collide with sufficient energy to overcome the activation energy and they must collide with the correct orientation with respect to each other.

9. An increase in the temperature increases the rate of an elementary step according to the Arrhenius equation.

10. The Arrhenius equation is an expression for k (the rate constant) that includes all the factors that affect a reaction other than concentration.

$$k \text{ (rate constant)} = A\, e^{-\frac{E_A}{RT}}$$

A is a parameter that is related to the collision frequency and the orientation requirements. The exponential term is the fraction of molecules having the minimum energy E_A required for the reaction.

11. The transition state is the configuration of atoms at the point of highest potential energy between the reactants and the products. The rearrangement of atoms (the reaction) requires that the system pass through the transition state.

12. Increase the concentrations of the reactants. The rate increases because collisions between the molecules increase in frequency.

Increase the temperature. The rate increases because more energy is available at higher temperatures and the fraction of molecules possessing sufficient energy to overcome the activation energy barrier is higher. The collision frequency is also increased but this is a relatively minor effect.

Add a catalyst. The rate increases because the catalyst provides an alternative mechanism for the reaction with a lower activation energy.

13. The catalyst provides a different route for the reaction. The new route has a lower activation energy than the uncatalyzed route and the rate of the reaction increases. A homogeneous catalyst is a catalyst in the same phase as the reactants. A heterogeneous catalyst is a catalyst in a different phase from the reactants.

End-of-Unit Problems

1. Write rate laws for the following elementary steps:
    a. $O_3(g) + NO(g) \rightarrow O_2(g) + NO_2(g)$
    b. $N_2O_2(g) \rightarrow 2\ NO(g)$
    c. $COCl(g) + Cl_2(g) \rightarrow COCl_2(g) + Cl(g)$

2. Write rate laws for the following elementary steps:
    a. $O_3(g) + Cl(g) \rightarrow ClO(g) + O_2(g)$
    b. $I^-(aq) + ClO^-(aq) \rightarrow IO^-(aq) + Cl^-(aq)$
    c. $CO(g) + NO_3(g) \rightarrow CO_2(g) + NO_2(g)$

3. The following mechanisms have been proposed for the reaction of nitric oxide and chlorine to produce nitrosyl chloride:

$$2\ NO(g) + Cl_2(g) \rightarrow 2\ NOCl(g)$$

Mechanism I: $2\ NO \rightleftharpoons N_2O_2$
$N_2O_2 + Cl_2 \rightarrow 2\ NOCl$

Mechanism II: $NO + Cl_2 \rightarrow NOCl_2$
$NO + NOCl_2 \rightarrow 2\ NOCl$

For each mechanism,
    a. What is the molecularity of each step?
    b. Which species are reaction intermediates?
    c. Do the elementary steps add up to the correct balanced equation for the reaction?
    d. If the first step is the rate determining step, does either mechanism match the observed rate law: Rate = $k[NO]^2[Cl_2]$?
    e. If the second step is the rate determining step, does either mechanism match the observed rate law?

4. The experimental rate law for the reaction

$$2H_2 + 2NO \rightarrow N_2 + 2H_2O$$

is Rate = $k[H_2][NO]^2$. Three proposed mechanisms for this reaction are:

Mechanism I: $H_2 + NO \rightarrow N + H_2O$ Slow
$N + NO \rightarrow N_2 + O$ Fast
$O + H_2 \rightarrow H_2O$ Fast

Mechanism II: $H_2 + 2NO \rightarrow N_2O + H_2O$ Slow
$N_2O + H_2 \rightarrow N_2 + H_2O$ Fast

Mechanism III: $2NO \rightleftharpoons N_2O_2$ Very fast
$N_2O_2 + H_2 \rightarrow N_2O + H_2O$ Slow
$N_2O + H_2 \rightarrow N_2 + H_2O$ Fast

For each mechanism,
    a. What is the molecularity of each step?
    b. Which species are reaction intermediates?
    c. Do the elementary steps add up to the correct balanced equation for the reaction?
    d. Which, if any, of these mechanisms agrees with the observed experimental rate equation? Can any of the mechanisms be ruled out?

5. Nitrogen reacts with hydrogen to produce ammonia.

$$N_2(g) + 3H_2(g) \rightarrow 2NH_3(g)$$

A proposed mechanism for this reaction is

$N_2 + H_2 \rightleftharpoons N_2H_2$ Fast
$N_2H_2 + H_2 \rightarrow N_2H_4$ Slow
$N_2H_4 + H_2 \rightarrow 2NH_3$ Fast

    a. What are reaction intermediates in this reaction mechanism?
    b. What is the rate equation for the reaction according to this mechanism?
    c. What is the overall order for the reaction?

6. A proposed mechanism for a reaction is:

$C_4H_9Br \rightarrow C_4H_9^+ + Br^-$ Slow
$C_4H_9^+ + H_2O \rightarrow C_4H_9OH_2^+$ Fast
$C_4H_9OH_2^+ + H_2O \rightarrow C_4H_9OH + H_3O^+$ Fast

    a. What are reaction intermediates in this reaction mechanism?
    b. What is the rate equation for the reaction according to this mechanism?
    c. What is the overall chemical reaction?

7. The following mechanisms have been proposed for the reduction of iodine monochloride by hydrogen.

$$2\ ICl(g) + H_2(g) \rightarrow 2\ HCl(g) + I_2(g)$$

Mechanism I:	$H_2 + ICl \rightarrow HI + HCl$	Fast
	$HI + ICl \rightarrow HCl + I_2$	Slow
Mechanism II:	$H_2 + ICl \rightarrow HI + HCl$	Slow
	$HI + ICl \rightarrow HCl + I_2$	Fast
Mechanism III:	$H_2 + ICl \rightarrow HICl + H$	Slow
	$H + ICl \rightarrow HCl + I$	Fast
	$HICl \rightarrow HCl + I$	Fast
	$I + I \rightarrow I_2$	Fast

For each mechanism,

a. What is the molecularity of each step?

b. Which species are reaction intermediates?

c. Do the elementary steps add up to the correct balanced equation for the reaction?

d. If the observed rate law is: Rate = $k[H_2][ICl]$, which, if any, of these mechanisms is possible and which can be ruled out?

8. The experimental rate law for the reaction

$$2NO + O_2 \rightarrow 2\ NO_2$$

is Rate = $k[NO]^2[O_2]$. Three proposed mechanisms for this reaction are:

Mechanism I:	$O_2 + NO \rightarrow O + NO_2$	Slow
	$O + NO \rightarrow NO_2$	Fast
Mechanism II:	$O_2 + NO \rightleftharpoons NO_3$	Fast
	$NO_3 + NO \rightarrow 2\ NO_2$	Slow
Mechanism III:	$2\ NO \rightleftharpoons N_2O_2$	Fast
	$N_2O_2 + O_2 \rightarrow 2\ NO_2$	Slow

For each mechanism,

a. What is the molecularity of each step?

b. Which species are reaction intermediates?

c. Do the elementary steps add up to the correct balanced equation for the reaction?

d. Which mechanisms agree with the observed experimental rate equation?

9. Sometimes the reaction orders for reactants in a chemical reaction are fractional. These fractional exponents arise because of the mechanism of the reaction. For example, consider the reaction of chloroform and chlorine in the gas phase to produce carbon tetra-chloride:

$$CHCl_3(g) + Cl_2(g) \rightarrow CCl_4(g) + HCl(g)$$

The following mechanism has been suggested:

Step 1: $Cl_2 \rightleftharpoons 2Cl$	Fast
Step 2: $Cl + CHCl_3 \rightarrow HCl + CCl_3$	Slow
Step 3: $Cl + CCl_3 \rightarrow CCl_4$	Fast

a. Show that the sum of the elementary steps equals the overall equation.

b. Derive the rate law from this mechanism.

c. What is the overall order of reaction?

10. Sometimes the reaction orders for reactants in a chemical reaction are negative. These negative exponents arise because of the mechanism of the reaction. For example, consider the reaction of iodide ion and hypochlorite ion in basic aqueous solution:

$$I^-(aq) + ClO^-(aq) \rightarrow Cl^-(aq) + IO^-(aq)$$

The following mechanism has been suggested:

Step 1: $ClO^- + H_2O \rightleftharpoons HClO + OH^-$	Fast
Step 2: $HClO + I^- \rightarrow HIO + Cl^-$	Slow
Step 3: $HIO + OH^- \rightleftharpoons IO^- + H_2O$	Fast

a. Show that the sum of the elementary steps equals the overall equation.

b. Derive the rate law from this mechanism.

c. What is the overall order of reaction?

11. The gas phase decomposition of acetaldehyde CH_3CHO to methane CH_4 and carbon monoxide occurs by a chain reaction. Some of the steps involved are:

$$CH_3CHO \rightarrow \cdot CH_3 + \cdot CHO$$
$$\cdot CH_3 + CH_3CHO \rightarrow CH_4 + \cdot CH_2CHO$$
$$\cdot CH_2CHO \rightarrow \cdot CH_3 + CO$$
$$\cdot CH_3 + \cdot CH_3 \rightarrow C_2H_6$$
$$\cdot CH_3 + \cdot CHO \rightarrow CH_3CHO$$

Characterize each step as initiation, propagation, or termination.

12. The reaction between methane and chlorine to produce chloromethane and hydrogen chloride occurs by a chain reaction. Some of the steps involved are:

$$Cl_2 \rightarrow Cl\cdot + Cl\cdot$$
$$CH_4 + Cl\cdot \rightarrow \cdot CH_3 + HCl$$
$$CH_4 + Cl_2 \rightarrow \cdot CH_3 + HCl + Cl\cdot$$
$$\cdot CH_3 + Cl_2 \rightarrow CH_3Cl + Cl\cdot$$
$$\cdot Cl + \cdot Cl \rightarrow Cl_2$$
$$\cdot CH_3 + \cdot Cl \rightarrow CH_3Cl$$

Characterize each step as initiation, propagation, or termination.

13. If the rate of a reaction increases tenfold when the temperature increases from 25°C to 60°C, what is the activation energy E_A for the reaction?

14. If the rate of a reaction increases by a factor of 15 when the temperature increases from 10°C to 55°C, what is the activation energy E_A for the reaction?

15. The activation energy for a reaction is 95 kJ mol^{-1}. If the rate of formation of product at 25°C is 0.231 mol L^{-1} s^{-1}, what would the rate of product formation be at 40°C? Assume the the frequency factor A remains the same.

16. The activation energy for a reaction is 125 kJ mol^{-1}. If the rate of formation of product at 35°C is 20.4 mol L^{-1} min^{-1}, what would the rate of product formation be at 55°C? Assume the the frequency factor A remains the same.

17. Calculate the activation energy, E_A, for the reaction below, given that k the rate constant has a value of 3.46×10^{-5} s^{-1} at 25°C and value of 1.48×10^{-4} s^{-1} at 35°C.

$$N_2O_5(g) \rightarrow 2\ NO(g) + \tfrac{1}{2}\ O_2(g)$$

18. Calculate the activation energy, E_A, for the production of phosgene, given that k the rate constant at 250°C has a value 1000 times higher than at 175°C.

$$CO(g) + Cl_2(g) \rightarrow COCl_2(g)$$

19. The activation energy for the first order isomerization of methyl isonitrile CH_3NC to acetonitrile CH_3CN is 160 kJ mol^{-1} and the rate constant for the reaction at 300°C is 0.28 s^{-1}. What is the value of the rate constant at 600°C?

20. The activation energy for the first order isomerization of cyclopropane C_3H_6 to propene C_3H_6 is 272 kJ mol^{-1} and the rate constant for the reaction at 500°C is 6.0×10^{-4} s^{-1}. What is the value of the rate constant at 25°C?

21. The rate of the reaction between nitrogen dioxide and ozone was studied at different temperatures and the rate constant determined. The following results were obtained:

$$NO_2 + O_3 \rightarrow NO_3 + O_2$$

Temperature (°C)	k(L mol^{-1} s^{-1})
−70	4.15×10^5
−60	7.32×10^5
−50	1.24×10^6
−40	2.00×10^6
−30	3.10×10^6

a. Graph the data and determine the activation energy E_A for the reaction.

b. From the graph, determine the value of the rate constant k at 25°C.

22. The isotope exchange between hydrogen H and deuterium D in the following reaction was studied at different temperatures. The results were:

$$H + D_2 \rightarrow HD + D$$

Temperature (K)	k(L mol^{-1} s^{-1})
300	1.60×10^4
328	3.80×10^4
345	7.50×10^4
440	1.07×10^6
550	8.70×10^6

a. Graph the data and determine the activation energy E_A for the reaction.

b. From the graph, determine the value of the rate constant k at 1000 K.

23. Urea hydrolyses to ammonia and carbon dioxide:

$$NH_2CONH_2 + H_2O \rightarrow 2\ NH_3 + CO_2$$

In the absence of a catalyst the activation energy for the reaction is 125 kJ mol^{-1}. However, in the presence of the enzyme urease, the activation energy is reduced to 46 kJ mol^{-1}. Assuming that the frequency factor A is approximately the same in both cases,

a. how much faster does the reaction proceed in the presence of the catalyst?

b. what temperature would be required of the uncatalyzed reaction to achieve the rate of the catalyzed reaction at 25°C?

24. The enzyme catalase catalyzes the decomposition of hydrogen peroxide to water and oxygen:

$$2\ H_2O_2 \rightarrow 2\ H_2O + O_2$$

In the absence of a catalyst the activation energy for the reaction is 42 kJ mol^{-1}. In the presence of the enzyme catalase, the activation energy is reduced to 7.0 kJ mol^{-1}. Assuming that the frequency factor A is approximately the same in both cases,

a. how much faster does the reaction proceed in the presence of the catalyst?

b. what temperature would be required of the uncatalyzed reaction to achieve the rate of the catalyzed reaction at 25°C?

Acids and Bases

38.1   What Are Acids and Bases?

In Unit 8 we learned that electrolytes in aqueous solution can be classified as acids, bases, or salts. Acids were defined as solutes that produce the hydrogen ion H^+ when they dissolve in water. Bases were defined as solutes that produce the hydroxide ion OH^- when they dissolve in water. These are the definitions of acids and bases suggested by Arrhenius in 1884.

Ask a chemist now what an acid is and you may get a different answer. For example, an acid may be defined as an electron-pair acceptor. In fact, scientists have defined acids and bases in several different ways. Some definitions are without doubt more useful than others and in this unit we will review the more common definitions of acids and bases and determine the underlying principles.

Acids and bases have been known since the early days of alchemy a thousand years ago. Old names for some common strong acids reflect their long history. Sulfuric acid was known as *oil of vitriol* or simply as *vitriol*. It was made by distilling *green vitriol* (iron(II) sulfate). If the green vitriol was mixed with salt (sodium chloride) and then distilled, *aqua salis* (or spirit of salt) was obtained—an acid now known as hydrochloric acid. The third common strong acid, nitric acid, was made by distilling a mixture of green vitriol, alum ($KAl(SO_4)_2 \cdot 12H_2O$), and saltpetre (potassium nitrate) and was known as *aqua fortis* (strong water). A mixture of one part nitric acid and three parts hydrochloric acid was, and still is, known as *aqua regia*. This mixture is able to oxidize noble metals such as gold and platinum.

Characteristic properties of acids and bases have been established over many years. Acids, for example, tend to be sour. Bases tend to feel slippery and have a bitter taste. Acids react with many metals to produce hydrogen gas. The reaction between an acid and a base often produced effervescence—an example is the reaction between vinegar and baking soda. Robert Boyle (1627–1691) made an important contribution when he found that a blue vegetable substance called *syrup of violets* turned red when added to acids and turned green when added to bases. This was the first use of an **acid-base indicator** and provided useful operational definitions of an acid and a base: An acid was defined as a substance that changes the color of syrup of violets red and a base was defined as a substance that changes the color of syrup of violets green. Boyle was able to use his indicator to monitor the neutralization of an acid and a base.

38.2   Arrhenius Definitions

Svante Arrhenius was the first person to suggest that some compounds exist as ions in solution. In particular, he classified acids as those solutes that ionize in aqueous solution to produce the hydrogen ion H^+. Typical examples are the three strong acids mentioned earlier: sulfuric acid H_2SO_4, hydrochloric acid HCl, and nitric acid HNO_3. Notice the H present in the formulas of all three of these acids—all Arrhenius acids have an H in their formula. Note that these are atoms of hydrogen in the acid molecules not H^+ ions—the hydrogen ions are produced only when the acid ionizes during the solution process. The sour taste typical of acids is caused by the presence of these hydrogen ions in solution.

Arrhenius classified bases as those solutes that increase the concentration of hydroxide ions OH^- in aqueous solution. It is the reaction of the hydroxide ion with the

The word *vitriolic* describes caustic or hostile speech. Green vitriol is $FeSO_4 \cdot 7H_2O$. Blue vitriol is $CuSO_4 \cdot 5H_2O$.

Pure colorless nitric acid is still made in the lab by adding sulfuric acid to potassium nitrate and distilling the product under vacuum. The acid should be stored below 0°C to avoid decomposition to nitrogen dioxide which gives nitric acid its typical pale yellow color.

The word *acid* is derived from the Latin *acidus* meaning sour. Citric acid is responsible for the sour taste of lemons.

As we learned in Unit 8, the hydrogen ion H^+ released by the acid molecule immediately attaches itself to a water molecule to produce an ion called the hydronium ion H_3O^+. This hydronium ion is itself heavily hydrated and is written as $H_3O^+(aq)$.

oils in your skin that causes the slippery feeling. Very often Arrhenius bases contain hydroxide ions. Examples are sodium hydroxide NaOH and barium hydroxide $Ba(OH)_2$.

Arrhenius definitions: An **acid** is a substance that increases the concentration of hydronium ion H_3O^+ when dissolved in water. A **base** is a substance that increases the concentration of hydroxide ion OH^- when dissolved in water.

When an acid and a base react, the two neutralize each other and a salt is formed. According to Arrhenius, **neutralization** occurs when hydronium ions H_3O^+ from the acid in solution react with hydroxide ions OH^- from the base in solution to form the solvent water. The net ionic equation is:

$$H_3O^+(aq) + OH^-(aq) \rightarrow 2\,H_2O(l)$$

This description of neutralization explains why the heat released in the neutralization reaction of a strong acid and a strong base is always the same—regardless of the identities of the acid and base. The reaction, illustrated by the net ionic equation, is always the same. The identity of the spectator ions does not affect the heat of reaction.

As we noted in Unit 8, some acids and bases are strong and others are weak—it depends upon the extent to which the ionization takes place. For example, hydrochloric acid ionizes almost completely in water to produce hydronium ions $H_3O^+(aq)$ and chloride ions $Cl^-(aq)$. There are essentially no HCl molecules in solution. This acid is a **strong acid**:

Review (*cf.* Unit 8) and learn the seven common strong acids.

$$HCl(aq) + H_2O(l) \rightleftharpoons H_3O^+(aq) + Cl^-(aq) \qquad \text{complete ionization}$$

The equilibrium constant for this system, K_a, is very large.

K_a because this is an *acid* ionization reaction.

On the other hand, hydrofluoric acid is a **weak acid** because it ionizes very little in aqueous solution. Most of the hydrofluoric acid molecules remain in the molecular form and very few break up to form ions:

$$HF(aq) + H_2O(l) \rightleftharpoons H_3O^+(aq) + F^-(aq) \qquad \text{little ionization}$$

The equilibrium constant for this system, K_a, is very small (6.8×10^{-4} at 25°C).

The difference in the behavior of these two acids is illustrated in Figure 38.1.

Sodium hydroxide is an example of a **strong base**. When sodium hydroxide dissolves, the ions dissociate and exist in solution as hydrated sodium and hydroxide ions. There are essentially no NaOH 'molecular units' in dilute solution:

The (aq) indicates that the Na^+ and OH^- ions in aqueous solution are surrounded by water molecules. The ion-dipole attraction between the Na^+ and OH^- ions and the water molecules is strong. The energy released is sufficient to more than compensate for the energy required to break up the NaOH crystalline lattice.

$$NaOH(s) + H_2O(l) \rightleftharpoons Na^+(aq) + OH^-(aq) + H_2O(l) \qquad \text{complete ionization}$$

The equilibrium constant for this system, K_b, is very large.

K_b because this is a *base*.

Ammonia is an example of a **weak base**. The concentration of hydroxide ions produced in an aqueous solution of ammonia is low, most of the ammonia molecules remain molecules:

$$NH_3(aq) + H_2O(l) \rightleftharpoons NH_4^+(aq) + OH^-(aq) \qquad \text{little ionization}$$

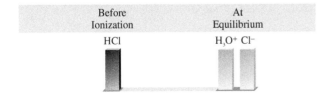

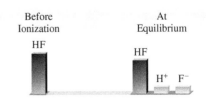

FIGURE 38.1   The extent of ionization of a strong acid such as HCl (left) and a weak acid such as HF (right).
Initially, there were 6 HCl and 6 HF molecules present. The strong acid is assumed to be completely ionized in solution. The proton exists in solution as the hydronium ion (H_3O^+).

The equilibrium constant for this system, K_b, is very small (1.8×10^{-5} at 25°C).

The descriptions strong and weak are relative terms. In aqueous solution strong means that an acid is stronger than H_3O^+ and a base is stronger than OH^-. A strong acid or base in water may be weak in a different solvent, and *vice versa*.

38.3 Brønsted-Lowry Definitions

All Arrhenius acids are Brønsted-Lowry acids, but Brønsted-Lowry acids are not necessarily Arrhenius acids. The same is true of bases. The Brønsted-Lowry definitions are broader and more useful than the Arrhenius definitions.

The Arrhenius definitions of acid and base are simple and, for aqueous systems, quite useful. However, more general definitions of an acid and a base were proposed independently by Johannes Brønsted and Thomas Lowry in 1923. Their definitions of acid and base emphasize the fact that many acid-base reactions, particularly those in aqueous solution, involve the transfer of a hydrogen ion from the acid to the base.

They defined an acid as a substance that donates a hydrogen ion to another substance (the base). A base is defined as a substance that accepts a hydrogen ion from another substance (the acid). This is such a useful concept that we will use the Brønsted-Lowry definitions in analyzing all aqueous equilibria in subsequent units.

Brønsted-Lowry definitions: An **acid** is a substance that donates a hydrogen ion H^+. A **base** is a substance that accepts a hydrogen ion H^+.

In any acid-base reaction, there is an acid and a base. The two always work together. If an acid donates a hydrogen ion, then some other substance, the base, must be present to accept it, and *vice versa*. In a system in equilibrium, in which there are two opposite reactions occurring at the same rate, there must be an acid and a base on the reactant side and another acid and base on the product side. Both reactions, the forward reaction and the reverse reaction, involve the transfer of a hydrogen ion from an acid to a base. For example, look at the ionization of hydrochloric acid in water:

$$\underset{\text{acid}}{HCl(aq)} + \underset{\text{base}}{H_2O(l)} \rightleftharpoons \underset{\text{acid}}{H_3O^+(aq)} + \underset{\text{base}}{Cl^-(aq)}$$

On the reactant side, the HCl molecule donates a hydrogen ion to the water molecule. The HCl molecule is an acid and the water molecule is a base. The base accepts the hydrogen ion from the acid. On the product side, the hydronium ion donates a hydrogen ion to the chloride ion. The hydronium ion is an acid and the chloride ion is a base. There is an acid and a base on both sides of the equation. Moreover, the acid on one side is the partner of the base on the other side. For example, when HCl donates its hydrogen ion, it forms the chloride ion—a base. The HCl/Cl⁻ acid-base pair is called a **conjugate pair**, and HCl and Cl⁻ are called **conjugate partners**. In other words, the chloride ion Cl⁻ is the **conjugate base** of hydrochloric acid HCl and hydrochloric acid HCl is the **conjugate acid** of the chloride ion Cl⁻.

The word conjugate comes from Latin and means joined together as in a partnership.

$$\underset{\text{acid}}{HCl(aq)} + \underset{\text{base}}{H_2O(l)} \rightleftharpoons \underset{\text{acid}}{H_3O^+(aq)} + \underset{\text{base}}{Cl^-(aq)}$$

In a Brønsted-Lowry acid-base system, there are only four components: an acid and base on one side of the equation and an acid and a base on the other side. These systems always have two conjugate acid-base pairs. Equations representing Brønsted-Lowry acid-base equilibria are net ionic equations. Spectator ions should be omitted. We will look at Brønsted-Lowry acid-base reactions in more detail in subsequent units.

EXAMPLE 38.1 BRØNSTED-LOWRY ACID-BASE EQUILIBRIA

For the following acid-base reactions, write the net ionic equation, characterize each component as acid or base, and pair the conjugate partners.

   a. the ionization of ammonia in aqueous solution

   b. the neutralization of nitric acid with potassium hydroxide

UNDERSTAND THE QUESTION

A Brønsted-Lowry acid-base equilibrium consists of an acid and base on one side (the reactant side) and an acid and base on the other side (the product side). The acid on one side is the conjugate partner of the base on the other side. The conjugate partners differ in that the acid has one H^+ more than its conjugate base. The acid must have an H^+ to give away! The immediate task is to write a chemical equation representing the reaction and then eliminate spectator ions to derive the net ionic equation. There should be four components in the net ionic equation: two acids and two bases.

PLAN THE SOLUTION

Write the chemical equation and derive the net ionic equation. Determine the transfer of the hydrogen ions in the reaction. The hydrogen ion is always transferred *from the acid to the base*. Assign the acid and base labels and pair the conjugate partners. Check that the acid has one more H+ than its conjugate base.

SOLVE THE PROBLEM

   a. The chemical equation is (this is also the net ionic equation):

$$NH_3 \ + \ H_2O \ \rightleftharpoons \ NH_4^+ \ + \ OH^-$$

   base   acid   acid   base

When assigning the acid and base labels, it is often useful to look for the conjugate partners. For example, NH_3 and NH_4^+ belong together as partners; the NH_4^+ has one more H^+ than NH_3, and so the NH_4^+ is the acid of the partnership. Note also the presence of hydroxide OH^-, which is almost always a base in aqueous solution and is a good place to start assigning the labels. Since there is always an acid and a base on each side of the equation, if OH^- is a base, then NH_4^+ must be an acid.

   b. The chemical equation is:

$$HNO_3 + KOH \rightleftharpoons KNO_3 + H_2O$$

The detailed ionic equation is (write the hydrogen ion H^+ as the hydronium ion H_3O^+):

$$H_3O^+ + NO_3^- + K^+ + OH^- \rightleftharpoons K^+ + NO_3^- + 2 \ H_2O$$

Cancel the K^+ and NO_3^- ions from both sides and the net ionic equation is:

$$H_3O^+ \ + \ OH^- \ \rightleftharpoons \ H_2O \ + \ H_2O$$

   acid   base   base   acid

The hydronium ion H_3O^+ is always an acid in aqueous solution. Note that the assignment of the labels on the right side is arbitrary.

For the following acid-base reactions, write the net ionic equation, characterize each component as acid or base, and pair the conjugate partners.

a. the ionization of acetic acid in aqueous solution

b. the neutralization of hydrocyanic acid with sodium hydroxide

For the following acid-base reactions, write the net ionic equation, characterize each component as acid or base, and pair the conjugate partners.

a. the reaction of ammonia and hydrobromic acid in aqueous solution

b. the ionization of nitric acid in water

38.4 Nonaqueous Solvents

There are, of course, solvents other than water. Some examples are liquid ammonia NH_3, bromine trifluoride BrF_3, pure acetic acid CH_3CO_2H, liquid sulfur dioxide SO_2, and many organic solvents such as ethanol C_2H_5OH, diethylether $(C_2H_5)_2O$, acetone $(CH_3)_2CO$, hexane C_6H_{14}, and benzene C_6H_6, to name but a few. Many of these solvents are suitable for acid-base reactions. What is an acid in solvents such as these?

It is convenient to divide these **nonaqueous solvents** into various categories. The first category are **protonic solvents** such as ammonia, glacial acetic acid, and ethanol. A second category are **nonprotonic solvents** such as bromine trifluoride—note the absence of any H in the formula BrF_3. A third category are basic **coordinating solvents** such as diethylether. We'll restrict the discussion in this section to the first two categories. We'll meet examples of the third category in the next section and also when we look at the chemistry of magnesium, boron, and aluminum later.

An acid in a protonic nonaqueous solvent is a substance that produces the solvent cation when dissolved in the solvent. Let's examine liquid ammonia as an example. Just as an acid in water produces the solvent cation of water (the hydronium ion H_3O^+), an acid dissolved in liquid ammonia produces the solvent cation of ammonia (the ammonium ion NH_4^+). The solvent cation for a protonic solvent is generated by adding an H^+ to the solvent molecule.

Pure acetic acid (m.pt.16.6 °C) is often called glacial acetic acid because the solid looks very like ice.

These definitions of acids and bases require that the solvent is capable of autoionization—and this is not always the case for nonaqueous solvents. Autoionization is the self ionization of the solvent. For example, for water:

$$H_2O + H_2O \rightleftharpoons H_3O^+ + OH^-$$

$$
\begin{array}{cccccc}
 & & & \text{solvent} & & \text{solvent cation} \\
\text{In water:} & HA & + & H_2O & \rightleftharpoons & H_3O^+ & + & A^- \\
\text{In ammonia:} & HA & + & NH_3 & \rightleftharpoons & NH_4^+ & + & A^- \\
 & \text{acid} & & \text{base} & & \text{acid} & & \text{base}
\end{array}
$$

In Brønsted-Lowry terms, these equilibria can be divided into two acid-base conjugate partnerships. The anion A^- for example is the conjugate base of the acid HA.

A base in a protonic nonaqueous solvent is a substance that produces the solvent anion when dissolved in the solvent. In water, a base produces the solvent anion of water (the hydroxide ion OH^-). In liquid ammonia, a base produces the solvent anion of ammonia (the amide ion NH_2^-). The solvent anion for a protonic solvent is generated by removing an H^+ from the solvent molecule.

$$
\begin{array}{ccccccccc}
 & & & \text{solvent} & & & & \text{solvent anion} \\
\text{In water:} & B & + & H_2O & \rightleftharpoons & HB^+ & + & OH^- \\
\text{In ammonia:} & B & + & NH_3 & \rightleftharpoons & HB^+ & + & NH_2^- \\
 & \text{base} & & \text{acid} & & \text{acid} & & \text{base}
\end{array}
$$

Again in Brønsted-Lowry terms, the equilibria can be divided into two acid-base conjugate partnerships. In this case the ammonia molecule NH_3 is the conjugate acid of the amide ion NH_2^- and HB^+ is the conjugate acid of the base B.

In nonprotonic solvents, the same principle applies, except that the solvent cation is not formed by the addition of a hydrogen ion. An example is the solvent bromine trifluoride. An acid in BrF_3 does not donate a hydrogen ion—BrF_3 is *not* a protonic solvent. Instead an acid accepts a fluoride ion. An example of an acid in bromine trifluoride is antimony pentafluoride:

$$
\begin{array}{ccccccccc}
 & & & \text{solvent} & & \text{solvent cation} & & \\
\text{In } BrF_3: & SbF_5 & + & BrF_3 & \rightleftharpoons & BrF_2^+ & + & SbF_6^- \\
 & \text{acid} & & \text{base} & & \text{acid} & & \text{base}
\end{array}
$$

Antimony pentafluoride is an acid because it produces the solvent cation BrF_2^+. A base in the solvent BrF_3 would produce the solvent anion BrF_4^-.

We will restrict our look at acid-base equilibria to protonic systems in aqueous solution. However, the descriptive chemistry of the elements discussed in later units is easier to characterize if this kind of acid-base interaction is understood. The same is true of the Lewis definitions of acids and bases discussed in the next section.

EXAMPLE 38.2   OTHER PROTONIC SOLVENTS

Suppose pure acetic acid is used as a solvent for an acid-base reaction. What species is produced by an acid, for example HCl, when it is dissolved in the acetic acid? Write an equation for the reaction between the HCl and the solvent. What species is produced when a base is dissolved in the acetic acid?

UNDERSTAND THE QUESTION

In any protonic solvent, including water, an acid always produces the solvent cation and a base always produces the solvent anion. The solvent cation is a protonated solvent molecule—a solvent molecule to which an H^+ has been added. A solvent anion is a solvent molecule from which a hydrogen ion has been removed.

PLAN THE SOLUTION

Write the formula for the solvent molecule and add an H^+ and remove an H^+ to determine the formulas for the solvent cation and solvent anion respectively.

SOLVE THE PROBLEM

The solvent in this example is pure acetic acid—formula CH_3CO_2H. Addition of a hydrogen ion generates the solvent cation $CH_3CO_2H_2^+$. Removal of a hydrogen ion generates the solvent anion, the acetate ion $CH_3CO_2^-$. When HCl is dissolved in pure acetic acid, the solvent cation is produced:

$$\underset{\text{base}}{CH_3CO_2H} + \underset{\text{acid}}{HCl} \rightleftharpoons \underset{\substack{\text{solvent cation}\\ \text{acid}}}{CH_3CO_2H_2^+} + \underset{\text{base}}{Cl^-}$$

The equilibrium can be divided into two Brønsted-Lowry acid-base conjugate partnerships. In pure acetic acid, a base, for example sodium hydroxide, produces the acetate ion.

PROBLEM 38.2A

Suppose ethanol CH_3CH_2OH is used as a solvent for an acid-base reaction. What species is produced by an acid and what species is produced by a base when they are dissolved in ethanol? Write a net ionic equation representing the reaction of a strong acid and a strong base in ethanol solution.

PROBLEM 38.2B

Hydrazine NH_2NH_2 is a liquid similar in some respects to ammonia. If hydrazine is used as a solvent for an acid-base reaction, what species is produced by an acid and what species is produced by a base when they are dissolved in the solvent?

38.5   Lewis Definitions

In the same year that Johannes Brønsted and Thomas Lowry defined acid-base reactions in aqueous solution as the transfer of a hydrogen ion between the acid and the base, Gilbert N. Lewis proposed even broader definitions.

This is the same Gilbert N. Lewis whose work on covalent bonding we discussed in Unit 20.

Lewis described an acid-base reaction in terms of what happens to the valence electrons of the participants. He defined an acid as a substance that accepts a share in an electron pair from the base, and he defined a base as a substance that partially donates an electron pair to the acid. The acid-base reaction results in the formation of a **coordinate covalent bond**.

> **Lewis definitions**: An **acid** is a substance that accepts an electron pair. A **base** is a substance that donates an electron pair.

A typical Arrhenius acid-base reaction is the formation of the ammonium ion NH_4^+ from ammonia NH_3 in acidic solution:

$$H^+ + NH_3 \rightleftharpoons NH_4^+$$

In Brønsted-Lowry terms the reaction would be written:

$$H_3O^+ + NH_3 \rightleftharpoons NH_4^+ + H_2O$$

Lewis's view of the reaction is a partial transfer of the lone pair of electrons from the ammonia molecule to the hydrogen ion and the formation of a bond between the two:

$$H^+ \; + \; \overset{\displaystyle H}{\underset{\displaystyle H}{:N-H}} \longrightarrow \left[\overset{\displaystyle H}{\underset{\displaystyle H}{H-N-H}}\right]^+$$

All Brønsted-Lowry acid-base reactions are Lewis acid-base reactions. This is because a Brønsted-Lowry base must have an available electron pair in order to accept a hydrogen ion. Similarly a Brønsted-Lowry acid must be able to supply a hydrogen ion, which is an electron pair acceptor. However, there are Lewis acid-base reactions that are not Brønsted-Lowry reactions. The Lewis definitions are more general than the Brønsted-Lowry definitions (Figure 38.2).

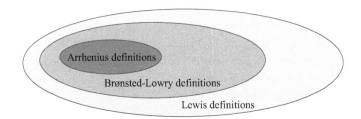

FIGURE 38.2   Arrhenius, Brønsted-Lowry, and Lewis acid-base definitions.
The Arrhenius definitions are a subset of the Brønsted-Lowry definitions, which are in turn a subset of the Lewis definitions.

An example of a Lewis acid-base reaction that does not involve the transfer of a hydrogen ion is the reaction between ammonia and boron trifluoride. The nitrogen atom of the ammonia molecule supplies the lone pair of electrons and the boron atom of the boron trifluoride molecule accepts a share of the pair of electrons. The product is called an **acid-base adduct** or more simply, an **adduct**. A coordinate covalent bond is formed between the two molecules. The bond is indistinguishable from an ordinary covalent bond but is usually referred to as a coordinate covalent bond to indicate that both electrons originate from one of the participants in the bond—rather than one electron from each participant. Notice how the structure around the boron changes from a trigonal sp^2 hybridization to a tetrahedral sp^3 hybridization:

$$
\begin{array}{ccccc}
& F & & H & \\
& | & & | & \\
F\!-\!B & + & :\!N\!-\!H & & \\
& | & & | & \\
& F & & H & \\
\text{acid} & & \text{base} & &
\end{array}
\longrightarrow
\begin{array}{c}
F \quad H \\
| \quad\; | \\
F\!-\!B\!-\!N\!-\!H \\
| \quad\; | \\
F \quad H
\end{array}
$$

Another example of a Lewis acid-base reaction is the transfer of a fluoride ion from bromine trifluoride to antimony pentafluoride discussed earlier. The fluoride ion is the electron pair donor (the Lewis base) and the antimony pentafluoride molecule is the electron pair acceptor (the Lewis acid):

$$
\begin{array}{c}
F \\
| \quad F \\
F\!-\!Sb \diagup \\
| \diagdown F \\
F
\end{array}
+ \; F^- \longrightarrow
\left[
\begin{array}{c}
F \\
| \quad F \\
F\!-\!Sb \diagup \!-\!F \\
F \diagup | \\
\;\;\; F
\end{array}
\right]^-
$$

In this case the antimony does not appear to have an orbital available into which to accept the electron pair but its structure is adjusted to make one available. This adjustment, in valence bond terms a change in hybridization from sp^3d to sp^3d^2, is often referred to as an **expansion of the valence shell**.

Another type of Lewis acid-base reaction outside the scope of the Brønsted-Lowry definitions is the coordination of molecules possessing a lone pair of electrons to metal cations. An example is the coordination of cyanide ions to nickel(II) ions in solution:

$$Ni^{2+} \ + \ 4\,CN^- \ \longrightarrow \ \begin{bmatrix} & N & \\ & C & \\ & | & \\ NC - & Ni & - CN \\ & | & \\ & C & \\ & N & \end{bmatrix}^{2-}$$

In this case the metal cation is the Lewis acid and the four cyanide ions are Lewis bases, each supplying a pair of electrons in the formation of a coordinate bond between the cyanide ion and the nickel(II) ion. The result is called a **coordination compound** or **complex ion** and we shall meet compounds such as these again when we examine the chemistry of transition metals.

A similar process occurs when a salt of a transition metal dissolves in water. The water molecules act as Lewis bases and coordinate to the transition metal cation. For example, when a cobalt(III) salt dissolves in water, the water acts as a coordinating solvent:

$$Co^{3+} \ + \ 6\,H_2O \ \longrightarrow \ \begin{bmatrix} & \overset{H_2}{O} & & \\ & | & & OH_2 \\ H_2O - & Co & - OH_2 \\ H_2O & | & \\ & O & \\ & H_2 & \end{bmatrix}^{3+}$$

A similar coordination of solvent molecules occurs when compounds such as ethylmagnesium bromide dissolve in diethyl ether. The diethylether molecule contains an oxygen atom with two lone pairs of electrons. One lone electron pair from the oxygen is partially donated to the magnesium atom of the ethyl magnesium bromide completing the valence shell of the magnesium and facilitating the solution process:

$$C_2H_5MgBr \ + \ 2\,C_2H_5OC_2H_5 \ \longrightarrow \ \begin{matrix} C_2H_5OC_2H_5 \\ | \\ C_2H_5 - Mg - Br \\ | \\ C_2H_5OC_2H_5 \end{matrix}$$

There are many coordination compounds that play an important role in biochemistry. Chlorophyll is a coordination compound containing magnesium ions surrounded by four nitrogen atoms in a **macrocyclic ring**. Each nitrogen atom possesses a lone pair of electrons that is donated to the magnesium ion at the center of the ring. Hemoglobin, responsible for the transport of oxygen in the blood supply, contains four heme groups with a similar macrocyclic ring. In this case an iron(II) or iron(III) ion is at the center (Figure 38.3).

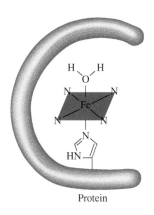

FIGURE 38.3 The structure of one of the four heme groups of hemoglobin.
In each molecule a metal ion at the center acts as a Lewis acid and accepts electron pairs from the four nitrogen atoms in the macrocyclic ring.

Other examples of Lewis acids are the nonmetal oxides, often referred to as acidic oxides. Some typical examples are carbon dioxide CO_2, nitrogen dioxide NO_2, sulfur trioxide SO_3, and chlorine dioxide ClO_2. When sulfur dioxide dissolves in water, the slightly positively-charged sulfur atom of the SO_2 molecule partially accepts an electron pair from a water molecule. The sulfur atom acts as a Lewis acid. At the same time, a hydrogen ion breaks away from the water molecule and attaches itself to an oxygen atom of the sulfur dioxide molecule—another Lewis acid-base reaction. The product of the reaction is sulfurous acid H_2SO_3:

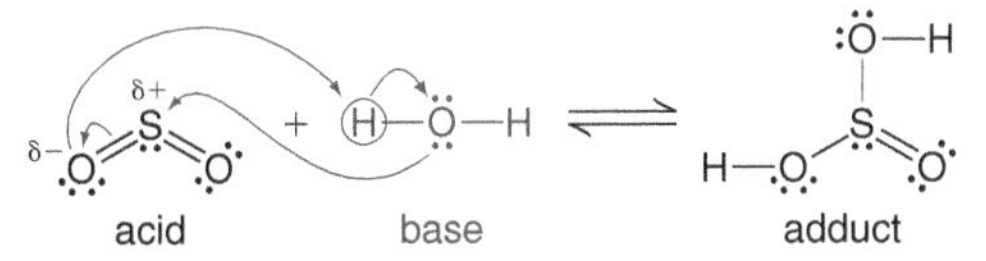

EXAMPLE 38.3   LEWIS ACID-BASE REACTIONS

Identify the Lewis acid and the Lewis base in the following reactions:

a. $BeCl_2 + 2\ Cl^- \rightarrow BeCl_4{}^{2-}$

b. $Cr^{3+} + 6\ NH_3 \rightarrow [Cr(NH_3)_6]^{3+}$

c. $BF_3 + F^- \rightarrow BF_4{}^-$

UNDERSTAND THE QUESTION

A Lewis acid-base reaction involves the partial transfer of an electron pair from the base to the acid and the formation of a coordinate covalent bond. The acid typically has an orbital available into which to accept the electron pair and the base has a lone pair of electrons to donate.

PLAN THE SOLUTION

Determine the structures of the participants and establish the transfer of electrons that takes place when the product is formed.

SOLVE THE PROBLEM

a. Beryllium chloride is an electron deficient molecule—there are only two pairs of electrons in valence shell of the beryllium. In other words, there are two vacant orbitals. This electron deficiency is typical of many molecules of elements to the left of Group 4A in the Periodic Table. The chloride ion has four pairs of nonbonding electrons and is able to donate one pair to the beryllium. The chloride ion is the Lewis base and the beryllium chloride molecule (specifically the beryllium atom) is the Lewis acid.

b. Ammonia has a nonbonding pair of electrons on the nitrogen atom and is a typical Lewis base. Transition metal ions such as Cr^{3+} accept electron pairs from Lewis bases in the formation of coordination compounds. The Cr^{3+} ion in solution exists as $[Cr(H_2O)_6]^{3+}$, a complex in which water molecules act as Lewis bases. Ammonia is a stronger Lewis base than water and the ammonia molecules displace the water molecules in the complex ion.

c. This reaction is similar to (a). The fluoride ion is the Lewis base and the electron deficient boron trifluoride molecule accepts an electron pair from the fluoride ion in the formation of a coordinate covalent bond. The hybridization of the atomic orbitals of the boron changes from sp^2 to sp^3.

PROBLEM 38.3A

Identify the Lewis acid and the Lewis base in the following reactions:

a. $2\ AlCl_3 \rightarrow Al_2Cl_6$

b. $SO_2 + OH^- \rightarrow HSO_3{}^-$

c. $CaO + SO_2 \rightarrow CaSO_3$

Identify the Lewis acid and the Lewis base in the following reactions:

a. $H^+ + H_2O \rightarrow H_3O^+$

b. $Ni + 4\,CO \rightarrow Ni(CO)_4$

c. $AlCl_3 + Cl^- \rightarrow AlCl_4^-$

38.6 Donor-acceptor Theory

This is very similar to the Lewis set of definitions. In Lewis acid-base reactions the electron pair on the base is invariably a lone pair of electrons.

An extension of the Lewis definitions of acids and bases is called **donor-acceptor theory**. Again the emphasis is on what happens to the electrons. Recall that the principal classification of chemical reactions is achieved by an analysis of what happens to the electrons when atoms are rearranged in a chemical reaction. If the transfer of electrons from one species to another is sufficient to cause a change in the oxidation number of the elements involved, then the reaction is classified as redox. If the movement of the electrons is more limited, with no change in the oxidation numbers, then the reaction is classified as acid-base.

In an acid-base reaction there is some movement of electrons. The species donating the electrons is the base and the species accepting the electrons is the acid. In the donor-acceptor theory of acid-base reactions, the donated electrons can be any pair of electrons—nonbonding, σ bonding, or π bonding. The orbital of the acid, into which electrons are accepted can be any vacant orbital—an atomic orbital, a hybrid atomic orbital, or an empty molecular (antibonding) orbital.

The orbital on the base from which the electron pair is donated is typically the **highest occupied molecular orbital (HOMO)** and the orbital on the acid into which the electrons are partially transferred is the **lowest unoccupied molecular orbital (LUMO)**. The general scheme is illustrated in Figure 38.4. The bonding molecular orbital between the acid and the base is the coordinate covalent bond referred to earlier.

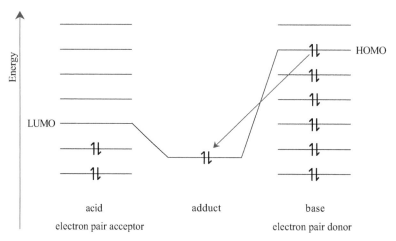

FIGURE 38.4 The donation of an electron pair from the highest occupied molecular orbital of the base to the lowest unoccupied molecular orbital of the acid.

An example of this type of donor-acceptor description of a reaction is the dimer-ization of borane BH_3 to form diborane B_2H_6. In this case the electron pair donated is a σ bonding pair of electrons. The acid is the boron atom of the other BH_3 molecule (Figure 38.5).

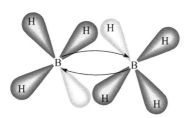

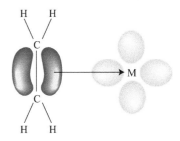

FIGURE 38.5   The dimerization of borane BH_3 to form diborane B_2H_6.
A σ bonding electron pair in a B—H bond is partially donated to the boron atom of the other borane molecule. The electron pair is now shared by the two boron atoms and the hydrogen atom.

FIGURE 38.6   The coordination of an ethylene molecule to a transition metal ion.
The π bonding electron pair in the ethylene molecule is partially donated to the transition metal. This weakens the bond between the two carbon atoms of the ethylene molecule.

Another example of a donor-acceptor acid-base reaction involving a different electron pair is the coordination of a molecule such as ethylene to a transition metal. In this case the electron pair donated is the π bonding electron pair of the double bond. The transition metal is the acid (Figure 38.6).

EXAMPLE 38.4   SUMMARY OF ACID-BASE DEFINITIONS

Classify the following reactions in terms of the Arrhenius definitions, the Brønsted-Lowry definitions, and the Lewis definitions. Any one of the reactions may fit one, two, or all three definitions. All three reactions occur in aqueous solution.

a. $S^{2-} + H_2O \rightleftharpoons HS^- + OH^-$

b. $HCl + H_2O \rightleftharpoons H_3O^+ + Cl^-$

c. $CuCl_2 + 2\,Cl^- \rightleftharpoons [CuCl_4]^{2-}$

UNDERSTAND THE QUESTION

Acids and bases have been defined in a variety of different ways. The different definitions represent different ways of looking at the behavior of acids and bases. The most general definitions are those of Lewis—the Lewis definitions encompass the Brønsted-Lowry and the Arrhenius definitions. Whereas the Arrhenius and Brønsted-Lowry defini-tions emphasize the movement of hydrogen ions, the Lewis definitions concentrate on the transfer of electron pairs. A reaction classified as a Brønsted-Lowry acid-base reaction is always a Lewis acid-base reaction but the reverse is not always true.

PLAN THE SOLUTION

Examine each reaction and match the behavior of the substances with the different sets of definitions.

SOLVE THE PROBLEM

a. In this reaction the sulfide ion dissolves in water to produce hydroxide ions—therefore the sulfide ion is an Arrhenius base. The sulfide ion is also a Brønsted-Lowry base—it accepts a hydrogen ion from the water. In Lewis terms, the sulfide ion donates an electron pair to a hydrogen ion from the water molecule. This reaction is therefore an acid-base reaction according to all three sets of definitions.

b. Hydrochloric acid is a typical strong acid; it ionizes almost completely in aqueous solution to increase the concentration of hydronium (hydrogen) ions. It is therefore an Arrhenius acid. The HCl molecule donates a hydrogen ion to a water molecule and therefore is a Brønsted-Lowry acid. According to the Lewis definitions, a lone pair of electrons on the oxygen atom of a water molecule is donated to the hydrogen ion from the HCl molecule. Again this reaction is an acid-base reaction according to all three definitions.

c. This reaction cannot be an acid-base reaction according to the definitions of Arrhenius or Brønsted-Lowry—there are no hydrogen ions involved. In Lewis terms, however, the chloride ion is a base. It donates an electron pair to the copper of the $CuCl_2$ and forms a coordinate covalent bond. According to the Lewis definitions, the $CuCl_2$ is a Lewis acid and the chloride ions are Lewis bases.

PROBLEM 38.4A

Classify the following reactions in terms of the Arrhenius definitions, the Brønsted-Lowry definitions, and the Lewis definitions. Any one of the reactions may fit one, two, or all three definitions. All three reactions occur in aqueous solution.

a. $HS^- + H_2O \rightleftharpoons H_2S + OH^-$

b. $H_3O^+ + OH^- \rightleftharpoons 2\,H_2O$

c. $Co^{3+} + 6\,NH_3 \rightleftharpoons [Co(NH_3)_6]^{3+}$

PROBLEM 38.4B

Classify the following reactions in terms of the Arrhenius definitions, the Brønsted-Lowry definitions, and the Lewis definitions. Any one of the reactions may fit one, two, or all three definitions. All three reactions occur in aqueous solution.

a. $Cu^{2+} + 6\,H_2O \rightleftharpoons [Cu(H_2O)_6]^{2+}$

b. $NH_3 + H_2O \rightleftharpoons NH_4^+ + OH^-$

c. $B(OH)_3 + Cl^- \rightleftharpoons B(OH)_3Cl^-$

Review Questions

1. Many acid-base reactions occur in aqueous solution. Describe how Arrhenius defined an acid and a base. Explain what happens in solution when an acid and a base react.

2. How do the definitions of Brønsted and Lowry differ from those of Arrhenius. Give an example of a substance that is a Brønsted-Lowry base but is not an Arrhenius base. Give an example of a substance that is both a Brønsted-Lowry base and an Arrhenius base.

3. What is the difference between a strong acid and a weak acid?

4. Nonaqueous solvents can be classified as protonic or nonprotonic. Explain what this means and give examples of each.

5. Describe the Lewis definitions of acids and bases and explain how these definitions differ from those of Brønsted and Lowry. Give an example of a substance that is a Lewis acid but is not a Brønsted-Lowry acid. Give an example of a substance that is both a Lewis acid and a Brønsted-Lowry acid.

Solutions to Problems

PROBLEM 38.1A

a. the ionization of acetic acid in aqueous solution

$$CH_3CO_2H(aq) \; + \; H_2O(l) \; \rightleftharpoons \; H_3O^+(aq) \; + \; CH_3CO_2^-(aq)$$
$$\text{acid} \qquad\qquad \text{base} \qquad\qquad \text{acid} \qquad\qquad \text{base}$$

b. the neutralization of hydrocyanic acid with sodium hydroxide

$$HCN(aq) \; + \; OH^-(aq) \; \rightleftharpoons \; CN^-(aq) \; + \; H_2O(l)$$
$$\text{acid} \qquad\qquad \text{base} \qquad\qquad \text{base} \qquad\qquad \text{acid}$$

PROBLEM 38.2A

An acid produces the solvent cation $CH_3CH_2OH_2^+$

A base produces the solvent anion $CH_3CH_2O^-$

Reaction of a strong acid and a strong base:

$$CH_3CH_2OH_2^+ + CH_3CH_2O^- \rightleftharpoons 2\,CH_3CH_2OH$$
$$\text{solvent cation} \qquad \text{solvent anion} \qquad\qquad \text{solvent molecule}$$

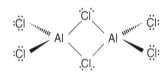

Dimeric structure of aluminum chloride

PROBLEM 38.3A

a. $2\,AlCl_3 \rightarrow Al_2Cl_6$

The aluminum accepts a pair of electrons from a chlorine atom of an adjacent $AlCl_3$ molecule.

The chlorine is the base; the aluminum is the acid.

b. $SO_2 + OH^- \rightarrow HSO_3^-$

The oxygen atom of the hydroxide ion donates a pair of electrons to the sulfur atom of the sulfur dioxide molecule.

The oxygen is the base; the sulfur atom is the acid.

c. $CaO + SO_2 \rightarrow CaSO_3$

The oxide ion donates a pair of electrons to the sulfur atom of the sulfur dioxide. The calcium ion is a spectator ion.

The oxygen is the base; the sulfur atom of the sulfur dioxide is the acid.

PROBLEM 38.4A

a. $HS^- + H_2O \rightleftharpoons H_2S + OH^-$

The hydrogen sulfide ion HS^- is an Arrhenius base—it produces hydroxide ions in solution. The equation represents a typical Brønsted-Lowry acid-base equilibrium:

$$HS^- \; + \; H_2O \; \rightleftharpoons \; H_2S \; + \; OH^-$$
$$\text{base} \qquad \text{acid} \qquad\qquad \text{acid} \qquad \text{base}$$

By default, a Brønsted-Lowry acid must be a Lewis acid and a Brønsted-Lowry base must be a Lewis base. In this case the sulfur of the HS^- donates a pair of electrons to the H^+ from the water molecule. In the reverse direction the oxygen of the hydroxide ion donates a pair of electrons to the H^+ from the H_2S molecule.

b. $H_3O^+ + OH^- \rightleftharpoons 2\,H_2O$

This equation represents a neutralization reaction between an acid and a base.

The hydronium ion is an Arrhenius acid. The hydroxide ion is an Arrhenius base.

Written in Brønsted-Lowry terms:

$$H_3O^+ \; + \; OH^- \; \rightleftharpoons \; H_2O \; + \; H_2O$$
$$\text{acid} \qquad\quad \text{base} \qquad\qquad \text{base} \qquad \text{acid}$$

Again, by default, a Brønsted-Lowry acid must be a Lewis acid and a Brønsted-Lowry base must be a Lewis base.

c. $Co^{3+} + 6\,NH_3 \rightleftharpoons [Co(NH_3)_6]^{3+}$

This is not an Arrhenius acid–base reaction, nor a Brønsted-Lowry acid–base reaction; there is no hydrogen ion transfer. The cobalt(III) ion is a Lewis acid and accepts a share of the electron pairs on the six ammonia molecules.

Answers to Review Questions

1. Arrhenius defined an acid as a solute that ionizes in aqueous solution to produce the hydrogen ion H^+—the concentration of hydrogen ion in the solution increases. He defined a base as a solute that increases the concentration of hydroxide ions OH^- in solution. When an acid and a base react, the two neutralize each other and a salt is formed. According to Arrhenius, neutralization occurs when the hydrogen ion H^+ from the acid reacts with the hydroxide ions OH^- from the base to form water molecules.

2. The Brønsted and Lowry definitions are broader than those of Arrhenius. A base is defined as a hydrogen ion acceptor, which may or may not be a hydroxide ion. For example the chloride ion is a Brønsted-Lowry base (the conjugate base of hydrochloric acid) but is not an Arrhenius base. Ammonia is both an Arrhenius base (it produces hydroxide ions in water) and a Brønsted-Lowry base. All Arrhenius bases are Brønsted-Lowry bases.

3. A strong acid is completely ionized in aqueous solution whereas a weak acid is only partially ionized.

4. A protonic solvent is a solvent in which an acid-base reaction involves the transfer of a hydrogen ion from the acid to the base. Examples are water, liquid ammonia, and glacial acetic acid. A nonprotonic solvent is a solvent in which an acid-base reaction involves the transfer of some species other than a hydrogen ion. An example is bromine trifluoride in which the species transferred is a fluoride ion.

5. Lewis described an acid-base reaction in terms of what happens to the valence electrons of the participants. He defined an acid as a substance that accepts a share in an electron pair from the base, and he defined a base as a substance that partially donates an electron pair to the acid. The acid-base reaction results in the formation of a coordinate covalent bond. These definitions expand the classification of acid-base reactions beyond the scope of the Brønsted-Lowry definitions. Brønsted-Lowry acid-base reactions involve the transfer of a hydrogen ion from the acid to the base. The Lewis definitions include acid-base reactions that do not involve the transfer of a hydrogen ion. An example of a substance that is a Lewis acid but is not a Brønsted-Lowry acid is nickel metal when it accepts pairs of electrons from carbon monoxide molecules in the formation of $[Ni(CO)_4]$. Any Brønsted-Lowry acid is also a Lewis acid.

End-of-Unit Problems

1. Of the following acids and bases, identify those that are strong electrolytes.

   H_2BrO_2 HF H_2SO_3 KOH HNO_3

2. Of the following acids and bases, identify those that are strong electrolytes.

   HNO_2 H_2SO_4 HI NH_3 $Ba(OH)_2$

3. For the following acid-base reactions, write the net ionic equation, identify both acids and both bases and pair the conjugate partners.
   a. $NH_4^+ + H_2O \rightleftharpoons H_3O^+ + NH_3$
   b. $H_2PO_4^- + H_2O \rightleftharpoons H_3O^+ + HPO_4^{2-}$

4. For the following acid-base reactions, write the net ionic equation, identify both acids and both bases and pair the conjugate partners.
   a. $CO_3^{2-} + H_2O \rightleftharpoons HCO_3^- + OH^-$
   b. $HNO_2 + H_2O \rightleftharpoons H_3O^+ + NO_2^-$

5. What is the formula for the conjugate acid of
   a. the chlorite ion in aqueous solution?
   b. the hydrogen sulfate ion in aqueous solution

6. What is the formula for the conjugate acid of
   a. the hydroxide ion in aqueous solution?
   b. the cyanide ion in aqueous solution?

7. What is the formula for the conjugate base of
   a. water in aqueous solution?
   b. the hydrogen sulfite ion in aqueous solution

8. What is the formula for the conjugate base of
   a. the ammonium ion in aqueous solution?
   b. acetic acid in aqueous solution?

9. Write the formula of the conjugate acid of the following bases:
   a. SO_3^{2-}
   b. H^-
   c. $(CH_3)_2NH$

10. Write the formula of the conjugate acid of the following bases:
    a. PO_4^{3-}
    b. NH_2^-
    c. CN^-

11. Write the formula of the conjugate base of the following acids:

    a. H_2SO_3

    b. NH_4^+

    c. C_6H_5OH

12. Write the formula of the conjugate base of the following acids:

    a. H_2CO_3

    b. HF

    c. $H_2PO_3^-$

13. For the following acid-base reactions, write the net ionic equation, characterize each component as acid or base, and pair the conjugate partners.

    a. the ionization of hydrocyanic acid in aqueous solution

    b. the neutralization of methylamine CH_3NH_2 with nitric acid

14. For the following acid-base reactions, write the net ionic equation, characterize each component as acid or base, and pair the conjugate partners.

    a. the reaction of perchloric acid and potassium hydroxide

    b. the ionization of hypochlorous acid in aqueous solution

15. Of the following molecules or ions:

    $BeCl_2$ HSO_4^- SO_2 O^{2-} OH^-

    a. Which can act as Brønsted-Lowry acids?

    b. Which can act as Brønsted-Lowry bases?

    c. Which can act as Lewis acids?

    d. Which can act as Lewis bases?

    In each case explain your reasoning.

16. Of the following molecules or ions:

    H_2SO_3 CO_2 HCN Cl^- $AlCl_3$

    a. Which can act as Brønsted-Lowry acids?

    b. Which can act as Brønsted-Lowry bases?

    c. Which can act as Lewis acids?

    d. Which can act as Lewis bases?

    In each case explain your reasoning.

17. For each of the following reactions, identify the Lewis acid and the Lewis base

    a. $Co_3+(aq) + 6\ NH_3(aq) \rightarrow [Co(NH_3)_6]^{3+}(aq)$

    b. $H^-(s) + H_2O(l) \rightarrow H_2(g) + OH^-(aq)$

    c. $BCl_3(g) + Cl^-(aq) \rightarrow BCl_4^-(aq)$

18. For each of the following reactions, identify the Lewis acid and the Lewis base

    a. $H_3O^+(aq) + NH_3(aq) \rightarrow NH_4^+(aq) + H_2O(l)$

    b. $CuCl_2(aq) + 2\ Cl^-(aq) \rightarrow [CuCl_4]^{2-}(aq)$

    c. $SO_3(aq) + OH^-(aq) \rightarrow HSO_4^-(aq)$

19. For each of the following reactions, identify the Lewis acid and the Lewis base

    a. $(CH_3)_2NH(l) + BF_3(g) \rightarrow (CH_3)_2NHBF_3(s)$

    b. $ZnCl_2(aq) + 4\ NH_3(aq) \rightarrow [Zn(NH_3)_4]^{2-}(aq) + 2\ Cl^-(aq)$

    c. $NiBr_2(s) + 6\ H_2O(l) \rightarrow [Ni(H_2O)_6]^{2-}(aq) + 2\ Br^-(aq)$

20. For each of the following reactions, identify the Lewis acid and the Lewis base

    a. $HCN(aq) + H_2O(l) \rightarrow H_3O^+(aq) + CN^-(aq)$

    b. $BeCl_2(s) + 2\ Cl^-(aq) \rightarrow [BeCl_4]^{2-}(aq)$

    c. $CO_2(g) + H_2O(l) \rightarrow H_2CO_3(aq)$

21. When glacial acetic acid is used as a solvent, bromic acid is weak. Write an equation representing what happens when bromic acid dissolves in glacial acetic acid.

22. Methylamine can be used as a solvent for acid base reactions. Write an equation representing what happens when hydroiodic acid dissolves in liquid methylamine.

23. In liquid ammonia, HI is an acid and $NaNH_2$ (sodium amide) is a base. Derive a net ionic equation representing the reaction that occurs in liquid ammonia between HI and $NaNH_2$.

24. Write an equation for the reaction between hydrogen chloride (HCl) and potassium ethoxide (KC_2H_5O) dissolved in ethanol (C_2H_5OH).

Aqueous Solutions and pH

39.1 The Autoionization of Water

When water is used as a solvent for acid-base reactions it can act as an acid or as a base. In Brønsted-Lowry terms, a water molecule can either accept a hydrogen ion (when it acts as a base) or it can donate a hydrogen ion (when it acts as an acid). A substance able to do this is called **amphiprotic**.

In pure water there are always a few hydronium ions and hydroxide ions present. One water molecule may donate a hydrogen ion to another water molecule to form a hydronium ion and a hydroxide ion in a process referred to as **autoionization**. Imagine two water molecules adjacent to one another in the liquid. The intermolecular attraction between the two molecules is a hydrogen bond (*cf.* Unit 28). In the liquid the water molecules are continually moving about, breaking these intermolecular hydrogen bonds and making new ones. Occasionally, but not very often, the bond *in* a water molecule breaks instead of the hydrogen bond *between* the water molecules (Figure 39.1). The hydronium and hydroxide ions are formed.

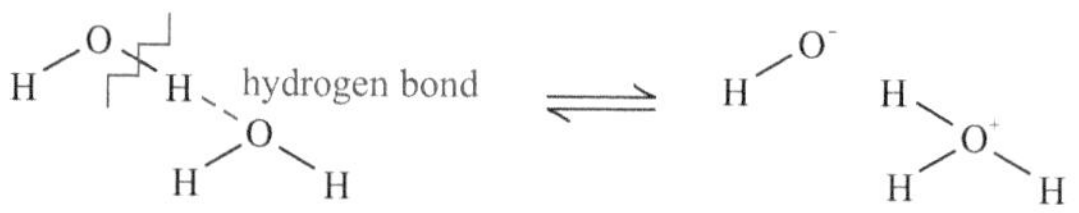

FIGURE 39.1   The autoionization of water to produce hydronium and hydroxide ions.

The O—H bond in the water molecule is much stronger than the intermolecular hydrogen bond and very few hydronium ions and hydroxide ions are produced. At 25°C, the concentration of H_3O^+ and OH^- ions in pure water is only 1.0×10^{-7} mol L^{-1}. At this temperature the concentration of water molecules in pure water is 55.35 mol L^{-1}. Therefore only two molecules of water in half a billion undergo autoionization.

It's interesting that as the temperature is increased more energy is available and the concentration of hydronium and hydroxide ions increases as more molecules are able to undergo autoionization.

The equation and the equilibrium constant for the autoionization process can be written:

$$H_2O + H_2O \rightleftharpoons H_3O^+ + OH^-$$

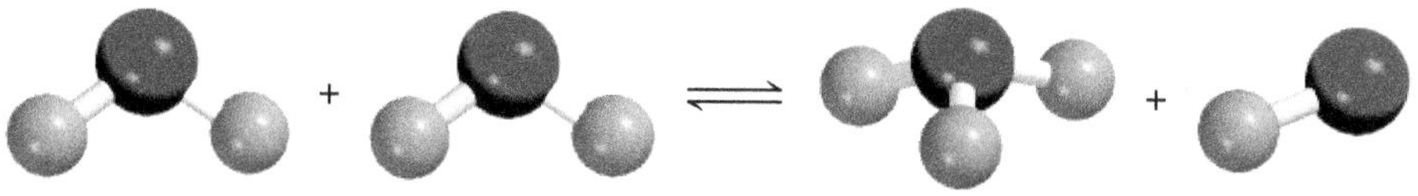

$$K = \frac{[H_3O^+][OH^-]}{[H_2O]^2}$$

The [H_2O] terms in the denominator are incorporated into the value for K, and the new K is given the symbol K_w:

$$K_w = [H_3O^+][OH^-] = 1.0 \times 10^{-14} \text{ at } 25°C$$

K_w is called the **ion product** for water and, because $[H_3O^+]$ and $[OH^-]$ depend upon the temperature, its value also depends upon the temperature. At $0°C$ the value of K_w is approximately 1.0×10^{-15} and at $60°C$ the value is approximately 1.0×10^{-13}. Values at other temperatures are listed in Table 39.1.

In pure water the concentration of hydronium ion $[H_3O^+]$ must equal the concentration of hydroxide ion $[OH^-]$—the charges must balance. A solution in which the two concentrations are equal is said to be **neutral**. In most aqueous solutions, however, the two concentrations are not equal. For example, in acidic solutions, the hydronium ion concentration $[H_3O^+]$ exceeds the hydroxide ion concentration $[OH^-]$. In basic solutions, the hydroxide ion concentration $[OH^-]$ exceeds the hydronium ion concentration $[H_3O^+]$:

$$\text{Acidic:} \quad [H_3O^+] > [OH^-]$$

$$\text{Neutral:} \quad [H_3O^+] = [OH^-]$$

$$\text{Basic:} \quad [H_3O^+] < [OH^-]$$

What is always true in dilute aqueous solutions is that the product of the two concentrations is constant, 1.0×10^{-14} at $25°C$. This is very useful because it means that if one of the two concentrations is known, the other can always be calculated.

We learned in Unit 10 that the hydronium ion concentration is often expressed as the pH, where the pH is defined as the $-\log_{10}[H_3O^+]$, or $-\log_{10}[H^+]$. The pH scale is a very convenient way of expressing the hydronium ion concentration in a solution (Figure 39.2).

The hydroxide ion concentration $[OH^-]$ can similarly be expressed as the pOH, where the pOH is defined as the $-\log_{10}[OH^-]$. In fact the prefix p before any quantity means the $-\log_{10}$ of that quantity. For example pK_w means $-\log_{10}K_w$.

If $\quad K_w = [H_3O^+][OH^-] = 1.0 \times 10^{-14}$ at $25°C$

then $\quad pK_w = pH + pOH = 14$ at $25°C$

In a neutral solution at $25°C$, in which the two concentrations $[H_3O^+]$ and $[OH^-]$ are equal, each must equal $1.0 \times 10^{-7}M$. The pH and the pOH are both equal to 7.0.

TABLE 39.1 Values of K_w at various temperatures

0°C	1.14×10^{-15}
10°C	2.92×10^{-15}
20°C	6.78×10^{-15}
25°C	1.00×10^{-14}
30°C	1.46×10^{-14}
40°C	2.87×10^{-14}
50°C	5.37×10^{-14}
60°C	9.33×10^{-14}
70°C	1.53×10^{-13}
80°C	2.39×10^{-13}
90°C	3.55×10^{-13}
100°C	5.05×10^{-13}

Remember that as the concentration of $[H_3O^+]$ *increases*, the pH *decreases*.

The pH scale was formulated by a Danish brewer Søren Sørensen in 1909.

EXAMPLE 39.1   THE RELATIONSHIP BETWEEN $[H_3O^+]$ AND $[OH^-]$

A solution of acetic acid in water at $25°C$ has a hydronium ion concentration equal to 2.0×10^{-5} M. Calculate the hydroxide ion concentration, the pH, and the pOH.

UNDERSTAND THE QUESTION

In aqueous solution the product of the $[H_3O^+]$ and $[OH^-]$ concentrations is constant, equal to 1.0×10^{-14} at $25°C$. If the $[H_3O^+]$ concentration is known, then the $[OH^-]$ concentration can be calculated, and *vice versa*. From these concentrations the pH and pOH can be determined.

PLAN THE SOLUTION

Use the relationship $K_w = [H_3O^+][OH^-] = 1.0 \times 10^{-14}$ to determine the hydroxide ion concentration. Then calculate the pH and pOH.

SOLVE THE PROBLEM

$$[H_3O^+] = 2.0 \times 10^{-5}\,M$$

$$[OH^-] = 1.0 \times 10^{-14} / 2.0 \times 10^{-5}\,M = 5.0 \times 10^{-10}\,M$$

$$pH = -\log_{10}[H_3O^+] = -\log_{10}(2.0 \times 10^{-5}) = 4.70$$

Note that the number of significant figures after the decimal point in the pH or pOH should equal the number of figures in the concentration.

$$pOH = -\log_{10}[OH^-] = -\log_{10}(5.0 \times 10^{-10}) = 9.30$$

Note that pH + pOH = 4.70 + 9.30 = 14.0

A quicker way to calculate the pOH if the pH is known is to subtract the pH from 14.0.

PROBLEM 39.1A

The pH of blood is maintained within a narrow range. A typical pH is 7.44—slightly basic. Calculate the hydronium ion concentration, the hydroxide ion concentration, and the pOH at 37°C if the pH is 7.44 and K_w at 37°C = 2.42×10^{-14}.

PROBLEM 39.1B

A solution of milk of magnesia, an antacid, has a pH of 10.50. Calculate the hydronium ion concentration, the hydroxide ion concentration, and the pOH of the solution.

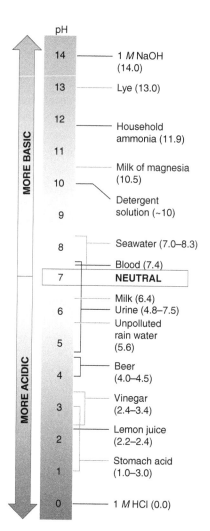

FIGURE 39.2 The pH scale.

39.2 Calculation of the pH of Solutions of Strong Acids and Bases

The calculation of the hydronium ion concentration and the pH of a solution of a strong acid or base is straightforward assuming that the strong acid or base is completely ionized—which it is in dilute solution.

One mole of any monoprotic strong acid will produce one mole of hydronium ions when it dissolves in water. The situation is a little more complicated for the diprotic strong acid sulfuric acid (H_2SO_4) because some hydronium ions are also produced in the second ionization—we'll deal with this later in Unit 42. Similarly, one mole of any strong base will produce one mole of hydroxide ions in aqueous solution.

EXAMPLE 39.2   THE pH OF A STRONG ACID OR BASE

A solution of sodium hydroxide in water at 25°C has a concentration of 0.20 mol L^{-1}.

Calculate the hydroxide ion concentration, the pOH, and the pH.

UNDERSTAND THE QUESTION

In aqueous solution, one mole of any strong base will produce one mole of hydroxide ions. A sodium hydroxide solution that is 0.20 M will have a hydroxide concentration equal to 0.20 M. Once the hydroxide [OH$^-$] concentration is known, the [H$_3$O$^+$] concentration can be calculated and from these concentrations the pH and pOH can be determined.

PLAN THE SOLUTION

Determine the hydroxide ion concentration; then the pOH; then the pH.

SOLVE THE PROBLEM

$$[OH^-] = 0.20 \ M$$
$$pOH = -\log_{10}[OH^-] = -\log_{10}(0.20) = 0.70$$
$$pH = 14 - pOH = 13.30$$

PROBLEM 39.2A

A solution of perchloric acid in water is prepared such that the concentration of perchloric acid is 3.0×10^{-2} M. Calculate the hydronium ion concentration, the hydroxide ion concentration, the pH, and the pOH.

PROBLEM 39.2B

A solution of potassium hydroxide is 0.0050 M. Calculate the hydroxide ion concentration, the hydronium ion concentration, the pOH, and the pH of the solution.

39.3   Calculation of the pH of Solutions of Weak Acids and Bases

The calculation of the hydronium ion concentration and the pH of a solution of a weak acid or base involves the same sort of calculation discussed in Unit 35. The use of a table to organize the initial and equilibrium concentrations is highly recommended. The key to all equilibrium calculations for aqueous solutions is to recognize what happens when the solute dissolves. Always write an equation representing the reaction, preferably in Brønsted-Lowry terms, and from this equation derive the expression for the equilibrium constant K. In this section we will look at solutions of weak acids and bases. In later units we will look at solutions of salts, mixtures of conjugate partners, polyprotic acids and their salts, and sparingly soluble salts.

The first example involves the calculation of the hydrogen ion concentration and the pH of a 0.10 M solution of acetic acid CH$_3$CO$_2$H.

EXAMPLE 39.3   CALCULATION OF THE pH OF A SOLUTION OF A WEAK ACID

Calculate the hydrogen ion concentration and the pH of a 0.10 M solution of acetic acid CH_3CO_2H. The equilibrium constant K_a for acetic acid at 25°C is 1.8×10^{-5}.

UNDERSTAND THE QUESTION

Acetic acid is a weak acid and ionizes in aqueous solution to produce a small concentration of hydronium ions.

PLAN THE SOLUTION

Write the equation representing the ionization of the acid in water. Derive the expression for the equilibrium constant K_a. Set up an ICE table to summarize the initial concentrations and the equilibrium concentrations of the acid, the hydronium ion, and the acetate ion (the conjugate base of acetic acid).

SOLVE THE PROBLEM

The ionization of acetic acid is represented by the equation:

$$CH_3CO_2H + H_2O \rightleftharpoons H_3O^+ + CH_3CO_2^-$$

The equilibrium constant $K_a = \dfrac{[H_3O^+][CH_3CO_2^-]}{[CH_3CO_2H]}$

It is often convenient, although not necessary, to introduce a quantity x to represent an unknown concentration. In this case, for example, we can represent the hydronium ion concentration by x. The stoichiometry of the reaction indicates that the two concentrations $[H_3O^+]$ and $[CH_3CO_2^-]$ must be equal, both equal to x.

The ICE table is (with concentrations in M):

	$CH_3CO_2H + H_2O$	$\rightleftharpoons$	H_3O^+	$+ CH_3CO_2^-$
Initial:	0.10		0	0
Change:	− x		+ x	+ x
Equilibrium concentrations:	0.10 − x		x	x

The equilibrium concentrations are now substituted into the expression for the equilibrium constant K_a and the value of x calculated.

$$K_a = \frac{[H_3O^+][CH_3CO_2^-]}{[CH_3CO_2H]} = \frac{x^2}{(0.10 - x)}$$

To simplify the calculation, we make the assumption that x is a very small number compared to 0.10, so that (0.10 − x) is essentially equal to 0.10. So,

$$K_a = 1.8 \times 10^{-5} = \frac{x^2}{0.10} \text{ and } x = 1.3 \times 10^{-3}$$

The value of x is indeed small (0.0013) compared to 0.10.

x represents the concentrations of the hydronium ion and the acetate ion:

$$[H_3O+] = 1.3 \times 10^{-3} \, M$$

$$pH = -\log_{10}[H_3O^+] = -\log_{10}(1.3 \times 10^{-3}) = 2.89$$

A general expression sometimes used is:

$$[H_3O^+] = \sqrt{(K_a[HA]_o)}$$

where $[HA]_o$ is the initial concentration of the weak acid. This can be modified by taking the negative log of both sides to produce an expression for the pH directly:

$$pH = \tfrac{1}{2}pK_a - \tfrac{1}{2}\log[HA]_o$$

PROBLEM 39.3A

Calculate the hydrogen ion concentration and the pH of a 0.20 M solution of hypochlorous acid HClO. The equilibrium constant K_a for HClO at 25°C is 3.0×10^{-8}.

PROBLEM 39.3B

Calculate the hydrogen ion concentration and the pH of a 0.25 M solution of benzoic acid $C_6H_5CO_2H$. The equilibrium constant K_a for $C_6H_5CO_2H$ at 25°C is 6.3×10^{-5}.

Two questions arise from Example 39.3. One is: when is it possible to make the assumption that the concentration of the weak electrolyte remains essentially unchanged? In other words, when is it permissible to ignore the x in the denominator of the equilibrium constant expression? The answer depends upon the relative magnitude of x and the initial concentration of the acid. Is the difference in the magnitude of these two quantities greater or less than the precision of the data? As the initial concentration of the acid decreases, or the value of the equilibrium constant increases, the assumption becomes less valid.

A useful empirical rule is that the approximation is permissible if the initial concentration of the acid is greater than $100 \times K_a$. In Example 39.3, the initial concentration of the acid was 0.10 M, which exceeded the value of $100 \times K_a$ (= 0.0018), and so the assumption was permissible. In other words, the change in the concentration of the acid molecules is negligible. Example 39.4 is one for which the x in the denominator cannot be neglected.

The other question concerning Example 39.3 that may have crossed your mind is: Surely there are hydronium ions present in the solution arising from the autoionization of water. Why wasn't this hydronium ion concentration included in the total?

Hydronium ions are present due to the autoionization of water but the concentration is extremely small. The autoionization is suppressed by the addition of the acid (*cf.* LeChatelier's Principle discussed in Unit 35) and the concentration is certainly far less than 10^{-7} M. Compare this to the concentration 1.3×10^{-3} M from the ionization of the acetic acid. The hydronium ion concentration from the autoionization of the water need only be considered when the hydronium ion concentration from the ionization of the acid is equally small (or smaller).

However, if K_a is very small, or the solution of the acid is very dilute, then the $[H_3O^+]$ from the autoionization of water cannot be neglected. For example, suppose you are asked to calculate the pH of a 1.0×10^{-8} M solution of a strong acid. You might be tempted to take the $-\log_{10}(10^{-8})$ and state the pH to be 8. This is clearly incorrect—a solution of a strong acid cannot be basic!

In this case the $[H_3O^+]$ from the strong acid is 1.0×10^{-8} M. The $[H_3O^+]$ from the autoionization of water will be the same as the $[OH^-]$ from the water (you can't get one without the other); let's call this x. The total $[H_3O^+]$ is (1.0×10^{-8}) from the acid plus x from the water. We can now use the expression for K_w to solve for x:

$$K_w = 1.0 \times 10^{-14} = [H_3O^+][OH^-] = [(1.0 \times 10^{-8}) + x][x]$$
$$\text{or } x^2 + 1.0 \times 10^{-8} x - 1.0 \times 10^{-14} = 0$$

This can be solved using the quadratic formula or by iteration to obtain $x = 9.51 \times 10^{-8}$.

Then,

$$[H_3O^+] = 1.0 \times 10^{-8} + 9.51 \times 10^{-8} = 1.05 \times 10^{-7} \text{ M}$$
$$[OH^-] = 9.51 \times 10^{-8} \text{ M}$$

and the pH = 6.98—very near 7 as you would anticipate. Most of the hydronium ion in solution in this case comes from the autoionization of water.

The situation is more complicated for very dilute solutions of weak acids. Although we will not derive it here, it can be shown that . . .

$$K_a = \frac{[H_3O^+] \times \{[H_3O^+] - K_w/[H_3O^+]\}}{[HA]_0 - \{[H_3O^+] - K_w/[H_3O^+]\}}$$

where $[HA]_0$ is the initial concentration of the weak acid.

Rearrangement leads to a cubic equation for the $[H_3O^+]$ concentration x:

$$x^3 + K_a x^2 - (K_w + K_a[HA]_0)x - K_a K_w = 0$$

> These cubic equations are best solved using a graphing calculator or computer. We will not encounter these problems in this text.

The next example is the calculation of the pH of a dilute solution of a weak base. There are several weak bases that have structures similar to ammonia and that behave in the same way. A nitrogen atom with a lone pair of electrons acts as a hydrogen ion acceptor. Some examples of nitrogen-based weak bases are listed in Table 39.2.

TABLE 39.2 Some nitrogen-based weak bases and their K_b.

Name	Formula	K_b	pK_b
Triethylamine	$(C_2H_5)_3N$	1.0×10^{-3}	3.00
Ethylamine	$C_2H_5NH_2$	6.4×10^{-4}	3.19
Dimethylamine	$(CH_3)_2NH$	5.4×10^{-4}	3.27
Methylamine	CH_3NH	4.4×10^{-4}	3.43
Trimethylamine	$(CH_3)_3N$	6.5×10^{-5}	4.19
Ammonia	NH_3	1.8×10^{-5}	4.74
Hydrazine	N_2H_4	1.3×10^{-6}	5.89
Hydroxylamine	NH_2OH	1.0×10^{-8}	8.00
Pyridine	C_5H_5N	1.8×10^{-9}	8.74
Aniline	$C_6H_5NH_2$	4.3×10^{-10}	9.37

EXAMPLE 39.4 CALCULATION OF THE pH OF A SOLUTION OF A WEAK BASE

Calculate the hydrogen ion concentration and the pH of a 0.010 M solution of methylamine CH_3NH_2. The equilibrium constant K_b for methylamine at 25°C is 4.4×10^{-4}.

UNDERSTAND THE QUESTION

Methylamine is a weak base and ionizes in aqueous solution to produce a small concentration of hydroxide ions. Its behavior is similar to that of ammonia NH_3.

PLAN THE SOLUTION

Write the equation representing the ionization of the base and derive the expression for the equilibrium constant K_b. As in the previous example, set up an ICE table to summarize the initial and equilibrium concentrations.

SOLVE THE PROBLEM

The ionization of methylamine is represented by the equation:

$$CH_3NH_2 + H_2O \rightleftharpoons CH_3NH_3^+ + OH^-$$

The equilibrium constant $K_b = \dfrac{[CH_3NH_3^+][OH^-]}{[CH_3NH_2]}$

The ICE table is (with concentrations in M):

$$CH_3NH_2 + H_2O \rightleftharpoons CH_3NH_3^+ + OH^-$$

	CH_3NH_2	$CH_3NH_3^+$	OH^-
Initial:	0.010	0	0
Change:	$-x$	$+x$	$+x$
Equilibrium concentrations:	$0.010 - x$	x	x

The equilibrium concentrations are substituted into the expression for the equilibrium constant K_a and the value of x calculated.

$$K_b = \frac{[CH_3NH_3^+][OH^-]}{[CH_3NH_2]} = \frac{x^2}{(0.010 - x)}$$

Is it justifiable to neglect the x in the denominator? In this case the initial concentration (0.010 M) does not exceed the value of $100 \times K_b$ (= 0.044) and the approximation is *not* justifiable. The solution is dilute and the value for K_b is comparatively high.

There are two methods that can be used to solve the problem. The quadratic equation can be solved using the quadratic formula. This yields the result x = 1.89 × 10^{-3} M.

> When $ax^2 + bx + c = 0$, solve for x using the quadratic formula:
>
> $$x = \frac{-b \pm \sqrt{b^2 - 4ac}}{2a}$$

Another method is successive approximation—this method is often quicker than using the quadratic formula and is recommended.

The equation is first solved assuming x in the denominator *can* be neglected.

$$x^2 = (4.4 \times 10^{-4}) \times 0.010$$

$x = 2.098 \times 10^{-3}$ M—more than 10% different from the true value 1.89×10^{-3} M

Then this value is used in the denominator and the calculation repeated.

$$x^2 = (4.4 \times 10^{-4}) \times (0.010 - 0.002098)$$
$$x = 1.865 \times 10^{-3}\ M$$

> Maintain several significant figures in this series of calculations until the end.

This procedure is again repeated using the new value of x:

$$x^2 = (4.4 \times 10^{-4}) \times (0.010 - 0.001865)$$
$$x = 1.89 \times 10^{-3} \ M$$

If the procedure repeated yet again, the same value is obtained. Successive approximations are continued until a consistent value is obtained—usually the procedure does not take long and is faster and more foolproof than using the quadratic formula.

The x in these calculations is the hydroxide concentration.

$$[OH^-] = 1.9 \times 10^{-3} \ M$$
$$[H_3O^+] = 5.3 \times 10^{-12} \ M$$
$$pH = -\log_{10}[H_3O^+] = -\log_{10}(5.3 \times 10^{-12}) = 11.28$$

> A common mistake is to assume that x is the desired concentration or to forget what x represents. Remember what concentration you have used x for.

PROBLEM 39.4A

Calculate the hydrogen ion concentration and the pH of a 0.020 M solution of chloroacetic acid CH_2ClCO_2H. The equilibrium constant K_a for CH_2ClCO_2H at 25°C = 1.4×10^{-3}.

PROBLEM 39.4B

Calculate the hydrogen ion concentration and the pH of a 0.025 M solution of dimethylamine $(CH_3)_2NH$. The equilibrium constant K_b for dimethylamine $(CH_3)_2NH$ at 25°C = 5.4×10^{-4}.

> You may wonder, if K_a is constant, how this is possible—for the expression for K_a does not include $[H_2O]$. Dilution decreases the concentrations of all species in solution and, in the expression for K_a, the numerator contains two concentration terms but the denominator only one. Dilution by 2, for example, decreases the numerator by 4 but the denominator by 2. The reaction quotient decreases and the system must move to the right.

39.4 Percent Ionization

Another way to express the strength of a weak acid or weak base is the **percent ionization**. This is defined as the fraction of acid molecules that are ionized in solution multiplied by 100. If, for example, a 0.10 M solution of acetic acid is prepared, the concentrations $[H_3O^+]$, $[CH_3CO_2^-]$, and $[CH_3CO_2H]$ can be calculated (*cf.* Example 39.2).

The percent ionization in a 0.10 M solution of acetic acid is:

$$\text{Percent ionization} = \frac{[CH_3CO_2^-]}{[CH_3CO_2H]} \times 100\% = \frac{1.3 \times 10^{-3}}{0.10} \times 100\% = 1.3\%$$

The percent ionization depends upon the strength of the acid or base. A strong acid is 100% ionized in dilute solution. A weak acid, such as acetic acid just discussed, is only very slightly ionized.

The percent ionization of a weak acid also depends upon the initial concentration of acid. The percent ionization of a weak acid is greater in a more dilute solution. This is something you might have anticipated from LeChatelier's Principle:

$$CH_3CO_2H + H_2O \rightleftharpoons H_3O^+ + CH_3CO_2^-$$

Addition of water, to make the solution more dilute, should shift the equilibrium to the right, increasing the ionization of the acid. The variation of the percent ionization as the solution concentration is changed, is illustrated in Figure 39.3.

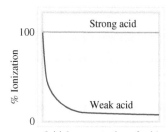

FIGURE 39.3 The percent ionization in a solution of acetic acid increases as solution is made more dilute.

Review Questions

1. Water is an amphiprotic solvent. Explain what this means.

2. Write an expression for K_w, the ion product for water. Is the value of Kw constant? Is the pH of a neutral solution always equal to 7.0?

3. Explain when the change in the concentration of a weak acid or weak base can be neglected in the calculation of the pH of the solution and when it cannot. In other words, when can the 'x' in the denominator be ignored?

Solutions to Problems

PROBLEM 39.1A

$pH = -\log_{10}[H_3O^+] = 7.44$

$[H_3O^+] = 3.63 \times 10^{-8}$ M

$[OH^-] = 2.42 \times 10^{-14} / 3.63 \times 10^{-8} = 6.67 \times 10^{-7}$ M

$pOH = -\log_{10}[OH^-] = -\log_{10}(6.67 \times 10^{-7}) = 6.18$

Or, $pOH = pK_w - pH = 13.62 - 7.44 = 6.18$

PROBLEM 39.2A

$[H_3O^+]$ = the concentration of the strong acid = 3.0×10^{-2} M

$pH = -\log_{10}[H_3O^+] = -\log_{10}[3.0 \times 10^{-2}] = 1.52$

$pOH = 14 - pH = 12.48$

$[OH^-] = 1.0 \times 10^{-14} / 3.0 \times 10^{-2} = 3.3 \times 10^{-13}$ M

PROBLEM 39.3A

The ionization of hypochlorous acid HClO is represented by the equation:

$$HClO + H_2O \rightleftharpoons H_3O^+ + ClO^-$$

The equilibrium constant

$$K_a = \frac{[H_3O^+][ClO^-]}{[HClO]} = 3.0 \times 10^{-8}$$

The ICE table is (with concentrations in M):

	HClO + H$_2$O $\rightleftharpoons$ H$_3$O$^+$ + ClO$^-$		
Initial:	0.20	0	0
Change:	$-x$	$+x$	$+x$
Equilibrium:	$0.20 - x$	x	x

$$K_a = \frac{[H_3O^+][ClO^-]}{[HClO]} = \frac{x^2}{(0.20 - x)}$$

The initial concentration (0.020 M) exceeds the value of $100 \times K_a$ (= 3.0×10^{-6}) and the approximation that the x in the denominator can be neglected is justifiable.

$$K_a = 3.0 \times 10^{-8} = \frac{x^2}{0.20} \text{ and } x = 7.75 \times 10^{-5}$$

x represents the concentration of hydronium ion:

$[H_3O^+] = 7.7 \times 10^{-5}$ M

$pH = -\log_{10}[H_3O^+] = -\log_{10}(7.7 \times 10^{-5}) = 4.11$

PROBLEM 39.4A

The ionization of chloroacetic acid CH_2ClCO_2H is represented by the equation:

$$CH_2ClCO_2H + H_2O \rightleftharpoons H_3O^+ + CH_2ClCO_2^-$$

The equilibrium constant

$$K_a = \frac{[H_3O^+][CH_2ClCO_2^-]}{[CH_2ClCO_2H]} = 1.4 \times 10^{-3}$$

The ICE table is (with concentrations in M):

	H$_2$O + CH$_2$ClCO$_2$H $\rightleftharpoons$ H$_3$O$^+$ + CH$_2$ClCO$_2^-$		
I:	0.020	0	0
C:	$-x$	$+x$	$+x$
E:	$0.020 - x$	x	x

$$K_a = \frac{[H_3O^+][CH_2ClCO_2^-]}{[CH_2ClCO_2H]} = \frac{x^2}{(0.20 - x)} = 1.4 \times 10^{-3}$$

The initial concentration (0.010 M) does *not* exceed the value of $100 \times K_b$ (= 0.14) and the approximation is *not* justifiable.

Solve the equation assuming x in the denominator *can* be neglected:

$$x^2 = (1.4 \times 10^{-3}) \times 0.020$$
$$x = 5.29 \times 10^{-3} \, M$$

Then use this value in the denominator in a repeat calculation:

$$x^2 = (1.4 \times 10^{-3}) \times (0.020 - 5.29 \times 10^{-3})$$
$$x = 4.54 \times 10^{-3} \, M$$

Repeating the process:

$$x^2 = (1.4 \times 10^{-3}) \times (0.020 - 4.54 \times 10^{-3})$$
$$x = 4.65 \times 10^{-3} \, M$$

And again:

$$x^2 = (1.4 \times 10^{-3}) \times (0.020 - 4.65 \times 10^{-3})$$

$$x = 4.64 \times 10^{-3} \, M$$

x represents the concentration of hydronium ion:

$$[H_3O^+] = 4.6 \times 10^{-3} \, M$$

$$pH = -\log_{10}[H_3O^+] = -\log_{10}(4.6 \times 10^{-3}) = 2.33$$

Answers to Review Questions

1. An amphiprotic solvent is a solvent that can either donate a hydrogen ion and act as an acid or accept a hydrogen ion and act as a base.

2. $K_w = [H_3O^+][OH^-] = 1.0 \times 10^{-14}$ at 25°C.

   The value of K_w increases if the temperature increases because the concentrations of hydronium ion $[H_3O^+]$ and hydroxide $[OH^-]$ ion increase. The pH of a neutral solution decreases: the pH = $-\log_{10}[H_3O^+]$.

   For example, at 80°C, $K_w = 2.39 \times 10^{-14}$ and therefore in a neutral solution $[H_3O^+] = 4.89 \times 10^{-7}$ and the pH decreases to 6.31.

3. The decision whether or not to ignore the 'x' in the denominator depends upon the precision of the data and the precision required in the answer. Generally the data provided do not warrant a precision greater than ± 5% and this means that the x can be ignored if it is less than 5% of the initial concentration of weak electrolyte. The decision to ignore the x depends both upon the magnitude of the equilibrium constant and the initial concentration. A useful rule is that in order to ignore the x, the initial concentration should be greater than 100 × K.

End-of-Unit Problems

1. Vinegar, a solution of acetic acid, has a hydronium ion concentration $[H_3O^+]$ equal to $3.5 \times 10^{-3} \, M$. Calculate the hydroxide ion concentration $[OH^-]$, the pH, and the pOH of the solution.

2. A freshly brewed beer was tested for acidity and found to have a hydronium ion concentration $[H_3O^+]$ equal to $8.3 \times 10^{-5} \, M$. Calculate the hydroxide ion concentration $[OH^-]$, the pH, and the pOH of the beer.

3. A sample of lemon juice has a pH of 2.31. Calculate the hydronium ion concentration $[H_3O^+]$, the hydroxide ion concentration $[OH^-]$, and the pOH of the juice.

4. A household detergent solution has a pH of 10.44. Calculate the hydronium ion concentration $[H_3O^+]$, the hydroxide ion concentration $[OH^-]$, and the pOH of the solution.

5. A drain cleaner has a pOH of 1.21. Calculate the hydronium ion concentration $[H_3O^+]$, the hydroxide ion concentration $[OH^-]$, and the pH of the cleaner.

6. Household ammonia solution has a pOH of 2.38. Calculate the hydronium ion concentration $[H_3O^+]$, the hydroxide ion concentration $[OH^-]$, and the pH of the solution.

7. A nitric acid solution was diluted until its pH was equal to 4.23. Calculate the hydronium ion concentration $[H_3O^+]$, the hydroxide ion concentration $[OH^-]$, and the pOH of the solution.

8. A potassium hydroxide solution was diluted until its pH was equal to 11.80. Calculate the hydronium ion concentration $[H_3O^+]$, the hydroxide ion concentration $[OH^-]$, and the pOH of the solution.

9. A neutral solution at body temperature (37°C) has a pH equal to 6.80. Calculate the hydronium ion concentration $[H_3O^+]$, the hydroxide ion concentration $[OH^-]$, and the pOH of this neutral solution.

10. At 90°C, $K_w = 3.55 \times 10^{-13}$. Calculate the pH and pOH of a neutral solution at this temperature and the corresponding hydronium ion concentration $[H_3O^+]$ and hydroxide ion concentration $[OH^-]$.

11. An acidic solution with a pH = 5.60 at 25°C was heated to 70°C. Does the pH of the solution change? If so, what is the pH of the solution at 70°C? The ion product for water K_w at 70°C = 3.55×10^{-13}.

12. A basic solution with a pH = 9.43 at 80°C was cooled to 0°C. Does the pH of the solution change? If so, what is the pH of the solution at 0°C? The ion product for water K_w at 80°C = 2.39×10^{-13} and at 0°C = 1.14×10^{-15}.

13. Calculate the hydrogen ion concentration and the pH of a 0.180 M solution of acetic acid CH_3CO_2H. The equilibrium constant K_a for acetic acid at 25°C = 1.8×10^{-5}.

14. Calculate the hydrogen ion concentration and the pH of a 0.500 M solution of formic acid HCO_2H. The equilibrium constant K_a for formic acid at 25°C = 1.8×10^{-4}.

15. Calculate the hydrogen ion concentration and the pH of a 0.25 M solution of hydroxylamine NH_2OH. The equilibrium constant K_b for hydroxylamine at 25°C = 1.0×10^{-8}.

16. Calculate the hydrogen ion concentration and the pH of a 0.015 M solution of pyridine C_5H_5N. The equilibrium constant K_b for pyridine at 25°C = 1.8×10^{-9}.

17. Calculate the hydrogen ion concentration and the pH of a 0.020 M solution of triethylamine $(C_2H_5)_3N$.

The equilibrium constant K_b for triethylamine at 25°C = 1.0×10^{-3}. Explain why it is not possible to neglect the change in the initial concentration of the base in this case.

18. Calculate the hydrogen ion concentration and the pH of a 0.250 M solution of iodic acid HIO_3. The equilibrium constant K_a for iodic acid at 25°C = 1.6×10^{-1}. Explain why it is not possible to neglect the change in the initial concentration of the acid in this case.

19. Calculate the percent ionization of the acetic acid, formic acid, triethylamine, and pyridine in the solutions described in Questions 13 through 16.

20. If the pOH of a calcium hydroxide $Ca(OH)_2$ solution is 3.61, what is the molarity of the solution?

21. If the pH of a barium hydroxide $Ba(OH)_2$ solution is 10.22, what is the molarity of the solution?

The Strengths of Acids and Bases

40.1   Hydrogen Ion Transfer

According to the Brønsted-Lowry definitions, an acid is a species that transfers a hydrogen ion to a base and the base is the species that accepts the hydrogen ion from the acid. The acid-base reaction is a hydrogen ion transfer. Brønsted-Lowry acid-base reactions are reversible. The acid and base formed in the forward reaction—the conjugate partners of the acid and base on the reactant side—can also participate in a hydrogen ion transfer and reform the reactants. At equilibrium, the rate in the forward direction equals the rate of the reaction in the reverse direction.

The ionization of ammonia in aqueous solution is an example: In the forward direction the water molecule donates a hydrogen ion to the ammonia molecule and in the reverse direction the ammonium ion donates a hydrogen ion to the hydroxide ion:

$$\text{forward reaction} \qquad\qquad \text{reverse reaction}$$
$$\underset{\text{base}}{NH_3(aq)} + \underset{\text{acid}}{H_2O(l)} \rightleftharpoons \underset{\text{acid}}{NH_4^+(aq)} + \underset{\text{base}}{OH^-(aq)}$$

The strength of a Brønsted-Lowry acid reflects its tendency to donate a hydrogen ion. A strong acid is a molecule, or ion, that releases a hydrogen ion easily. Similarly, a strong base is a molecule, or ion, that has a high affinity for a hydrogen ion. As we will see, a Brønsted-Lowry acid-base equilibrium can be viewed as a competition for the hydrogen ion—which of the two bases wants the hydrogen ion more and wins the competition?

40.2   Proton Affinity

The proton affinity of an anion or neutral molecule is a measure of how strong a base it is in the gas phase. It is the enthalpy change when a hydrogen ion is added to the isolated anion or molecule. Conventionally, the proton affinity is listed as a positive number although it is the energy *released* when the hydrogen ion is added and therefore ΔH is negative. In this sense, proton affinities follow the same convention as electron affinities.

anion: $A^-(g) + H^+(g) \rightarrow HA(g)$

molecule: $B(g) + H^+(g) \rightarrow BH+(g)$

It is possible to measure the proton affinites of simple anions and molecules and some values are listed in Table 40.1.

It's not surprising that the proton affinity of a negatively charged anion is greater than that of a neutral molecule. The attraction between the two oppositely charged ions is greater.

Any two bases can be compared to determine which is the stronger and which would win the competition for a hydrogen ion. For example, compare the proton affinities of the hydroxide ion and ammonia in the gas phase:

$$NH_3(g) + H_2O(g) \rightleftharpoons NH_4^+(g) + OH^-(g)$$
$$854 \text{ kJ mol}^{-1} \qquad\qquad\qquad 1635 \text{ kJ mol}^{-1}$$

TABLE 40.1   Gas phase proton affinities of some anions and molecules. By convention, these energies are listed as positive numbers representing the energy *released* when a hydrogen ion is added. The enthalpy change is the negative of these numbers.

Anions		Molecules	
Base	**Proton Affinity**	**Base**	**Proton Affinity**
H^-	1675 kJ mol^{-1}	CH_3NH_2	896 kJ mol^{-1}
NH_2^-	1672	NH_3	854
OH^-	1635	C_2H_5OH	788
F^-	1554	HCN	717
CN^-	1477	H_2S	712
$CH_3CO_2^-$	1458	H_2O	697
Cl^-	1395	HI	628
NO_3^-	1358	HBr	569
Br^-	1354	HCl	564
I^-	1315	H_2	424

The hydroxide ion has the higher proton affinity and wins the competition—it forms water and the system lies predominantly on the left. Now compare the proton affinities of water and the chloride ion in the gas-phase:

$$HCl(g) + H_2O(g) \rightleftharpoons H_3O^+(g) + Cl^-(g)$$
$$697 \text{ kJ mol}^{-1} \qquad\qquad 1395 \text{ kJ mol}^{-1}$$

Again the negative ion (Cl^-) has the higher proton affinity; it wins the competition for the hydrogen ion and forms HCl; the equilibrium lies on the left. This behavior is quite different from what happens in aqueous solution. In solution, the Cl^- ion is a weaker base than water (the HCl is a stronger acid than H_3O^+), and the equilibrium lies on the right. The difference between the two situations is the presence of the solvent—the solvent affects the relative strengths of the bases. The two situations can be related by the energy cycles illustrated in Figure 40.1.

In each cycle the upper arrow represents the addition of a hydrogen ion *in solution* and the lower arrow represents the addition of a hydrogen ion *in the gas phase*. Connecting the two are the hydration energies of the bases and their conjugate acids.

Unless there is some unusual interaction between the solute and solvent, the ion–dipole attraction between ions and the water molecules in aqueous solution is greater than the attraction between neutral molecules and the water molecules. This means that in the first case shown in Figure 40.1, less energy is required to take the molecular base B out of solution and into the gas phase than is released when its conjugate acid BH$^+$ is put back into solution. Using Hess's Law for the cycle, this results in an increase in the energy released when the hydrogen ion is added in solution, compared to the energy released when the hydrogen ion is added in the gas phase. The proton affinity of molecular bases is increased in solution.

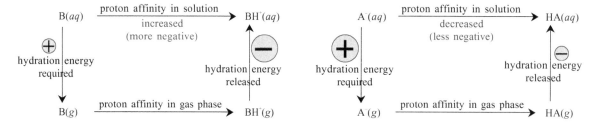

FIGURE 40.1 **Proton affinities of molecules (B) and anions (A⁻) in solution compared to the gas phase.**
The proton affinities of neutral molecules are increased in solution and the proton affinities of anions are decreased in solution.

The opposite is true for anionic (negatively charged) bases. In this case more energy is required to take the base A⁻ out of solution and into the gas phase than is released when the conjugate acid HA is put back into solution.

The overall effect for several bases is illustrated in Figure 40.2.

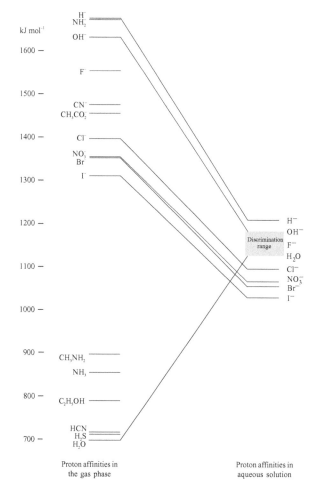

FIGURE 40.2 **The effect of the solvent (water) on the basic strength (proton affinity) of some molecular and anionic bases.**
The basic strength of neutral molecules is increased in solution and the basic strength of anions is decreased in solution.

40.3 Conjugate Partners

Two bases relevant in aqueous equilibria are water itself and the hydroxide ion. In the righthand column in Figure 40.2, corresponding to base strengths in aqueous solution, the range between H_2O and OH^- is called the **discrimination range**. Bases stronger than hydroxide OH^- (for example the hydride ion H^- in Figure 40.2) are defined as strong bases—these bases will react with water to produce hydroxide ions. Water, as a solvent, cannot discriminate between any bases stronger than the hydroxide ion—this is referred to as the **levelling effect**. In other words, the hydroxide ion is the strongest base that can exist in aqueous solution. Any base stronger than hydroxide cannot exist in aqueous solution because it reacts with water to produce the hydroxide ion.

At the other end of the discrimination range, the bases Cl^-, NO_3^-, etc., are weaker bases than water. This means that their conjugate acids, HCl, HNO_3, etc. are all stronger than the hydronium ion; that is, they are all classified as strong acids. Water, as a solvent, cannot discriminate between the strong acids; they are all equally strong in aqueous solution. As in the case with strong bases described above, any acid stronger than the hydronium ion reacts with water to produce the hydronium ion in aqueous solution. The hydronium ion is the strongest acid that can exist in aqueous solution.

Within the discrimination range, the relative strengths of various weak acids, and the corresponding weak conjugate bases, can be determined. This is most easily seen on another diagram (Figure 40.3) which includes some representative bases with their conjugate acids. The acids are in the left column and their conjugate bases are in the right column. The diagram is shown in its usual orientation with the acids increasing in strength from bottom to top on the left and the bases increasing in strength from top to bottom on the right. Note that this is the reverse of Figure 40.2 in which the base strength increases going up.

When an acid releases a hydrogen ion, it forms its conjugate base. The more readily the acid releases the hydrogen ion, the less its conjugate base wants to accept the hydrogen ion back. In other words, the stronger the acid, the weaker its conjugate base. For example, consider the strong acid HCl. This acid is completely ionized in dilute aqueous solution:

$$HCl + H_2O \rightarrow H_3O^+ + Cl^-$$

The HCl molecule readily releases a hydrogen ion in aqueous solution and the chloride ion has little tendency to accept the hydrogen ion back. The acid is strong and the equilibrium lies predominantly on the right. Of the two acids present, HCl and H_3O^+, the HCl is the stronger.

From our point of view, there are two bases present, the H_2O and the Cl^-. Which of these two bases is the stronger? The water is the stronger base and it wins the competition for the hydrogen ion:

$$
\begin{array}{cccccc}
& \overset{\displaystyle H^+ \longrightarrow}{} & & & \overset{\displaystyle H^+ \longrightarrow}{} & \\
HCl & + & H_2O & \rightleftharpoons & H_3O^+ & + & Cl^- \\
\text{acid} & & \text{base} & & \text{acid} & & \text{base} \\
\text{stronger} & & \text{stronger} & & \text{weaker} & & \text{weaker}
\end{array}
$$

The transfer of the hydrogen ion from the strong acid to the strong base is the predominant reaction. This makes sense because the stronger acid donates a hydrogen ion more readily than the weaker acid and the stronger base accepts the hydrogen ion

The enthalpy change for the autoionization of water,

$$2\,H_2O \rightleftharpoons H_3O^+ + OH^-$$

is the difference between the proton affinities of H_2O and OH^- in aqueous solution:

$$\Delta H° = +55.86 \text{ kJ mol}^{-1}$$

The corresponding changes in entropy and free energy are:

$\Delta S° = -80.40$ JK^{-1}
$\Delta G° = +79.9$ kJ mol^{-1} at 25°C

$\Delta G° = -RT\ln K$
or $K = e^{-(\Delta G°/RT)}$
$\quad = 1.01 \times 10^{-14}$

which is K_w, the autoionization constant for water at 25°C.

To discriminate better between the strong acids, a more acidic solvent (for example, glacial acetic acid) or less basic solvent (for example, diethylether) is required.

	ACID			BASE	

<table>
<tr><td>Perchloric acid</td><td>$HClO_4$</td><td>ClO_4^-</td><td>Perchlorate ion</td></tr>
<tr><td>Hydrochloric acid</td><td>HCl</td><td>Cl^-</td><td>Chloride ion</td></tr>
<tr><td>Sulfuric acid</td><td>H_2SO_4</td><td>HSO_4^-</td><td>Hydrogen sulfate ion</td></tr>
<tr><td>Nitric acid</td><td>HNO_3</td><td>NO_3^-</td><td>Nitrate ion</td></tr>
<tr><td>Hydronium ion</td><td>H_3O^+</td><td>H_2O</td><td>Water</td></tr>
<tr><td>Hydrogen sulfate ion</td><td>HSO_4^-</td><td>SO_4^{2-}</td><td>Sulfate ion</td></tr>
<tr><td>Phosphoric acid</td><td>H_3PO_4</td><td>$H_2PO_4^-$</td><td>Dihydrogen phosphate ion</td></tr>
<tr><td>Nitrous acid</td><td>HNO_2</td><td>NO_2^-</td><td>Nitrite ion</td></tr>
<tr><td>Hydrofluoric acid</td><td>HF</td><td>F^-</td><td>Fluoride ion</td></tr>
<tr><td>Acetic acid</td><td>CH_3CO_2H</td><td>$CH_3CO_2^-$</td><td>Acetate ion</td></tr>
<tr><td>Hydrosulfuric acid</td><td>H_2S</td><td>HS^-</td><td>Hydrogen sulfide ion</td></tr>
<tr><td>Dihydrogen phosphate ion</td><td>$H_2PO_4^-$</td><td>HPO_4^{2-}</td><td>Hydrogen phosphate ion</td></tr>
<tr><td>Hypochlorous acid</td><td>$HClO$</td><td>ClO^-</td><td>Hypochlorite ion</td></tr>
<tr><td>Ammonium ion</td><td>NH_4^+</td><td>NH_3</td><td>Ammonia</td></tr>
<tr><td>Hydrocyanic acid</td><td>HCN</td><td>CN^-</td><td>Cyanide ion</td></tr>
<tr><td>Hydrogen phosphate ion</td><td>HPO_4^{2-}</td><td>PO_4^{3-}</td><td>Phosphate ion</td></tr>
<tr><td>Water</td><td>H_2O</td><td>OH^-</td><td>Hydroxide</td></tr>
<tr><td>Ammonia</td><td>NH_3</td><td>NH_2^-</td><td>Amide ion</td></tr>
<tr><td>Hydrogen</td><td>H_2</td><td>H^-</td><td>Hydride ion</td></tr>
<tr><td>Methane</td><td>CH_4</td><td>CH_3^-</td><td>Methide ion</td></tr>
<tr><td>Hydroxide</td><td>OH^-</td><td>O^{2-}</td><td>Oxide ion</td></tr>
</table>

Left margin: STRONG ACIDS; Acid strength increases up
Right margin: Base strength increases down; STRONG BASES

FIGURE 40.3 Acids and their conjugate bases arranged in order of their strength. Strong acids are on the left at the top and strong bases are at the bottom on the right. The dividing line between strong and weak acids is the hydronium ion and the dividing line between strong and weak bases is the hydroxide ion.

more readily than the weaker base. Notice how the stronger of the two acids and the stronger of the two bases lie on the same side. Similarly the weaker of the two acids and the weaker of the two bases lie on the other side.

As a result, an equilibrium system such as this *always* lies on the side of the weaker acid and base—all aqueous systems move spontaneously to form weaker electrolytes.

To summarize, the acids and bases shown in Figure 40.3 are divided into three groups:

- Strong acids are those acids stronger than the hydronium ion H_3O^+. Water cannot discriminate between these acids. The conjugate bases of these acids are extremely weak.

- Weak acids and bases are those acids weaker than H_3O^+ and those bases weaker than OH^-.

- Strong bases are those bases stronger than the hydroxide ion OH⁻. Water cannot discriminate between these bases. The conjugate acids of these bases are extremely weak.

As we have seen in Unit 39, equilibria are characterized by an equilibrium constant K which describes the ratio between the ⇌ ntrations of the products and reactants at equilibrium. A general equation for the ionization of an acid in aqueous solution is

$$HA + H_2O \rightleftharpoons H_3O^+ + A^-$$

and the equilibrium constant is

$$K_a = \frac{[H_3O^+][A^-]}{[HA]}$$

These equilibrium constants are called **acid ionization constants** and, as shown, they are given the symbol K_a. If the value of K_a is large (>1), then system lies more on the product side and the acid is strong. Conversely, if the value of K_a is small (<1), then system lies more on the reactant side and the acid is weak.

A list of some acids is shown in Table 40.2 arranged in order of their relative strengths with values of their K_a and pK_a.

The acid ionization constant is often called the acid dissociation constant.

TABLE 40.2 The relative strengths of some acids in aqueous solution. Acids above the hydronium ion in the table are strong. Acids below the hydronium ion in the table are weak.

Name	Formula	K_a	pK_a
Hydroiodic acid	HI	large ~10^{11}	−11
Perchloric acid	$HClO_4$	large ~10^{10}	−10
Hydrobromic acid	HBr	large ~10^9	−9
Hydrochloric acid	HCl	large ~10^7	−7
Chloric acid	$HClO_3$	large ~10^3	−3
Sulfuric acid	H_2SO_4	large ~10^2	−2
Nitric acid	HNO_3	large ~10	−1
Hydronium ion	H_3O^+	1.0	0
Trichloroacetic acid	CCl_3CO_2H	3.0×10^{-1}	0.52
Iodic acid	HIO_3	1.6×10^{-1}	0.80
Sulfurous acid	H_2SO_3	1.5×10^{-2}	1.82
Hydrogen sulfate	HSO_4^-	1.2×10^{-2}	1.92
Chlorous acid	$HClO_2$	1.1×10^{-2}	1.96
Phosphoric acid	H_3PO_4	7.5×10^{-3}	2.12
Hydrofluoric acid	HF	6.8×10^{-4}	3.17
Nitrous acid	HNO_2	4.5×10^{-4}	3.35
Formic acid	HCO_2H	1.8×10^{-4}	3.74
Benzoic acid	$C_6H_5CO_2H$	6.3×10^{-5}	4.20
Acetic acid	CH_3CO_2H	1.8×10^{-5}	4.74
Propionic acid	$CH_3CH_2CO_2H$	1.3×10^{-5}	4.89
Carbonic acid	H_2CO_3	4.3×10^{-7}	6.37
Hydrogen sulfite	HSO_3^-	1.2×10^{-7}	6.91
Dihydrogen phosphate	$H_2PO_4^-$	6.2×10^{-8}	7.21
Hypochlorous acid	HClO	3.0×10^{-8}	7.52
Hypobromous acid	HBrO	2.3×10^{-9}	8.64
Ammonium ion	NH_4^+	5.6×10^{-10}	9.26
Hydrocyanic acid	HCN	4.0×10^{-10}	9.40
Phenol	C_6H_5OH	1.6×10^{-10}	9.80
Hydrogen carbonate	HCO_3^-	5.6×10^{-11}	10.25
Hypoiodous acid	HIO	2.3×10^{-11}	10.64
Hydrogen phosphate	HPO_4^{2-}	3.6×10^{-13}	12.44

These K_a values for the strong acids are meaningless for aqueous solution—all strong acids are equally strong in aqueous solution due to the levelling effect. The values are provided to indicate the relative strengths in a more acidic solvent.

Bromic acid $HBrO_3$ is weaker than chloric acid but stronger than the hydronium ion and is classified as strong. It is *not* a commonly encountered acid.

Note that *stronger* acids have *lower* pK_a values. The strong acids have negative pK_a values.

EXAMPLE 40.1 BRØNSTED-LOWRY ACID-BASE EQUILIBRIA

Use the data in Figure 40.3 to write an equation representing what happens when

a. NH_3 dissolves in water

b. a salt of the F^- ion (eg. NaF) dissolves in water

Determine the conjugate acid-base pairs and establish which side of the equation is the weaker side and therefore what are the predominant species present in aqueous solution.

UNDERSTAND THE QUESTION

Figure 40.3 can be used to predict what happens when an electrolyte is dissolved in water. The table indicates the conjugate partner of the species dissolved in water and the relative strengths of the two acids and the two bases involved in the equilibrium.

PLAN THE SOLUTION

Find the substance in Figure 40.3 and identify the conjugate partner. If the substance is in the acid column, then water acts as a base and the substance produces hydronium ion when dissolved. Similarly, if the substance is in the base column, then water acts as an acid and the substance produces hydroxide ion when dissolved.

SOLVE THE PROBLEM

a. Ammonia NH_3 is in both columns. However, ammonia cannot act as an acid in aqueous solution—water is above ammonia in the acid column and is the stronger acid of the two. Therefore ammonia acts as a base in aqueous solution.

Ammonia reacts with water to produce the conjugate base of water and its own conjugate acid, the ammonium ion NH_4^+:

acid strength ↑	acid		base	base strength ↓
	NH_4^+	⟵	NH_3	
	H_2O	⟶	OH^-	

The equilibrium is:

$$\underset{\text{base}}{NH_3} + \underset{\text{acid}}{H_2O} \rightleftharpoons \underset{\text{acid}}{NH_4^+} + \underset{\text{base}}{OH^-}$$

weaker weaker stronger stronger

⟵

The system lies predominantly on the weaker side, K_b is small (1.8×10^{-5})—the predominant species in solution is NH_3 (and H_2O).

b. The fluoride ion F^- is in the base column. (It cannot act as an acid—it has no hydrogen.) The fluoride ion reacts with water to produce the conjugate base of water and its own conjugate acid, HF:

acid strength ↑	acid		base	base strength ↓
	HF	⟵	F^-	
	H_2O	⟶	OH^-	

The equilibrium is:

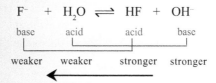

The system lies predominantly on the weaker side, K_b is very small (1.5×10^{-11}) —the predominant species in solution is F^- (and H_2O). This is an example of the hydrolysis of a salt—we will examine this in more detail in the next unit, Unit 41.

PROBLEM 40.1A

Use the data in Table 40.2 to write an equation representing what happens when

a. Nitric acid HNO_3 dissolves in water.

b. Sodium hydride NaH dissolves in water.

Determine the conjugate acid-base pairs and establish which side of the equation is the weaker side and therefore what are the predominant species present in aqueous solution.

PROBLEM 40.1B

Use the data in Table 40.2 to write an equation representing what happens when

a. Sodium sulfite Na_2SO_3 dissolves in water.

b. Acetic acid CH_3CO_2H dissolves in water.

Determine the conjugate acid-base pairs and establish which side of the equation is the weaker side and therefore what are the predominant species present in aqueous solution.

40.4   The Relative Strengths of Acids and Bases

What makes one acid stronger than another? The ease with which a molecule releases a hydrogen ion depends upon its chemical structure. In order to release a hydrogen ion readily . . .

• the bond between the hydrogen atom and the remainder of the molecule should be relatively weak.

• the bond between the hydrogen atom and the remainder of the molecule should be polarized such that the bonding electrons are withdrawn from the hydrogen atom.

• the fragment of the molecule remaining after the hydrogen ion has broken away (the conjugate base) should be stable.

• any negative charge on the species should be low (it is more difficult to remove a positive hydrogen ion from a negatively charged particle than from a neutral particle).

Let's look at these factors in turn and examine how they influence the strengths of acids. Remember, however, that the effect of the solvent is very important. Most of the following comments refer to an isolated (gaseous) molecule.

Bond Energy

The release of a hydrogen ion involves breaking a covalent bond between the hydrogen atom and the remainder of the molecule. Examine, for example, the bond strengths of the binary hydrides of the halogens.

HF	565 kJ mol^{-1}
HCl	431 kJ mol^{-1}
HBr	366 kJ mol^{-1}
HI	298 kJ mol^{-1}

It is tempting to assume that the ease with which the hydrogen ion is lost is directly related to the strength of the bond—the acid strength increases down the series. Hydrofluoric acid is weak and the three remaining acids HCl, HBr, and HI are all strong, increasing in strength in that order. This explanation, however, completely ignores the effect of the solvent. In fact, the comparatively large HF bond energy is more than compensated for by the high heat of solvation of the fluoride ion—the solvation energy of the fluoride ion is –505 kJ mol^{-1} compared to –365 kJ mol^{-1} for the chloride ion—partly due to a hydrogen bonding interation between the fluoride ion, water molecules, and hydronium ions. The weak acid strength of HF in aqueous solution must be caused by some other effect.

Referring back to the second cycle in Figure 40.1, we can compare the two ions F$^-$ and Cl$^-$ and ask the question: why is F$^-$ a stronger base than Cl$^-$? In other words, why is HF weak and HCl strong in aqueous solution? One significant difference between HF and HCl in aqueous solution is the ability of HF to hydrogen bond with the solvent water molecules. The increased energy of this interaction means that the F$^-$ ion will be a stronger base than the Cl$^-$ ion in solution—the decrease in the gas phase proton affinity will be less for F$^-$ compared with Cl$^-$.

Another thing to remember is that the equilibrium constant K depends upon $\Delta G°$, not just upon $\Delta H°$. We have not considered any entropy effects. The high charge density of the small fluoride ion attracts the solvent water molecules very strongly and this results in a decrease in the entropy for the fluoride ion in solution compared to the other halide ions in solution. This means that when HF reacts with water there is a large decrease in entropy ($\Delta S°$ is negative), compared to the decrease when HCl, HBr, and HI react with water. This results in a more positive $\Delta G°$ for HF and a correspondingly smaller equilibrium constant K. Estimates for $\Delta G°$ for HF and HCl are +18 kJ mol^{-1} and –46 kJ mol^{-1} respectively.

Hydrogen bonding not only between HF molecules and water molecules, but also between fluoride ions, hydronium ions, and water molecules, has a complicated but very significant effect upon the acid strength of hydrofluoric acid.

$$\Delta G° = -RT\ln K$$
$$\Delta G° = \Delta H° - T\Delta S°$$

Bond Polarity

The hydrogen breaks away from the acid as H$^+$, not as an H atom. For this reason the strength of the acid depends not only upon the strength of the bond but also upon the extent to which the electrons are polarized in the bond. The more the electrons are withdrawn from the hydrogen atom, the easier it is for the H$^+$ ion to break away. As an example look at the binary hydrides of carbon, nitrogen, oxygen, and fluorine:

	Electronegativity Difference		**Approximate** K_a =
CH$_4$	0.24		$\sim 10^{-40}$
NH$_3$	0.77		$\sim 10^{-32}$
H$_2$O	1.31		$\sim 10^{-16}$
HF	1.89		$\sim 10^{-4}$

The acid strength of these four compounds increases as the electronegativity difference increases and the polarity of the bond increases. Even though the H—F bond is stronger than the C—H, N—H, or O—H bonds, HF is the strongest acid of the four molecules because the H—F bond is the most polarized. The hydrogen atoms of the methane molecule CH_4 are not acidic at all (K_a is extremely small).

A similar trend in acid strength is observed in the oxoacids. You may have noticed that HNO_3 is strong but HNO_2 is weak, H_2SO_4 is strong but H_2SO_3 is weak, and $HClO_4$ and $HClO_3$ are strong but $HClO_2$ and $HClO$ are weak. The strength of the acid appears to depend upon the number of oxygen atoms.

There are two factors to consider. One is the identity of the element to which the oxygen atoms are bonded. Examine the hypohalous acids and their values for K_a:

HIO $\qquad$ $K_a = 2.3 \times 10^{-11}$ $\qquad\qquad$ I—O—H

HBrO $\qquad$ $K_a = 2.3 \times 10^{-9}$ $\qquad\qquad$ Br—O—H

HClO $\qquad$ $K_a = 3.0 \times 10^{-8}$ $\qquad\qquad$ Cl—O—H

As the electronegativity of the halogen increases, electrons are pulled away from the oxygen atom to which the hydrogen is attached. This polarizes the bond between the oxygen and hydrogen atoms and makes it easier for the hydrogen ion to break away.

A similar trend is seen in the oxyacids of the third period elements illustrated in Figure 40.4. As the electronegativity of the central atom increases, the acid strength increases.

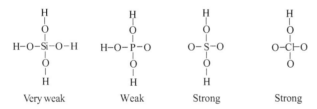

FIGURE 40.4 As the electronegativity of the central atom increases, the strength of the acid increases.

The other factor is the number of oxygen atoms without a hydrogen attached. Each of these oxygen atoms withdraws electrons from the halogen, increasing its effective electronegativity. This in turn pulls electrons away from the oxygen with a hydrogen, again making it easier for the hydrogen ion to break away. The more oxygen atoms there are, the greater the polarization of the O—H bond, and the more easily the hydrogen ion is detached. This effect can be seen in the relative strengths of the chlorine oxoacids (Figure 40.5).

FIGURE 40.5 As the number of oxygen atoms around the chlorine atom increases, more electron density is withdrawn from the O—H bond, making the bond more polar, and making it easier for the H^+ to break away. The strengths of the acids increase HOCl < HOClO < HOClO₂ < HOClO₃.

There is an empirical rule that states that oxyacids that have at least two more oxygen atoms than acidic hydrogen atoms are strong.

For example, in H_2SO_4, the difference between the number of oxygen atoms and acidic hydrogen atoms is 2, therefore the acid is strong. In H_2SO_3, the difference is only 1, therefore weak.

The rule works well for the common acids but it is not without exceptions. For example, iodic acid HIO_3 and periodic acid HIO_4 might be predicted to be strong but in fact they are slightly weaker than H_3O^+:

Iodic acid HIO_3 $K_a = 1.6 \times 10^{-1}$

Periodic acid HIO_4 $K_a = 2.3 \times 10^{-2}$

Note that the structure of periodic acid is concentration dependent:

dilute solution: HIO_4
concentrated solution: H_5IO_6

Another empirical rule allows an estimate of the pK_a of an oxoacid from the formula: $pK_a \approx 8 - 5n$ where n is the number of hydrogen-free oxygen atoms in the oxoacid: $XO_n(OH)_m$. For example, in HNO_2, n = 1, so 8 − 5n = 3. The actual pK_a = 3.35. In HOCl, n = 0, so 8 − 5n = 8. The actual pK_a = 7.52.

The two rules are obviously related because if n is 2 or greater, then pK_a is negative (8 − 10 = −2), and the acid is strong.

Stability of the Anion (the Conjugate Base)

When a hydrogen ion H^+ breaks away from a molecule, the electrons in the covalent bond stay with the remainder of the molecule, creating a negative charge—it is an anion. If this negative charge can be delocalized (spread out) over the anion, then the anion is more stable and the molecule loses the hydrogen ion more readily—it is a stronger acid. In other words, the anion is less willing to accept the hydrogen ion back—it is a weaker base.

Compare, for example, phenol and ethanol (Figure 40.6). When ethanol loses a hydrogen ion, the negative charge on the ethoxide anion is localized on the oxygen atom. When phenol loses a hydrogen ion, the negative charge on the phenoxide ion is delocalized around the benzene ring in the π bonding network (the $\delta-$ indicates a partial negative charge). The phenoxide ion is more stable and less basic than the ethoxide ion. Although both are quite weak, phenol ($K_a = 10^{-10}$) is a stronger acid than ethanol ($K_a = 10^{-16}$) by a factor of one million.

$$CH_3-CH_2-OH \quad \rightarrow \quad CH_3-CH_2-O^-$$

ethanol $\rightarrow$ ethoxide ion   phenol $\rightarrow$ phenoxide ion

FIGURE 40.6   Phenol is one million times stronger ($K_a = 10^{-10}$) than ethanol ($K_a = 10^{-16}$) as an acid in aqueous solution.
When ethanol loses a hydrogen ion, the negative charge on the ethoxide anion remains localized on the oxygen atom. When phenol loses a hydrogen ion, the negative charge is delocalized around the benzene ring.

The delocalization of the negative charge on anions plays an important role in their stability. For example the double negative charge on the sulfate ion and on the carbonate ion is shared by all the oxygen atoms in these ions. The single negative charge on the acetate ion (and other carboxylate anions) is shared by both oxygen atoms and this delocalization increases the stability of the anions and increases the strength of the corresponding acid (Figure 40.7).

$$CH_3-CH_2-C \overset{O}{\underset{O}{\diagdown}} \quad \longleftrightarrow \quad CH_3-CH_2-C \overset{O}{\underset{O^-}{\diagdown}}$$

FIGURE 40.7   The delocalization of the negative charge on anions plays an important role in their stability.
The negative charge on the acetate ion is shared by both oxygen atoms and this delocalization increases the stability of the acetate anion and increases the strength of acetic acid. The two resonance structures are shown.

> An indication of how well a negative charge is delocalized on an anion can be determined by the number of resonance Lewis structures that can be drawn for the ion (*cf.* Unit 19).

Charge

As mentioned earlier, it is more difficult to detach a hydrogen ion from a negatively charged ion than from the corresponding neutral molecule. Similarly, it is easier to remove a hydrogen ion from a positively charged ion than from the corresponding molecule. For example, a hydrogen ion is removed more easily from a hydronium ion H_3O^+ than from a water molecule H_2O. Likewise, the ammonium ion NH_4^+ is more acidic than the ammonia molecule NH_3. The effect is seen in the relative acid strengths of the anions of a polyprotic acid such as phosphoric acid:

$$HPO_4^{2-} \quad K_{a3} = 3.6 \times 10^{-13}$$
$$H_2PO_4^- \quad K_{a2} = 6.2 \times 10^{-8}$$
$$H_3PO_4 \quad K_{a1} = 7.5 \times 10^{-3}$$

Phosphoric acid is a polyprotic acid (*cf.* Unit 8)—it has more than one acidic hydrogen atom. The removal of the second hydrogen ion is much more difficult than the removal of the first hydrogen ion because the H^+ ion has to be removed from a particle that already has a negative charge. The removal of the third hydrogen ion is even more difficult. The magnitude of K_a decreases by a factor of about 100,000 for each successive ionization. We will examine polyprotic acids in more detail in Unit 42.

EXAMPLE 40.2   ACID STRENGTHS

Order the substances in the following groups in increasing acid strength.

a. $HBrO_3$, H_2O, H_2CO_3, OH^-

b. CH_3OH, NH_4^+, CH_3CO_2H, NH_3

UNDERSTAND THE QUESTION

The strength of an acid depends upon its molecular structure, the charge, if any, on the molecule, and the effect of the solvent. For oxoacids, the number of oxygen atoms attached to the central atom determines the strength of the acid. The electronegativity of the central atom is important. For binary compounds, the strength and polarity of the bond to the acidic hydrogen atom influences the strength of the acid. Positively charged species donate a hydrogen ion more readily than the corresponding neutral molecules and neutral molecules donate a hydrogen ion more readily than negatively charged species.

PLAN THE SOLUTION

Identify the acids, or determine their structures, and estimate their relative strengths.

SOLVE THE PROBLEM

a. The four substances are $HBrO_3$, H_2O, H_2CO_3, OH^-.

First divide them into acids and bases, and into strong and weak acids. $HBrO_3$ is not one of the seven strong acids you have memorized—is it strong or is it weak? If not strong, you might predict that it is at least a very strong weak acid. The hydroxide ion is a strong base. Carbonic acid H_2CO_3 is a weak acid. The order, in increasing acid strength is:

$$OH^- < H_2O < H_2CO_3 < HBrO_3$$

b. The four substances are CH_3OH, NH_4^+, CH_3CO_2H, NH_3.

Ammonia NH_3 is a base. Alcohols in general are very weak acids; methanol CH_3OH is extremely weak. The remaining two substances, the ammonium ion NH_4^+ and acetic acid CH_3CO_2H, are acids and perhaps a more difficult decision is to estimate their relative strengths. The ammonium ion is positively charged and might be expected to lose a hydrogen relatively easily. However, acetic acid, like most carboxylic acids, is a relatively strong weak acid ($K_a = 1.8 \times 10^{-5}$), approximately 100,000 times stronger than the ammonium ion ($K_a = 5.6 \times 10^{-10}$). We will discover in the next chapter how to calculate the equilibrium constants for conjugate acids and bases. The order, in increasing strength, is:

$$NH_3 < CH_3OH < NH_4^+ < CH_3CO_2H$$

PROBLEM 40.2A

For each pair of substances, choose the more acidic in aqueous solution:

a. HSO_3^- and HSO_4^-

b. HIO and $HBrO_2$

c. NH_3 and NH_4^+

d. C_2H_5OH and CH_3CO_2H

PROBLEM 40.2B

For each of the following pairs of acids, choose the more acidic in aqueous solution:

a. HBr and HBrO

b. $HClO_4$ and $HClO_2$

c. H_2SO_3 and H_2SeO_3

d. H_2S and HS^-

Review Questions

1. Describe the various factors that influence the strength of an acid.

2. How are the strengths of an acid and its conjugate base related?

3. Explain why an aqueous system in equilibrium lies predominantly on the weaker side.

4. What is the levelling effect. Why is the hydronium ion the strongest acid that can exist in water?

Solutions to Problems

PROBLEM 40.1A

a. Nitric acid reacts with water to produce its conjugate base and the conjugate base of water:

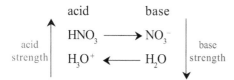

The equilbrium is:

$$HNO_3 + H_2O \rightleftharpoons I_3O^+ + NO_3^-$$

acid   base   acid   base

stronger   stronger   weaker   weaker

The predominant species in solution are the hydronium ion H_3O^+ and the nitrate ion NO_3^-

b. The sodium ion is a spectator ion. The hydride ion reacts with water to produce hydroxide ion and its own conjugate acid, hydrogen gas.

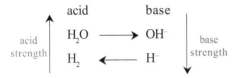

The equilbrium is:

$$H^- \; + \; H_2O \; \rightleftharpoons \; H_2 \; + \; OH^-$$

base   acid   acid   base

stronger   stronger   weaker   weaker

The predominant species in solution are the hydrogen H_2 and the hydroxide ion OH^-

PROBLEM 40.2A

a. HSO_3^- and HSO_4^-

HSO_4^- is the stronger—more oxygen atoms around the sulfur atom.

b. HIO and $HBrO_2$

$HBrO_2$—the bromine is more electronegative and there are more oxygen atoms.

c. NH_3 and NH_4^+

NH_4^+—the NH_4^+ ion is the conjugate acid of NH_3.

d. C_2H_5OH and CH_3CO_2H

CH_3CO_2H—carboxylic hydrogen atoms are more acidic than alcohol hydrogen atoms.

Answers to Review Questions

1. The strength of an acid depends upon how easily the molecules release hydrogen ions and the ease with which this happens depends upon the molecular structure and the charge, if any, on the molecule. To release a hydrogen ion relatively easily the bond between the hydrogen atom and the remainder of the molecule should be relatively weak, the bond should be polarized so that the bonding electrons are pulled away from the hydrogen atom, and the remainder of the molecule (the conjugate base) should be stable. It is more difficult to remove a positive hydrogen ion from a negatively charged particle than from a neutral particle. In a polyprotic acid, for example, the loss of hydrogen ions becomes progressively more difficult.

2. The strengths of an acid and its conjugate base are inversely proportional. The stronger the acid—the more readily it releases a hydrogen ion—the weaker the conjugate base—the less willing the base is to accept the hydrogen ion back. As we will see in Unit 41, the K_a for the acid multiplied by the K_b for the base equals K_w.

3. In a Brønsted-Lowry equilibrium there are two conjugate acid-base pairs. Therefore there are two acids and two bases. One acid is always stronger than the other acid. Similarly, one base is always stronger than the other base. The stronger acid donates a hydrogen ion more readily than the weaker acid and the stronger base accepts the hydrogen ion more readily than the weaker base. Therefore the transfer of the hydrogen ion from the strong acid to the strong base is the predominant reaction. The weaker acid and the weaker base are formed and the system lies predominantly on the weaker side.

4. Equal molar amounts of any monoprotic strong acid produce solutions of equal acidity—the solutions contain exactly the same concentration of hydronium ion. All strong acids produce solutions of hydronium ion. The only difference between the solutions is the identity of the conjugate base. The equal acidity of all strong acids in aqueous solution is called the levelling effect. It doesn't matter how strong the strong acid is, it produces a solution of hydronium ion. The hydronium ion is the strongest acid that is able to exist in aqueous solution because any acid stronger than the hydronium ion reacts with water and is levelled to hydronium ion.

The same behavior is exhibited by bases stronger than the hydroxide ion in aqueous solution. The hydroxide ion is the strongest base that can exist in aqueous solution. Any base stronger than the hydroxide ion is levelled to hydroxide ion in aqueous solution.

End-of-Unit Problems

1. Write formulas for the conjugate acids of the following species:

   a. NO_2^-

   b. SO_4^{2-}

   c. HCO_3^-

   d. CH_3NH_2

   e. H_2O

2. Write formulas for the conjugate bases of the following species:

   a. NH_4^+

   b. H_2SO_4

   c. HCO_3^-

   d. $H_2PO_4^-$

   e. NH_3

3. For the following pairs of acids, determine which of the pair is stronger and explain your decision:

   a. HF and HBr

   b. HNO_3 and HNO_2

   c. H_3PO_4 and H_3AsO_4

4. For the following pairs of acids, determine which of the pair is stronger and explain your decision:

   a. HIO and HClO

   b. $HBrO_3$ and $HBrO_2$

   c. H_3PO_4 and $HClO_4$

5. The molecular structures of picric acid and phenol are shown. Picric acid ($K_a = 4 \times 10^{-1}$) is stronger than phenol ($K_a = 1.6 \times 10^{-10}$). Suggest why.

6. The molecular structures of acetic acid and trichloroacetic acid are shown. Trichloroacetic acid ($K_a = 3 \times 10^{-1}$) is stronger than acetic acid ($K_a = 1.8 \times 10^{-5}$). Suggest why.

7. Basing your arguments on the empirical rule that oxyacids that have at least two more oxygen atoms than acidic hydrogen atoms are strong, decide which, if any, of the following acids you expect to be strong in aqueous solution:

   a. H_2SeO_4

   b. H_6TeO_6

   c. $HBrO_2$

8. Basing your arguments on the empirical rule that oxyacids that have at least two more oxygen atoms than acidic hydrogen atoms are strong, decide which, if any, of the following acids you expect to be strong in aqueous solution:

   a. H_2SeO_3

   b. H_3PO_2

   c. $HClO_3$

9. Write a net-ionic equation representing what happens when hydrogen cyanide HCN dissolves in water. Determine the Brønsted-Lowry conjugate acid-base pairs and establish which side of the equation is the weaker side and therefore what are the predominant species present in aqueous solution.

10. Write a net-ionic equation representing what happens when potassium nitrite dissolves in water. Determine the Brønsted-Lowry conjugate acid-base pairs and establish which side of the equation is the weaker side and therefore what are the predominant species present in aqueous solution.

11. The following species in aqueous solution make up two conjugate acid-base pairs. Using the data in Table 40.3, write a net-ionic equation representing the equilibrium that exists in solution and indicate the conjugate pairs. Label the species acid or base. Establish which side of the equation is the weaker side and therefore what are the predominant species present:

$$Cl^-, HCO_3^-, H_2CO_3, HCl$$

12. The following species in aqueous solution make up two conjugate acid-base pairs. Using the data in Table 40.3, write a net-ionic equation representing the equilibrium that exists in solution and indicate the conjugate pairs. Label the species acid or base. Establish which side of the equation is the weaker side and therefore what are the predominant species present:

$$CH_3CO_2H, HPO_4^{2-}, CH_3CO_2^-, H_2PO_4^-$$

13. In the following equation, label the species acid or base according to the Brønsted-Lowry definitions. Establish which side of the equation is the weaker side and therefore what are the predominant species present:

$$NH_3 + H_2O \rightleftharpoons NH_4^+ + OH^-$$

14. In the following equation, label the species acid or base according to the Brønsted-Lowry definitions. Establish which side of the equation is the weaker side and therefore what are the predominant species present:

$$HClO_4 + H_2O \rightleftharpoons H_3O^+ + ClO_4^-$$

15. In the following equation, label the species acid or base according to the Brønsted-Lowry definitions. Establish which side of the equation is the weaker side and therefore what are the predominant species present:

$$SO_4^{2-} + H_2O \rightleftharpoons HSO_4^- + OH^-$$

16. In the following equation, label the species acid or base according to the Brønsted-Lowry definitions. Establish which side of the equation is the weaker side and therefore what are the predominant species present:

$$HClO_4 + CH_3CO_2H \rightleftharpoons CH_3CO_2H_2^+ + ClO_4^-$$

Salts in Aqueous Solution

41.1 What Happens to Salts in Solution?

When a salt dissolves in water, the ionic lattice of the solid breaks down and the ions separate. Provided that the solution is sufficiently dilute we will assume that the salt exists predominantly in an ionic form in solution and ignore any association between the ions. In reality, as we learned in Unit 8, there is considerable association between ions, particularly when the solution is concentrated and when the ions have high charges.

As the ions separate from one another, they are surrounded by water molecules in a process called **hydration**, or more generally, **solvation**. The positive ions attract the negative ends of the water molecules (the oxygen atom) and the negative ions attract the positive ends of the water molecules (the hydrogen atoms) (Figure 41.1). The ion-dipole attraction between the ions and the solvent releases energy. This compensates, at least in part, for the energy required to break up the ionic lattice.

FIGURE 41.1   The solution process.
The water molecules surround and solvate the ions as they break away from the crystalline lattice. The water molecules are drawn far apart from each other for clarity. In reality the water molecules touch one another.

What happens next depends upon the identity of the salt. If either of the two ions is a conjugate partner of a weak electrolyte (acid or base), then **hydrolysis** will occur. To explain what this means, let's examine what happens when sodium fluoride dissolves in water.

The fluoride ion is the conjugate base of hydrofluoric acid (a weak acid). When the fluoride ion is surrounded by water molecules, the fluoride ion competes for one of the hydrogen ions of a water molecule (Figure 41.2). In most cases the hydroxide ion wins the competition—it is a stronger base than fluoride, but occasionally the fluoride ion gains the hydrogen ion and a hydroxide ion is released. The solution becomes slightly basic.

$$-\overset{|}{\underset{/}{F}}\!\!-\!\!H^+ \,\, O\!\!-\!\!^H \;\rightleftharpoons\; F\!\!-\!\!H \;+\; ^-O\!\!-\!\!H$$

hydrated
F⁻ ion

FIGURE 41.2 The competition between the fluoride ion and the hydroxide ion for the hydrogen ion in aqueous solution.
Most often the hydroxide ion wins—it is the stronger base—but occasionally the fluoride gains the hydrogen ion and the weak electrolyte HF is formed. Hydroxide ions are released making the solution basic.

This is the process called hydrolysis. Literally the word hydrolysis means the splitting of a water molecule and the reaction can be represented by the equation:

$$F^- + H_2O \rightleftharpoons HF + OH^-$$

Does the hydration of the sodium ion result in any hydrolysis? No—sodium hydroxide is a strong base and the sodium ion has no desire to detach a hydroxide ion from a water molecule.

Hydrolysis will only occur when the ion that is hydrated is a conjugate partner of a weak acid or base. Hydrolysis results in the formation of that weak acid or base. In our case, the fluoride ion is the conjugate base of the weak acid HF and hydrolysis occurs to produce the weak acid HF.

Are there any cations that cause hydrolysis in solution? Any cation that is the conjugate acid of a weak base will. For example, the ammonium ion is the conjugate acid of the weak base ammonia and when an ammonium salt is dissolved in water the ammonium ion will hydrolyse to produce a small concentration of ammonia and hydronium ions:

$$NH_4^+ + H_2O \rightleftharpoons H_3O^+ + NH_3$$

Acidic solutions are also produced when small highly charged metal cations dissolve in water. For example, when an iron(III) salt is dissolved in water, the Fe^{3+} ions are hydrated. The high 3+ charge on the Fe^{3+} ion pulls electrons away from the oxygen atom of the water molecule (Figure 41.3). This in turn polarizes the O—H bond in the water molecule and allows the hydrogen ion to break away. This release of a hydrogen ion produces an acidic solution.

The reaction can be viewed as competition for H^+ between a hydroxide attached to Fe^{3+} and a water molecule. Usually the hydroxide wins:

$$[Fe(H_2O)_6]^{3+} + H_2O \rightleftharpoons H_3O^+ + [Fe(H_2O)_5OH]^{2+}$$

However, $[Fe(H_2O)_6]^{3+}$ is quite acidic in aqueous solution with a K_a of 3.5×10^{-3}. The acid ionization constants of some other hydrated metal ions are listed in Table 41.1.

The extent to which hydrolysis occurs is usually quite small. In the competition for the hydrogen ion, or the competition for the hydroxide ion, the stronger acid or base wins and the equilibrium always lies on the weak side:

$$F^- \; + \; H_2O \; \rightleftharpoons \; HF \; + \; OH^-$$

base	acid	acid	base
weaker	weaker	stronger	stronger

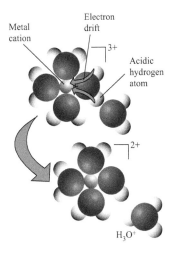

FIGURE 41.3 Fe^{3+} ions are hydrated in aqueous solution. The high charge on the Fe^{3+} ion pulls electrons away from the oxygen atom of the water molecule polarizing the O—H bond in the water molecule. This allows the hydrogen ion to break away and join another water molecule to form a hydronium ion.

Recall that all Brønsted-Lowry aqueous equilibria can be viewed as a competition between two bases for a hydrogen ion.

The system lies predominantly on the weaker side, K_b is small.

TABLE 41.1 The acid ionization constants K_a of some hydrated metal ions. Note that the metal ions with the highest charges are the most acidic.

Metal Ion	K_a	pK_a
$[Fe(H_2O)_6]^{3+}$	3.5×10^{-3}	2.46
$[Cr(H_2O)_6]^{3+}$	1.3×10^{-4}	3.89
$[Al(H_2O)_6]^{3+}$	7.9×10^{-6}	5.10
$[Cu(H_2O)_6]^{2+}$	3.2×10^{-8}	7.49
$[Co(H_2O)_6]^{2+}$	1.3×10^{-9}	8.89
$[Ni(H_2O)_6]^{2+}$	2.5×10^{-11}	10.6
$[Mg(H_2O)_6]^{2+}$	zero	
$[Na(H_2O)_6]^{+}$	zero	

The system lies predominantly on the weaker side, K_b is small.

$$\underset{\text{weaker}}{\underset{\text{acid}}{NH_4^+}} + \underset{\text{weaker}}{\underset{\text{base}}{H_2O}} \rightleftharpoons \underset{\text{stronger}}{\underset{\text{acid}}{H_3O^+}} + \underset{\text{stronger}}{\underset{\text{base}}{NH_3}}$$

$\longleftarrow$

The system lies predominantly on the weaker side, K_a is small.

However, the hydrolysis of many salts is sufficient to generate a significant concentration of hydronium ions or hydroxide ions.

A useful table illustrating possible salts derived from strong and weak acids and bases is shown in Table 41.2. If the acid is strong and the base is weak, then the salt hydrolyses to produce an acidic solution. If, on the other hand, the acid is weak and the base is strong, then the salt hydrolyses to produce a basic solution. If both acid and base are weak, the salt will hydrolyse. Whether the solution is acidic or basic depends upon the relative strengths of the acid and base.

TABLE 41.2 Acid-base properties of salts in aqueous solution.

Acid	Base	pH of the Solution	Example
strong	strong	neutral	NaCl
strong	weak	acidic	NH_4NO_3
weak	strong	basic	$NaCH_3CO_2$
weak	weak	acidic if $K_a > K_b$	NH_4IO_3
		basic if $K_b > K_a$	NH_4CN
		neutral if $K_a = K_b$	$NH_4CH_3CO_2$

EXAMPLE 41.1   HYDROLYSIS OF SALTS

Predict whether hydrolysis will occur when the following salts dissolve in water and, if so, whether the solution will be acidic or basic. Write equations representing the hydrolysis reaction if it occurs.

  a. $Mg(NO_3)_2$

  b. $NaNO_2$

  c. $CoCl_3$

UNDERSTAND THE QUESTION

An ion of a salt will hydrolyse if it is the conjugate partner of a weak electrolyte. Sometimes not so obvious is the hydrolysis by small highly charged cations such as Fe^{3+} and Al^{3+}.

PLAN THE SOLUTION

Examine the salt and determine the acid and base from which the salt is derived. If either is weak, then hydrolysis will occur.

SOLVE THE PROBLEM

  a. Magnesium nitrate $Mg(NO_3)_2$ is derived from nitric acid HNO_3 and magnesium hydroxide $Mg(OH)_2$. Both are strong electrolytes. This means that neither the magnesium ions nor the nitrate ions will hydrolyse in aqueous solution. The solution is neutral.

b. Sodium nitrite $NaNO_2$ is derived from nitrous acid HNO_2 and sodium hydroxide NaOH. Sodium hydroxide is a strong base—the sodium ion has no tendency to compete for a hydroxide ion and does not hydrolyse. Nitrous acid, however, is a weak acid. This means that the nitrite ion will hydrolyse in aqueous solution to produce some nitrous acid—the weak acid from which it is derived. This results in a basic solution:

$$NO_2^- + H_2O \rightleftharpoons HNO_2 + OH^-$$

c. Cobalt(III) chloride is a salt of Co^{3+}. This ion is highly hydrated in solution and some hydrolysis occurs to produce hydronium ions. The chloride ion is the conjugate base of the strong acid HCl and has no tendency to detach a hydrogen ion from water and reform the strong acid. The chloride ion does not hydrolyse. The solution is acidic.

> $[Co(H_2O)_6]^{3+}$ is a complex ion; the six water molecules form coordinate bonds with the Co^{3+} ion (*cf.* Unit 59).

$$[Co(H_2O)_6]^{3+} + H_2O \rightleftharpoons H_3O^+ + [Co(H_2O)_5OH]^{2+}$$

PROBLEM 41.1A

Predict whether hydrolysis will occur when the following salts dissolve in water and, if so, whether the solution will be acidic or basic. Write equations representing the hydrolysis reaction if it occurs.

a. $NH_4CH_3CO_2$

b. KCN

c. $LiClO_4$

PROBLEM 41.1B

Predict whether hydrolysis will occur when the following salts dissolve in water and, if so, whether the solution will be acidic or basic. Write equations representing the hydrolysis reaction if it occurs.

a. NH_4Cl

b. $[Cu(H_2O)_6]Cl_2$

c. KF

41.2 The Equilibrium Constants K_a and K_b

A weak acid such as hydrofluoric acid ionizes to some small extent in water:

$$HF + H_2O \rightleftharpoons H_3O^+ + F^-$$

The acid ionization constant is written: $K_a = \dfrac{[H_3O^+][F^-]}{[HF]}$

For hydrofluoric acid the value of K_a at 25°C is 6.8×10^{-4}.

As we have seen, the conjugate base of HF, the fluoride ion F^-, hydrolyses in aqueous solution to produce a slightly basic solution:

$$F^- + H_2O \rightleftharpoons HF + OH^-$$

The equilibrium constant for this reaction is written: $K_b = \dfrac{[HF][OH^-]}{[F^-]}$

In this case the value of K_b is 1.5×10^{-11}. The fluoride ion is a very weak base! This means that the hydrolysis does not occur to any great extent. If the K_a for the acid HF is multiplied by the K_b for its conjugate base F^-, the result is 1.0×10^{-14} at 25°C:

$$K_a \times K_b = 6.8 \times 10^{-4} \times 1.5 \times 10^{-11} = 1.0 \times 10^{-14} = K_w$$

This relationship is true for any weak acid and its conjugate base, or any weak base and its conjugate acid. The reason for this can be seen if the expressions for K_a and K_b are multiplied:

$$K_a \times K_b = \frac{[H_3O^+][F^-]}{[HF]} \times \frac{[HF][OH^-]}{[F^-]} = [H_3O^+][OH^-] = K_w$$

Alternatively,

$$pK_a + pK_b = pK_w = 14 \text{ at } 25°C$$

The relationship is very useful because it allows the calculation of the K_b (or pK_b) for a conjugate base if the K_a (or pK_a) for the acid is known, and *vice versa*. It also illustrates the observation made earlier that the stronger the acid, the weaker its conjugate base. In other words, if K_a is large then K_b must be small—because the two multiplied together must equal K_w. The relationship between K_a and K_b for a series of conjugate acid-base pairs is illustrated in Figure 41.4.

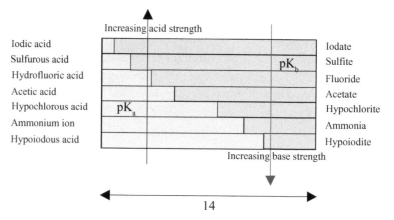

FIGURE 41.4 **The relationship between the pK$_a$ for an acid and the pK$_b$ for its conjugate base.**
The stronger the acid the weaker the conjugate base, and *vice versa*. At 25°C in dilute solution, pK$_a$ + pK$_b$ always equals 14.0. A smaller pK$_a$ corresponds to a larger K$_a$ and a stronger acid.

EXAMPLE 41.2   CALCULATING K FOR A CONJUGATE PARTNER

Use the acid ionization constants listed in Table 40.2 (Unit 40) to calculate the K_b for the following ions. If the sodium salts of these three ions were dissolved separately in water, which would produce the most basic solution?

a. CN^-

b. $CH_3CO_2^-$

c. F^-

UNDERSTAND THE QUESTION

K_a and K_b for a conjugate acid-base pair are related. The product of the two is always equal to K_w. If K_a is known then K_b can be calculated and *vice versa*.

PLAN THE SOLUTION

Look up the value of K_a for the conjugate acid of the anion listed and then calculate K_b. The salt with the highest K_b produces the most basic solution. The most acidic solution will be formed by the salt with the lowest K_b.

SOLVE THE PROBLEM

a. The conjugate acid is HCN, $K_a = 4.0 \times 10^{-10}$.

$$K_b \text{ for } CN^- = K_w/K_a = 1.0 \times 10^{-14}/4.0 \times 10^{-10} = 2.5 \times 10^{-5}$$

b. The conjugate acid is CH_3CO_2H, $K_a = 1.8 \times 10^{-5}$.

$$K_b \text{ for } CH_3CO_2^- = K_w/K_a = 1.0 \times 10^{-14}/1.8 \times 10^{-5} = 5.6 \times 10^{-10}$$

c. The conjugate acid is HF, $K_a = 6.8 \times 10^{-4}$.

$$K_b \text{ for } F^- = K_w/K_a = 1.0 \times 10^{-14}/6.8 \times 10^{-4} = 1.5 \times 10^{-11}$$

All of these salts produce basic solutions due to hydrolysis. Sodium cyanide produces the most basic solution—the cyanide ion hydrolyses the most because HCN is the weakest acid.

PROBLEM 41.2A

The values of K_b for some bases are listed below. Calculate the values of K_a for their conjugate acids (also listed).

a. base: ammonia NH_3 $K_b = 1.8 \times 10^{-5}$ conjugate acid: NH_4^+

b. base: nicotine $C_{10}H_{14}N_2$ $K_b = 1.0 \times 10^{-6}$ conjugate acid: $C_{10}H_{14}N_2H^+$

c. base: pyridine C_5H_5N $K_b = 1.8 \times 10^{-9}$ conjugate acid: $C_5H_5NH^+$

PROBLEM 41.2B

Use the acid ionization constants listed in Table 40.2 to calculate the K_b for the following ions. If the sodium salts of these three ions were dissolved separately in water, which would produce the most acidic solution?

a. IO_3^-

b. IO^-

c. HCO_2^-

41.3 The pH of Salt Solutions

The determination of the hydronium ion concentration and the pH of a solution of a salt involves the same kind of calculation we have discussed before. Again, it is important to write the equation for the equilibrium in solution and from this equation derive the expression for the equilibrium constant. As an example, let's calculate the pH of a 0.25 *M* solution of sodium cyanide.

EXAMPLE 41.3 CALCULATION OF THE pH OF A SALT SOLUTION

Calculate the pH of a 0.25 *M* aqueous solution of sodium cyanide at 25°C. The acid ionization constant for hydrocyanic acid at 25°C is 4.0×10^{-10}.

UNDERSTAND THE QUESTION

If a salt contains the conjugate partner of a weak electrolyte, that conjugate partner will hydrolyse producing a slightly acidic or basic solution.

PLAN THE SOLUTION

Determine what acid and what base would be used to make the salt. In other words determine the conjugate acid of the anion and the conjugate base of the cation. Recognize if either one is a weak electrolyte. Write an equation representing the hydrolysis of any ion that is the conjugate of a weak electrolyte. Remember that the product of the hydrolysis is that weak electrolyte. Then write an expression for the equilibrium constant, set up an ICE table, and solve for the unknown concentration of H_3O^+ or OH^-.

SOLVE THE PROBLEM

Sodium cyanide NaCN is a salt of HCN and NaOH. HCN, hydrocyanic acid, is a weak acid. This means that the cyanide ion will hydrolyse to produce some HCN in solution:

$$CN^- + H_2O \rightleftharpoons HCN + OH^-$$

The ionization constant is $K_b = \dfrac{[HCN][OH^-]}{[CN^-]}$

K_a for HCN $= 4.0 \times 10^{-10}$

K_b for $CN^- = K_w/K_a = 1.0 \times 10^{-14}/4.0 \times 10^{-10} = 2.5 \times 10^{-5}$

The stoichiometry of the hydrolysis reaction indicates that the two concentrations [HCN] and [OH$^-$] must be equal. Let's use the unknown x to represent both.

The ICE table is (with concentrations in M):

	$CN^- + H_2O \rightleftharpoons$	HCN	+ OH$^-$
Initial:	0.25	0	0
Change:	$-x$	$+x$	$+x$
Equilibrium concentrations:	$0.25 - x$	x	x

The equilibrium concentrations are now substituted into the expression for the equilibrium constant K_b and the value of x calculated.

$$K_b = \frac{[HCN][OH^-]}{[CN^-]} = \frac{x^2}{(0.25 - x)}$$

The initial concentration (0.25 M) exceeds the value of $100 \times K_b$ ($= 0.0025$), and so we will make the assumption that the x in the denominator can be ignored.

$$K_b = 2.5 \times 10^{-5} = \frac{x^2}{0.25} \text{ and } x = 2.5 \times 10^{-3}$$

The x in these calculations is the hydroxide concentration:

$[OH^-] = 2.5 \times 10^{-3} M$

$[H_3O^+] = 4.0 \times 10^{-12} M$

$pH = -\log_{10}[H_3O^+] = -\log_{10}(4.0 \times 10^{-12}) = 11.40$

PROBLEM 41.3A

Calculate the pH of a 0.15 M aqueous solution of ammonium chloride at 25°C. The ionization constant K_b for ammonia NH_3 at 25°C is 1.8×10^{-5}.

PROBLEM 41.3B

Calculate the pH of a 0.30 M aqueous solution of potassium nitrite at 25°C. The ionization constant for nitrous acid HNO_2 at 25°C is 4.5×10^{-4}.

41.4   The pH of a Salt of a Weak Acid and a Weak Base

The calculation of the pH of a solution of a salt of a weak acid and a weak base is a little more complicated because two hydrolysis reactions occur simultaneously. The relative magnitudes of the K_a and K_b can be used to predict relatively easily whether the solution will be acidic or basic, or even perhaps neutral, but how is the pH of the solution calculated?

The calculation is best described by example. Suppose that we want to calculate the pH of a 0.10 M solution of ammonium fluoride NH_4F. The ammonium ion will hydrolyse to the weak base ammonia and the fluoride ion will hydrolyse to the weak acid hydrofluoric acid:

$$NH_4^+ + F^- \rightleftharpoons NH_3 + HF \qquad\qquad K = \frac{[NH_3][HF]}{[NH_4^+][F^-]}$$

In this reaction, the $[NH_4^+]$ must equal the $[F^-]$, and the $[NH_3]$ must equal the $[HF]$, so we can rewrite the expression for K as:

$$K = \frac{[NH_3]^2}{[NH_4^+]^2}$$

The $[NH_3]$ and the $[NH_4^+]$ are related by the equation for the hydrolysis of NH_4^+:

$$NH_4^+ + H_2O \rightleftharpoons NH_3 + H_3O^+ \qquad\qquad K_{a(NH_4^+)} = \frac{[NH_3][H_3O^+]}{[NH_4^+]}$$

Rearranging, and squaring: $\dfrac{[NH_3]^2}{[NH_4^+]^2} = \dfrac{K_{a(NH_4^+)}^2}{[H_3O^+]^2}$

This equals the equilibrium constant K for the hydrolysis reaction above.

We can derive an alternative expression for this equilibrium constant by writing the individual hydrolysis reactions and adding them together:

$$NH_4^+ + H_2O \rightleftharpoons NH_3 + H_3O^+ \qquad\qquad K_{a(NH_4^+)}$$

$$F^- + H_2O \rightleftharpoons HF + OH \qquad\qquad K_b = \frac{K_w}{K_{a(HF)}}$$

$$H_3O^+ + OH^- \rightleftharpoons 2\,H_2O \qquad\qquad \frac{1}{K_w}$$

Adding these three equations yields the overall equation:

$$NH_4^+ + F^- \rightleftharpoons NH_3 + HF$$

Multiplying the equilibrium constants yields the K for the overall reaction:

$$K = K_{a(NH_4^+)} \times \frac{K_w}{K_{a(HF)}} \times \frac{1}{K_w} = \frac{K_{a(NH_4^+)}}{K_{a(HF)}}$$

We now have two expressions for K and we can set them equal to each other:

$$K = \frac{K_{a(NH_4^+)}}{K_{a(HF)}} = \frac{K_{a(NH_4^+)}^2}{[H_3O^+]^2}$$

> We could have chosen to rewrite the K in terms of [HF] and [F⁻]— the end result is the same.

Rearranging, and cancelling one $K_{a(NH_4^+)}$:

$$[H_3O^+]^2 = K_{a(HF)} \times K_{a(NH_4^+)}$$

or

$$[H_3O^+] = \sqrt{(K_{a(HF)} \times K_{a(NH_4^+)})}$$

or, taking the negative logarithms:

$$pH = \tfrac{1}{2}(pK_{a(HF)} + pK_{a(NH_4^+)})$$

In other words, the pH of the solution is the average of the two pK_as. Notice that the pH does not depend upon the concentration of the salt.

In our example of ammonium fluoride, the pK_a for the ammonium ion is 9.26 and the pK_a for hydrofluoric acid is 3.17. The average of the two is 6.22—slightly acidic. This would have been predicted on the basis of the relative strengths of the acid and base used to make the salt. Ammonia has a $K_b = 1.8 \times 10^{-5}$ and hydrofluoric acid has a K_a of 6.8×10^{-4}. The acid is slightly stronger than the base.

EXAMPLE 41.4   CALCULATION OF THE pH OF A SALT OF A WEAK ACID AND WEAK BASE

Predict whether pyridinium acetate will be acidic or basic in aqueous solution. Then calculate the pH of a 0.10 M aqueous solution of pyridinium acetate at 25°C. The acid ionization constant for acetic acid K_a at 25°C is 1.8×10^{-5} and the base ionization constant for pyridine K_b at 25°C is 1.8×10^{-9}.

UNDERSTAND THE QUESTION

If a salt contains two ions both of which are conjugate partners of weak electrolytes, then both ions will simultaneously hydrolyse. The pH will depend upon which of the two ions has the stronger conjugate partner.

PLAN THE SOLUTION

Determine what acid and what base would be used to make the salt. In other words determine the conjugate acid of the anion and the conjugate base of the cation. Predict the acidity or basicity of the solution from the relative magnitudes of the ionization constants of the acid and base used to make the salt. The pH of the solution is the average of the two pK_as (*not* the pK_a and pK_b!)

SOLVE THE PROBLEM

Pyridinium acetate is a salt of acetic acid and pyridine. Both are weak electrolytes; this means that both ions will hydrolyse in aqueous solution:

The acid ionization constant for acetic acid K_a at 25°C is 1.8×10^{-5}

The base ionization constant for pyridine K_b at 25°C is 1.8×10^{-9}.

The acid ionization constant is larger than the base ionization constant and the solution will be acidic.

> pK_a for acetic acid = 4.74
>
> K_a for the pyridinium ion = K_w/K_b = $1.0 \times 10^{-14}/1.8 \times 10^{-9}$ = 5.56×10^{-6}
>
> pK_a for the pyridinium ion = 5.26
>
> $pH = \tfrac{1}{2}(pK_{a(acetic\ acid)} + pK_{a(pyridinium\ ion)})$ = 5.00—acidic as predicted

PROBLEM 41.4A

Calculate the pH of a 0.20 M aqueous solution of ammonium acetate at 25°C. The acid ionization constant for acetic acid K_a at 25°C is 1.8×10^{-5} and the base ionization constant K_b for ammonia NH_3 at 25°C is 1.8×10^{-5}.

PROBLEM 41.4B

Predict whether hydrazinium cyanide will be acidic or basic in aqueous solution. Then calculate the pH of a 0.20 M aqueous solution of hydrazinium cyanide at 25°C. The acid ionization constant for hydrocyanic acid K_a at 25°C is 4.0×10^{-10} and the base ionization constant K_b for hydrazine NH_2NH_2 at 25°C is 1.3×10^{-6}.

Review Questions

1. Describe the difference between an ionization reaction and a hydrolysis reaction.

2. Describe how to determine if an ion in solution will hydrolyse.

3. What is the relationship between the K_a for an acid and the K_b for its conjugate base.

Solutions to Problems

PROBLEM 41.1A

a. Ammonium acetate $NH_4CH_3CO_2$ is an interesting case because both ions are conjugate partners of weak electrolytes. The ammonium ion hydrolyses to produce some ammonia and the acetate ion hydrolyses to produce some acetic acid:

$$NH_4^+ + H_2O \rightleftharpoons H_3O^+ + NH_3$$
$$CH_3CO_2^- + H_2O \rightleftharpoons CH_3CO_2H + OH^-$$

The curious feature of these hydrolysis reactions is that the ionization constants for ammonia and acetic acid are the same value (1.8×10^{-5}). As a result the concentrations of H_3O^+ and OH^- are the same and the solution is neutral.

b. The cyanide ion is the conjugate base of the weak acid HCN. The cyanide ion therefore hydrolyses to produce a basic solution:

$$CN^- + H_2O \rightleftharpoons HCN + OH^-$$

c. Lithium perchlorate $LiClO_4$ is a salt of the strong acid $HClO_4$ and the strong base LiOH. No hydrolysis occurs; the solution is neutral.

PROBLEM 41.2A

a. K_a for the ammonium ion
$$NH_4^+ = K_w/K_b = 1.0 \times 10^{-14}/1.8 \times 10^{-5} = 5.6 \times 10^{-10}$$

b. K_a for $C_{10}H_{14}N_2H^+ = K_w/K_b = 1.0 \times 10^{-14}/1.0 \times 10^{-6}$
$= 1.0 \times 10^{-8}$

c. K_a for $C_5H_5NH^+ = K_w/K_b = 1.0 \times 10^{-14}/1.8 \times 10^{-9} = 5.6 \times 10^{-6}$

PROBLEM 41.3A

Ammonium chloride is acidic in aqueous solution due to the hydrolysis of the ammonium cation:

$$NH_4^+ + H_2O \rightleftharpoons H_3O^+ + NH_3 \quad K_a = K_w/K_b = 5.6 \times 10^{-10}$$

The ICE table is (with concentrations in M):

	$NH_4^+ + H_2O \rightleftharpoons H_3O^+ + NH_3$		
Initial:	0.15	0	0
Change:	$-x$	$+x$	$+x$
Equilibrium concentrations:	$0.15 - x$	x	x

$$K_a = \frac{[H_3O^+][NH_3]}{[NH_4^+]} = \frac{x^2}{(0.15 - x)} = 5.6 \times 10^{-10}$$

The x in the denominator can be neglected, so x = 9.2×10^{-6}

$$[H_3O^+] = 9.2 \times 10^{-6} \, M$$

$$pH = 5.04$$

PROBLEM 41.4A

As mentioned in the solution to Problem 41.1A, the curious feature of the hydrolysis of ammonium acetate is that the ionization constants for ammonia and acetic acid are the same value (1.8×10^{-5}). As a result the concentrations of H_3O^+ and OH^- are the same and the solution is neutral.

Using our formula for the pH of a salt of a weak acid and a weak base:

$$pH = \tfrac{1}{2}(pK_{a(CH_3CO_2H)} + pK_{a(NH_4^+)})$$

where $pK_{a(CH_3CO_2H)} = -\log_{10}(1.8 \times 10^{-5}) = 4.74$

and $pK_{a(NH_4^+)} = pK_w - pK_b = (14.00 - 4.74)$

$$pH = \tfrac{1}{2}(4.74 + (14.00 - 4.74))$$
$$= 7.0$$

Note that the concentration of the salt has no effect on the pH.

Answers to Review Questions

1. An ionization reaction is a reaction in which an acid or base reacts with water to produce its conjugate partner and hydronium ions or hydroxide ions. Examples are the ionization of acetic acid and the ionization of ammonia:

$$CH_3CO_2H + H_2O \rightleftharpoons H_3O^+ + CH_3CO_2^-$$
$$NH_3 + H_2O \rightleftharpoons NH_4^+ + OH^-$$

A hydrolysis reaction is a reaction in which the conjugate partner of a weak acid or weak base (one of the ions of a salt) reacts with water to produce some of the acid or base from which the salt was formed. Again hydronium ions or hydroxide ions are produced to make the solution slightly acidic or basic. Examples are the hydrolysis of an acetate ion or an ammonium ion:

$$CH_3CO_2^- + H_2O \rightleftharpoons CH_3CO_2H + OH^-$$
$$NH_4^+ + H_2O \rightleftharpoons H_3O^+ + NH_3$$

2. An ion will hydrolyse in aqueous solution only if it is the conjugate partner of a weak acid or weak base. For example, the acetate ion hydrolyses because it is the conjugate base of the weak acid acetic acid. The nitrate ion does not hydrolyse because it is the conjugate base of the strong acid nitric acid. A conjugate base of a strong acid has no affinity for a hydrogen ion and no tendency to accept one back.

3. The equilibrium constant K_a is a measure of the strength of the acid—the higher the value of K_a the stronger the acid. The more readily the acid releases a hydrogen ion, the less readily the conjugate base accepts it. So the K_a for the acid and the K_b for the base are inversely proportional. In fact, the two multiplied together equals K_w.

End-of-Unit Problems

1. Which, if any, of the following salts will hydrolyse in aqueous solution? Determine whether the solution is acidic, basic, or neutral.
   a. NH_4CN
   b. KNO_2
   c. NaF
   d. $MgCl_2$

2. Which, if any, of the following salts will hydrolyse in aqueous solution? Determine whether the solution is acidic, basic, or neutral.
   a. KCN
   b. KIO_3
   c. $NaBr$
   d. $NH_4CH_3CO_2$

3. After the neutralization reactions of the following acids and bases, is the solution acidic, neutral or basic?
   a. HBr and KOH
   b. CH_3CO_2H and $NaOH$
   c. HF and NH_3

4. After the neutralization reactions of the following acids and bases, is the solution acidic, neutral or basic?
   a. HCO_2H and KOH
   b. HI and NH_3
   c. HCl and NH_2NH_2

5. Predict whether aqueous solutions of the following salts are acidic, basic, or neutral:

    a. CH_3NH_3Cl

    b. $FeCl_3$

    c. NH_4Br

    d. $Sr(CH_3CO_2)_2$

6. Predict whether aqueous solutions of the following salts are acidic, basic, or neutral:

    a. $CuCl_2$

    b. $KClO$

    c. NH_4F

    d. $CaCl_2$

7. Using Table 39.2 as a resource, determine which of the following pairs of salts is the stronger acid:

    a. ammonium nitrate NH_4NO_3 and methylammonium nitrate $CH_3NH_3NO_3$

    b. triethylammonium chloride $(C_2H_5)_3NHCl$ and dimethylammonium chloride $(CH_3)_2NH_2Cl$

8. Using Table 40.2 as a resource, determine which of the following pairs of salts is the stronger base:

    a. potassium chlorite $KClO_2$ and sodium nitrite $NaNO_2$

    b. lithium acetate $LiCH_3CO_2$ and magnesium formate $Mg(HCO_2)_2$

9. Write balanced net-ionic equations representing the reactions of the following ions with water. In each case identify the Brønsted-Lowry acid-base pairs:

    a. PO_4^{3-}

    b. $N_2H_5^+$

    c. ClO_2^-

10. Write balanced net-ionic equations representing the reactions of the following ions with water. In each case identify the Brønsted-Lowry acid-base pairs:

    a. SO_3^{2-}

    b. $[Cu(H_2O)_6]^{2+}$

    c. IO_3^-

11. The following salts are dissolved in water to produce 0.10 M solutions. Arrange the solutions in order of increasing pH:

    NaBr, $Ca(NO_2)_2$, NH_4NO_3, KBrO

12. The following salts are dissolved in water to produce 0.10 M solutions. Arrange the solutions in order of increasing pH:

    $NaCH_3CO_2$, $Mg(NO_3)_2$, NH_4ClO, KCN

13. Refer to Table 40.2 for the values of K_a and determine the K_b for the following salts:

    a. potassium iodate KIO_3

    b. sodium nitrite $NaNO_2$

    c. sodium phenate NaC_6H_5O

14. Refer to Table 40.2 for the values of K_a and determine the K_b for the following salts:

    a. magnesium fluoride MgF_2

    b. lithium formate $LiHCO_2$

    c. sodium chlorite $NaClO_2$

15. Calculate the hydronium ion concentration and pH of a 0.40 M solution of potassium fluoride.

16. Calculate the hydronium ion concentration and pH of a 0.25 M solution of sodium nitrite.

17. Calculate the hydronium ion concentration and pH of a 0.60 M solution of ammonium nitrate.

18. Calculate the hydronium ion concentration and pH of a 0.075 M solution of hydrazinium perchlorate.

19. Calcium hypochlorite $Ca(ClO)_2$ is used as a disinfectant for swimming pools. What is the pH of a 0.100 M solution of calcium hypochlorite. K_a for hypochlorous acid HClO is 3.0×10^{-8}.

20. Sodium benzoate $NaC_6H_5CO_2$ is used as a food preservative. What is the pH of a 0.075 M solution of sodium benzoate. K_a for benzoic acid $C_6H_5CO_2H$ is 6.3×10^{-5}.

21. Determine whether the following salts are acidic, neutral, or basic in aqueous solution:

    a. ammonium bicarbonate

    b. ammonium iodate

Polyprotic Acids and Their Salts

42.1 Polyprotic Acids

Polyprotic acids are acids that have more than one hydrogen atom that can be detached as a H^+ ion. It's useful to label the successive ionization constants K_{a1}, K_{a2}, and K_{a3} to distinguish one from another. For example, for phosphoric acid:

$$H_3PO_4 + H_2O \rightleftharpoons H_3O^+ + H_2PO_4^- \qquad K_{a1} = 7.5 \times 10^{-3}$$
$$H_2PO_4^- + H_2O \rightleftharpoons H_3O^+ + HPO_4^{2-} \qquad K_{a2} = 6.2 \times 10^{-8}$$
$$HPO_4^{2-} + H_2O \rightleftharpoons H_3O^+ + PO_4^{3-} \qquad K_{a3} = 3.6 \times 10^{-13}$$

Some other examples of common polyprotic acids are listed in Table 42.1. Note that for these acids the loss of the second hydrogen ion is considerably more difficult than the first. The values for K_a for the successive ionizations usually differ by a factor of about 100,000. This means that the first hydrogen ions are removed from all the molecules before any of the second hydrogen ions are removed. If there is a third hydrogen ion then this is detached with even more difficulty.

TABLE 42.1 Some polyprotic acids and their K_a constants.

Acid		K_{a1}	pK_{a1}	K_{a2}	pK_{a2}	K_{a3}	pK_{a3}
Sulfuric acid	H_2SO_4	strong		1.2×10^{-2}	1.92		
Sulfurous acid	H_2SO_3	1.5×10^{-2}	1.82	1.2×10^{-7}	6.91		
Phosphorous acid	H_3PO_3	1.0×10^{-2}	2.00	2.6×10^{-7}	6.59		
Phosphoric acid	H_3PO_4	7.5×10^{-3}	2.12	6.2×10^{-8}	7.21	3.6×10^{-13}	12.44
Arsenic acid	H_3AsO_4	5.6×10^{-3}	2.25	1.0×10^{-7}	7.00	3.0×10^{-12}	11.52
Selenous acid	H_2SeO_3	2.3×10^{-3}	2.64	5.3×10^{-9}	8.28		
Carbonic acid	H_2CO_3	4.3×10^{-7}	6.37	5.6×10^{-11}	10.25		
Hydrosulfuric acid	H_2S	8.9×10^{-8}	7.05	$\sim 10^{-19}$	~ 19		

This makes the calculation of the pH of a solution of these polyprotic acids relatively straightforward because almost all the hydronium ions in solution are the result of the first ionization and so few result from the second ionization that the amount can usually be ignored. The calculation of the pH of the solution of a polyprotic acid is therefore exactly the same as the examples in Unit 39.

There is another class of polyprotic acids in which the acidic hydrogen atoms belong to different carboxylic acid groups sometimes located quite far from each other on the same molecule. Some examples are listed in Table 42.2. If the chain of carbon atoms between the two carboxylic groups is 2, 3, 4, or higher, the pK_a values of the different acids are similar and the pK_{a1} and pK_{a2} values differ only by about 1 unit— the pK_{a1} and pK_{a2} are much closer compared to the acids in Table 42.1. Compare succinic, glutaric, and adipic acids in Table 42.2.

If the —CO_2H groups are closer in the molecule, as in oxalic acid or malonic acid, the presence of one group increases the acidity of the other (the —CO_2H group is electron withdrawing), so the pK_{a1} values are lower. Compare $pK_{a1} = 1.23$ for oxalic acid to $pK_{a1} = 4.21$ for succinic acid—oxalic acid is 1000 times more acidic.

As noted earlier, for most of the polyprotic acids in Table 42.1, only the first ionization need be considered in determining the hydronium ion concentration. The amount of hydronium ion resulting from the second ionization, or third, is often negligible in comparison.

TABLE 42.2   Some organic polyprotic acids and their K_a constants.

Acid		K_{a1}	pK_{a1}	K_{a2}	pK_{a2}	K_{a3}	pK_{a3}
Oxalic acid	$HO_2C{-}CO_2H$	5.9×10^{-2}	1.23	6.4×10^{-5}	4.19		
Malonic acid	$HO_2C{-}CH_2{-}CO_2H$	1.4×10^{-3}	2.86	2.0×10^{-6}	5.70		
Citric acid	$HO_2C{-}CH_2{-}C(OH)(CO_2H){-}CH_2{-}CO_2H$	7.4×10^{-4}	3.13	1.7×10^{-5}	4.77	4.0×10^{-7}	6.40
Tartaric acid	$HO_2C{-}(CHOH)_2{-}CO_2H$	6.0×10^{-4}	3.22	1.5×10^{-5}	4.82		
Ascorbic acid	$H_2C_6H_6O_6$ (see figure)	8.0×10^{-5}	4.10	1.6×10^{-12}	11.80		
Succinic acid	$HO_2C{-}(CH_2)_2{-}CO_2H$	6.2×10^{-5}	4.21	2.3×10^{-6}	5.64		
Glutaric acid	$HO_2C{-}(CH_2)_3{-}CO_2H$	4.6×10^{-5}	4.34	5.4×10^{-6}	5.27		
Adipic acid	$HO_2C{-}(CH_2)_4{-}CO_2H$	3.9×10^{-5}	4.41	5.2×10^{-6}	5.28		

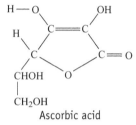

Ascorbic acid

Consider for a moment a strong diprotic acid for which both ionizations are complete—in this case the second ionization would release an equal number of hydrogen ions. The most complicated case would be a strong acid for which the second ionization is not complete but still has a fairly high value for K_{a2}. Let's examine the diprotic acid H_2SO_4—there are three situations to consider:

A concentrated solution of the acid (approximately 0.50 M or above)—in this case we can ignore the second ionization.

A very dilute solution of the acid (approximately 1×10^{-3} M or below)—in this dilute solution we can assume that the second ionization is complete.

An intermediate concentration—in this case the second ionization will contribute a significant concentration of $[H_3O^+]$ that cannot be ignored and has to be calculated.

The situation is illustrated in Figure 42.1.

FIGURE 42.1   The effect of concentration on the relative importance of the second ionization of sulfuric acid.

The number of hydrogen ions released per molecule changes from approximately 1 at a concentration of 1.0 M to approximately 2 at a concentration of 1.0×10^{-4} M.

EXAMPLE 42.1 CALCULATION OF THE pH OF THREE SOLUTIONS OF SULFURIC ACID

Calculate the pH of

a. a 0.50 M solution of sulfuric acid

b. a 1.0×10^{-3} M solution of sulfuric acid

c. a 0.050 M solution of sulfuric acid

$$K_{a2} \text{ for } HSO_4^- = 1.2 \times 10^{-2}$$

UNDERSTAND THE QUESTION

These three solutions illustrate the relative importance of the second ionization. The second ionization increases in importance, producing more and more of the $[H_3O^+]$ as the solution becomes more dilute.

PLAN THE SOLUTION

In each case, calculate the $[H_3O^+]$ for the first ionization and then determine the additional $[H_3O^+]$ that results from the second ionization.

SOLVE THE PROBLEM

The first ionization is complete:

$$H_2SO_4 + H_2O \rightarrow H_3O^+ + HSO_4^- \qquad K_{a1} = \text{very large}$$

The ICE table is (with concentrations in M):

	$H_2SO_4 + H_2O \rightarrow$	H_3O^+	$+ HSO_4^-$
Initial concentrations:	0.50	0	0
Equilibrium concentrations:	0	0.50	0.50

Some additional hydronium ion comes from the second ionization:

$$HSO_4^- + H_2O \rightleftharpoons H_3O^+ + SO_4^{2-} \qquad K_{a2} = 1.2 \times 10^{-2}$$

The ICE table is (with concentrations in M):

	$HSO_4^- + H_2O \rightleftharpoons$	H_3O^+	$+$	SO_4^{2-}
Initial:	0.50	0.50		0
Change:	$- x$	$+ x$		$+ x$
Equilibrium concentrations:	$0.50 - x$	$0.50 + x$		x

$$K_{a2} = \frac{[H_3O^+][SO_4^{2-}]}{[HSO_4^-]} = \frac{(0.50 + x)x}{(0.50 - x)} = 1.2 \times 10^{-2}$$

Solving the quadratic equation, using the quadratic formula or by successive approximation, x = 0.0114. The unknown x in this case represents the concentration of the sulfate ion in the solution and the additional hydronium ion produced as a result of the second ionization. This amount, 0.0114 M, is very small (~2%) compared to the 0.50 M from the first ionization. The additional hydronium ion scarcely has a noticeable effect.

Now let's repeat the calculation for the second case, where the initial concentration of the sulfuric acid is 1.0×10^{-3} M. As above, the hydronium ions $[H_3O^+]$ from the first ionization will be 1.0×10^{-3} M. In the second ionization:

The ICE table is (with concentrations in M):

$$HSO_4^- + H_2O \rightleftharpoons H_3O^+ \quad + \quad SO_4^{2-}$$

Initial:	0.0010	0.0010	0
Change:	$-x$	$+x$	$+x$
Equilibrium concentrations:	$0.0010 - x$	$0.0010 + x$	x

$$K_{a2} = \frac{[H_3O^+][SO_4^{2-}]}{[HSO_4^-]} = \frac{(0.0010 + x)x}{(0.0010 - x)} = 1.2 \times 10^{-2}$$

x = the $[H_3O^+]$ from the second ionization = $8.66 \times 10^{-4}\,M$

This is almost as much as the $[H_3O^+]$ from the first ionization ($1.0 \times 10^{-3}\,M$).

So, for dilute solutions, each sulfuric acid molecule ionizes to produce *two* hydrogen ions.

Now let's look at the third case, where the initial concentration of the sulfuric acid is 0.050 M. As above, the hydronium ions $[H_3O^+]$ from the first ionization will be 0.050 M. In the second ionization:

The ICE table is (with concentrations in M):

$$HSO_4^- + H_2O \rightleftharpoons H_3O^+ \quad + \quad SO_4^{2-}$$

Initial:	0.050	0.050	0
Change:	$-x$	$+x$	$+x$
Equilibrium concentrations:	$0.050 - x$	$0.050 + x$	x

$$K_{a2} = \frac{[H_3O^+][SO_4^{2-}]}{[HSO_4^-]} = \frac{(0.050 + x)x}{(0.050 - x)} = 1.2 \times 10^{-2}$$

x = the $[H_3O^+]$ from the second ionization = $8.51 \times 10^{-3}\,M$

This is about 17% of the $[H_3O^+]$ from the first ionization (0.050 M). For intermediate solutions, the second ionization contributes significantly to the hydronium ion concentration and cannot be ignored.

PROBLEM 42.1A

Repeat the calculation illustrated in Example 42.1 for a solution of sulfuric acid that is 0.010 M. Comment on the contribution of the second ionization to the hydronium ion concentration in light of the results described in Example 42.1.

PROBLEM 42.1B

Calculate the pH of a 0.010 M solution of tartaric acid neglecting the second ionization. Then adjust your answer to take into account the second ionization and comment on the difference of the two results.

$$K_{a1} = 6.0 \times 10^{-4} \quad K_{a2} = 1.5 \times 10^{-5}$$

For solutions of the weak polyprotic acids in Table 42.1 the values of K_{a1}, K_{a2}, and K_{a3} differ by approximately 10^5. In these cases the second or third ionization can be ignored—only the first ionization contributes significantly to the hydronium ion concentration. The following example illustrates that the concentrations of the species resulting from the second ionization are typically very small. The comparatively high concentration of hydronium ion from the first ionization suppresses the second ionization.

EXAMPLE 42.2 CALCULATION OF THE CONCENTRATIONS OF SPECIES PRESENT IN A SOLUTION OF A POLYPROTIC ACID

Calculate the concentrations of species present in a 0.100 M solution of sulfurous acid.

UNDERSTAND THE QUESTION

Sulfurous acid is a diprotic acid. However the values of pK_{a1} and pK_{a2} differ by more than 5 and virtually all the hydronium ion in solution is a result of the first ionization.

PLAN THE SOLUTION

Calculate the $[H_3O^+]$ and $[HSO_3^-]$ for the first ionization. Then use these concentrations for the second ionization to calculate the $[SO_3^{2-}]$ concentration.

SOLVE THE PROBLEM

For the first ionization:

$$H_2SO_3 + H_2O \rightleftharpoons H_3O^+ + HSO_3^- \qquad K_{a1} = 1.5 \times 10^{-2}$$

The ICE table is (with concentrations in M):

	$H_2SO_3 + H_2O \rightleftharpoons$	$H_3O^+ +$	HSO_3^-
Initial concentrations:	0.10	0	0
Change:	$-x$	$+x$	$+x$
Equilibrium concentrations:	$0.10 - x$	x	x

> Like carbonic acid, which exists predominantly in aqueous solution as dissolved carbon dioxide, sulfurous acid exists predominantly as dissolved sulfur dioxide. Pure sulfurous acid cannot be isolated. However, it is easier to describe the reactions of sulfurous acid by writing it as H_2SO_3.

$$K_{a1} = \frac{[H_3O^+][HSO_3^-]}{[H_2SO_3]} = \frac{x^2}{(0.10 - x)} = 1.5 \times 10^{-2}$$

The x in the denominator is too large to neglect. Solution using the quadratic formula, or by successive approximation, yields x = 0.032.

x in this problem is the hydronium ion concentration $[H_3O^+]$ and the hydrogen sulfite ion concentration $[HSO_3^-]$. These concentrations can now be used in the calculation for the second ionization:

The second ionization is:

$$HSO_3^- + H_2O \rightleftharpoons H_3O^+ + SO_3^{2-}$$

$$K_{a2} = \frac{[H_3O^+][SO_3^{2-}]}{[HSO_3^-]} = 1.2 \times 10^{-7}$$

Note, however, that if we neglect the very small amount of $[H_3O^+]$ from the second ionization, the $[H_3O^+]$ and $[HSO_3^-]$ are equal and $[SO_3^{2-}] = K_{a2} = 1.2 \times 10^{-7}\ M$.

This is true for the concentration of the anion resulting from the second ionization for any polyprotic acid—provided that the amount of $[H_3O^+]$ from the second ionization can be ignored.

In summary, the concentrations of the species present in 0.100 M sulfurous acid are:

$[H_2SO_3] = 6.8 \times 10^{-2}\ M$ $[SO_3^{2-}] = 1.2 \times 10^{-7}\ M$

$[H_3O^+] = 3.2 \times 10^{-2}\ M$ $[OH^-] = 3.1 \times 10^{-13}\ M$

$[HSO_3^-] = 3.2 \times 10^{-2}\ M$

PROBLEM 42.2A

Ascorbic acid (Vitamin C) is a diprotic acid with $K_{a1} = 8.0 \times 10^{-5}$ and $K_{a2} = 1.6 \times 10^{-12}$.

Abbreviate the symbol for ascorbic acid as H_2A. Calculate the concentrations of H_2A, HA^-, A^{2-}, H_3O^+, and OH^- in a 0.050 M solution of ascorbic acid.

PROBLEM 42.2B

Phosphorous acid H_3PO_3 is a diprotic acid with $K_{a1} = 1.0 \times 10^{-2}$ and $K_{a2} = 2.6 \times 10^{-7}$. Calculate the concentrations of H_3PO_3, $H_2PO_3^-$, HPO_3^{2-}, H_3O^+, and OH^- in a 0.250 M solution of phosphorous acid.

42.2   Ionization *vs.* Hydrolysis

Intermediate ions derived from a polyprotic acid are amphiprotic. These ions can accept a hydrogen ion and act as a base or they can donate a hydrogen ion and act as an acid. An example is the dihydrogen phosphate ion $H_2PO_4^-$. In Table 40.3, you may remember, these ions were listed both in the acid column and in the base column.

Hydrolysis: $\underset{\text{base}}{H_2PO_4^-} + H_2O \rightleftharpoons \underset{\text{conjugate acid}}{H_3PO_4} + OH^-$

Ionization: $\underset{\text{acid}}{H_2PO_4^-} + H_2O \rightleftharpoons H_3O^+ + \underset{\text{conjugate base}}{HPO_4^{2-}}$

When a salt containing the dihydrogen phosphate ion, for example sodium dihydrogen phosphate NaH_2PO_4, is dissolved in water, is the solution acidic or basic? In other words, what happens—does the dihydrogen phosphate ion hydrolyse and produce a basic solution or does it ionize and produce an acidic solution? The answer depends upon the relative magnitude of the equilibrium constants for the two processes. What does the dihydrogen phosphate ion tend to do—lose another hydrogen ion or accept one back?

The equilibrium constant for the hydrolysis reaction is K_b, which equals K_w/K_{a1}, where K_{a1} is the acid ionization constant for the acid formed in the hydrolysis H_3PO_4.

The equilibrium constant for the ionization reaction is K_{a2}, the acid ionization constant for $H_2PO_4^-$.

For the dihydrogen phosphate ion $H_2PO_4^-$:

$$K_b = K_w/K_{a1} = 1.0 \times 10^{-14}/7.5 \times 10^{-3} = 1.3 \times 10^{-12}$$

and $K_{a2} = 6.2 \times 10^{-8}$

The ionization constant (K_a) is much larger than the hydrolysis constant (K_b). The dihydrogen phosphate ion ionizes in solution to release another hydrogen ion. It has little desire to hydrolyse and accept a hydrogen ion. The solution is acidic.

EXAMPLE 42.3 IONIZATION *VS.* HYDROLYSIS

Is sodium hydrogen phosphate Na_2HPO_4 acidic or basic in aqueous solution?

UNDERSTAND THE QUESTION

The hydrogen phosphate HPO_4^{2-} ion is amphiprotic—it can accept a hydrogen ion and act as a base or it can donate a hydrogen ion and act as an acid:

Hydrolysis: $HPO_4^{2-} + H_2O \rightleftharpoons H_2PO_4^- + OH^-$ $K_b = K_w/K_{a2}$

Ionization: $HPO_4^{2-} + H_2O \rightleftharpoons H_3O^+ + PO_4^{3-}$ K_{a3}

Evaluation of the K_b and K_{a3} determines the predominant reaction. It is important to note that the K_a in the relationship K_w/K_a is the acid ionization constant for the conjugate acid of the base—in other words the acid formed in the hydrolysis reaction.

PLAN THE SOLUTION

Look up the value of K_{a2} and calculate K_b. Compare with the value of K_{a3}. The reaction with the larger K will predominate.

SOLVE THE PROBLEM

$$K_{a2} = 6.2 \times 10^{-8}$$
$$K_b \text{ for } HPO_4^{2-} = K_w/K_{a2} = 1.0 \times 10^{-14}/6.2 \times 10^{-8} = 1.6 \times 10^{-7}$$
$$K_{a3} = 3.6 \times 10^{-13}$$

K_b is much larger than K_{a3} and the hydrolysis reaction predominates. Sodium hydrogen phosphate Na_2HPO_4 is basic in aqueous solution.

PROBLEM 42.3A

Oxalic acid $(CO_2H)_2$ is an acid found in the stems and leaves of many plants such as chives, parsley, spinach, and rhubarb. Oxalic acid is a diprotic acid. Is sodium hydrogen oxalate $NaH(CO_2)_2$ acidic or basic in aqueous solution?

$$K_{a1} = 5.9 \times 10^{-2} \text{ and } K_{a2} = 6.5 \times 10^{-5}$$

Large amounts of oxalic acid are toxic due to the formation of calcium (and other) oxalates. Calcium oxalate is insoluble in water and ingestion of oxalic acid leads to kidney stones.

PROBLEM 42.3B

Carbonic acid, H_2CO_3, produced when carbon dioxide dissolves in water, is a diprotic acid. You may know the answer without any calculation, but prove that sodium hydrogen carbonate $NaHCO_3$ (baking soda) is basic in aqueous solution.

$$K_{a1} = 4.3 \times 10^{-7} \text{ and } K_{a2} = 4.8 \times 10^{-11}$$

42.3   Salts of Polyprotic Acids

Note that the hydrogen sulfate ion is not amphiprotic. In aqueous solution hydrolysis never occurs because to do so the *strong* acid H_2SO_4 would be formed. Hydrolysis only occurs if *weak* electrolytes are formed.

Some salts of polyprotic acids do not hydrolyse—instead, as we have seen, they ionize to produce acidic solutions. Comparison of the K_b for the hydrolysis and the K_a for the ionization establishes the predominant reaction. There are in fact relatively few salts of inorganic polyprotic oxyacids that do ionize. The common examples are salts containing the dihydrogen phosphate $H_2PO_4^-$ ion, the dihydrogen phosphite $H_2PO_3^-$ ion, the hydrogen sulfate HSO_4^- ion, and the hydrogen sulfite HSO_3^- ion.

How can we calculate the pH of a salt of a polyprotic acid? For example, what is the pH of a solution of sodium dihydrogen phosphate NaH_2PO_4? We have established that the dihydrogen phosphate $H_2PO_4^-$ ion is acidic in aqueous solution. What happens to the hydrogen ions released by the $H_2PO_4^-$ ion? They will be donated to the strongest base present—which is the $H_2PO_4^-$ ion! Notice in Table 40.3 that the $H_2PO_4^-$ ion is a stronger acid than H_2O (in the left column) and it is also a stronger base than H_2O (in the right column). The reaction can be written:

$$H_2PO_4^- + H_2PO_4^- \rightleftharpoons H_3PO_4 + HPO_4^{2-}$$

The equilibrium constant for this reaction can be derived from the two equations written earlier for the ionization and hydrolysis of the dihydrogen phosphate ion and the equation for the autoionization of water written in reverse:

Ionization: $H_2PO_4^- + H_2O \rightleftharpoons H_3O^+ + HPO_4^{2-}$ K_{a2}

Hydrolysis: $H_2PO_4^- + H_2O \rightleftharpoons H_3PO_4 + OH^-$ $K_b = K_w/K_{a1}$

$\underline{\qquad H_3O^+ + OH^- \rightleftharpoons \quad 2\,H_2O \qquad\qquad 1/K_w \qquad}$

$H_2PO_4^- + H_2PO_4^- \rightleftharpoons H_3PO_4 + HPO_4^{2-}$ K

The K for the overall reaction equals the product of the equilibrium constants for the individual equilibria:

$$K = K_{a2} \times K_w/K_{a1} \times 1/K_w = K_{a2}/K_{a1}$$

In this case, $K = 6.2 \times 10^{-8}/7.5 \times 10^{-3} = 8.3 \times 10^{-6}$

In the equilibrium, the concentration $[H_3PO_4]$ must equal the concentration $[HPO_4^{2-}]$—according to the stoichiometry one cannot form without the other. Therefore:

$$K = \frac{[H_3PO_4]^2}{[H_2PO_4^-]^2}$$

But $[H_3PO_4]$ and $[H_2PO_4^-]$ are related by the equation for the ionization of phosphoric acid:

$$H_3PO_4 + H_2O \rightleftharpoons H_3O^+ + H_2PO_4^- \qquad K_{a1} = \frac{[H_3O^+][H_2PO_4^-]}{[H_3PO_4]}$$

Rearranging this: $\dfrac{[H_3PO_4]}{[H_2PO_4^-]} = [H_3O^+]/K_{a1}$

Squaring this: $\dfrac{[H_3PO_4]^2}{[H_2PO_4^-]^2} = [H_3O^+]^2/K_{a1}^2$, which, from above $= K = K_{a2}/K_{a1}$

$$[H_3O^+]^2/K_{a1}^2 = K_{a2}/K_{a1}$$

The hydronium ion concentration $[H_3O^+] = \sqrt{(K_{a1} \times K_{a2})}$

Or, the pH of the solution $= \frac{1}{2}(pK_{a1} + pK_{a2})$

This is a very useful result because it means that the pH of any intermediate salt of a polyprotic acid (containing an ion that is amphiprotic)

- is independent of the concentration of the salt.
- equals the average of the pK_as for the anion of the salt and its conjugate acid.
- can be used to determine whether ionization or hydrolysis is the predominant reaction. If the average of the pK_as is below 7, the solution is acidic and ionization is the predominant reaction. If the average of the pK_as is above 7, the solution is basic and hydrolysis is the predominant reaction.

Note also that HPO_3^{2-} is not amphiprotic. The third hydrogen of phosphorous acid is *not* acidic. This hydrogen atom is attached to the phosphorus atom, not an oxygen atom.

This reaction is analogous to the autoionization of water. Because the salt is already 'ionized', this type of reaction is often referred to as **autoprotolysis**.

This derivation is very similar to the derivation of the expression:
$pH = \frac{1}{2}(pK_a + pK_a)$
for a solution of a salt of a weak acid and a weak base
(*cf.* Unit 41).

EXAMPLE 42.4   CALCULATION OF THE pH OF AN AMPHIPROTIC SALT OF A POLYPROTIC ACID

Calculate the hydronium ion concentration and pH of a 0.20 M solution of sodium dihydrogen phosphite NaH_2PO_3.

K_{a1} for phosphorous acid $= 1.0 \times 10^{-2}$

K_{a2} for phosphorous acid $= 2.6 \times 10^{-7}$

UNDERSTAND THE QUESTION

The pH of a salt containing an amphiprotic ion of a polyprotic acid equals the average of the pK_as for the ion of the salt and its conjugate acid. The pH is independent of the concentration.

PLAN THE SOLUTION

Calculate the average of pK_{a1} and pK_{a2}.

SOLVE THE PROBLEM

$pKa_1 = -\log_{10}(1.0 \times 10^{-2}) = 2.00$

$pKa_2 = -\log_{10}(2.6 \times 10^{-7}) = 6.59$

The pH of the solution $= (2.00 + 6.59)/2 = 4.29$

The $[H_3O^+] = 5.10 \times 10^{-5}$

Alternatively, $[H_3O^+] = \sqrt{(K_{a1} \times K_{a2})} = \sqrt{(1.0 \times 10^{-2} \times 2.6 \times 10^{-7})} = 5.10 \times 10^{-5}$

PROBLEM 42.4A

Using the pK_a values listed in Table 42.2 as a resource, determine the pH of a solution of sodium hydrogen oxalate $NaHC_2O_4$.

PROBLEM 42.4B

Using the pK_a values listed in Table 42.1 as a resource, determine the pH of a solution of sodium dihydrogen phosphite NaH_2PO_3.

The use of the formula $pH = \frac{1}{2}(pK_{a1} + pK_{a2})$ is restricted to salts that contain amphiprotic ions. For example, for phosphoric acid and its salts, the calculation of the pH of various solutions can be summarized:

H_3PO_4:   ionization of a weak acid using K_{a1}

$H_2PO_4^-$: $pH = \frac{1}{2}(pK_{a1} + pK_{a2})$

HPO_4^{2-}: $pH = \frac{1}{2}(pK_{a2} + pK_{a3})$

PO_4^{3-}:   hydrolysis of a salt using K_b $(= K_w/K_{a3})$

The question remains: How is the pH of a solution containing a mixture of two of the species listed above calculated? What, for example, is the pH of a solution containing both H_3PO_4 and $H_2PO_4^-$? This is the subject of the next unit.

Review Questions

1. Describe the difference between an ionization reaction and a hydrolysis reaction.

2. Describe how to determine if an ion in solution will hydrolyse.

3. What is the relationship between the K_a for an acid and the K_b for its conjugate base.

4. What does the description amphiprotic mean? Give an example of an amphiprotic substance and the different reactions it can undergo.

5. Describe how to determine whether an amphiprotic ion of a polyprotic acid will ionize or hydrolyse.

Solutions to Problems

PROBLEM 42.1A

For the first ionization:

$$H_2SO_4 + H_2O \rightleftharpoons H_3O^+ + HSO_4^- \quad K_{a1} = \text{very large}$$

The ICE table is (with concentrations in M):

$$H_2SO_4 + H_2O \rightleftharpoons H_3O^+ + HSO_4^-$$

Initial concentrations: 0.010 0 0

Equilibrium concentrations: 0 0.010 0.010

Some additional hydronium ion comes from the second ionization:

$$HSO_4^- + H_2O \rightleftharpoons H_3O^+ + SO_4^{2-} \quad K_{a2} = 1.2 \times 10^{-2}$$

The ICE table is (with concentrations in M):

	$HSO_4^- + H_2O \rightleftharpoons$	H_3O^+	$+ SO_4^{2-}$
Initial:	0.010	0.010	0
Change:	$- x$	$+ x$	$+ x$
Equilibrium concentrations:	$0.010 - x$	$0.010 + x$	x

$$K_{a2} = \frac{[H_3O^+][SO_4^{2-}]}{[HSO_4^-]} = \frac{(0.010 + x)x}{(0.010 - x)} = 1.2 \times 10^{-2}$$

Solving the quadratic equation using the quadratic formula, $x = 4.52 \times 10^{-3}$. The unknown x in this case represents the additional hydronium ion produced as a result of the second ionization:

$[H_3O^+]$ from the first ionization = 0.010 M

$[H_3O^+]$ from the second ionization = 0.0045 M

Total $[H_3O^+]$ = 0.010 M + 0.0045 M = 0.015 M

pH = 1.84

In this dilute solution of sulfuric acid the second ionization is significant.

PROBLEM 42.2A

For the first ionization:

$$H_2A + H_2O \rightleftharpoons H_3O^+ + HA^- \quad K_{a1} = 8.0 \times 10^{-5}$$

The ICE table is (with concentrations in M):

	$H_2A + H_2O \rightleftharpoons$	H_3O^+	$+ HA^-$
Initial concentrations:	0.050	0	0
Change:	$- x$	$+ x$	$+ x$
Equilibrium concentrations:	$0.050 - x$	x	x

$$K_{a1} = \frac{[H_3O^+][HA^-]}{[H_2A]} = \frac{x^2}{(0.050 - x)} = 8.0 \times 10^{-5}$$

The x in the denominator can be ignored and $x = 2.0 \times 10^{-3}$. The x in this problem is the hydronium ion concentration $[H_3O^+]$ and the hydrogen ascorbate ion concentration $[HA^-]$. Therefore, the concentrations of the species present in 0.050 M ascorbic acid are:

$[H_2A] = [H_2A]_{init} - [HA^-] = 0.050\,M - 2.0 \times 10^{-3}\,M = 0.048\,M$

$[H_3O^+] = 2.0 \times 10^{-3}\,M$

$[HA^-] = 2.0 \times 10^{-3}\,M$

$[A^{2-}] = K_{a2} = 1.6 \times 10^{-12}\,M$

$[OH^-] = 5.0 \times 10^{-12}\,M$

PROBLEM 42.3A

For hydrolysis (where Hox^- represents the hydrogen oxalate ion):

$$Hox^- + H_2O \rightleftharpoons H_2ox + OH^- \quad K_b = K_w/K_{a1} = 1.7 \times 10^{-13}$$

For ionization (where ox^{2-} represents the oxalate ion):

$$Hox^- + H_2O \rightleftharpoons H_3O^+ + ox^{2-} \quad K_{a2} = 6.5 \times 10^{-5}$$

K_{a2} exceeds K_b by a factor of about 400 million. Sodium hydrogen oxalate $NaH(CO_2)_2$ is acidic in aqueous solution. This is confirmed by the answer to Problem 42.4A.

PROBLEM 42.4A

$$pKa_1 = -\log_{10}(5.9 \times 10^{-2}) = 1.23$$
$$pKa_2 = -\log_{10}(6.4 \times 10^{-5}) = 4.19$$

The pH of the solution = (1.23 + 4.19)/2 = 2.71

Answers to Review Questions

1. An ionization reaction is a reaction in which an acid or base reacts with water to produce its conjugate partner and hydronium ions or hydroxide ions. Examples are the ionization of acetic acid and the ionization of ammonia:

$$CH_3CO_2H + H_2O \rightleftharpoons H_3O^+ + CH_3CO_2^-$$
$$NH_3 + H_2O \rightleftharpoons NH_4^+ + OH^-$$

A hydrolysis reaction is a reaction in which the conjugate partner of a weak acid or weak base (one of the ions of a salt) reacts with water to produce some of the acid or base from which the salt was formed. Again hydronium ions or hydroxide ions are produced to make the solution slightly acidic or basic. Examples are the hydrolysis of an acetate ion or an ammonium ion:

$$CH_3CO_2^- + H_2O \rightleftharpoons CH_3CO_2H + OH^-$$
$$NH_4^+ + H_2O \rightleftharpoons H_3O^+ + NH_3$$

2. An ion will hydrolyse in aqueous solution only if it is the conjugate partner of a weak acid or weak base. For example, the acetate ion hydrolyses because it is the conjugate base of the weak acid acetic acid. The nitrate ion does not hydrolyse because it is the conjugate base of the strong acid nitric acid. A conjugate base of a strong acid has no affinity for a hydrogen ion and no tendency to accept one back.

3. The equilibrium constant K_a is a measure of the strength of the acid—the higher the value of K_a the stronger the acid. The more readily the acid releases a hydrogen ion, the less readily the conjugate base accepts it. So the K_a for the acid and the K_b for the base are inversely proportional. In fact, the two multiplied together equals K_w.

4. An amphiprotic substance can accept a hydrogen ion and act as a base, or it can donate a hydrogen ion and act as an acid. Water is amphiprotic. Another example is the dihydrogen phosphate ion $H_2PO_4^-$:

Ionization (acting as an acid):

$$H_2PO_4^- + H_2O \rightleftharpoons H_3O^+ + HPO_4^{2-}$$

Hydrolysis (acting as a base):

$$H_2PO_4^- + H_2O \rightleftharpoons H_3PO_4 + OH^-$$

5. The magnitudes of K_a for the ionization reaction and K_b for the hydrolysis reaction can be compared. The reaction with the larger value for K will be the predominant reaction. Alternatively, the average of pK_{a1} and pK_{a2} for the amphiprotic species can be calculated. If the average is above 7 (at 25°C), then the solution is basic and hydrolysis must have occurred. If the average is below 7 (at 25°C), then the solution is acidic and ionization must have occurred.

End-of-Unit Problems

1. Calculate the concentrations of all species present in a solution of 0.250 *M* arsenic acid. What is the pH of the solution?

2. Calculate the concentrations of all species present in a solution of 0.500 *M* phosphorous acid. What is the pH of the solution?

3. The dihydrogen phosphate ion $H_2PO_4^-$ is amphiprotic. Does this ion hydrolyse or ionize in aqueous solution. What is the pH of a solution of potassium dihydrogen phosphate?

4. The hydrogen carbonate ion HCO_3^- is amphiprotic. Does this ion hydrolyse or ionize in aqueous solution. What is the pH of a solution of sodium hydrogen carbonate?

5. When potassium dihydrogen arsenate dissolves in water, is ionization or hydrolysis the predominant reaction? What is the pH of the solution?

6. When sodium hydrogen sulfite dissolves in water, is ionization or hydrolysis the predominant reaction? What is the pH of the solution?

7. Using the pK_a values listed in Table 42.2, calculate the pH of a 0.10 *M* solution of sodium hydrogen malonate.

8. Using the pK_a values listed in Table 42.2, calculate the pH of a 0.10 *M* solution of sodium hydrogen ascorbate.

9. When sodium hydrogen succinate dissolves in water, is ionization or hydrolysis the predominant reaction? What is the pH of the solution?

10. Suppose that 0.10 *M* acetic acid is added to 0.10 *M* disodium hydrogen phosphate. What happens? Write a Brønsted-Lowry acid-base equilibrium and identify the conjugate acid-base pairs. Determine whether K for the reaction is large or small.

11. Write a Brønsted-Lowry acid-base equilibrium describing what happens when 0.10 *M* sulfurous acid is added to 0.10 *M* potassium hydrogen carbonate. Identify the conjugate acid-base pairs. Determine whether K for the reaction is large or small.

Acid-Base Reactions in Aqueous Solution

43.1 Acid-base Neutralization Reactions

Acids and bases react together in a process called **neutralization**. This is not necessarily because the solution at the end is neutral—most often it is not—but because the acid and the base neutralize each other. Consider, for example, the reaction between hydrochloric acid and ammonia in aqueous solution. The reaction of the acid and the base leads to the formation of the salt ammonium chloride:

$$HCl + NH_3 \rightleftharpoons NH_4^+ + Cl^-$$

Some questions you might ask are: What are the predominant species present in the solution? In other words, how far does this reaction go to completion? How can the equilibrium constant be calculated?

Hydrochloric acid is a strong acid. In aqueous solution the molecules are essentially completely ionized:

$$HCl + H_2O \rightarrow H_3O^+ + Cl^- \qquad K_a \text{ very large}$$

In aqueous solution ammonia is a weak base and exists in equilibrium with a small concentration of ammonium ions and hydroxide ions:

$$NH_3 + H_2O \rightleftharpoons NH_4^+ + OH^- \qquad K_b = 1.8 \times 10^{-5}$$

If this equation is added to the equation for the autoionization of water written in reverse, the net ionic equation for the neutralization reaction between hydrochloric acid and ammonia is obtained:

$NH_3 + H_2O \rightleftharpoons NH_4^+ + OH^-$	$K_b = 1.8 \times 10^{-5}$
$H_3O^+ + OH^- \rightleftharpoons 2\,H_2O$	$1/K_w = 1.0 \times 10^{14}$
$H_3O^+ + NH_3 \rightleftharpoons NH_4^+ + H_2O$	$K_{neut} = 1.8 \times 10^9$

> The chloride ion is a spectator ion and is not present in the net ionic equation.

> Recall (*cf.* Unit 34) that if an equation is reversed, the K is the reciprocal of the original K.

The equilibrium constant K_{neut} for the reaction between hydrochloric acid and ammonia is obtained by multiplying the two equilibrium constants K_b and $1/K_w$:

$$K_{neut} = \frac{K_b}{K_w} = 1.8 \times 10^9$$

The result is a large number—this means that the system lies predominantly on the product side. Very little acid (H_3O^+) and base (NH_3) is present in the solution. The system consists almost entirely of ammonium ions (NH_4^+) and chloride (Cl^-) spectator ions when the neutralization is complete.

In order to distinguish this type of reaction we will denote the equilibrium constant, at least for the moment, as K_{neut}. Why is the value of the equilibrium constant K_{neut} so large? In other words, why does a neutralization such as this lie predominantly on the product side? Examination of the values of the equilibrium constants K_b and $1/K_w$ indicates that it is the large value for $1/K_w$ that drives the reaction to the product side:

$$H_3O^+ + OH^- \rightleftharpoons 2\,H_2O \qquad 1/K_w = 1.0 \times 10^{14}$$

Neutralization reactions are driven to completion due to the formation of water. It is the combination of hydronium ions and hydroxide ions to form water that drives all neutralization reactions. Water is a weak electrolyte and all aqueous systems move spontaneously to form weaker electrolytes (*cf.* Unit 40).

If both a weak acid and a weak base are used in the neutralization reaction, then the magnitude of the equilibrium constant K_{neut} is usually still large—the actual value depends upon the strengths of the acid and base. For example, consider the neutralization reaction between acetic acid and ammonia. Acetic acid is a weak acid—it exists in aqueous solution predominantly as CH_3CO_2H molecules. Ammonia is a weak base as we have seen. The net ionic equation for the neutralization reaction is:

$$CH_3CO_2H + NH_3 \rightleftharpoons NH_4^+ + CH_3CO_2^-$$

We can calculate the equilibrium constant for this neutralization reaction in the same way as before by adding the individual equations for the ionization of the weak acid, the ionization of the weak base, and the autoionization of water written in reverse.

$$CH_3CO_2H + H_2O \rightleftharpoons H_3O^+ + CH_3CO_2^- \qquad K_a = 1.8 \times 10^{-5}$$

$$NH_3 + H_2O \rightleftharpoons NH_4^+ + OH^- \qquad K_b = 1.8 \times 10^{-5}$$

$$H_3O^+ + OH^- \rightleftharpoons 2\,H_2O \qquad 1/K_w = 1.0 \times 10^{14}$$

$$CH_3CO_2H + NH_3 \rightleftharpoons NH_4^+ + CH_3CO_2^- \qquad K = \frac{K_a \times K_b}{K_w} = 3.2 \times 10^4$$

The fact that K_a for acetic acid and K_b for ammonia are both equal to 1.8×10^{-5} is coincidental.

You may remember that at the beginning of Unit 40 we noted that the extent to which an acid-base reaction goes toward the product side of the equation depends upon both the strength of the acid—its willingness to release a hydrogen ion—and the strength of the base—its willingness to accept the hydrogen ion. According to the expression for K_{neut}, the larger the values of K_a and K_b (the stronger the acid and the base), the greater its value.

As we saw earlier, the equilibrium constant for a strong acid – weak base neutralization is:

$$K_{neut} = \frac{K_b}{K_w}$$

For a weak acid–strong base neutralization, the equilibrium constant is:

$$K_{neut} = \frac{K_a}{K_w}$$

And if both acid and base are weak, the equilibrium constant is:

$$K_{neut} = \frac{K_a \times K_b}{K_w}$$

EXAMPLE 43.1 CALCULATION OF THE EQUILIBRIUM CONSTANT FOR A NEUTRALIZATION REACTION

Write the equation representing the neutralization reaction between nitrous acid and sodium hydroxide and calculate the equilibrium constant for the reaction.

$$K_a \text{ for nitrous acid} = 4.5 \times 10^{-4}$$

UNDERSTAND THE QUESTION

Neutralization reactions are product-favored; the equilibrium constants are large numbers. In fact, the stronger the acid and the base used in the reaction, the greater the equilibrium constant for the reaction. The general relationship is:

$$K_{neut} = \frac{K_a \times K_b}{K_w}$$

If the acid is strong, omit the K_a. If the base is strong, omit the K_b. If both are strong, omit both K_a and K_b and then $K_{neut} = 1/K_w$.

PLAN THE SOLUTION

In this case the base is strong, so $K_{neut} = K_a/K_w$.

SOLVE THE PROBLEM

The overall equation for the reaction is:

$$HNO_2 + NaOH \rightleftharpoons NaNO_2 + H_2O$$

The net ionic equation is (the sodium ion is a spectator ion):

$$HNO_2 + OH^- \rightleftharpoons NO_2^- + H_2O$$

$$K_{neut} = K_a/K_w = 4.5 \times 10^{-4}/1.0 \times 10^{-14} = 4.5 \times 10^{10}$$

PROBLEM 43.1A

Write equations representing the ionization of nitric acid and potassium hydroxide in water. Show that the equilibrium constant for the neutralization reaction of nitric acid and potassium hydroxide is equal to 1.0×10^{14}.

PROBLEM 43.1B

Write the equation representing the neutralization reaction between methylamine and formic acid and calculate the equilibrium constant for the reaction.

$$K_b \text{ for methylamine} = 3.6 \times 10^{-4}$$

$$K_a \text{ for formic acid} = 1.8 \times 10^{-4}$$

You may have recognized from the net ionic equation in Example 43.1 that the equilibrium constant for the neutralization reaction to form the nitrite ion NO_2^- is the reciprocal of the hydrolysis constant K_b for the nitrite ion:

In other words, the neutralization reaction is simply the reverse of the hydrolysis reaction discussed in Unit 41:

Neutralization: $HNO_2 + OH^- \rightleftharpoons NO_2^- + H_2O$ K_{neut}

Hydrolysis: $NO_2^- + H_2O \rightleftharpoons HNO_2 + OH^-$ K_b

The neutralization constant $K_{neut} = \dfrac{K_a}{K_w}$

The hydrolysis constant $K_b = \dfrac{K_w}{K_a}$

43.2   Mixtures of Conjugate Partners

The maintenance of the pH of a solution in biological systems is often critical. Even small deviations from the required pH can lead to sickness and death. The pH of blood, for example, must be maintained within the range 7.35 to 7.45. In agriculture the pH of the soil must be maintained at some optimal level that depends upon the crop being cultivated. How is this achieved?

Let's look again at a solution of acetic acid in water. The system is represented by the equation:

$$CH_3CO_2H + H_2O \rightleftharpoons H_3O^+ + CH_3CO_2^-$$

The equilibrium constant $K_a = \dfrac{[H_3O^+][CH_3CO_2^-]}{[CH_3CO_2H]} = 1.8 \times 10^{-5}$

Suppose some source of acetate ion (e.g. sodium acetate $NaCH_3CO_2$) is added to this system—what would happen? According to LeChâtelier's principle, the system would shift to the left. The added acetate ion combines with hydronium ion to produce acetic acid molecules—the reverse reaction occurs. This decreases the concentration of hydronium ion $[H_3O^+]$ and raises the pH. This effect is called the **common ion effect**. The acetate ion is the common ion—it is present in solution due to the ionization of the acetic acid *and* as a result of the dissociation of the added salt sodium acetate. In other words, it is an ion common to both systems.

The pH of an aqueous solution of a weak acid (acetic acid) and its conjugate base (the acetate ion) can therefore be adjusted by varying the relative amounts of the two components present. For example let's calculate the pH of a solution of acetic acid and sodium acetate.

EXAMPLE 43.2   CALCULATING THE pH OF A MIXTURE OF A WEAK ACID AND ITS CONJUGATE BASE

Calculate the pH of a solution in which the concentration of acetic acid is 0.100 *M* and the concentration of sodium acetate is 0.050 *M*.

UNDERSTAND THE QUESTION

Sodium acetate is a strong electrolyte. Because the acetate ion is the conjugate base of a weak acid, it hydrolyses in solution. The sodium ion is a spectator ion. Acetic acid is a weak acid and ionizes slightly in aqueous solution. Start by writing an equation either for the hydrolysis of the conjugate base or the ionization of the weak acid. Each approach will yield the same answer although writing the ionization of the weak acid is perhaps easier.

PLAN THE SOLUTION

Write the equation representing the ionization of acetic acid. Derive the expression for the equilibrium constant K_a. Set up an ICE table to summarize the initial concentrations and the equilibrium concentrations of the acetic acid, the hydronium ion, and the acetate ion.

SOLVE THE PROBLEM

As we have just seen, the ionization reaction is represented by the equation:

$$CH_3CO_2H + H_2O \rightleftharpoons H_3O^+ + CH_3CO_2^-$$

The equilibrium constant $K_a = \dfrac{[H_3O^+][CH_3CO_2^-]}{[CH_3CO_2H]} = 1.8 \times 10^{-5}$

The ICE table is (with concentrations in M):

$$CH_3CO_2H + H_2O \rightleftharpoons H_3O^+ + CH_3CO_2^-$$

Initial:	0.100	0	0.050
Change:	– x	+ x	+ x
Equilibrium:	0.100 – x	x	0.050 + x

The equilibrium concentrations are now substituted into the expression for the equilibrium constant K_a and the value of x is calculated.

$$K_a = \frac{[H_3O^+][CH_3CO_2^-]}{[CH_3CO_2H]} = \frac{(x)(0.050 + x)}{(0.100 - x)} = 1.8 \times 10^{-5}$$

In this case x is a small number compared to 0.050, and the x in both (0.050 + x) and (0.100 – x) can be ignored. So,

$$x = (1.8 \times 10^{-5})(0.100)/(0.050) = 3.6 \times 10^{-5}$$

The x is the hydronium ion concentration.

Having calculated x, you can check that it is indeed much smaller than 0.050 M.

$$[H_3O^+] = 3.6 \times 10^{-5}\ M \text{ and the pH} = 4.44$$

As expected, because the ionization of the acid is suppressed by the common ion, the pH is higher than that for 0.100 M acetic acid alone (pH = 2.89).

PROBLEM 43.2A

Calculate the pH of a solution in which the concentration of ammonia is 0.040 M and the concentration of ammonium chloride is 0.060 M.

PROBLEM 43.2B

Calculate the pH of a solution in which the concentration of nitrous acid is 0.150 M and the concentration of potassium nitrite is 0.100 M.

43.3   Buffer Solutions

Solutions that contain a weak electrolyte and its conjugate partner are called **buffer solutions**. The reason for this name is their ability to resist a change in pH when either an acid or base is added to the solution.

Let's examine again the mixture of acetic acid and sodium acetate for which we calculated the pH in Example 43.2. What happens to this solution if some strong acid is added?

EXAMPLE 43.3   CALCULATING THE EFFECT OF ADDING ACID TO A BUFFER SOLUTION

Calculate the pH of a solution of 100 mL 0.10 M acetic acid and 0.050 M sodium acetate after adding 1.0 mL of a 1.0 M HCl solution. Compare the result to adding 1.0 mL of a 1.0 M HCl solution to 100 mL of pure water.

UNDERSTAND THE QUESTION

The mixture of acetic acid and sodium acetate is a buffer solution—it is a mixture of a weak acid (acetic acid) and its conjugate base (the acetate ion). The pH of the solution was calculated in Example 43.2 and equals 4.44.

$$CH_3CO_2H + H_2O \rightleftharpoons H_3O^+ + CH_3CO_2^-$$

According to LeChâtelier's principle, if hydronium ion (a strong acid) is added to this system, the system will shift to the left. In other words, the added hydronium ion will combine with acetate ion to form acetic acid molecules. The added hydronium ion is 'absorbed' by the acetate ion and as a result the concentration of hydronium ion in the solution changes very little.

PLAN THE SOLUTION

Start by writing the equation for the ionization of the acetic acid and, as usual, derive the expression for the equilibrium constant K_a. The initial concentrations of acetic acid and acetate change slightly when the hydrochloric acid is added because of the slight dilution. But because the change is small and both change in the same ratio, this dilution can usually be ignored. The hydrochloric acid is also diluted when added to the 100 mL of the buffer solution—by a factor of (1 mL/101 mL).

The added hydronium ion is almost totally absorbed in the reaction with the acetate ion—neutralization reactions generally go to completion—and the easiest way to solve this problem is to assume that the system moves *all* the way to completion (to the left) and then backs off a little to the right. In this way, the small adjustment x is indeed a small number. Set up an ICE table to summarize the initial concentrations and the equilibrium concentrations of the acetic acid, the hydronium ion, and the acetate ion.

SOLVE THE PROBLEM

The initial concentration of the added HCl in the solution is $1.0\ M \times (1\ \text{mL}/101\ \text{mL}) = 0.010\ M$.

The ICE table is (with concentrations in M):

$$CH_3CO_2H + H_2O \rightleftharpoons H_3O^+ + CH_3CO_2^-$$

Initial:	0.10	0	0.050
Add 1.0 mL 1.0 M HCl:		+0.010	

Assume complete movement to left using up all the added H_3O^+. The added H_3O^+ combines with acetate ion to produce acetic acid. The acetate ion concentration deceases to 0.040 M:

	0.11	0	0.040

Then there is a small adjustment of the system back to the right to reach equilibrium:

Change:	$-x$	$+x$	$+x$
Equilibrium:	$0.11 - x$	x	$0.040 + x$

The equilibrium concentrations are now substituted into the expression for the equilibrium constant K_a and the value of x calculated.

$$K_a = \frac{[H_3O^+][CH_3CO_2^-]}{[CH_3CO_2H]} = \frac{x(0.04 - x)}{(0.11 - x)} = 1.8 \times 10^{-5}$$

Neglecting the small change x in the concentrations of the acetic acid and the acetate ion, $x = (1.8 \times 10^{-5})(0.11)/(0.040) = 4.9 \times 10^{-5}$.

The x is the hydronium ion concentration.

$$[H_3O^+] = 4.95 \times 10^{-5}\ M \text{ and the pH} = 4.31$$

The original pH was 4.44, so the pH has changed but not by very much. Compare this small change to what happens when the same 1.0 mL of 1.0 M HCl is added to 100 mL of pure water:

When the 1.0 M HCl is added to the water, the solution is diluted from 1.0 M to 0.010 M.

Initial pH of pure water = 7.0

The pH of 0.010 M HCl solution = 2.0—a change of 5.0 pH units, representing a change in the hydronium ion concentration by a factor of 100,000.

PROBLEM 43.3A

The buffer system responsible for maintaining the pH of blood at 7.40 is carbonic acid H_2CO_3 and its conjugate base the hydrogen carbonate ion HCO_3^-. Calculate the ratio of the concentrations of these two conjugate partners necessary to establish a pH of 7.40.

K_a for carbonic acid = 8.0×10^{-7} at 37°C (a little higher than at 25°C).

PROBLEM 43.3B

Basic buffer solutions are prepared using a weak base and its conjugate acid. Suppose that such a buffer solution consists of 100 mL of 0.10 M ammonia and 0.10 M ammonium chloride. Calculate the pH of the solution. Calculate the pH of the solution after 0.0020 mole of sodium hydroxide (80 mg) has been added. Assume that the change in the volume when the NaOH is added is negligible.

K_b for ammonia = 1.8×10^{-5}.

Buffer solutions resist a change in pH upon addition of acid or base. This is because in a buffer solution there are two components. In the buffer solution just discussed, for example, the two components are acetic acid and acetate ion. The acetate ion, as we have seen, reacts with any hydronium ion added to produce acetic acid. The acetic acid reacts with any hydroxide ion added to produce acetate ion. Both of these reactions go largely to completion.

The acetic acid–acetate ion conjugate acid-base system has the capacity to go in either direction. There is a reservoir of base (the acetate ion) to absorb any added hydronium ion and there is a reservoir of acid (acetic acid) to absorb any added base. The amount of acid or base a buffer system can absorb without a significant change in the pH is called the **buffer capacity**. The buffer capacity depends upon the amount—concentration, volume, or both—of the two conjugate partners present in the solution. The greater the amount of the buffer, the greater the amount of acid or base that can be added without a significant change in the pH. If too much acid or base is added to a buffer solution, the buffer will be exhausted and the pH will begin to change dramatically.

43.4 The Henderson-Hasselbalch Equation

As we have noted, buffer solutions play a critical role in maintaining the pH of biological systems. Many reactions in the human body, and many experiments in chemical and biochemical laboratories, are performed in buffered media. Because of this, an equation has been developed to make the determination of the pH of a buffer solution relatively straightforward.

The general equation for the ionization of a weak acid is:

$$\text{Acid} + H_2O \rightleftharpoons H_3O^+ + \text{Conjugate base}$$

$$K_a \text{ for the acid} = \frac{[H_3O^+][\text{Conjugate base}^-]}{[\text{Acid}]}$$

Rearranging this expression:

$$[H_3O^+] = K_a \times \left(\frac{[\text{Acid}]}{[\text{Conjugate base}]} \right)$$

Taking the $-\log_{10}$ of both sides of this equation:

$$pH = pK_a - \log_{10} \left(\frac{[\text{Acid}]}{[\text{Conjugate base}]} \right)$$

Or, since $-\log_{10}x = +\log_{10}(1/x)$:

$$pH = pK_a + \log_{10} \left(\frac{[\text{Conjugate base}]}{[\text{Acid}]} \right)$$

The same treatment of a weak base leads to the expression:

$$pH = pK_a + \log_{10} \left(\frac{[\text{Base}]}{[\text{Conjugate acid}]} \right) = 14 - pK_b + \log_{10} \left(\frac{[\text{Base}]}{[\text{Conjugate acid}]} \right)$$

where the pK_a refers to the conjugate acid of the weak base and pK_b refers to the weak base itself.

The general expression for a weak acid or a weak base is

$$pH = pK_a + \log_{10} \left(\frac{[\text{base}]}{[\text{acid}]} \right)$$

This equation is the **Henderson-Hasselbalch equation** for determining the pH of any buffer solution where [acid] and [base] represent the initial concentrations of the two conjugate partners. The change in the initial concentrations of the acid and the base when the buffer solution is prepared is negligible. The acid ionizes to some extent to produce its conjugate base, but the conjugate base hydrolyses to some extent to produce the acid and the results cancel to some extent. Another way to think of this is that, according to LeChâtelier's principle, the presence of the conjugate base suppresses the ionization of the acid and the presence of the acid suppresses the hydrolysis of the base.

The Henderson-Hasselbalch equation provides an efficient way to determine the pH of a buffer solution. Realize, however, that the equation is nothing more than a different way of expressing the ionization constant of a weak acid when the change in the initial concentration of the acid can be ignored.

The equation is useful because it shows that the pH of a buffer solution depends primarily upon the pK_a of the acid. The choice of an acid with a suitable pK_a can be considered to be the coarse adjustment of the buffer pH. The variation of the ratio ([base]/[acid]) is the fine adjustment. In order to have a reasonable capacity to buffer in both directions—resisting a change in pH upon addition of both acid and base—the ratio ([base]/[acid]) should be no greater than 10:1 and no less than 1:10. This means that the acid chosen should have a pK_a within the range of the desired pH $\pm$ 1.

$$pH = \underset{\substack{\text{coarse} \\ \text{adjustment}}}{pK_a} + \log_{10} \left(\frac{[\text{base}]}{\underset{\substack{\text{fine} \\ \text{adjustment}}}{[\text{acid}]}} \right)$$

EXAMPLE 43.4   CHOOSING A BUFFER SOLUTION FOR A SPECIFIED pH

Using Table 40.2 as a resource, choose a suitable conjugate acid-base system for the preparation of a buffer solution having a pH of 2.20.

UNDERSTAND THE QUESTION

The Henderson-Hasselbalch equation is the easiest way to determine the pH of a buffer solution. The pH of a buffer solution depends primarily upon the pK_a of the acid. The ratio of the concentration of the base to the concentration of the acid can be adjusted to achieve the exact pH required.

PLAN THE SOLUTION

Look for an acid with a pK_a near to the desired pH. Then calculate the ratio ([base]/[acid]) necessary for the exact pH.

SOLVE THE PROBLEM

The acid with a pK_a nearest to 2.20 is phosphoric acid (pK_a = 2.13). This means that a buffer system consisting of equimolar amounts of phosphoric acid H_3PO_4 and its conjugate base $H_2PO_4^-$ would have a pH of 2.13. This value 2.13, and the desired pH 2.20, can be substituted in the Henderson-Hasselbalch equation to obtain the necessary ratio ($[H_2PO_4^-]/[H_3PO_4]$):

$$pH = pK_a + \log_{10}\left(\frac{[base]}{[acid]}\right)$$

$$2.20 = 2.13 + \log_{10}\left(\frac{[base]}{[acid]}\right)$$

$$\log_{10}\left(\frac{[base]}{[acid]}\right) = 2.20 - 2.13 = 0.07$$

$$\left(\frac{[base]}{[acid]}\right) = 1.18$$

The ratio of the concentrations necessary is 1.18 to 1—a small excess of the conjugate base $H_2PO_4^-$. This makes sense because the desired pH (2.20) is slightly more basic then the pK_a of the acid (2.13).

PROBLEM 43.4A

A culture medium for an experiment in a biochemical lab is required to be maintained at a pH of 9.0. Choose a conjugate acid-base system for the preparation of a suitable buffer solution.

PROBLEM 43.4B

A buffer solution is required to maintain the pH of a solution at 7.0 at 25°C. Select a suitable acid-base system and calculate the required concentrations. Explain why you can't just use pure water.

In practice, buffer solutions are often prepared by a partial neutralization of a weak acid or base using a strong base or acid. To prepare an acidic buffer, a weak acid is chosen that has a pK_a near the desired pH. A strong base such as sodium hydroxide is added to a solution of the weak acid until the desired pH is reached. The added base reacts with the acid to produce the conjugate base of the weak acid and the final buffer solution therefore contains the required weak acid and its conjugate base. In a similar way, a basic buffer solution can be prepared by choosing an appropriate weak base and then adding a strong acid until the desired pH is reached. Again the final solution contains the weak base and the conjugate acid formed in the partial neutralization of the base. This method has the advantage that the buffer solution has exactly the pH required. Buffer solutions prepared by mixing calculated amounts of the acid and conjugate base, or base and conjugate acid, usually have to be adjusted to the precise pH required because of the nonideal behavior of ionic solutions and the approximations employed in the derivation of the Henderson-Hasselbalch equation.

The Henderson-Hasselbalch equation can be used to calculate the composition of a solution of a weak acid at a particular pH. In other words, if the pH is known, and the pK_a for the weak acid is known, the ratio ([base]/[acid]) can be calculated. For example, suppose sufficient base is added to a solution of acetic acid to make the pH of the solution 4.00. What are the relative concentrations of acetic acid and acetate ion in the solution? We know using LeChâtelier's principle that addition of H_3O^+ will suppress the ionization of the acetic acid and the addition of OH^- will shift the equilibrium to the right. Using the Henderson-Hasselbalch equation we can calculate just how much the equilibrium is shifted.

$$CH_3CO_2H + H_2O \rightleftharpoons H_3O^+ + CH_3CO_2^-$$

addition of H_3O^+ suppresses the ionization

addition of OH^- shifts the equilibrium to the right

EXAMPLE 43.5   CALCULATING THE COMPOSITION OF A SOLUTION OF A WEAK ACID AND ITS CONJUGATE BASE

Calculate the relative concentrations of acetic acid and acetate ion in a solution having a pH of 4.00.

UNDERSTAND THE QUESTION

We can use the Henderson-Hasselbalch equation to calculate the composition of a solution of a weak acid at any pH. If the pH is known, and the pK_a for the weak acid is known, the ratio ([base]/[acid]) can be calculated. The calculation is basically the same as that of Example 43.4.

PLAN THE SOLUTION

Use the Henderson-Hasselbalch equation. Substitute the pH of the solution and the pK_a of acetic acid. Then calculate the ratio ([base]/[acid]).

SOLVE THE PROBLEM

The pK_a for acetic acid is 4.74

$$pH = pK_a + \log_{10}\left(\frac{[base]}{[acid]}\right)$$

$$4.0 = 4.74 + \log_{10}\left(\frac{[base]}{[acid]}\right)$$

$$\log_{10}\left(\frac{[base]}{[acid]}\right) = 4.00 - 4.74 = -0.74$$

$$\left(\frac{[base]}{[acid]}\right) = 0.18$$

The ratio of the acetate ion concentration $[CH_3CO_2^-]$ to the acetic acid concentration $[CH_3CO_2H]$ at a pH of 4.74 is 1:1—the concentrations are equal. The solution is said to be equimolar. At a pH of 4.00 (more acidic), the equilibrium is shifted to the left, increasing the $[CH_3CO_2H]$ and decreasing the $[CH_3CO_2^-]$ so that the ratio is 0.18. This is in agreement with the prediction of LeChâtelier's principle.

PROBLEM 43.5A

Benzoic acid $C_6H_5CO_2H$ is a weak acid ($K_a = 6.3 \times 10^{-5}$). Calculate the ratio of $C_6H_5CO_2^-$ ions to $C_6H_5CO_2H$ molecules in a solution with a pH = 4.00 at 25°C.

PROBLEM 43.5B

The pK_b for ammonia equals 4.74. Calculate the ratio of ammonia $[NH_3]$ to ammonium ions $[NH_4^+]$ in an aqueous solution at a pH of 9.50.

An important feature of buffer solutions apparent in the Henderson-Hasselbalch equation is that the pH of a buffer solution is not affected by dilution. If a buffer solution is diluted, the concentrations of the base and acid are equally affected. In other words the ratio ([base]/[acid]) remains constant. If this ratio remains constant then the pH must remain the same.

Review Questions

1. Describe how the magnitude of the equilibrium constant for a neutralization reaction depends upon the strengths of the acid and base used in the neutralization.

2. Describe the common ion effect and how a common ion influences the equilibrium between a weak acid and its conjugate base in aqueous solution.

3. Explain what a buffer solution is and how such a solution resists a change in pH when a small amount of a strong acid or strong base is added.

4. What does buffer capacity mean? What happens if the buffer capacity is exceeded?

5. Describe what the Henderson-Hasselbalch equation is used for and why it is so useful. Use the equation to explain why the pH of a buffer solution is not affected by dilution.

Solutions to Problems

PROBLEM 43.1A

Nitric acid HNO_3 is a strong acid—it exists in aqueous solution predominantly as hydronium ions and nitrate ions:

$$HNO_3 + H_2O \rightleftharpoons H_3O^+ + NO_3^-$$

Potassium hydroxide is a strong base—it is dissociated in aqueous solution:

$$KOH + H_2O \rightleftharpoons K^+ + OH^-$$

The two equations are added to obtain the detailed ionic equation for the neutralization reaction:

$$H_3O^+ + NO_3^- + K^+ + OH^- \rightleftharpoons NO_3^- + K^+ + 2 H_2O$$

The nitrate ion and the potassium ion are spectator ions. The net ionic equation is:

$$H_3O^+ + OH^- \rightleftharpoons 2 H_2O \qquad K_{neut} = 1/K_w = 1.0 \times 10^{14}$$

This equation is the net ionic equation for any strong acid–strong base neutralization.

PROBLEM 43.2A

The ionization of ammonia is represented by the equation:

$$NH_3 + H_2O \rightleftharpoons NH_4^+ + OH^-$$

The equilibrium constant $K_b = \dfrac{[NH_4^+][OH^-]}{[NH_3]} = 1.8 \times 10^{-5}$

The ICE table is (with concentrations in M):

	$NH_3 + H_2O \rightleftharpoons$	NH_4^+	+	OH^-
Initial:	0.040	0.060		0
Change:	$-x$	$+x$		$+x$
Equilibrium:	$0.040 - x$	$0.060 + x$		x

The equilibrium concentrations are now substituted into the expression for the equilibrium constant K_a and the value of x is calculated.

$$K_a = \frac{[NH_4^+][OH^-]}{[NH_3]} = \frac{(0.060 + x)(x)}{(0.040 - x)} = 1.8 \times 10^{-5}$$

x is a small number compared to 0.040, so:

$$x = (1.8 \times 10^{-5})(0.040)/(0.060) = 1.2 \times 10^{-5}$$

The x is the hydroxide ion concentration.

$[OH^-] = 1.2 \times 10^{-5}\ M$, pOH = 4.92, and the pH = 9.08

PROBLEM 43.3A

The equilibrium is: $H_2CO_3 + H_2O \rightleftharpoons H_3O^+ + HCO_3^-$

$$K_a = \frac{[H_3O^+][HCO_3^-]}{[H_2CO_3]} = 8.0 \times 10^{-7} \text{ at } 37°C$$

We neglect the small changes in the concentrations of the carbonic acid and the hydrogen carbonate ion. The pH is 7.40 which corresponds to a hydronium ion concentration of 4.0×10^{-8}.

$$8.0 \times 10^{-7} = (4.0 \times 10^{-8}) \times [HCO_3^-]/[H_2CO_3]$$

The ratio $[HCO_3^-]/[H_2CO_3] = 20$.

In blood the actual concentrations of $[HCO_3^-]$ and $[H_2CO_3]$ are approximately 0.024 M and 0.0012 M respectively.

PROBLEM 43.4A

Examination of the acids in Table 40.2 indicates that the ammonium ion has a pK_a near 9.0 ($pK_a = 9.25$). A buffer system based on the NH_4^+/NH_3 system would be a good choice. Typically an acid should be chosen that has a pK_a within the range pH ± 1.

$$pH = pK_a + \log_{10}\left(\frac{[base]}{[acid]}\right)$$

$$9.0 = 9.25 + \log_{10}\left(\frac{[base]}{[acid]}\right)$$

$$\log_{10}\left(\frac{[base]}{[acid]}\right) = -0.25$$

$$[base/[acid] = [NH_3]/[NH_4^+] = 0.56$$

A little more acid (NH_4^+) than base (NH_3) to make the solution more acidic (pH = 9.0) than pK_a (9.4).

PROBLEM 43.5A

$$pH = pK_a + \log_{10}\left(\frac{[base]}{[acid]}\right)$$

$$4.0 = 4.20 + \log_{10}\left(\frac{[base]}{[acid]}\right)$$

$$\log_{10}\left(\frac{[base]}{[acid]}\right) = -0.20$$

$$[base/[acid] = [C_6H_5CO_2^-]/[C_6H_5CO_2H] = 0.63$$

The concentration of the conjugate base $C_6H_5CO_2^-$ is less than the concentration of benzoic acid $C_6H_5CO_2H$. An equimolar solution would have a pH = 4.20. The solution at a pH of 4.0 contains more acid.

Answers to Review Questions

1. The extent to which an acid-base reaction goes to completion depends upon both the strength of the acid—its willingness to release a hydrogen ion—and the strength of the base—its willingness to accept the hydrogen ion.

   The relationship $K_{neut} = \dfrac{K_a \times K_b}{K_w}$ illustrates that the larger the values of K_a and K_b—the stronger the acid and the base—the greater the value of the equilibrium constant for the neutralization, K_{neut}.

2. If, in a solution, there are two sources of the same ion, the ion is referred to as a common ion. A typical example is a solution of a weak electrolyte and a salt of the same electrolyte. The weak electrolyte ionizes to yield its conjugate partner. The salt of the weak electrolyte contains the same conjugate partner. The conjugate partner is the common ion. Consider ammonia in solution with an ammonium salt: The ammonia ionizes in solution to form the ammonium ion and the ammonium ion is also present from the

ammonium salt—the ammonium ion is the ion common to both systems. According to LeChâtelier's principle the presence of the common ion will suppress the ionization of the weak electrolyte.

3. Buffer solutions resist a change in pH upon addition of acid or base. This is because in a buffer solution there are two components—a weak electrolyte and its conjugate partner. In a buffer solution, therefore, there is a reservoir of base to absorb any added hydronium ion and there is a reservoir of acid to absorb any added hydroxide ion.

4. The amount of acid or base a buffer system can absorb without a significant change in the pH is called the buffer capacity. The buffer capacity depends upon the amount of the two conjugate partners present in the solution. The greater the amount of the buffer, the greater the amount of acid or base that can be added without a significant change in

the pH. If too much acid or base is added to a buffer solution, the buffer will be exhausted and the pH will begin to change.

5. The Henderson-Hasselbalch equation is

$$pH = pK_a + \log_{10}\left(\frac{[\text{base}]}{[\text{acid}]}\right)$$

where [acid] and [base] represent the concentrations of the two conjugate partners. The equation provides an efficient way to determine the pH of a buffer solution. The pH of a buffer solution depends primarily upon the pK_a of the acid. The variation of the ratio ([base]/[acid]) can be adjusted to established the exact pH required. If a buffer solution is diluted, the concentrations of the base and acid are equally affected and the ratio ([base]/[acid]) remains constant. The pH must therefore remain the same.

End-of-Unit Problems

1. Derive the following equation for the neutralization reaction between ammonia and formic acid from the corresponding equations for the ionization of the acid and the base. From the K_a for formic acid, the K_b for ammonia, and K_w for the autoionization of water, derive the expression for K_{neut} and calculate its value:

$$HCO_2H + NH_3 \rightleftharpoons NH_4^+ + HCO_2^-$$

Values of ionization constants are listed in Tables 39.2 and 40.2.

2. Derive the following equation for the neutralization reaction between methylamine and benzoic acid from the corresponding equations for the ionization of the acid and the base. From the K_a for benzoic acid, the K_b for methylamine, and K_w for the autoionization of water, derive the expression for K_{neut} and calculate its value:

$$C_6H_5CO_2H + CH_3NH_2 \rightleftharpoons CH_3NH_3^+ + C_6H_5CO_2^-$$

Values of ionization constants are listed in Tables 39.2 and 40.2.

3. Write the net ionic equation for the following neutralization reaction between sodium hydroxide and hypochlorous acid and then derive the same equation from the corresponding equation for the ionization of the acid. From the K_a for hypochlorous acid and K_w for the autoionization of water, derive the expression for K_{neut} and calculate its value:

$$HClO + NaOH \rightleftharpoons NaClO + H_2O$$

Values of ionization constants are listed in Table 40.2.

4. Write the net ionic equation for the following neutralization reaction between potassium hydroxide and iodic acid and then derive the same equation from the corresponding equation for the ionization of the acid. From the K_a for iodic acid and K_w for the autoionization of water, derive the expression for K_{neut} and calculate its value:

$$HIO_3 + KOH \rightleftharpoons KIO_3 + H_2O$$

Values of ionization constants are listed in Table 40.2.

5. Calculate the value of the equilibrium constant for the neutralization reaction between hydrochloric acid and hydrazine. Values of ionization constants are listed in Tables 39.2 and 40.2.

6. Calculate the value of the equilibrium constant for the neutralization reaction between hydrobromic acid and pyridine. Values of ionization constants are listed in Tables 39.2 and 40.2.

7. Most neutralization reactions are product-favored. In other words they have equilibrium constants that are quite large. However, if the base and the acid are really weak, the neutralization reaction is more reactant-favored. For example, calculate the K_{neut} for

the reaction in aqueous solution between the weak base aniline ($K_b = 4.3 \times 10^{-10}$) and the weak acid phenol ($K_a = 1.6 \times 10^{-10}$).

8. Pyridine is a very weak base ($K_b = 1.8 \times 10^{-9}$) and hypochlorous acid is almost as weak as an acid ($K_a = 3.0 \times 10^{-8}$). Calculate the value of the neutralization constant K_{neut} for the reaction between pyridine and hypochlorous acid. Is this a neutralization that is heavily product-favored?

9. Describe what happens to the ionization of acetic acid in aqueous solution when

   a. a strong acid is added to the solution

   b. a strong base is added to the solution

   c. sodium acetate is added to the solution

10. Describe what happens to the ionization of ammonia in aqueous solution when

    a. a strong acid is added to the solution

    b. a strong base is added to the solution

    c. ammonium nitrate is added to the solution

11. According to LeChâtelier's principle, addition of which of the following substances affects the position of equilibrium in an aqueous solution of acetic acid? If the equilibrium is affected, describe how the system shifts.

    a. potassium acetate

    b. ammonia

    c. sodium hydroxide

12. According to LeChâtelier's principle, addition of which of the following substances affects the position of equilibrium in an aqueous solution of the weak base hydrazine? If the equilibrium is affected, describe how the system shifts.

    a. hydrochloric acid

    b. ammonia

    c. acetic acid

13. Describe how the pH of a 0.10 M solution of nitrous acid changes when an equimolar amount of sodium nitrite is added to the solution.

14. Describe what happens to the pH of 50 mL of a 0.25 M solution of formic acid when 25 mL of 0.25 M potassium hydroxide solution is added.

15. Calculate the pH of a solution in which the concentration of nitrous acid is 0.010 M and the concentration of sodium nitrite is 0.025 M.

16. Calculate the pH of a solution in which the concentration of sodium benzoate is 0.050 M and the concentration of benzoic acid is 0.020 M.

17. Calculate the pH of a solution in which the concentration of ammonia is 0.080 M and the concentration of ammonium chloride is 0.050 M.

18. Calculate the pH of a solution in which the concentration of dimethylammonium chloride $(CH_3)_2NH_2Cl$ is 0.120 M and the concentration of dimethylamine is 0.090 M.

19. Basic buffer solutions are prepared using a weak base and its conjugate acid. Calculate the pH of a buffer solution that consists of 100 mL of 0.10 M pyridine and 0.80 M pyridinium chloride. Calculate the pH of the solution after 0.0025 mole of sodium hydroxide (0.10 gram) has been added. Assume that the change in the volume when the NaOH is added is negligible.

20. Acidic buffer solutions are prepared using a weak acid and its conjugate base. Calculate the pH of a buffer solution that consists of 100 mL of 0.50 M benzoic acid and 0.30 M sodium benzoate. Calculate the pH of the solution after 0.0025 mole of hydrochloric acid (1.0 mL of a 2.5 M solution) has been added. Assume that the change in the volume when the HCl is added is negligible.

21. One way to prepare an acidic buffer solution is to make a solution of a weak acid and then add a strong base until the desired pH is reached. The base reacts with the acid to produce the conjugate base of the weak acid and the final solution therefore contains the weak acid and its conjugate base—a buffer solution. Calculate how many mL of a 0.10 M NaOH solution should be added to 100 mL of a 0.050 M phosphoric acid solution to produce a buffer solution with a pH of 2.30.

22. Calculate how many mL of a 0.25 M HCl solution should be added to 100 mL of a 0.0150 M ammonia solution to produce a buffer solution with a pH of 9.10.

23. Given appropriate amounts of each component, which of the following solutions can act as buffer solutions?

    a. NaH_2PO_4 and Na_2HPO_4

    b. HCl and NaCl

    c. HF and NaF

    d. CH_3CO_2H and NaOH

24. Given appropriate amounts of each component, which of the following solutions can act as buffer solutions?

    a. HCl and Na_2HPO_4

    b. HNO_2 and $NaNO_2$

    c. NH_4NO_3 and NH_3

    d. $HClO_3$ and $NaClO_3$

25. Using the data in Tables 39.2, 40.2, and 42.1 as a resource, choose a conjugate acid-base system suitable for the preparation of buffer solutions having a pH equal to

    a. 7.25

    b. 10.80

    c. 4.00

26. Using the data in Tables 39.2, 40.2, and 42.1 as a resource, choose a conjugate acid-base system suitable for the preparation of buffer solutions having a pH equal to

    a. 2.10

    b. 3.68

    c. 9.25

27. Calculate the ratio of sodium benzoate $[NaC_6H_5CO_2]$ to benzoic acid $[C_6H_5CO_2H]$ in a buffer solution with a pH = 6.50 at 25°C. K_a for benzoic acid = 6.3×10^{-5}.

28. Calculate the ratio of potassium propionate $[KC_2H_5CO_2]$ to propionic acid $[C_2H_5CO_2H]$ in a buffer solution with a pH = 4.50 at 25°C. K_a for propionic acid = 1.3×10^{-5}.

29. Calculate the ratio of ethylammonium bromide $[C_2H_5NH_2Br]$ to ethylamine $[C_2H_5NH_2]$ in a buffer solution with a pH = 10.60 at 25°C. K_b for ethylamine = 6.4×10^{-4}.

30. Calculate the ratio of ammonium nitrate $[NH_4NO_3]$ to ammonia $[NH_3]$ in a buffer solution with a pH = 8.95 at 25°C. K_b for ammonia = 1.8×10^{-5}.

Acid-Base Titrations

44.1   Titrations

We have seen that most acid-base neutralization reactions are strongly product-favored. The equilibrium constant for a strong acid–strong base neutralization reaction is 1.0×10^{14} and is still quite large for most weak acid–weak base reactions. When a strong acid or a strong base is involved, the reaction can be assumed to go to completion. This means that quantitative experiments, called **titrations**, can be done in which the amount of acid can be determined if the amount of base is known, and *vice versa*. Quantitative titrations involving weak acid–weak base neutralization reactions are rarely performed because a strong electrolyte can always be chosen in preference.

In a titration a solution of an acid is added to a solution of a base, or *vice versa*. The solution in the buret (the solution that is added) is commonly referred to as the **titrant** and the solution in the flask is called the **analyte**. If the concentration of the titrant is known, and the volume of the titrant added has been measured, then the number of moles of analyte in the flask can be calculated.

The success of the procedure depends upon the detection of the **equivalence point**—the point at which the amounts of acid and base are exactly equal. The **endpoint** of a titration is experimental evidence that the equivalence point of the neutralization reaction has been reached. It is detected either by the use of a suitable **acid-base indicator** or by monitoring the pH using a pH meter.

44.2   Calculating the pH at the Equivalence Point

At the equivalence point in a reaction of an acid and a base, the acid is completely neutralized by the base and *vice versa*. All that remains in the solution is a salt. For example, suppose that nitrous acid and sodium hydroxide react to form sodium nitrite. At the equivalent point the number of moles of nitrous acid used, the number of moles of sodium hydroxide used, and the number of moles of sodium nitrite formed are all exactly the same.

The calculation of the pH of the solution at the equivalence point can be approached by two different routes.

We can write the equation for the neutralization reaction, derive the expression for the equilibrium constant K_{neut}, set up an ICE table, and solve to obtain the hydroxide ion concentration.

$$HNO_2 + OH^- \rightleftharpoons H_2O + NO_2^- \qquad K_{neut} = \frac{[NO_2^-]}{[HNO_2][OH^-]}$$

Or, we can examine the solution at the equivalence point and write the equation for the hydrolysis of the salt that is present:

$$NO_2^- + H_2O \rightleftharpoons HNO_2 + OH^- \qquad K_b = \frac{[HNO_2][OH^-]}{[NO_2^-]}$$

As we noted in the last unit, one equation is the reverse of the other, and K_{neut} for the neutralization is the reciprocal of K_b for the hydrolysis.

We have already examined hydrolysis reactions in Unit 41. Although the solution using the hydrolysis reaction is probably more straightforward, let's solve this problem using the neutralization reaction.

EXAMPLE 44.1   CALCULATING THE pH AT THE EQUIVALENCE POINT

Calculate the pH at the equivalence point when 25 mL of 0.10 M nitrous acid reacts with 25 mL of 0.10 M sodium hydroxide.

UNDERSTAND THE QUESTION

This is a neutralization reaction of a weak acid and a strong base. At the equivalence point, the number of moles of acid equals the number of moles of base used. The only species present in solution is the salt sodium nitrite. We'll solve the problem using the equation for the neutralization reaction. Remember that the solution is diluted when the acid and base are mixed.

PLAN THE SOLUTION

Write the equation representing the neutralization reaction. Derive the expression for the equilibrium constant K_{neut}. Set up an ICE table to summarize the initial and equilibrium concentrations of the salt, the hydroxide ion, and the weak acid nitrous acid. Note that when the solutions are mixed, the volume changes, and the concentrations decrease.

SOLVE THE PROBLEM

The neutralization reaction is represented by the equation:

$$HNO_2 + OH^- \rightleftharpoons H_2O + NO_2^-$$

The equilibrium constant $K_{neut} = \dfrac{K_a}{K_w} = \dfrac{[NO_2^-]}{[HNO_2][OH^-]} = \dfrac{4.5 \times 10^{-4}}{1.0 \times 10^{-14}} = 4.5 \times 10^{10}$

The equilibrium constant is very large—the reaction goes to completion. The best approach in this case is to assume that the reaction goes to completion and then backs off very slightly. This, you may recognize, is just another way to represent the hydrolysis of the nitrite ion.

When the two 25 mL solutions are mixed, the volume increases to 50 mL. The initial concentrations of the acid and base can be written in the ICE table as 0.10 M × (25 mL/50 mL) = 0.050 M. The stoichiometry of the reaction indicates that one mole of salt is formed from one mole of acid (or base), so the concentration of the salt formed in the reaction is the same.

The ICE table is therefore (with concentrations in M):

$$HNO_2 + OH^- \rightleftharpoons H_2O + NO_2^-$$

	HNO$_2$	OH$^-$	H$_2$O	NO$_2^-$
Initial:	0.050	0.050	0	0

Assume the reaction goes to completion:

	0	0		0.050

Then adjusts by shifting slightly to the left:

Change:	+ x	+ x		− x
Equilibrium concentrations:	x	x		0.050 − x

The equilibrium concentrations are now substituted into the expression for the equilibrium constant K_{neut} and the value of x calculated.

$$K_{neut} = \frac{[NO_2^-]}{[HNO_2][OH^-]} = \frac{(0.050 - x)}{x^2} = 4.5 \times 10^{10}$$

In this case x is a very small number compared to 0.050, and the x in (0.050 – x) can be ignored. So,

$$x^2 = \frac{0.050}{4.5 \times 10^{10}}$$

$x = 1.05 \times 10^{-6}$ The value of x is indeed small compared to 0.050.

The x in these calculations is the hydroxide concentration.

$$[OH^-] = 1.05 \times 10^{-6}\,M$$

$$[H_3O^+] = 9.5 \times 10^{-9}\,M \text{ and the pH} = 8.02\text{—slightly basic as predicted.}$$

PROBLEM 44.1A

Calculate the pH at the equivalence point when 50 mL of 0.50 M hydrochloric acid reacts with 100 mL of 0.25 M diethylamine $(C_2H_5)_2NH$.

PROBLEM 44.1B

Calculate the pH at the equivalence point when 25 mL of 0.40 M formic acid reacts with 50 mL of 0.20 M potassium hydroxide.

44.3   Titration Curves and Distribution Diagrams

The pH of the solution during an acid-base titration can be measured or calculated at any point during the titration. If the pH of the solution is plotted against the amount of acid or base added, then a **titration curve** is obtained. The shape of the titration curve depends upon the strengths of the acid and base used. We'll examine three cases: a strong acid–strong base titration, a weak acid–strong base titration, and a strong acid–weak base titration.

A Strong Acid–Strong Base Titration

Figure 44.1 illustrates the titration of a strong acid such as 0.10 M HCl *vs.* a strong base such as 0.10 M NaOH. We can divide the titration curve into various sections:

- At the beginning (0 mL NaOH) the solution contains only the acid HCl; no base has been added. At this point the pH depends only upon the concentration of the hydrochloric acid.

- As the sodium hydroxide (a base) is added, the base neutralizes the acid and the salt sodium chloride is formed. In this region the solution contains a mixture of the acid HCl and the salt NaCl.

- At the equivalence point, the number of moles of sodium hydroxide added equals the number of moles of hydrochloric acid originally present. The solution contains only sodium chloride and is neutral.

- After the equivalence point, the sodium hydroxide is in excess of the acid HCl. The solution contains the sodium chloride salt and becomes more basic as increasing amounts of excess sodium hydroxide base are added.

The initial change in pH as the base is added is relatively small but as the equivalence point is reached the slope of the curve increases. At the equivalence point the

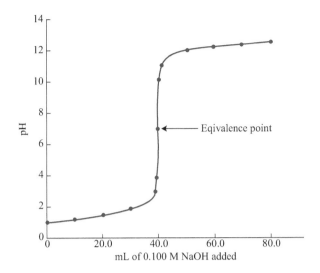

FIGURE 44.1   A strong acid–strong base titration curve.
In this titration 0.10 *M* HCl is titrated against 0.10 *M* NaOH.

curve is almost vertical. In practice, just one drop of the titrant from the buret will cause a change of several pH units across the equivalence point. It is this very sharp change in the pH across the equivalence point that makes a titration such an accurate analytical method. After the equivalence point the curve levels out and additional base has relatively little effect on the pH.

If the composition of the solution at any point during the titration is known, the pH can be calculated.

EXAMPLE 44.2   CALCULATION OF THE pH DURING A STRONG ACID–STRONG BASE TITRATION

A 0.100 M solution of sodium hydroxide is titrated against 50 mL of 0.100 M hydrochloric acid. Calculate the pH of the solution

  a. at the beginning of the titration

  b. after 20 mL of the sodium hydroxide solution has been added

  c. after 45 mL of the sodium hydroxide solution has been added

  d. after 55 mL of the sodium hydroxide solution has been added (more than enough)

UNDERSTAND THE QUESTION

Assume that the strong acid is completely ionized in solution. The 0.100 *M* hydrochloric acid solution therefore contains 0.100 *M* $[H_3O^+]$. Similarly the 0.100 *M* sodium hydroxide solution contains 0.100 *M* $[OH^-]$. As the base is added to the acid, the hydronium ions and hydroxide ions react to form water—a neutralization reaction that is virtually complete ($K_{neut} = 1.0 \times 10^{14}$). Up to the equivalence point, the number of moles of hydronium ions in the solution equals the initial number minus the number of moles of hydroxide ion added. It is advisable to work in moles because this makes it easier to calculate the effect of diluting the solution as the solution of base is added. After the equivalence point, the excess hydroxide ion added is responsible for the increase in the pH.

PLAN THE SOLUTION

Calculate the number of moles of hydronium ion in the solution at any point up to the equivalence point. Divide this by the volume of the solution to obtain the concentration (M) of hydronium ions and then calculate the pH. After the equivalence point determine the excess hydroxide present in the solution and use this to determine the pH.

SOLVE THE PROBLEM

a. at the beginning of the titration:

$$[H_3O^+] = 0.100 \ M; pH = 1.00$$

b. after 20 mL of the sodium hydroxide solution has been added:

Initial number of moles of HCl = 50 mL × 0.100 M × (1 L/1000 mL) = 5.0×10^{-3} moles

Number of moles of NaOH added = 20 mL × 0.100 M × (1 L/1000 mL) = 2.0×10^{-3} moles

Number of moles of HCl remaining = 5.0×10^{-3} moles − 2.0×10^{-3} moles = 3.0×10^{-3} moles

Volume of solution = 50 mL + 20 mL = 70 mL = 0.070 L

$[H_3O^+] = 3.0 \times 10^{-3}$ moles/0.070 L = $4.29 \times 10^{-2} M$; pH = 1.37

> All the pH values in these calculations have been rounded to 2 decimal places.

c. after 45 mL of the sodium hydroxide solution has been added:

Initial number of moles of HCl = 50 mL × 0.100 M × (1 L/1000 mL) = 5.0×10^{-3} moles

Number of moles of NaOH added = 45 mL × 0.100 M × (1 L/1000 mL) = 4.5×10^{-3} moles

Number of moles of HCl remaining = 5.0×10^{-3} moles − 4.5×10^{-3} moles = 5.0×10^{-4} moles

Volume of solution = 50 mL + 45 mL = 95 mL = 0.095 L

$[H_3O^+] = 5.0 \times 10^{-4}$ moles/0.095 L = $5.26 \times 10^{-3} M$; pH = 2.28

d. after 55 mL of the sodium hydroxide solution has been added (more than enough):

50 mL of the NaOH is required to neutralize all the acid

5 mL NaOH remains in excess

Number of moles of NaOH in excess = 5 mL × 0.100 M × (1 L/1000 mL) = 5.0×10^{-4} moles

Volume of solution = 50 mL + 55 mL = 105 mL = 0.105 L

$[OH^-] = 5.0 \times 10^{-4}$ moles/0.105 L = $4.76 \times 10^{-3} M$; pOH = 2.32; pH = 11.68

Note the large increase in the pH, from 2.28 to 11.68, over the equivalence point.

PROBLEM 44.2A

For the same titration described in Example 44.2, calculate the pH of the solution

a. after 49.0 mL of the NaOH solution has been added

b. after 51.0 mL of the NaOH solution has been added

Comment on the results.

PROBLEM 44.2B

For the same titration described in Example 44.2, calculate the pH of the solution

a. when half the acid has been neutralized

b. at the equivalence point

c. when 100 mL of the NaOH solution has been added

A Weak Acid–Strong Base Titration

A pH titration curve for the titration of a weak acid *vs.* a strong base is similar to the strong acid–strong base curve. The difference is in the initial pH of the curve and the pH at the equivalence point, both of which are higher for the weak acid titration. A series of titration curves for weak acids of varying strengths is illustrated in Figure 44.2. The strong acid–strong base curve is included for comparison. As the pK_a of the weak acid increases (the acid is weaker), the equivalence point becomes more difficult to detect. This is because the change in pH across the equivalence point decreases as the acid strength decreases.

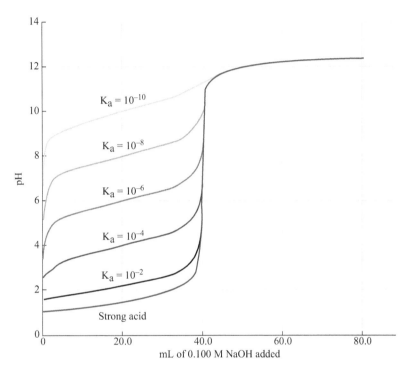

FIGURE 44.2   The change in a titration curve as the acid decreases in strength.
The titration curve for an acid with $K_a = 1.0 \times 10^{-2}$ is very similar to a strong acid–strong base titration. If the K_a for the acid is as low as 1.0×10^{-10}, the endpoint becomes impossible to detect accurately.

Like the strong acid–strong base curve, we can divide a weak acid–strong base curve into various sections. An example is the titration of 0.10 M acetic acid *vs.* 0.10 M sodium hydroxide:

- Initially, the solution contains only the weak acid CH_3CO_2H. No base has been added. At this point the pH depends only upon the concentration of the acetic acid. The calculation of the pH is the same calculation we discussed in Unit 39 (*cf.* Example 39.3). The K_a for acetic acid is 1.8×10^{-5}.

- As the sodium hydroxide base is added, the salt sodium acetate is formed. In this region the solution contains a mixture of acetic acid and sodium acetate. A significant point is reached when the concentration of the acid is equal to the concentration of the salt halfway to the equivalence point. We will calculate the pH at this point.

- At the equivalence point the number of moles of sodium hydroxide added equals the number of moles of acetic acid originally present. The solution contains the salt sodium acetate. As we have already noted, the pH at the equivalence point is greater than 7.

- After the equivalence point, the sodium hydroxide is in excess of the acid. The solution contains the sodium acetate salt and increasing amounts of excess base. This part of the curve is the same as for the strong acid– strong base titration curve.

EXAMPLE 44.3 CALCULATION OF THE pH DURING A WEAK ACID–STRONG BASE TITRATION

For a titration of 50 mL 0.050 M acetic acid $vs.$ 0.050 M sodium hydroxide, calculate the pH of the solution

a. at the beginning of the titration

b. midway between the initial solution and the equivalence point

c. after 49 mL of the sodium hydroxide solution has been added

d. at the equivalence point

e. after 51 mL of the sodium hydroxide solution has been added

UNDERSTAND THE QUESTION

These calculations differ from those for the strong acid–strong base calculations because the acid is *not* completely ionized in solution. However, as the base is added to the acid, the hydronium ions and hydroxide ions react to form water and more acetic acid ionizes until it is all used up. The neutralization reaction is virtually complete ($K_{neut} = K_a/K_w = 1.8 \times 10^{-5}/1.0 \times 10^{-14} = 1.8 \times 10^9$).

PLAN THE SOLUTION

We can calculate the initial pH using the same procedure described in Example 39.3.

Up to the equivalence point, there are both acetic acid molecules and acetate ions present in solution. We can calculate the amount of acetate ions from the stoichiometry of the reaction between the acetic acid and the added NaOH. We can then determine the pH of the solution using the equilibrium constant expression for acetic acid as we have done before or we could use the Henderson-Hasselbalch equation. Again, the initial calculations should be done in moles because this makes it easier to account for the dilution of the solution as the base is added.

At the equivalence point all the acid has been neutralized; only the salt sodium acetate is present. Calculation of the pH at the equivalence point is a hydrolysis problem like that described in Example 41.3.

SOLVE THE PROBLEM

a. at the beginning of the titration:

The ionization of acetic acid is represented by the equation:

$$CH_3CO_2H + H_2O \rightleftharpoons H_3O^+ + CH_3CO_2^-$$

The equilibrium constant $K_a = \dfrac{[H_3O^+][CH_3CO_2^-]}{[CH_3CO_2H]}$

The ICE table is (with concentrations in M):

$$CH_3CO_2H + H_2O \rightleftharpoons H_3O^+ + CH_3CO_2^-$$

Initial:	0.050	0	0
Change:	$-x$	$+x$	$+x$
Equilibrium concentrations:	$0.050 - x$	x	x

The equilibrium concentrations are now substituted into the expression for the equilibrium constant K_a and the value of x calculated.

$$K_a = \frac{[H_3O^+][CH_3CO_2^-]}{[CH_3CO_2H]} = \frac{x^2}{(0.050 - x)}$$

x is a small number compared to 0.050, so

$$K_a = 1.8 \times 10^{-5} = \frac{x^2}{0.050} \text{ and } x = 9.5 \times 10^{-4}$$

x represents the concentrations of hydronium ion and acetate ion:

$$[H_3O^+] = 9.5 \times 10^{-4} \, M$$
$$pH = -\log_{10}[H_3O^+] = -\log_{10}(9.5 \times 10^{-4}) = 3.02$$

b. midway between the initial solution and the equivalence point:

At the point midway between the initial solution and the equivalence point, half the acetic acid remains, and half the sodium acetate has been formed. The concentration of the acetic acid remaining equals the concentration of the sodium acetate that has been formed.

The equilibrium in solution is again represented by the equation:

$$CH_3CO_2H + H_2O \rightleftharpoons H_3O^+ + CH_3CO_2^-$$

The equilibrium constant $K_a = \dfrac{[H_3O^+][CH_3CO_2^-]}{[CH_3CO_2H]}$

In this case the two concentrations $[CH_3CO_2^-]$ and $[CH_3CO_2H]$ are equal and $K_a = [H_3O^+]$.

Or, the $pH = pK_a = -\log_{10}(K_a) = -\log_{10}(1.8 \times 10^{-5}) = 4.74$

c. after 49 mL of the sodium hydroxide solution has been added:

Initial number of moles of $CH_3CO_2H = 50 \text{ mL} \times 0.050 \, M \times (1 \text{ L}/1000 \text{ mL}) = 2.5 \times 10^{-3}$ moles

Number of moles of NaOH added $= 49 \text{ mL} \times 0.050 \, M \times (1 \text{ L}/1000 \text{ mL}) = 2.45 \times 10^{-3}$ moles

Number of moles of CH_3CO_2H remaining $= 2.5 \times 10^{-3}$ moles $- 2.45 \times 10^{-3}$ moles $= 5.0 \times 10^{-5}$ moles

Number of moles of $CH_3CO_2^-$ produced $= 2.45 \times 10^{-3}$ moles

Volume of solution $= 50 \text{ mL} + 49 \text{ mL} = 99 \text{ mL} = 0.099 \text{ L}$

$$[CH_3CO_2H] = 5.0 \times 10^{-5} \text{ moles}/0.099 \text{ L} = 4.95 \times 10^{-4} \, M$$
$$[CH_3CO_2^-] = 2.45 \times 10^{-3} \text{ moles}/0.099 \text{ L} = 2.43 \times 10^{-2} \, M$$

These concentrations can now be substituted in the equilibrium constant expression:

The equilibrium constant $K_a = \dfrac{[H_3O^+][CH_3CO_2^-]}{[CH_3CO_2H]} = \dfrac{[H_3O^+](2.43 \times 10^{-2})}{(4.95 \times 10^{-4})} = 1.8 \times 10^{-5}$

$[H_3O^+] = 3.7 \times 10^{-7}\ M;\ pH = 6.44$

It is easier to use the Henderson–Hasselbalch equation:

If 49 mL NaOH has been added, 49/50 of the CH_3CO_2H has been neutralized and 1/50 remains. The ratio of $[CH_3CO_2^-]$ to $[CH_3CO_2H]$ is 49/1 regardless of any dilution.

Therefore, pH $= pK_a + \log_{10}(49/1)$

$= 4.74 + 1.69$

$= 6.43$

d. at the equivalence point

Number of moles of $CH_3CO_2^-$ produced = number of moles of acid originally present or the number of moles of base added = 2.5×10^{-3} moles

Volume of solution = 50 mL + 50 mL = 100 mL = 0.100 L

$[CH_3CO_2^-] = 2.5 \times 10^{-3}$ moles/0.100 L = $2.5 \times 10^{-2}\ M$

The acetate ion hydrolyses to produce a slightly basic solution:

$$CH_3CO_2^- + H_2O \rightleftharpoons CH_3CO_2H + OH^-$$

The ionization constant is $K_b = \dfrac{[CH_3CO_2H][OH^-]}{[CH_3CO_2^-]}$

K_a for $CH_3CO_2H = 1.8 \times 10^{-5}$

K_b for $CH_3CO_2^- = K_w/K_a = 1.0 \times 10^{-14}/1.8 \times 10^{-5} = 5.6 \times 10^{-10}$

The ICE table is (with concentrations in M):

	$CH_3CO_2^- + H_2O \rightleftharpoons$	$CH_3CO_2H +$	OH^-
Initial:	2.5×10^{-2}	0	0
Change:	$- x$	$+ x$	$+ x$
Equilibrium concentrations:	$2.5 \times 10^{-2} - x$	x	x

The equilibrium concentrations are now substituted into the expression for the equilibrium constant K_b and the value of x calculated.

$$K_b = \frac{[CH_3CO_2H][OH^-]}{[CH_3CO_2^-]} = \frac{x^2}{(2.5 \times 10^{-2} - x)} = 5.6 \times 10^{-10}$$

The initial concentration ($2.5 \times 10^{-2}\ M$) exceeds the value of $100 \times K_b$ ($= 5.6 \times 10^{-8}$), and the x in the denominator can be ignored.

$$x = 3.73 \times 10^{-6}$$

The x in these calculations is the hydroxide concentration:

$$[OH-] = 3.73 \times 10^{-6}\ M;\ pOH = 5.43 \text{ and the } pH = 8.57$$

e. after 51 mL of the sodium hydroxide solution has been added

50 mL of the NaOH is required to neutralize all the acid

1 mL NaOH remains in excess

Number of moles of NaOH in excess = 1 mL $\times$ 0.050 M $\times$ (1 L/1000 mL) = 5.0×10^{-5} moles

Volume of solution = 50 mL + 51 mL = 101 mL = 0.101 L

$[OH^-] = 5.0 \times 10^{-5}$ moles/0.101 L = $4.95 \times 10^{-4}\ M$; pOH = 3.31; pH = 10.69

Notice that the pH at 49 mL of NaOH is 6.44 and that the pH at 51mL of NaOH is 10.69. The average of the two is 8.57—the pH at the equivalence point.

PROBLEM 44.3A

For a titration of 50 mL 0.100 *M* nitrous acid *vs.* 0.100 *M* sodium hydroxide, calculate the pH of the solution after 45 mL of the sodium hydroxide has been added to the acid.

PROBLEM 44.3B

For a titration of 50 mL 0.075 *M* hydrocyanic acid *vs.* 0.075 *M* sodium hydroxide, calculate the pH of the solution after exactly 25 mL of the sodium hydroxide has been added to the acid.

The series of calculations illustrated in Example 44.3 include the ionization of a weak acid, the calculation of the pH of a solution of a weak acid and its conjugate base, and the hydrolysis of a salt in solution. The key to all these problems is to identify the species present in solution and then to determine what, if anything, happens to these species. Questions to ask are: Is the solute a weak or strong electrolyte? Is the solute an acid or a base? Does the solute ionize or hydrolyse in solution? Always write an equation representing any reaction in solution and derive from this equation an expression for the equilibrium constant. If necessary, set up an ICE table and then solve for the $[H_3O^+]$ or $[OH^-]$.

The composition of the solution during the titration can be illustrated by a **distribution diagram**. An example is shown in Figure 44.3 correlated with the titration curve for the titration just described in Example 44.3. The composition of the solution is shown from 1 mL to 49 mL of added base. The titration begins (Point A) with a high concentration of the acid and zero concentration of the salt (the conjugate base of the acid). As the titration proceeds (between Points A and B), the concentration of the acid diminishes and the concentration of the salt increases. The lines cross (Point B) where the two concentrations are equal. At this point, the pH = pK_a. Note that the vertical axis on the distribution diagram is a fractional composition, where a value of 1 indicates that the species is the only species present. The horizontal axis is the pH of the solution. The ratio ([base]/[acid]) at any pH can be calculated using the Henderson-Hasselbalch equation.

A Strong Acid–Weak Base Titration

Figure 44.4 illustrates the pH titration curve for the titration of a 0.100 *M* ammonia solution *vs.* a 0.100 *M* hydrochloric acid solution. The titration curve is an inverted image of that for the weak acid–strong base titration. The pH decreases as the hydrochloric acid is added to the ammonia and the equivalence point occurs at a pH less than 7. Just as we did for the previous titration curves, we can divide this curve into various sections:

- The solution initially (no HCl added) contains only the weak base ammonia NH_3. The pH depends only upon the concentration of the ammonia. The calculation of the pH is the same calculation discussed in Unit 39 (*cf.* Example 39.4).

- As the hydrochloric acid is added, the salt ammonium chloride is formed. In this region the solution contains a mixture of ammonia and its conjugate acid, the ammonium ion.

- At the equivalence point the number of moles of hydrochloric acid added equals the number of moles of ammonia originally present. The solution contains the

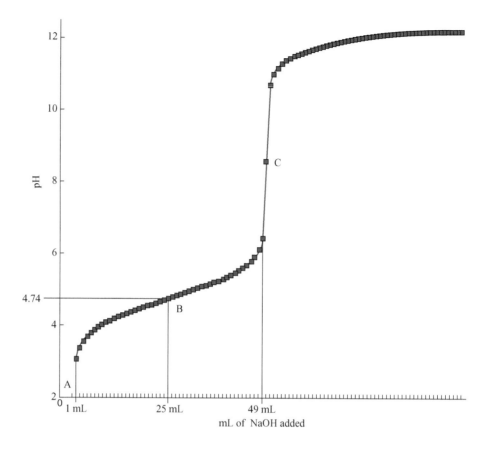

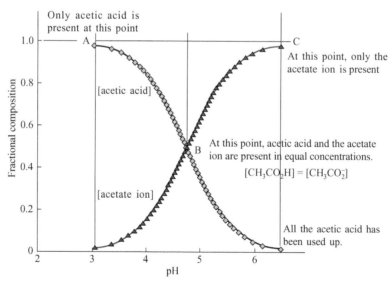

FIGURE 44.3 **The correlation of a distribution diagram with the titration curve (from 1 mL to 49 mL) for an acetic acid–sodium hydroxide titration.**

At point A, before any NaOH has been added, only acetic acid is present in solution.

At point B, one-half of the acetic acid has been neutralized and one-half of the acetate ions have been formed. The two concentrations are equal and the pH = 4.74.

At point C, the equivalence point, all the acetic acid has been neutralized. Additional sodium hydroxide increases the pH of the solution.

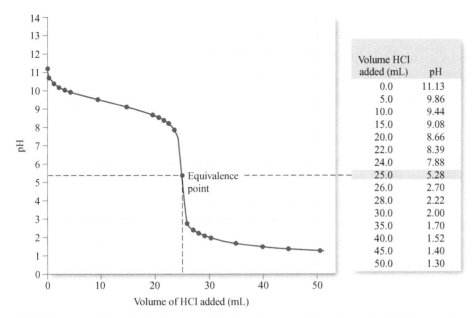

Volume HCl added (mL)	pH
0.0	11.13
5.0	9.86
10.0	9.44
15.0	9.08
20.0	8.66
22.0	8.39
24.0	7.88
25.0	5.28
26.0	2.70
28.0	2.22
30.0	2.00
35.0	1.70
40.0	1.52
45.0	1.40
50.0	1.30

FIGURE 44.4   **The pH titration curve for the titration of 25 mL of a 0.100 *M* ammonia solution *vs.* a 0.100 *M* hydrochloric acid solution.**
The titration curve is an inverted image of that for the weak acid–strong base titration shown in Figure 44.3. The equivalence point occurs at a pH below 7.

salt ammonium chloride. Hydrolysis of the ammonium ion yields a slightly acidic solution at the equivalence point.

• After the equivalence point, the hydrochloric acid is in excess of the base. The solution becomes more acidic as the excess hydrochloric acid increases.

We do not need to repeat all the calculations for this titration. They are analogous to those done for the weak acid–strong base titration. The following example is a calculation of the pH in the intermediate region before the equivalence point is reached. We will use the Henderson–Hasselbalch equation.

EXAMPLE 44.4   CALCULATION OF THE pH DURING A STRONG ACID–WEAK BASE TITRATION

For a titration of 50 mL 0.100 *M* ammonia *vs.* 0.100 *M* hydrochloric acid, calculate the pH of the solution after 48 mL of the acid has been added. If the pH at the equivalence point is 5.28, estimate the pH of the solution after 52 mL of the acid has been added.

UNDERSTAND THE QUESTION

In the region before the equivalence point is reached, there are both ammonia molecules and ammonium ions present in the solution. We can calculate the amount of ammonium ions from the stoichiometry of the reaction between the acid and the base. We can then determine the pH of the solution using the Henderson–Hasselbalch equation.

Titration curves in the region of the equivalence point tend to be quite symmetrical. The closer the values of the pK_a and the pK_b, the more symmetrical the curve is. As we saw for the weak acid–strong base titration, the pH at the equivalence point was the average of the pH at 49 mL of base and the pH at 51 mL of base. If the pH at the equivalence point is known, and we have calculated the pH at 48 mL of acid, then a reasonable estimate of the pH equidistant on the other side of the equivalence point can be made.

PLAN THE SOLUTION

We will use the Henderson–Hasselbalch equation.

SOLVE THE PROBLEM

The ionization of ammonia is represented by the equation:

$$NH_3 + H_2O \rightleftharpoons NH_4^+ + OH^-$$

If 48 mL HCl has been added, 48/50 of the ammonia has been neutralized and 2/50 remains. The ratio of $[NH_3]$ to $[NH_4^+]$ is 2/48 regardless of any dilution that occurs in the process.

This concentration ratio can now be substituted in the Henderson–Hasselbalch equation:

$$pH = pK_a + \log_{10}\left(\frac{[\text{base}]}{[\text{acid}]}\right) = 9.26 + \log_{10}(2/48) = 7.88$$

If the pH at the equivalence point is 5.28, we might anticipate that the pH after 52 mL of acid has been added would be approximately 2.68. (The actual pH is 2.71.)

PROBLEM 44.4A

Calculate the pH of the solution for the titration described in Example 44.4 after 40 mL of the HCl solution has been added.

PROBLEM 44.4B

Calculate the pH of the solution for the titration described in Example 44.4 after 60 mL of the HCl solution has been added.

44.4 Buffers and Titration Curves

We have seen that on the titration curve for a weak acid–strong base titration, at the point midway between the initial acid and the equivalence point, the concentration of acid equals the concentration of the salt. In other words, half the acid has been neutralized and half the salt has been formed. The pH at this point equals the pK_a (*cf.* Example 44.3(b)).

You may have recognized that the solution at this point in the titration is an ideal buffer solution—a solution of a weak acid and its conjugate base in which the two concentrations are equal. The effect of adding an acid or a base to this buffer solution can be seen on the titration curve (Figure 44.5).

Addition of a base moves the solution along the titration curve to the right, using up acid and forming more salt. Addition of an acid moves the solution along the titration curve to the left, reacting with the conjugate base and forming more acid. The slope of the titration curve in this region is low; the line is almost horizontal. Movement to the left or to the right causes little change in the pH of the solution.

If the buffer solution is poorly balanced, so that the ratio of acid to conjugate base exceeds 10:1 or is less than 1:10, then the solution is too near to one end of the horizontal region of the titration curve. In this case the buffer capacity in one direction is severely limited.

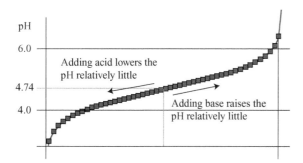

FIGURE 44.5   Addition of an acid or base to an acetic acid–acetate ion buffer solution illustrated on a titration curve.
Addition of a base moves the solution along the titration curve to the right, using up acid and forming more salt. Addition of an acid moves the solution along the titration curve to the left, reacting with the conjugate base and forming more acid. The slope of the titration curve in this region is low and movement to the left or to the right causes little change in the pH of the solution.

44.5   Indicators

An acid-base indicator changes color at the endpoint of a titration. As we learned in Unit 9, an indicator is a substance that has different colors in acidic and basic solutions. An indicator is often a weak acid that exists in a molecular form (acid) or an ionized form (conjugate base). The colors of the two forms are different. Removal of a hydrogen ion from the molecular form therefore changes the color of the indicator. The structures of the indicator phenolphthalein were illustrated earlier in Figure 10.5.

If an indicator is a very weak acid compared to the acid involved in the titration, the hydrogen ion of the indicator is not removed by the base until all the acid involved in the titration has been neutralized. In other words, the indicator does not change color until all the acid in the titration has been neutralized. However, most indicators have K_a values in the region of 1×10^{-4} to 1×10^{-8} and the relative concentrations of the two forms of the indicator in solution at any pH can be calculated using the Henderson-Hasselbalch equation. This is exactly the same calculation described in Example 43.5.

Phenolphthalein is colorless in its acidic form and red in its deprotonated form. The pK_a for phenolphthalein is 8.8 ($K_a = 1.6 \times 10^{-9}$). What is the predominant form of phenolphthalein in solution at a pH of 7? Using the Henderson-Hasselbalch equation:

$$pH = pK_a + \log_{10}\left(\frac{[base]}{[acid]}\right)$$

$$7.0 = 8.8 + \log_{10}\left(\frac{[red]}{[colorless]}\right)$$

$$\log_{10}\left(\frac{[red]}{[colorless]}\right) = 7.0 - 8.8 = -1.8$$

$$\left(\frac{[red]}{[colorless]}\right) = \frac{1}{63}$$

The predominant form in the solution at a pH of 7.0 is the colorless molecular form and the red conjugate form is probably too faint to be detected by eye. Usually about one tenth of the indicator must change color before the change is detectable by the human eye. This means that indicators have an observable color change over about 2 pH units, from $pK_{ind}-1$ to $pK_{ind}+1$.

The idea is to choose an indicator that changes color at an appropriate pH. In other words, the endpoint should coincide with the equivalence point. For a strong acid–strong base titration, almost any indicator will do because the change in pH at the equivalence point to so great. It is logical however, to choose an indicator with a pK_a of approximately 7 although phenolphthalein is often used because the color change is easy to detect visually. For a weak acid–strong base titration, phenolphthalein is ideal. For a strong acid–weak base titration, phenolphthalein is not a good indicator—the endpoint is far from the equivalence point (Figure 44.6). Methyl orange, methyl red, or thymol blue are often used.

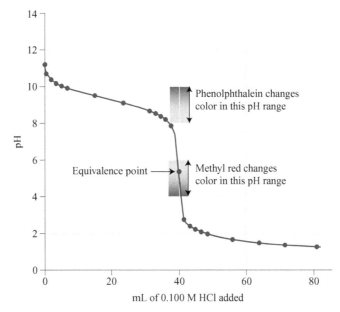

FIGURE 44.6 The unsuitability of phenolphthalein as an indicator for a strong acid–weak base titration.
The end point should coincide as nearly as possible with the equivalence point.

44.6   Titrations of Polyprotic Acids

Polyprotic acids have more than one hydrogen atom that can be detached as a hydrogen ion. There are relatively few triprotic acids—phosphoric acid H_3PO_4 is an example. Most are diprotic. As we have seen, if the difference between pK_{a1} and pK_{a2} is sufficiently large, all the first ionizable hydrogen atoms are lost before any of the second hydrogen atoms are removed. This makes the calculation of the pH at any stage during the titration relatively straightforward.

Interesting examples of diprotic species are the **amino acids**. These are the molecules that link to form proteins and are literally the building blocks of life. There are twenty amino acids found in nature, all of which are essential to support life. We will examine these amino acids further in Unit 66. An amino acid contains an amino $-NH_2$ group (which is basic) and a carboxylic acid $-CO_2H$ group (which is acidic). Two amino acids are illustrated in Figure 44.7. One is the simplest

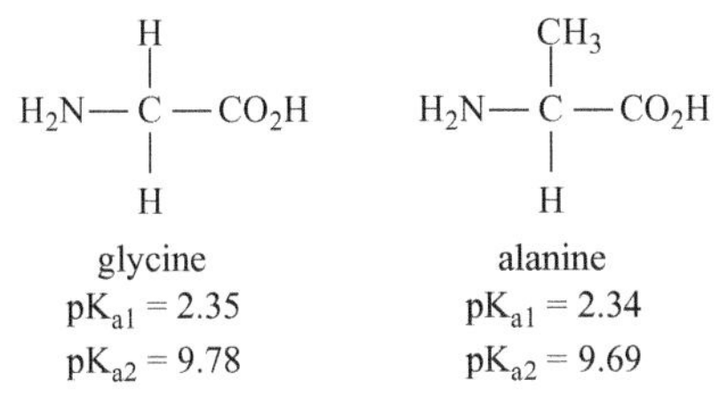

$$H_2N-\underset{\underset{H}{|}}{\overset{\overset{H}{|}}{C}}-CO_2H \qquad H_2N-\underset{\underset{H}{|}}{\overset{\overset{CH_3}{|}}{C}}-CO_2H$$

glycine

$pK_{a1} = 2.35$

$pK_{a2} = 9.78$

alanine

$pK_{a1} = 2.34$

$pK_{a2} = 9.69$

FIGURE 44.7 The two amino acids glycine and alanine.

amino acid, glycine, and the second is a close relative, alanine. Their pK_a values are listed—notice that the pK_a values of the two differ very little.

When base is added to the protonated form, the most acidic hydrogen ion is removed first. This is the carboxylic acid hydrogen ion, not the hydrogen ion attached to the amino group. This means that the intermediate species in solution is a doubly charged ion with a positive $-NH_3^+$ group on one end of the molecule and a negative CO_2^- group at the other end. Such an ion is called a **zwitterion** (Figure 44.8).

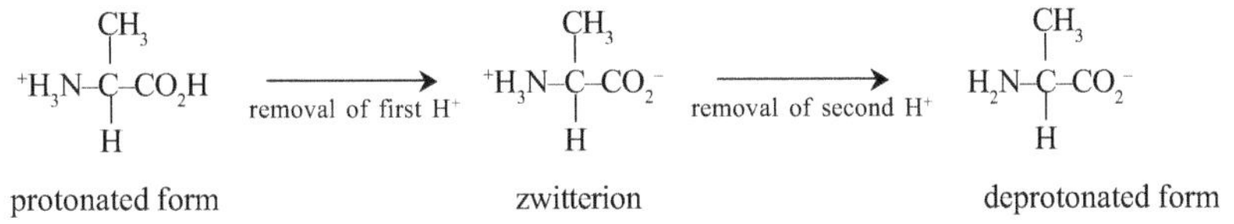

$$^+H_3N-\underset{\underset{H}{|}}{\overset{\overset{CH_3}{|}}{C}}-CO_2H \xrightarrow[\text{removal of first } H^+]{} {}^+H_3N-\underset{\underset{H}{|}}{\overset{\overset{CH_3}{|}}{C}}-CO_2^- \xrightarrow[\text{removal of second } H^+]{} H_2N-\underset{\underset{H}{|}}{\overset{\overset{CH_3}{|}}{C}}-CO_2^-$$

protonated form zwitterion deprotonated form

FIGURE 44.8 The protonated and deprotonated forms of alanine.

The titration curve for the titration of the protonated form of alanine *vs.* sodium hydroxide is is illustrated in Figure 44.9. We now know enough about aqueous equilibria to calculate the pH at any point along this titration curve:

At the beginning of the titration, before any base has been added, the calculation involves the ionization of a weak acid. This was described in Examples 39.3 and 44.3.

Along the curve to the first equivalence point, the calculation involves a mixture of a weak acid and its conjugate base, most easily solved using the Henderson-Hasselbalch equation. This was illustrated in Examples 39.4 and 44.4.

At the point exactly halfway to the first equivalence point, the pH = pK_{a1}. This is the pH of a buffer solution with an ideal buffer capacity.

At the first equivalence point, the species present is amphiprotic. In this case it is the zwitterion illustrated in Figure 44.8. The pH at this point is the average of the pK_{a1} and pK_{a2} for the amino acid. The pH = $\frac{1}{2}(pK_{a1} + pK_{a2})$. An example of this calculation was illustrated in Example 42.4. In biochemistry, this first equivalence point, where the predominant species present in solution is the amino acid as the zwitterion, and the small concentrations of the protonated and deprotonated forms are equal, is called the **isoelectric point**. Notice the symmetry of the titration curve about the first equivalence point, from the point at which the pH = pK_{a1} and the point at which the pH = pK_{a2}. It's not surprising that the pH at the equivalence point is the average of pK_{a1} and pK_{a2}.

Along the curve between the first and second equivalence points, the calculation again involves a mixture of a weak acid and its conjugate base. In this case the second ionization is the relevant process and the problem is again most easily solved using the Henderson-Hasselbalch equation.

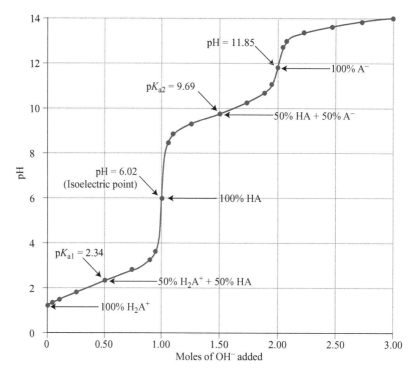

FIGURE 44.9 Titration of the diprotic protonated amino acid alanine **vs.** sodium hydroxide.

At the point exactly halfway between the first and second equivalence points, the pH = pK_{a2}. In the solution at this point there are equal concentrations of the zwitterion and the deprotonated form.

At the second equivalence point, the predominant species present is the deprotonated amino acid. The calculation of the pH is a hydrolysis problem. This calculation was described in Example 44.3.

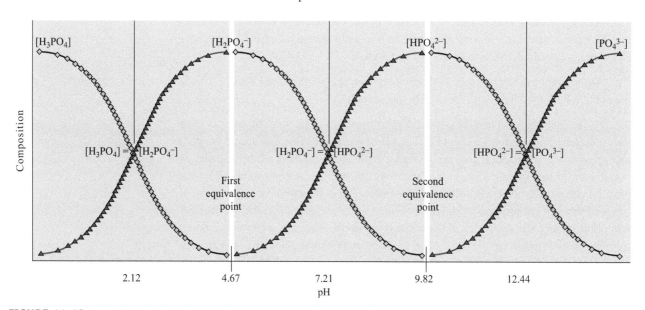

FIGURE 44.10   The distribution diagram for phosphoric acid—a triprotic acid.
The composition of the solution at various pHs is noted on the distribution diagram. The ratio of the two conjugate partners ([base]/[acid]) present at any pH can be calculated using the Henderson-Hasselbalch equation.

Beyond the second equivalence point, no acid remains in solution and any added sodium hydroxide is in excess. The pH of the solution depends upon the excess sodium hydroxide. This calculation was illustrated in Example 44.3.

Distribution diagrams are useful when examining the titration of a polyprotic acid or when deciding what the predominant species in the solution are at a particular pH. If the difference between successive ionization constants is sufficiently large—and often they are—there are only two species present in the solution in appreciable amounts at any one time. The distribution diagram for phosphoric acid illustrates this (Figure 44.10).

EXAMPLE 44.5 DETERMINATION OF THE COMPOSITION OF A SOLUTION AT A PARTICULAR pH

For a solution of carbonic acid H_2CO_3, sketch the distribution diagram and determine the predominant species in solution at a pH of 10.0. Calculate the composition of the solution at this pH.

UNDERSTAND THE QUESTION

A distribution diagram is an illustration of how the composition of an aqueous solution of a weak electrolyte varies as the pH of the solution changes. Such a diagram can be roughly sketched from the values of K_{a1} and K_{a2} for a diprotic acid such as H_2CO_3. The relative concentrations of the one or two predominant species present can be calculated using the Henderson-Hasselbalch equation.

PLAN THE SOLUTION

Look up the values of K_{a1} and K_{a2} for H_2CO_3 and sketch the distribution diagram. Determine the predominant species present. Use the Henderson-Hasselbalch equation to calculate the ratio of ([base]/[acid]).

SOLVE THE PROBLEM

$$H_2CO_3 + H_2O \rightleftharpoons HCO_3^- + H_3O^+ \qquad K_{a1} = 4.3 \times 10^{-7} \qquad pK_{a1} = 6.37$$
$$HCO_3^- + H_2O \rightleftharpoons CO_3^{2-} + H_3O^+ \qquad K_{a2} = 5.6 \times 10^{-11} \qquad pK_{a2} = 10.25$$

The approximate shape of the distribution curve is:

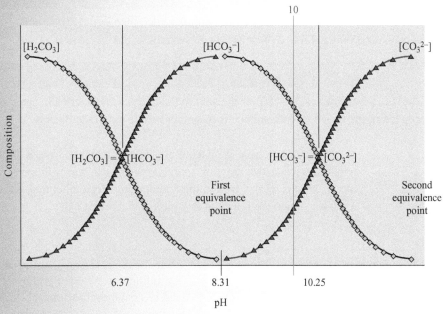

The principal component present at a pH of 10.0 is the hydrogen carbonate ion. The only other species present in significant amount is the carbonate ion. The ratio of [hydrogen carbonate] to [carbonate] can be calculated using the Henderson-Hasselbalch equation as we have done before:

$$pH = pK_{a2} + \log_{10}\left(\frac{[\text{base}]}{[\text{acid}]}\right)$$

$$10.0 = 10.25 + \log_{10}\left(\frac{[\text{base}]}{[\text{acid}]}\right)$$

$$\log_{10}\left(\frac{[\text{base}]}{[\text{acid}]}\right) = -0.25$$

$$[CO_3^{2-}]/[HCO_3^-] = 0.56$$

Expressed as fractions of the total,

the fraction of CO_3^{2-} is $0.56/1.56 = 0.36$ or 36%

the fraction of HCO_3^- is $1.0/1.56 = 0.64$ or 64%

There will a very small amount of H_2CO_3 present. If necessary this can be calculated using the Henderson Hasselbalch equation again:

$$pH = pK_{a1} + \log_{10}\left(\frac{[\text{base}]}{[\text{acid}]}\right)$$

$$10.0 = 6.37 + \log_{10}\left(\frac{[\text{base}]}{[\text{acid}]}\right)$$

$$\log_{10}\left(\frac{[\text{base}]}{[\text{acid}]}\right) = 3.63$$

$$[HCO_3^-]/[H_2CO_3] = 4.3 \times 10^3$$

The fraction of the total present as H_2CO_3 is $0.64 \times (1/4.3 \times 10^3) = 1.5 \times 10^{-4}$ or 0.015% which is negigible compared to the HCO_3^- and CO_3^{2-}.

PROBLEM 44.5A

Repeat the calculations described in Example 44.5 for the solution of carbonic acid, H_2CO_3, at a pH of 6.0. Determine the fraction of the two most predominant forms of carbonate present at this pH.

PROBLEM 44.5B

Repeat the calculations described in Example 44.5 for the solution of carbonic acid, H_2CO_3, again but now at a pH of 8.0. Determine the fraction of the two most predominant forms of carbonate present at this pH.

We have one topic in aqueous equilibria remaining. This is the study of equilibria involving species that are only sparingly soluble in water. In many ways, the fact that one of the species involved in the equilibrium is insoluble makes the analysis of such equilibria easier. We'll look at this subject in the next unit.

Review Questions

1. Describe how the magnitude of the equilibrium constant for a neutralization reaction depends upon the strengths of the acid and base used in the neutralization.

2. Describe the common ion effect and how a common ion influences the equilibrium between a weak acid and its conjugate base in aqueous solution.

3. Explain what a buffer solution is and how such a solution resists a change in pH when a small amount of a strong acid or strong base is added.

4. What does buffer capacity mean? What happens if the buffer capacity is exceeded?

5. Describe what the Henderson-Hasselbalch equation is used for and why it is so useful. Use the equation to explain why the pH of a buffer solution is not affected by dilution.

Solutions to Problems

PROBLEM 44.1A

The volume at the equivalence point = 50 mL + 100 mL = 150 mL

Concentration of diethylammonium chloride at the equivalence point

$$= 0.50 \text{ M} \times (50 \text{ mL}/150 \text{ mL}) = 0.167 \text{ M}$$

The salt hydrolyzes to produce a slightly acidic solution:

$$(C_2H_5)_2NH_2^+ + H_2O \rightleftharpoons H_3O^+ + (C_2H_5)_2NH$$

The ionization constant is $K_a = \dfrac{[H_3O^+][(C_2H_5)_2NH]}{[(C_2H_5)_2NH_2^+]}$

K_b for $(C_2H_5)_2NH = 6.4 \times 10^{-4}$

K_a for $(C_2H_5)_2NH_2^+ = K_w/K_b = 1.0 \times 10^{-14}/6.4 \times 10^{-4} = 1.56 \times 10^{-11}$

Two concentrations $[H_3O^+]$ and $[(C_2H_5)_2NH]$ are equal.

The ICE table is (with concentrations in M):

	$(C_2H_5)_2NH_2^+ + H_2O \rightleftharpoons$	H_3O^+	$+ (C_2H_5)_2NH$
Initial:	0.167	0	0
Change:	$-x$	$+x$	$+x$
Equilibrium concentrations:	$0.167 - x$	x	x

The equilibrium concentrations are now substituted into the expression for the equilibrium constant K_b and the value of x calculated.

$$K_a = \frac{[H_3O^+][(C_2H_5)_2NH]}{[(C_2H_5)_2NH_2^+]} = \frac{x^2}{(0.167 - x)}$$

K_a is very small and the x in the denominator can be ignored.

$$K_a = 1.56 \times 10^{-11} = \frac{x^2}{0.167} \text{ and } x = 1.6 \times 10^{-6}$$

The x in these calculations is the hydronium ion concentration:

$$[H_3O^+] = 1.6 \times 10^{-6} \text{ } M$$

$$pH = -\log_{10}[H_3O^+] = -\log_{10}(1.6 \times 10^{-6}) = 5.79$$

Slightly acidic as expected.

PROBLEM 44.2A

a. after 49 mL of the sodium hydroxide solution has been added

Initial number of moles of HCl = 50 mL × 0.100 M × (1 L/1000 mL) = 5.0 × 10⁻³ moles

Number of moles of NaOH added = 49 mL × 0.100 M × (1 L/1000 mL) = 4.9 × 10⁻³ moles

Number of moles of HCl remaining = 5.0 × 10⁻³ moles − 4.9 × 10⁻³ moles = 1.0 × 10⁻⁴ moles

Volume of solution = 50 mL + 49 mL = 99 mL = 0.099 L

$[H_3O^+]$ = 1.0 × 10⁻⁴ moles / 0.099 L = 1.01 × 10⁻³ M; pH = 3.00

b. after 51 mL of the sodium hydroxide solution has been added (more than enough)

50 mL of the NaOH is required to neutralize all the acid

1 mL NaOH remains in excess

Number of moles of NaOH in excess = 1 mL × 0.100 M × (1 L/1000 mL) = 1.0 × 10⁻⁴ moles

Volume of solution = 50 mL + 51 mL = 101 mL = 0.101 L

$[OH^-]$ = 1.0 × 10⁻⁴ moles / 0.101 L = 9.9 × 10⁻⁴ M; pOH = 3.00; pH = 11.00

From 45 mL to 49 mL of base added, the pH changes from 2.28 to only 3.00. The next 2 mL of base results in a change from 3.00 to 11.00—a large increase in the pH over the equivalence point. Notice that the average of 3.00 (1 mL before the equivalence point) and 11.00 (1 mL after the equivalence point) is 7.00 (the pH at the equivalence point).

PROBLEM 44.3A

pK_a for nitrous acid = 3.35

If 45 mL NaOH has been added, then 45/50 of the HNO₂ has been neutralized and 5/50 remains. The ratio of $[NO_2^-]$ to $[HNO_2]$ is 45 to 5 or 9/1 regardless of any dilution.

This concentration ratio can be substituted in the Henderson-Hasselbalch equation:

$$pH = pK_a + \log_{10}\left(\frac{[base]}{[acid]}\right)$$

$$pH = 3.35 + \log_{10}([NO_2^-]/[HNO_2]) = 3.35 + \log_{10}(9)$$
$$= 4.30$$

PROBLEM 44.4A

If 40 mL HCl has been added, then 4/5 of the ammonia has been neutralized and 1/5 remains. The ratio of $[NH_3]$ to $[NH_4^+]$ is 1/4 regardless of any dilution.

This concentration ratios can be substituted in the Henderson–Hasselbalch equation:

$$pH = pK_a + \log_{10}\left(\frac{[base]}{[acid]}\right) = 9.26 + \log_{10}(1/4) = 8.66$$

PROBLEM 44.5A

Examination of the distribution diagram indicates that the two species present are H_2CO_3 and HCO_3^-. Of these two, the H_2CO_3 is predominant.

$$pH = pK_{a1} + \log_{10}\left(\frac{[base]}{[acid]}\right)$$

$$6.0 = 6.37 + \log_{10}\left(\frac{[base]}{[acid]}\right)$$

$$\log_{10}\left(\frac{[base]}{[acid]}\right) = -0.37$$

$$[HCO_3^-]/[H_2CO_3] = 0.43$$

Expressed as fractions of the total,

the fraction of HCO_3^- is 0.43/1.43 = 0.30 or 30%

the fraction of H_2CO_3 is 1.0/1.43 = 0.70 or 70%

Answers to Review Questions

1. The calculation of the pH of the solution at the equivalence point can be accomplished in two different ways. We can write the equation for the neutralization reaction, derive the expression for the equilibrium constant K_{neut}, set up an ICE table, and solve to obtain the hydroxide ion concentration.

$$HNO_2 + OH^- \rightleftharpoons H_2O - NO_2^-$$

$$K_{neut} = \frac{[NO_2^-]}{[HNO_2][OH^-]}$$

Or the equation for the hydrolysis of the salt in the solution at the equivalence point can be written, the expression for K_b derived, and solved to obtain the hydroxide ion concentration.

$$NO_2^- + H_2O \rightleftharpoons HNO_2 + OH^-$$

$$K_b = \frac{[HNO_2][OH^-]}{[NO_2^-]}$$

One equation is the reverse of the other and both give the same results.

2. A titration curve is a plot of the pH of a solution as acid or base is added. The shape of the curve depends upon the strengths of the acid and base used.

3. At the beginning the solution contains only the weak acid CH_3CO_2H. The pH depends only upon the concentration of the weak acid acid.

As the strong base is added, the salt (conjugate base) of the acid is formed. The solution now contains a mixture of the weak acid and its conjugate base.

Halfway to the equivalence point the solution contains equal concentrations of the acid and its conjugate base. The $pH = pK_a$.

At the equivalence point the number of moles of base added equals the number of moles of weak acid originally present. The solution contains the salt (the conjugate base) of the weak acid.

After the equivalence point, the solution contains the salt and excess sodium hydroxide. The pH of the solution depends upon the amount of excess base.

4. A distribution diagram is an illustration of how the composition of an aqueous solution of a weak electrolyte varies as the pH of the solution changes. Such a diagram is particularly useful for polyprotic acids when it shows which two species are predominant in solution at a particular pH. The easiest way to calculate the concentration curves on a distribution diagram is by using the Henderson-Hasselbalch equation.

5. The primary requirement of an acid-base indicator is to match the equivalence point. Other requirements are an intense color so that the amount of indicator required is minimal and a distinct color change at the endpoint.

End-of-Unit Problems

1. Draw a pH titration curve for a reaction between a weak acid and a strong base. On the diagram indicate the points or regions where

    a. the pH equals the pK_a of the acid

    b. the equivalence point

    c. the pH depends only upon the concentration of the acid

2. Draw a pH titration curve for a reaction between a weak base and a strong acid. On the diagram indicate the points or regions where

    a. the pH depends only upon the concentration of the conjugate acid of the base

    b. the pH equals the pK_b for the base

    c. the pH depends only upon the amount of excess acid added

3. When 50 mL of 0.15 M nitric acid is titrated against 0.25 M sodium hydroxide,

    a. how many mL of the sodium hydroxide solution are necessary to reach the equivalence point?

    b. what is the pH at the equivalence point?

4. When 40 mL of 0.25 M hydrochloric acid is titrated against 0.10 M sodium hydroxide,

    a. how many mL of the sodium hydroxide solution are necessary to reach the equivalence point?

    b. what is the pH of the solution when twice this amount of sodium hydroxide has been added?

5. For a titration of 50 mL of 0.100 M chloric acid against 0.100 M potassium hydroxide, calculate the pH of the solution

    a. after 25 mL of the base has been added

    b. after 50 mL of the base has been added

    c. after 60 mL of the base has been added

6. For a titration of 40 mL of 0.250 M hydrochloric acid against 0.250 M sodium hydroxide, calculate the pH of the solution

    a. after 35 mL of the base has been added

    b. after 39 mL of the base has been added

    c. after 41 mL of the base has been added

7. For a titration of 0.150 M hydrochloric acid against 50 mL of 0.150 M methylamine CH_3NH_2, calculate the pH of the solution

    a. after 48 mL of the acid has been added

    b. after 50 mL of the acid has been added

    c. after 52 mL of the acid has been added

8. For a titration of 40 mL of 0.200 M formic acid against 0.200 M sodium hydroxide, calculate the pH of the solution

    a. after 39 mL of the base has been added

    b. after 40 mL of the base has been added

    c. after 41 mL of the base has been added

9. For a titration of 0.200 M hydrochloric acid against 50 mL of 0.100 M ammonia, calculate the pH of the solution

    a. before any acid has been added

    b. after 12.5 mL of the acid has been added

    c. at the equivalence point

10. For a titration of 40 mL of 0.100 M acetic acid against 0.250 M sodium hydroxide, calculate the pH of the solution

    a. before any base has been added

    b. at a point halfway to the equivalence point

    c. at the equivalence point

11. Calculate the pH halfway to the equivalence point in the titrations of

    a. 0.10 M HCl $vs.$ 0.20 M NH_3

    b. 0.20 M HCO_2H $vs.$ 0.10 M NaOH

12. Calculate the pH halfway to the equivalence point in the titrations of

    a. 0.25 M $HClO_4$ $vs.$ 0.20 M $C_2H_5NH_2$

    b. 0.20 M HNO_2 $vs.$ 0.15 M KOH

13. The weak acid methyl red is a popular indicator for acid-base titrations. Consult Figure 44.6 and determine the approximate range through which methyl red changes color. Of the three titrations, strong acid–strong base, strong acid–weak base, and weak acid–strong base, which is a titration for which you would not choose the indicator methyl red? Explain why.

14. The indicator phenolphthalein is one of the most commonly used acid-base indicators. Consult Figure 44.6 and determine the approximate range through which phenolphthalein changes color. Of the three titrations, strong acid–strong base, strong acid–weak base, and weak acid–strong base, which is a titration for which you would not choose this indicator? Explain why.

15. Three small samples were taken from a solution of unknown pH. A drop of different indicators was added to each sample. Phenolphthalein was colorless, methyl red was yellow, and alizarin was red. What is the approximate pH of the unknown solution?

16. Three small samples were taken from a solution of unknown pH. A drop of different indicators was added to each sample. Methyl orange was yellow, phenol red was red, phenolphthalein was red, and alizarin yellow was yellow. What is the approximate pH of the unknown solution?

17. Consult Figure 44.6 and determine an appropriate indicator for the titration of 0.01 M iodic acid $vs.$ 0.10 M potassium hydroxide.

18. Consult Figure 44.6 and determine an appropriate indicator for the titration of 0.01 M benzoic acid $vs.$ 0.10 M sodium hydroxide.

19. Arsenic acid, H_3AsO_4, is a weak polyprotic acid. The values for the successive ionizations are listed in Table 42.1. If the initial concentraion of arsenic acid is 0.100 M, calculate the concentrations at equilibrium of H_3AsO_4, $H_2AsO_4^-$, $HAsO_4^{2-}$, H_3O^+, and OH^-.

20. Selenous acid, H_2SeO_3, is a weak diprotic acid. The values for the successive ionizations are listed in Table 42.1. If the initial concentraion of selenous acid is 0.100 M, calculate the concentrations at equilibrium of H_2SeO_3, $HSeO_3^-$, SeO_3^{2-}, H_3O^+, and OH^-.

21. In the titration of 50 mL of 0.200 M phosphorous acid $vs.$ 0.200 M sodium hydroxide, calculate the pH of the solution

    a. before any acid has been added

    b. halfway to the first equivalence point

    c. at the first equivalent point

    d. halfway from the first equivalent point to the second equivalence point

    e. at the second equivalence point

    Values for K_{a1} and K_{a2} are listed in Table 42.1.

22. In the titration of 40 mL of 0.150 M phosphoric acid $vs.$ 0.300 M sodium hydroxide, calculate the pH of the solution

    a. before any acid has been added

    b. halfway to the first equivalence point

    c. at the first equivalent point

    d. halfway from the first equivalent point to the second equivalence point

    e. at the second equivalence point

    f. halfway from the second equivalent point to the third equivalence point

    Values for K_{a1}, K_{a2} and K_{a3} are listed in Table 42.1.

23. Maleic acid is a diprotic acid for which $K_{a1} = 1.4 \times 10^{-2}$ and $K_{a2} = 8.6 \times 10^{-7}$. If 50 mL of a 0.120 M solution of maleic acid is titrated against 0.120 M sodium hydroxide, calculate the pH of the solution when the following amounts of the sodium hydroxide solution have been added:

    a. 25 mL

    b. 40 mL

    c. 80 mL

    d. 100 mL

24. In a titration of 40 mL of 0.250 M oxalic acid ($K_{a1} = 5.9 \times 10^{-2}$ and $K_{a2} = 6.4 \times 10^{-5}$) against 0.125 M sodium hydroxide, calculate the pH of the solution when the following amounts of the sodium hydroxide solution have been added:

    a. 10 mL

    b. 20 mL

    c. 25 mL

    d. 30 mL

25. For an aqueous solution of phosphorous acid H_3PO_3, sketch the distribution diagram and determine the predominant species in solution at a pH of 3.0 and at a pH of 8.0. Calculate the composition of the solution at these pH. Values of K_{a1} and K_{a2} are listed in Table 42.1.

26. For an aqueous solution of selenous acid H_2SeO_3, sketch the distribution diagram and determine the predominant species in solution at a pH of 4.0 and at a pH of 7.0. Calculate the composition of the solution at these pH. Values of K_{a1} and K_{a2} are listed in Table 42.1.

Solubility Equilibria

45.1 The Solubility of Salts

We learned in Unit 8 that some salts are insoluble in water. The energy released in the solvation process is insufficient to overcome the energy required to break up the strong interaction between the ions in the solid ionic lattice. Even though the entropy change for the solution process is favorable (positive $\Delta S°$), the unfavorable enthalpy change (positive $\Delta H°$) makes $\Delta G°$ positive and the solution process is heavily reactant-favored:

$$\text{solid ionic compound} \rightleftharpoons \text{cation}(aq) + \text{anion}(aq)$$

$$\xleftarrow{\hspace{3cm}}$$

the system lies predominantly on the reactant side

The equilibrium position, where ΔG is zero, lies very close to reactant side. Although salts are often described as insoluble, in reality many are **sparingly soluble**. The solid ionic compound reaches equilibrium with low, sometimes extremely low, concentrations of its ions in solution. An equilibrium system such as this that involves two different phases is called a **heterogeneous equilibrium**.

A set of **solubility rules** provides guidelines for determining which salts are soluble and which are not. For example, salts of singly-charged oxoanions such as perchlorate, chlorate, nitrate, and acetate, tend to be soluble. Salts of the halides tend to soluble except those with a few doubly-charged cations. Salts of doubly- or triply-charged oxoanions such as carbonate, phosphate, oxalate, and chromate, tend to be insoluble, unless the cation is an ammonium cation or a singly-charged cation from Group 1A. A complete set of solubility rules are listed in Table 8.3.

Many biological, industrial, and environmental processes involve equilibria in which an ionic compound is sparingly soluble. We have already mentioned the precipitation of the insoluble calcium oxalate in the formation of kidney stones. Another example is the reaction of acids such as lactic acid (from the bacterial decay of foods trapped in plaque) with tooth enamel. Tooth enamel is principally hydroxyapatite, $Ca_5(PO_4)_3OH$, which is insoluble in water but slightly soluble in acidic solutions. The acid neutralizes the OH^- in the hydroxyapatite and converts some PO_4^{3-} to HPO_4^{2-} which dissolves—this causes cavities. Other acids such as the phosphoric acid in soda also cause tooth decay. Fluoride toothpaste converts some of the hydroxyapatite to fluorapatite $Ca_5(PO_4)_3F$ which is more resistant to acids—fluoride is a weaker base than hydroxide.

A dramatic example of heterogeneous equilibria in the environment is the formation of stalactites and stalagmites in limestone caves caused by the precipitation of the sparingly soluble calcium carbonate $CaCO_3$ from the water dripping from the roof (Figure 45.1).

In research laboratories and in the chemical industry, chemists make great use of the solution and precipitation of compounds to isolate and purify them.

When an ionic salt dissolves in water it is often assumed that the salt dissociates completely into its constituent ions. This is not true for the salts of the alkaline earth metals, and other metal cations with a high charge, except in very dilute solutions. For example, when magnesium fluoride dissolves in water, not only are there Mg^{2+} and F^- ions in solution but also MgF^+ ions. This complicates the treatment of heterogeneous

The presence of species such as MgF^+ increases the solubility of a salt.

FIGURE 45.1 **Stalactites and stalagmites in a cave at Nerja, Málaga, Spain form when sparingly soluble calcium carbonate precipitates from the water dripping from the roof of the cavern.**
In time the stalactites and stalagmites join to form pillars extending from the floor to the roof.

equilibria. Fortunately, for sparingly soluble salts the solutions are very dilute and, to keep things simple, we will assume in our calculations that the ions completely dissociate. The results of such calculations should be regarded as a first approximation only.

Another complicating factor is that many ions in solution hydrolyse (*cf.* Unit 41). This means that more than one equilibrium is involved in the solution process. We will examine simultaneous equilibria in Unit 46.

45.2   The Solubility Product

The equilibrium constant for a heterogeneous equilibrium between a solid salt and the ions in solution is called the **solubility product**. It is given the symbol K_{sp} (where sp indicates solubility product). For example, consider the sparingly soluble salt magnesium fluoride:

$$MgF_2(s) \rightleftharpoons Mg^{2+}(aq) + 2\,F^-(aq)$$
$$K_{sp} = [Mg^{2+}][F^-]^2$$

Note that the solid $MgF_2(s)$ does not appear in the equilibrium constant expression because it is a pure solid and its activity equals 1. The solubility constant expression is the product of the concentrations of the ions in solution with each concentration term raised to a power equal to the corresponding coefficient in the balanced equation for the solution process.

The value of the solubility product K_{sp} for magnesium fluoride is obtained experimentally by measuring the **solubility** of the salt in water at a particular temperature. The solubility is the concentration of magnesium fluoride formula units in

> The solubility product for a sparingly soluble salt is analogous to the ion product for water. It is the product of the concentrations of the ions in solution at equilibrium.

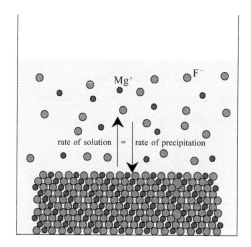

FIGURE 45.2   A saturated solution of magnesium fluoride MgF$_2$.
The concentration of fluoride ions F$^-$ is twice the concentration of magnesium ions Mg^{2+}.
At equilibrium, the rate of solution equals the rate of precipitation.

The solubility product is related to the solubility of a salt. However, comparison of K$_{sp}$ values does not necessarily indicate the relative solubilities of two salts—it depends upon the stoichiometry of the salts. For example:

K$_{sp}$ (AgCl) = 1.8 × 10^{-10}

Solubility = 1.3 × 10^{-5} M

K$_{sp}$ (Ag$_2$CrO$_4$) = 1.1 × 10^{-12}

Solubility = 6.5 × 10^{-5} M

The K$_{sp}$ for Ag$_2$CrO$_4$ is lower, but its solubility is slightly higher.

14.65 mg = 1.465 × 10^{-2} g

Molar mass MgF$_2$ = 62.31 g mol^{-1}

$\dfrac{1.465 \times 10^{-2}\ \text{g}}{62.31\ \text{g mol}^{-1}}$ = 2.351 × 10^{-4} mol

Most solubility products are written with only two significant figures. Additional precision is usually not justified.

a saturated solution in moles liter^{-1}. For example, consider what happens when an excess amount of magnesium fluoride is added to water. The salt slowly dissolves—a process that can be speeded up by stirring or agitating the solution. The system reaches an equilibrium state when the rate of the solution process equals the rate of the precipitation process (Figure 45.2). The solution is now saturated and the concentrations of magnesium ions and fluoride ions remain constant. If the saturated solution is analyzed, the amount of magnesium fluoride per volume of solution can be determined.

In the solution of magnesium fluoride the concentration of the fluoride ions is twice the concentration of magnesium ions because there are two fluoride ions for each magnesium ion:

$$[\text{F}^-] = 2 \times [\text{Mg}^{2+}]$$

Suppose that the solubility of magnesium fluoride is determined to be 14.65 mg/L. This corresponds to a molarity of magnesium fluoride formula units equal to 2.351 × 10^{-4} M. The concentration of magnesium ions is the same, 2.351 × 10^{-4} M, because there is one magnesium ion in each formula unit. The concentration of fluoride ions is twice this, 4.703 × 10^{-4} M because there are two fluoride ions per formula unit. The solubility product for magnesium fluoride is therefore:

$$\text{K}_{sp} = [\text{Mg}^{2+}][\text{F}^-]^2 = (2.351 \times 10^{-4})(4.703 \times 10^{-4})^2 = 5.2 \times 10^{-11}$$

An alternative way to determine the solubility product is to add a soluble source of fluoride ions, for example sodium fluoride, to a soluble source of magnesium ions, for example magnesium nitrate, until the first permanent precipitation of the insoluble magnesium fluoride occurs. The precipitation of the magnesium fluoride indicates that the product of the concentrations of the ions just exceeds the solubility product. Let's work through a typical experiment.

EXAMPLE 45.1 CALCULATING THE SOLUBILITY PRODUCT FROM SOLUBILITY DATA

A 0.0010 M solution of sodium fluoride is added to 100.0 mL of a 0.0010 M solution of magnesium nitrate. The first permanent precipitation of magnesium fluoride is detected after 36.0 mL of the sodium fluoride solution has been added. Calculate the solubility product for magnesium fluoride.

UNDERSTAND THE QUESTION

The solubility product for magnesium fluoride is the product of the concentration of the magnesium ions and the concentration of the fluoride ions squared. If the concentrations of the magnesium ions and the fluoride ions in a saturated solution can be determined, then the solubility product can be calculated.

PLAN THE SOLUTION

Determine the concentrations of the magnesium ions and fluoride ions at the moment that precipitation occurs. Take account of the fact that the solutions are diluted when they are mixed.

SOLVE THE PROBLEM

The final volume of the solution = 100.0 mL + 36.0 mL = 136.0 mL

$$[Mg^{2+}] = 0.0010\ M \times (100.0\ mL/136.0\ mL) = 0.000735\ M$$
$$[F^-] = 0.0010\ M \times (36.0\ mL/136.0\ mL) = 0.000265\ M$$
$$K_{sp} = [Mg^{2+}][F^-]^2 = (0.000735)(0.000265)^2 = 5.6 \times 10^{-11}$$

Additional significant figures are included until the calculation is complete.

This is the same value obtained earlier.

PROBLEM 45.1A

Sufficient silver chromate Ag_2CrO_4 is added to water to make a saturated solution. The solution is analyzed and found to contain a concentration of silver ions $[Ag^+]$ equal to $1.3 \times 10^{-4}\ M$. Calculate the solubility of silver chromate in water and calculate its solubility product K_{sp}.

PROBLEM 45.1B

A saturated solution of silver bromide AgBr is found to contain a concentration of silver ions $[Ag^+]$ equal to $7.35 \times 10^{-7}\ M$. Calculate the solubility of silver bromide in water and calculate its solubility product K_{sp}.

Notice that the concentrations of the magnesium ions and fluoride ions in the answer to Example 45.1 are not in the ratio 1:2. There's no restriction on the individual concentrations of the ions; it's the ion product K_{sp} that is important. There could be a lot of magnesium Mg^{2+} and very little fluoride F^- in the saturated solution, or *vice versa*. The presence of spectator ions ensures that the charges balance. Figure 45.3 illustrates the line along which the product of the concentration terms equals the solubility product. On the left the concentration of magnesium ions is high and the concentration of the fluoride ions is low. The reverse is true on the right. The plot is logarithmic and the line is straight: $pK_{sp} = pMg + 2pF$.

The solubility products K_{sp} for several salts are listed in Table 45.1. If the K_{sp} for a salt is known, then the solubility of the salt in moles L^{-1} can be calculated. The calculation is the reverse of the one we have just done. The relevant relationship is again the expression for the solubility product. Let's calculate the solubility of copper(II) iodate in water.

If $K_{sp} = [Mg^{2+}][F^-]^2$
then
$logK_{sp} = log[Mg^{2+}] + 2log[F^-]$
or
$pK_{sp} = pMg + 2pF$

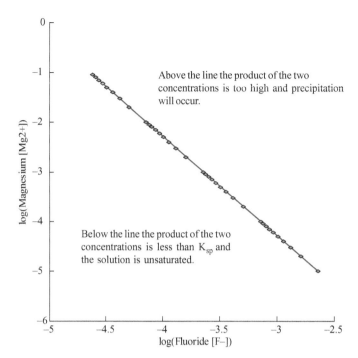

FIGURE 45.3 **The relationship between the concentration of magnesium ions and the concentration of fluoride ions in a saturated solution of magnesium fluoride MgF$_2$.**
The solution is saturated along the solid line. Above the line the product of the concentrations of the ions exceeds the solubility product and precipitation will occur. Below the line the solution is unsaturated. Note that both the [Mg^{2+}] and [F$^-$] axes are logarithmic.

EXAMPLE 45.2 CALCULATING THE SOLUBILITY OF A SALT FROM THE SOLUBILITY PRODUCT

Calculate the solubility of copper(II) iodate, Cu(IO$_3$)$_2$, if the K$_{sp}$ for the salt equals 6.9×10^{-8}.

UNDERSTAND THE QUESTION

The solubility product for a salt and the solubility of a salt are related by the solubility product expression. The solubility refers to the concentration of the salt in a saturated solution, in formula units per liter.

PLAN THE SOLUTION

Write the expression for the solubility product K$_{sp}$. Determine the relationship between the concentrations of the ions. It is often convenient to assign a label, e.g. an unknown x or s, to one of the concentrations.

SOLVE THE PROBLEM

The formula for copper(II) iodate is Cu(IO$_3$)$_2$

For every Cu^{2+} ion there are 2 IO$_3^-$ ions.

The concentration of the iodate ions [IO$_3^-$] must be twice the concentration of copper ions [Cu^{2+}]:

$$[IO_3^-] = 2 \times [Cu^{2+}]$$

Represent the [Cu^{2+}] by 's':

$$[Cu^{2+}] = s$$
$$[IO_3^-] = 2s$$

Therefore $K_{sp} = 6.9 \times 10^{-8} = [Cu^{2+}][IO_3^-]^2 = (s) \times (2s)^2 = 4s^3$

Solving for s:

$$s = 2.6 \times 10^{-3} \, M$$

s is the concentration of $[Cu^{2+}]$ and, because there is one Cu^{2+} ion in the formula unit for $Cu(IO_3)_2$, it also equals the molar solubility of copper iodate.

> If your calculator does not have a cube root key, you can use the y^x key (where x = 1/3).
>
> Or, use logarithms:
>
> press the ln key, divide by 3, then press the e^x key.

PROBLEM 45.2A

Calculate the solubility of lead(II) bromide, $PbBr_2$, if the K_{sp} for the salt equals 6.6×10^{-6}.

PROBLEM 45.2B

Calculate the solubility of lead(II) sulfate, $PbSO_4$, if the K_{sp} for the salt equals 2.5×10^{-8}.

TABLE 45.1 Solubility constants K_{sp} for some sparingly soluble salts.

Salt		K_{sp}	Salt		K_{sp}
Aluminum phosphate	$AlPO_4$	9.8×10^{-21}	Lithium fluoride	LiF	1.8×10^{-3}
Barium carbonate	$BaCO_3$	2.6×10^{-9}	Magnesium carbonate	$MgCO_3$	6.8×10^{-6}
Barium fluoride	BaF_2	1.8×10^{-7}	Magnesium fluoride	MgF_2	5.2×10^{-11}
Barium nitrate	$Ba(NO_3)_2$	4.6×10^{-3}	Magnesium hydroxide	$Mg(OH)_2$	5.6×10^{-12}
Barium sulfate	$BaSO_4$	1.1×10^{-10}	Mercury(I) bromide	Hg_2Br_2	6.4×10^{-23}
Cadmium carbonate	$CdCO_3$	1.0×10^{-12}	Mercury(I) chloride	Hg_2Cl_2	1.4×10^{-18}
Cadmium fluoride	CdF_2	6.4×10^{-3}	Mercury(II) bromide	$HgBr_2$	6.2×10^{-20}
Cadmium iodate	$Cd(IO_3)_2$	2.5×10^{-8}	Mercury(II) chloride	$HgCl_2$	2.9×10^{-29}
Calcium carbonate	$CaCO_3$	3.4×10^{-9}	Mercury(I) iodide	Hg_2I_2	5.2×10^{-29}
Calcium fluoride	CaF_2	3.5×10^{-11}	Nickel(II) carbonate	$NiCO_3$	1.4×10^{-7}
Calcium phosphate	$Ca_3(PO_4)_2$	2.1×10^{-33}	Nickel(II) hydroxide	$Ni(OH)_2$	5.5×10^{-16}
Calcium sulfate	$CaSO_4$	4.9×10^{-5}	Nickel(II) iodate	$Ni(IO_3)_2$	4.7×10^{-5}
Copper(I) bromide	CuBr	6.3×10^{-9}	Potassium perchlorate	$KClO_4$	1.1×10^{-2}
Copper(I) chloride	CuCl	1.7×10^{-7}	Potassium periodate	KIO_4	3.7×10^{-4}
Copper(I) cyanide	CuCN	3.5×10^{-20}	Silver acetate	$AgCH_3CO_2$	1.9×10^{-3}
Copper(I) iodide	CuI	1.3×10^{-12}	Silver bromide	AgBr	5.4×10^{-13}
Copper(II) iodate	$Cu(IO_3)_2$	6.9×10^{-8}	Silver carbonate	Ag_2CO_3	8.5×10^{-12}
Copper(II) phosphate	$Cu_3(PO_4)_2$	1.4×10^{-37}	Silver chloride	AgCl	1.8×10^{-10}
Iron(II) fluoride	FeF_2	2.4×10^{-6}	Silver chromate	Ag_2CrO_4	1.1×10^{-12}
Iron(II) carbonate	$FeCO_3$	3.1×10^{-11}	Silver cyanide	AgCN	6.0×10^{-17}
Iron(II) hydroxide	$Fe(OH)_2$	4.8×10^{-17}	Silver iodate	$AgIO_3$	3.2×10^{-8}
Iron(III) hydroxide	$Fe(OH)_3$	2.8×10^{-39}	Silver iodide	AgI	8.5×10^{-17}
Lead(II) bromide	$PbBr_2$	6.6×10^{-6}	Silver thiocyanate	AgSCN	1.0×10^{-12}
Lead(II) chloride	$PbCl_2$	1.7×10^{-5}	Strontium fluoride	SrF_2	4.3×10^{-9}
Lead(II) hydroxide	$Pb(OH)_2$	1.4×10^{-20}	Strontium sulfate	$SrSO_4$	3.4×10^{-7}
Lead(II) iodide	PbI_2	9.8×10^{-9}	Tin(II) hydroxide	$Sn(OH)_2$	5.5×10^{-27}
Lead(II) iodate	$Pb(IO_3)_2$	3.7×10^{-13}	Zinc carbonate	$ZnCO_3$	1.5×10^{-10}
Lead(II) sulfate	$PbSO_4$	2.5×10^{-8}	Zinc fluoride	ZnF_2	3.0×10^{-2}
Lithium carbonate	Li_2CO_3	8.2×10^{-4}	Zinc hydroxide	$ZnCO_3$	3.0×10^{-17}

45.3   The Common Ion Effect

Just as a common ion suppresses the ionization of a weak electrolyte, the presence of a common ion decreases the solubility of a sparingly soluble salt. This suppression of the solubility is in accord with LeChâtelier's principle. For example, consider again the solution of magnesium fluoride:

$$MgF_2(s) \rightleftharpoons Mg^{2+}(aq) + 2\,F^-(aq)$$

Addition of fluoride ion to this equilibrium will shift the system to the left and decrease the concentration of Mg^{2+} ions in solution. The fluoride ion is added as a soluble fluoride salt such as sodium fluoride. After the addition, the fluoride ion concentration in the solution is higher and the magnesium ion concentration is lower, but the solubility product $[Mg^{2+}][F^-]^2$ is the same. A plot of how the solubility of magnesium fluoride decreases as the added fluoride ion concentration increases is shown in Figure 45.4.

> Compare this figure with Figure 45.3 and understand why they are in fact the same.

The same suppression of the solubility will occur if a source of magnesium ions, for example magnesium nitrate, is added to the solution. In this case the magnesium ion is the common ion.

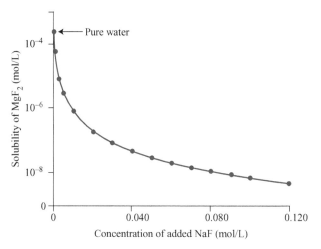

FIGURE 45.4   The decrease in the solubility of magnesium fluoride at 25°C as the concentration of fluoride ion in the solution is increased.
The common ion effect suppresses the solubility. The solubility (vertical axis) is plotted on a logarithmic scale.

EXAMPLE 45.3   CALCULATING THE SOLUBILITY OF A SALT IN THE PRESENCE OF A COMMON ION

Calculate the solubility of lead(II) iodide, PbI_2, if the K_{sp} for the salt equals 9.8×10^{-9}. Calculate the solubility of the salt in an aqueous solution of 0.10 *M* sodium iodide NaI.

UNDERSTAND THE QUESTION

The solubility product for a salt is a constant at constant temperature. If the concentration of one of the ions in the solubility product expression is changed then the concentration of the other ion must also change so that K_{sp} remains constant. The effect of the change can be predicted by LeChâtelier's principle—the solubility is suppressed by the addition of a common ion.

PLAN THE SOLUTION

Determine the relationship between the concentrations of the ions in the solution of the salt. Write the expression for the solubility product K_{sp} and solve for the unknown concentration. Repeat the calculation for the solution containing the common ion. Assume that all the common ion is derived from the added soluble salt (sodium iodide).

SOLVE THE PROBLEM

The formula for lead(II) iodide is PbI_2

For every Pb^{2+} ion there are 2 I^- ions.

The concentration of the iodide ions $[I^-]$ must be twice the concentration of lead ions $[Pb^{2+}]$:

$$[I^-] = 2 \times [Pb^{2+}]$$

Represent the $[Pb^{2+}]$ by 's':

$$[Pb^{2+}] = s$$
$$[I^-] = 2s$$

Therefore $K_{sp} = 9.8 \times 10^{-9} = [Pb^{2+}][I^-]^2 = (s) \times (2s)^2 = 4s^3$

Solving for s:

$$s = 1.35 \times 10^{-3} \, M$$

s is the concentration $[Pb^{2+}]$

There is one Pb^{2+} ion in the formula unit for PbI_2, so the molar solubility of lead iodide = $1.35 \times 10^{-3} \, M$.

In the presence of the additional iodide ion, K_{sp} must be the same:

$$K_{sp} = 9.8 \times 10^{-9} = [Pb^{2+}][I^-]^2$$

But in this case the $[I^-]$ concentration = 0.10 M.

$$9.8 \times 10^{-9} = [Pb^{2+}][I^-]^2 = [Pb^{2+}](0.10)^2$$
$$\text{and } [Pb^{2+}] = 9.8 \times 10^{-7} \, M.$$

The solubility of lead(II) iodide = $9.8 \times 10^{-7} \, M$.

Is the assumption to ignore the small amount of iodide from the lead(III) iodide justifiable? The concentration of iodide from the sodium iodide is 0.10 M. The concentration of iodide from the lead iodide = $2 \times 9.8 \times 10^{-7} \, M = 2.0 \times 10^{-6} \, M$—50,000 times less and negligible in comparison.

Notice how the solubility of the lead(II) iodide decreases from $1.4 \times 10^{-3} \, M$ to $9.8 \times 10^{-7} \, M$ in the presence of the common iodide ion.

PROBLEM 45.3A

Calculate the solubility of silver chromate, Ag_2CrO_4, in the presence of 0.050 M potassium chromate, K_2CrO_4. The solubility product K_{sp} for silver chromate = 1.1×10^{-12}.

PROBLEM 45.3B

Calculate the solubility of lead(II) sulfate, $PbSO_4$, in the presence of 0.15 M sodium sulfate, Na_2SO_4, if the K_{sp} for the salt equals 2.5×10^{-8}. Compare your answer with the solubility calculated in Problem 41.2.

45.4   Prediction of Precipitation

If a solution of sodium chloride is mixed with a solution of silver nitrate, the salt silver chloride precipitates from the solution. Individually, sodium chloride and silver nitrate are soluble in water, but when the solutions are mixed, the mixture contains silver ions and chloride ions and silver chloride is only sparingly soluble. Precipitation occurs because the solubility product of silver chloride is exceeded. The sodium ions and nitrate ions remain in solution.

In order to determine whether a salt will precipitate from solution, it is useful to calculate the reaction quotient for the solution process. The quotient, which we can call the **solubility quotient**, has the symbol Q_{sp} and is equal to the product of the concentrations of the ions in solution raised to powers equal to the coefficients in the balanced equation for the solution process. The expression has exactly the same form as the solubility product. In other words, to use our example magnesium fluoride:

$$K_{sp} = [Mg^{2+}][F^-]^2 \quad \text{at equilibrium}$$
$$Q_{sp} = [Mg^{2+}][F^-]^2 \quad \text{for any situation}$$

If Q_{sp} is less than K_{sp}, the solution is not yet saturated and more salt will dissolve.

If Q_{sp} equals K_{sp}, the solution is at equilibrium and the solution is saturated.

If Q_{sp} is greater than K_{sp}, the concentration of ions is too high and precipitation will occur. This is illustrated in Figure 45.5.

> The term *quotient* is misplaced in this case because the equation for Q_{sp} is a product not a quotient. However the name is retained because it is entirely analogous to the reaction quotient discussed in Unit 35.

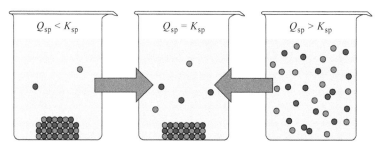

FIGURE 45.5   The determination whether precipitation will occur.
If $Q_{sp} < K_{sp}$ then the solution is unsaturated.
If $Q_{sp} = K_{sp}$ then the solution is saturated.
If $Q_{sp} > K_{sp}$ then precipitation of the excess solute will occur.

EXAMPLE 45.4   DETERMINING WHETHER PRECIPITATION WILL OCCUR

If 50 mL of a $5.0 \times 10^{-4}\,M$ solution of silver nitrate is mixed with 50 mL of a $5.0 \times 10^{-3}\,M$ solution of potassium chromate K_2CrO_4, will precipitation of silver chromate Ag_2CrO_4 occur? K_{sp} for silver chromate $= 1.1 \times 10^{-12}$.

UNDERSTAND THE QUESTION

A salt will precipitate from solution if the solubility product for the salt is exceeded. Note that when the solutions are mixed, they are both diluted. This dilution must be taken into account.

PLAN THE SOLUTION

Write the expression for the solubility product K_{sp}. Calculate the concentrations of the ions in solution and determine the value of Q_{sp}. If Q_{sp} exceeds K_{sp}, then precipitation will occur.

SOLVE THE PROBLEM

$$K_{sp} = [Ag^+]^2[CrO_4^{2-}] = 1.1 \times 10^{-12}$$

$[Ag^+]$ in the silver nitrate $AgNO_3$ solution $= 5.0 \times 10^{-4}\,M$

when the solutions are mixed, the volume doubles to 100 mL

the $[Ag^+]$ is reduced to $2.5 \times 10^{-4}\,M$

$[CrO_4^{2-}]$ in the potassium chromate K_2CrO_4 solution $= 5.0 \times 10^{-3}\,M$

when the solutions are mixed, the $[CrO_4^{2-}]$ is reduced to $2.5 \times 10^{-3}\,M$

$$Q_{sp} = [Ag^+]^2[CrO_4^{2-}] = (2.5 \times 10^{-4})^2(2.5 \times 10^{-3}) = 1.6 \times 10^{-10}$$

Q_{sp} exceeds K_{sp} and precipitation will occur.

PROBLEM 45.4A

If 100 mL of a 0.10 M solution of lead(II) nitrate $Pb(NO_3)_2$ is mixed with 50 mL of a 0.20 M solution of potassium chloride KCl, will precipitation of lead chloride $PbCl_2$ occur? K_{sp} for lead chloride $= 1.7 \times 10^{-5}$.

PROBLEM 45.4B

Will precipitation of silver bromide AgBr occur if 1.0 mL of 0.0010 M NaBr is added to 1000 mL of $1.0 \times 10^{-5}\,M$ silver nitrate solution? K_{sp} for AgBr $= 5.4 \times 10^{-13}$.

If a solution contains a mixture of ions, it is often possible to separate the ions through selective precipitation. Suppose, for example, that a metal object contains a mixture of silver and lead and the two metals have to be separated. The object could be dissolved in nitric acid to produce a solution of silver nitrate and lead nitrate. Sodium chloride could be added to the solution to produce a precipitate of silver chloride ($K_{sp} = 1.8 \times 10^{-10}$). Then, after all the silver has been precipitated and removed, addition of more sodium chloride would precipitate lead chloride ($K_{sp} = 1.7 \times 10^{-5}$).

EXAMPLE 45.5   SELECTIVE PRECIPITATION OF METAL IONS FROM SOLUTION

A solution containing 0.20 M Ag^+ and 0.20 M Pb^{2+} is treated with increasing amounts of sodium chloride.

   a. What concentration of sodium chloride is necessary to precipitate the silver as AgCl?

   b. What concentration of sodium chloride is necessary to precipitate the lead as $PbCl_2$?

   c. What is the concentration of silver in the solution when the lead starts to precipitate?

UNDERSTAND THE QUESTION

As noted earlier, a salt will precipitate from solution if the solubility product for the salt is exceeded ($Q_{sp} > K_{sp}$). If two different ions are present they can be separated based upon their relative solubilities—the less soluble salt will precipitate while the more soluble salt will remain in solution. As the silver is removed from the solution, its concentration decreases and the concentration of Cl^- must be increased to continue the precipitation. Even when the lead starts to precipitate there will still be some silver remaining in the solution.

PLAN THE SOLUTION

Calculate the initial concentration of Cl^- necessary to precipitate the silver. Repeat the calculation for the lead. The concentration of silver in solution at the point where the lead starts to precipitate can be calculated from the expression for K_{sp} for AgCl.

SOLVE THE PROBLEM

a. $K_{sp} = [Ag^+][Cl^-] = 1.8 \times 10^{-10}$

$[Ag^+] = 0.20\ M$, therefore $[Cl^-]$ required for initial precipitation $= 9.0 \times 10^{-10}\ M$

b. $K_{sp} = [Pb^{2+}][Cl^-]^2 = 1.7 \times 10^{-5}$

$[Pb^{2+}] = 0.20\ M$, therefore $[Cl^-]$ required for initial precipitation $= 9.2 \times 10^{-3}\ M$

As the sodium chloride concentration is increased from $9.0 \times 10^{-10}\ M$ to $9.2 \times 10^{-3}\ M$ silver is precipitated. Only when the sodium chloride concentration reaches $9.2 \times 10^{-3}\ M$ does the lead start to precipitate.

c. $K_{sp} = [Ag^+][Cl^-] = 1.8 \times 10^{-10}$

$[Cl^-] = 9.2 \times 10^{-3}\ M$, therefore the $[Ag^+] = 1.96 \times 10^{-8}\ M$ compared to an initial concentration of $0.20\ M$. This means that 99.99999% of the silver has been removed from the solution before the lead starts to precipitate.

PROBLEM 45.5A

Mercury(I) iodide Hg_2I_2 is less soluble ($K_{sp} = 5.2 \times 10^{-29}$) than mercury(I) chloride Hg_2Cl_2 ($K_{sp} = 1.4 \times 10^{-18}$). Calculate the maximum permissible concentration of iodide ions in a mixture of iodide ions and chloride ions when precipitation of mercury(I) chloride occurs from a 0.010 M solution of Cl^- ions. The mercury(I) ion is a diatomic ion Hg_2^{2+}.

PROBLEM 45.5B

Lead iodate ($K_{sp} = 3.7 \times 10^{-13}$) and copper(II) iodate ($K_{sp} = 6.9 \times 10^{-8}$) differ in their solubilities. In a mixture of Pb^{2+} and Cu^{2+}, calculate the concentration of Pb^{2+} in a solution of 0.10 M Cu^{2+} ions at the point at which the copper(II) iodate begins to precipitate from the solution.

In the next unit we will examine what happens to the ions of a sparingly soluble salt in solution. We already know that some ions hydrolyse in solution (*cf.* Unit 41). How does this hydrolysis affect the solubility of a salt and how is the solubility of the salt affected by the pH of the solution?

Review Questions

1. Explain the difference between the solubility of a salt and its solubility product. If the K_{sp} for one salt is higher than for another salt, does that mean its solubility is higher?

2. Write a general expression for the solubility product constant K_{sp} for a sparingly soluble salt MX where M^+ is a metal cation and X^- is an anion and the solubility of the salt is s mol L^{-1}. Write similar expressions for a salt MX_2, a salt MX_3, and a salt M_2X_3.

3. How does a common ion influence the solubility of a salt?

4. What is the solubility quotient Q_{sp}? Describe the possible relationships between Q_{sp} and K_{sp} and indicate what each situation represents.

Solutions to Problems

PROBLEM 45.1A

$$[Ag^+] = 1.3 \times 10^{-4} \, M$$
$$[CrO_4^{2-}] = \frac{1}{2} \times [Ag^+] = 6.5 \times 10^{-5} \, M$$

There is one chromate ion per formula unit, therefore the solubility = $6.5 \times 10^{-5} \, M$

$$K_{sp} = [Ag^+]^2[CrO_4^{2-}] = (1.3 \times 10^{-4})^2(6.5 \times 10^{-5}) = 1.1 \times 10^{-12}$$

PROBLEM 45.2A

The bromide ion concentration $[Br^-]$ must be twice the lead ion concentration $[Pb^{2+}]$:

$$[Br^-] = 2 \times [Pb^{2+}]$$

If $[Pb^{2+}] = s$ and $[Br^-] = 2s$

$$K_{sp} = [Pb^{2+}][Br^-]^2 = 6.6 \times 10^{-6} = (s) \times (2s)^2 = 4s^3$$
$$s = 1.2 \times 10^{-2} \, M$$

s is the concentration of $[Pb^{2+}]$ and, because there is one Pb^{2+} ion in the formula unit for $PbBr_2$, it also equals the molar solubility of lead bromide.

PROBLEM 45.3A

Essentially all the chromate ion in the solution comes from the potassium chromate salt.

$$K_{sp} = [Ag^+]^2[CrO_4^{2-}] = [Ag^+]^2(0.050) = 1.1 \times 10^{-12}$$
$$[Ag^+] = 4.7 \times 10^{-6} \, M$$

PROBLEM 45.4A

$[Cl^-]$ in the potassium chloride KCl solution = $0.20 \, M$

When the solutions are mixed, the solution is diluted by 50 mL/150 mL.

The concentration $[Cl^-]$ decreases to $0.20 \, M \times (50 \text{ mL}/150 \text{ mL}) = 0.067 \, M$

$[Pb^{2+}]$ in the lead(II) nitrate $Pb(NO_3)_2$ solution = $0.10 \, M$

When the solutions are mixed, the solution is diluted by 100 mL/150 mL.

The concentration $[Pb^{2+}]$ decreases to $0.10 \, M \times (100 \text{ mL}/150 \text{ mL}) = 0.067 \, M$

$$Q_{sp} = [Pb^{2+}][Cl^-]^2 = (0.067)(0.067)^2 = 3.0 \times 10^{-4}$$

Q_{sp} exceeds K_{sp} (1.7×10^{-5}) and precipitation will occur.

PROBLEM 45.5A

Concentration of chloride $[Cl^-] = 0.010 \, M$

If K_{sp} for $Hg_2Cl_2 = [Hg_2^{2+}][Cl]^2 = 1.4 \times 10^{-18}$, then $[Hg_2^{2+}] = 1.4 \times 10^{-14} \, M$ when precipitation of Hg_2Cl_2 occurs.

If $[Hg_2^{2+}] = 1.4 \times 10^{-14} \, M$, and K_{sp} for $Hg_2I_2 = [Hg_2^{2+}][I]^2 = 5.2 \times 10^{-29}$, then the maximum permissible concentration of iodide ion is $6.1 \times 10^{-8} \, M$.

Answers to Review Questions

1. The solubility of a salt is the concentration of the salt in a saturated solution. The solubility product is an equilibrium constant equal to the product of the concentrations of the ions in a saturated solution of the salt, each concentration term raised to a power equal to the corresponding coefficient in the balanced equation for the solution process. The relative magnitudes of the solubility products of different salts do not necessarily indicate their relative solubilities—it depends upon the stoichiometries of the salts. If the stoichiometries of the salts are the same, then the K_{sp} indicates the trend in solubility (the higher the K_{sp} the higher the solubility). If the stoichiometries are different then no such relationship exists.

2. For a sparingly soluble salt such as MX, where the molar solubility = s mol L^{-1},

   $[M^+] = s$ mol L^{-1} and $[X^-] = s$ mol L^{-1}

   $K_{sp} = [M^+][X^-] = s^2$

For a sparingly soluble salt such as MX_2, where the molar solubility = s mol L^{-1},

$[M^{2+}] = s$ mol L^{-1} and $[X^-] = 2s$ mol L^{-1}

$K_{sp} = [M^{2+}][X^-]^2 = (s) \times (2s)^2 = 4s^3$

For a sparingly soluble salt such as MX_3, where the molar solubility = s mol L^{-1},

$[M^{3+}] = s$ mol L^{-1} and $[X^-] = 3s$ mol L^{-1}

$K_{sp} = [M^{2+}][X^-]^3 = (s) \times (3s)^3 = 27s^4$

For a sparingly soluble salt such as M_2X_3, where the molar solubility = s mol L^{-1},

$[M^{3+}] = 2s$ mol L^{-1} and $[X^-] = 3s$ mol L^{-1}

$K_{sp} = [M^{2+}]^2[X^-]^3 = (2s)^2 \times (3s)^3 = 108s^5$

3. Addition of a common ion suppresses the solubility of the salt. This is an example of LeChatelier's principle. Addition of a common ion $X^-(aq)$ moves the equilibrium to the side of the solid salt $MX(s)$ and reduces the concentration of $M^+(aq)$:

$$MX(s) \rightleftharpoons M^+(aq) + X^-(aq)$$

4. Q_{sp} is the reactant quotient for a system involving the solution of a sparingly soluble salt. Comparison of Q_{sp} and K_{sp} determines whether more salt will dissolve, whether precipitation will occur, or whether the system is at equilibrium. For a salt MX:

$$Q_{sp} = [M^+][X^-]$$

If $Q_{sp} < K_{sp}$, the solution is not yet saturated and more salt will dissolve.

If $Q_{sp} = K_{sp}$, the solution is at equilibrium and the solution is saturated.

If $Q_{sp} > K_{sp}$, the concentration of ions is too high and precipitation will occur.

End-of-Unit Problems

1. Write the solubility product expressions for the following salts:

   a. aluminum phosphate $AlPO_4$

   b. beryllium hydroxide $Be(OH)_2$

   c. bismuth iodide BiI_3

2. Write the solubility product expressions for the following salts:

   a. cesium periodate $CsIO_4$

   b. iron(II) fluoride FeF_2

   c. lithium phosphate Li_3PO_4

3. Determine the solubility products K_{sp} for the following sparingly soluble salts from the molar solubilities:

   a. barium sulfate $BaSO_4$, molar solubility = 1.04×10^{-5} M

   b. lead selenate $PbSeO_4$, molar solubility = 3.70×10^{-4} M

4. Determine the solubility products K_{sp} for the following sparingly soluble salts from the molar solubilities:

   a. bismuth arsenate $BiAsO_4$, molar solubility = 2.10×10^{-5} M

   b. magnesium carbonate $MgCO_3$, molar solubility = 2.61×10^{-3} M

5. Determine the solubility products K_{sp} for the following sparingly soluble salts from the molar solubilities:

   a. barium fluoride $BaSO_4$, molar solubility = 3.58×10^{-3} M

   b. iron(II) hydroxide $Fe(OH)_2$, molar solubility = 2.30×10^{-6} M

6. Determine the solubility products K_{sp} for the following sparingly soluble salts from the molar solubilities:

   a. lead iodide PbI_2, molar solubility = 1.35×10^{-3} M

   b. calcium iodate $Ca(IO_3)_2$, molar solubility = 1.17×10^{-2} M

7. Determine the molar solubilities of the following salts, given their K_{sp}.

   a. silver thiocyanate AgSCN, $K_{sp} = 1.03 \times 10^{-12}$

   b. strontium iodate $Sr(IO_3)_2$, $K_{sp} = 1.14 \times 10^{-7}$

8. Determine the molar solubilities of the following salts, given their K_{sp}.

   a. silver bromate $AgBrO_3$, $K_{sp} = 5.38 \times 10^{-5}$

   b. tin(II) hydroxide $Sn(OH)_2$, $K_{sp} = 5.45 \times 10^{-27}$

9. Determine an expression for the relationship between the molar solubility of scandium fluoride ScF_3 and its K_{sp}. If the K_{sp} value is 5.81×10^{-24}, calculate the molar solubility of the salt.

10. Determine an expression for the relationship between the molar solubility of cobalt(II) arsenate $Co_3(AsO_4)_2$ and its K_{sp}. If the K_{sp} value for the salt is 6.80×10^{-29}, calculate the molar solubility.

11. The molar solubility of lanthanum iodate $La(IO_3)_3$ is 7.26×10^{-4}. Calculate the K_{sp} for this salt.

12. The molar solubility of cadmium arsenate $Cd_3(AsO_4)_2$ is 3.46×10^{-7}. Calculate the K_{sp} for this salt.

13. 100 mL of a saturated solution of calcium oxalate CaC_2O_4 was analyzed and found to contain 0.62 mg of calcium oxalate. Calculate the molar solubility of calcium oxalate and the K_{sp} for the salt.

14. 100 mL of a saturated solution of iron(II) fluoride FeF_2 was analyzed and found to contain 79 mg of iron(II) fluoride. Calculate the molar solubility of iron(II) fluoride and the K_{sp} for the salt.

15. 100 mL of a saturated solution of silver(I) carbonate was carefully evaporated to dryness to avoid decomposition of the carbonate and the solid salt weighed. 3.54 mg of the salt was obtained. Calculate the molar solubility of silver(I) carbonate and the K_{sp} for the salt.

16. 250 mL of a saturated solution of strontium fluoride was carefully evaporated to dryness to yield 32.25 mg of the solid salt. Calculate the molar solubility of strontium fluoride and the K_{sp} for the salt.

17. Calculate the solubility of cadmium iodate, $Cd(IO_3)_2$, if the solubility product K_{sp} for the salt is 2.5×10^{-8}. Calculate the solubility of the salt in an aqueous solution of 0.010 M sodium iodate $NaIO_3$.

18. Calculate the solubility of lithium fluoride, LiF, if the solubility product K_{sp} for the salt is 1.84×10^{-3}. Calculate the solubility of the salt in an aqueous solution of 0.15 M potassium fluoride KF.

19. Calculate the solubility of mercury(I) chloride, Hg_2Cl_2, if the solubility product K_{sp} for the salt is 1.43×10^{-18}. Calculate the solubility of the salt in an aqueous solution of 0.025 M sodium chloride NaCl. The mercury(I) ion is a diatomic ion Hg_2^{2+}.

20. Calculate the solubility of strontium sulfate, $SrSO_4$, if the solubility product K_{sp} for the salt is 3.44×10^{-7}. Calculate the solubility of the salt in an aqueous solution of 0.50 M potassium sulfate K_2SO_4.

21. Determine the molar solubility of silver iodide AgI in
    a. pure water
    b. 0.050 M sodium iodide
    c. 0.0010 M silver nitrate

22. Determine the molar solubility of lead(II) iodate $Pb(IO_3)_2$ in
    a. pure water
    b. 0.250 M potassium iodate
    c. 0.0015 M lead(II) acetate

23. Determine whether precipitation of a sparingly soluble salt will occur when the following solutions are mixed.
    a. 50 mL of 5.0×10^{-5} M silver nitrate and 100 mL of 5.0×10^{-6} M sodium chloride
    b. 50 mL of 2.5×10^{-4} M barium acetate and 50 mL of 3.0×10^{-6} M sodium sulfate

24. Determine whether precipitation of a sparingly soluble salt will occur when the following solutions are mixed.
    a. 20 mL of 5.0×10^{-10} M silver perchlorate and 40 mL of 4.0×10^{-8} M sodium cyanide
    b. 50 mL of 2.5×10^{-3} M lead nitrate and 50 mL of 3.0×10^{-3} M sodium iodide

25. A solution containing 0.025 M Ba^{2+} and 0.025 M Ca^{2+} is treated with increasing amounts of potassium fluoride.
    a. What concentration of KF is necessary to precipitate the barium as BaF_2?
    b. What concentration of KF is necessary to precipitate the calcium as CaF_2?
    c. What is the concentration of calcium Ca^{2+} in the solution when the barium fluoride starts to precipitate?

26. A solution containing 0.150 M Pb^{2+} and 0.300 M Ag^+ is treated with increasing amounts of sodium sulfate.
    a. What concentration of sodium sulfate is necessary to precipitate the lead as lead $PbSO_4$?
    b. What concentration of sodium sulfate is necessary to precipitate the silver as silver sulfate Ag_2SO_4?
    c. Which metal sulfate precipitates first?
    d. What is the concentration of this ion in the solution when the second metal starts to precipitate?

Simultaneous Equilibria

46.1 More than One Equilibrium

Very often two or more equilibria involving common ions occur simultaneously in solution. Suppose that sodium bromide (a soluble source of bromide ions) is added to a system consisting of solid silver chloride and a saturated solution of silver chloride. What happens? Two equilibria are involved:

$$AgCl(s) \rightleftharpoons Ag^+(aq) + Cl^-(aq) \qquad K_{sp} = 1.8 \times 10^{-10}$$
$$AgBr(s) \rightleftharpoons Ag^+(aq) + Br^-(aq) \qquad K_{sp} = 5.4 \times 10^{-13}$$

Because silver bromide is less soluble than silver chloride, the bromide ions combine with the silver ions in solution to precipitate silver bromide. Removal of silver ions from the solution causes more silver chloride to dissolve, and the process continues as long as the bromide ion (sodium bromide) is added to the solution and there is still AgCl(s) available (Figure 46.1):

$$AgCl(s) \rightleftharpoons Ag^+(aq) + Cl^-(aq) \qquad K_{sp} = 1.8 \times 10^{-10}$$

Reverse the second equation:

$$\frac{Ag^+(aq) + Br^-(aq) \rightleftharpoons AgBr(s)}{AgCl(s) + Br^-(aq) \rightleftharpoons AgBr(s) + Cl^-(aq)} \qquad \frac{K = 1/K_{sp} = 1.9 \times 10^{12}}{K = 333}$$

The equilibrium is product-favored.

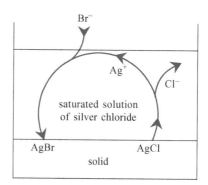

FIGURE 46.1   The addition of bromide ions to a saturated solution of silver chloride in equilibrium with solid silver chloride.
Silver bromide precipitates from the solution and more silver chloride dissolves. At equilibrium the ratio of chloride ions to bromide ions in the solution is 333 to 1.

EXAMPLE 46.1   SIMULTANEOUS EQUILIBRIA

Determine the relative concentrations of chloride ion and bromide ion in a AgCl(aq)/AgBr(aq) system after some sodium bromide is added to a saturated solution of silver chloride. Assume some solid AgCl remains at equilibrium.

UNDERSTAND THE QUESTION

As described above, the bromide of the sodium bromide salt causes silver bromide to precipitate. This removes Ag^+ from the solution and more silver chloride dissolves. The equilibrium is:

$$AgCl(s) + Br^-(aq) \rightleftharpoons AgBr(s) + Cl^-(aq) \qquad K = 333$$

PLAN THE SOLUTION

Write the equilibrium constant expression for this equilibrium and determine the ratio [Cl⁻]/[Br⁻]. Recall that the solids AgCl(s) and AgBr(s) are not included in the expression (their activities = 1).

SOLVE THE PROBLEM

$$K = \frac{[Cl^-]}{[Br^-]} = 333$$

The concentration [Cl⁻] is 333 times greater than the concentration [Br⁻].

PROBLEM 46.1A

Recalculate the answer to Problem 45.5A in the previous chapter using the approach in this example. Write the two equilibria involved and derive the overall equilibrium expression.

PROBLEM 46.1B

Determine the relative concentrations of bromide ion and iodide ion in a CuBr(s)/CuBr(aq) system after some potassium iodide is added. Assume some solid CuBr remains at equilibrium.

46.2 Solubility and pH

The pH of a solution can have a dramatic effect upon the solubility of a sparingly soluble salt. When the anion of the salt is the conjugate base of a weak acid, hydrolysis will always occur in the solution to produce a slightly basic solution. Consider again our example magnesium fluoride:

The solubility product is:

$$MgF_2(s) \rightleftharpoons Mg^{2+}(aq) + 2 F^-(aq) \qquad K_{sp} = 6.5 \times 10^{-9}$$

The fluoride ion hydrolyzes:

$$F^-(aq) + H_2O(l) \rightleftharpoons HF(aq) + OH^-(aq) \qquad K_b = K_w/K_a = 1.5 \times 10^{-11}$$

Doubling this equation and adding it to the first:

$$MgF_2(s) + 2 H_2O(l) \rightleftharpoons Mg^{2+}(aq) + 2 HF(aq) + 2 OH^-(aq)$$
$$K = 1.4 \times 10^{-30}$$

The equilibrium constant for this reaction is extremely small because the solubility product itself is small and HF is a relatively strong weak acid so the hydrolysis does not occur to any great extent.

However, the hydroxide ion in the equilibrium indicates what will happen if a source of hydronium ions (a strong acid) is added to the solution. The hydronium ions will combine with the hydroxide ions and shift the equilibrium to the right—increasing the concentration of magnesium ions in the solution.

The effect of the addition of hydronium ion on the solubility can be seen by adding the equation above to the equation for the autoionization of water doubled and written in reverse:

$$MgF_2(s) + 2\ H_2O(l) \rightleftharpoons Mg^{2+}(aq) + 2\ HF(aq) + 2\ OH^-(aq)$$
$$K = 1.4 \times 10^{-30}$$

$$2\ OH^-(aq) + 2\ H_3O^+(aq) \rightleftharpoons 4\ H_2O(l) \qquad 1/K_w^2 = 1.0 \times 10^{28}$$

$$MgF_2(s) + 2\ H_3O^+(aq) \rightleftharpoons Mg^{2+}(aq) + 2\ HF(aq) + 2\ H_2O(l)$$
$$K = 1.4 \times 10^{-2}$$

The equilibrium constant for this reaction is equal to K_{sp}/K_a^2, where K_a is the ionization constant for the conjugate acid (HF) of the anion of the salt (F$^-$). The equilibrium constant is relatively large and the concentration of Mg^{2+} is considerably higher when acid is added to the solution.

The pH will influence the solubility of any salt containing the conjugate base of a weak acid. The sulfide ion is the conjugate base of a particularly weak acid (the hydrogen sulfide ion HS$^-$). This means that the sulfide ion is a strong base and reacts with water to produce hydrogen sulfide ions and hydroxide ions:

$$S^{2-}(aq) \ + \ H_2O(l) \ \rightleftharpoons \ HS^-(aq) \ + \ OH^-(aq)$$

base   acid   acid   base

stronger   stronger   weaker   weaker

The system lies completely on the weaker side

K_{a2} for hydrosulfuric acid H_2S is about 10^{-19}. This means that the K_b for this hydrolysis reaction is about 10^5—the reaction is very much product-favored. When a sulfide salt dissolves very slightly in water, there are essentially no sulfide ions in solution, they hydrolyze completely to HS$^-$ ions. Consider zinc sulfide:

$$ZnS(s) \rightleftharpoons Zn^{2+}(aq) + S^{2-}(aq) \qquad K_{sp} = 1.8 \times 10^{-30}$$
$$S^{2-}(aq) + H_2O(l) \rightleftharpoons HS^-(aq) + OH^-(aq) \qquad K = {\sim}10^5$$

$$ZnS(s) + H_2O(l) \rightleftharpoons Zn^{2+}(aq) + HS^-(aq) + OH^-(aq) \qquad K = {\sim}1.8 \times 10^{-25}$$

Solubility products for sulfides are normally the equilibrium constants for this reaction (Table 46.1).

The hydronium ion (H_3O^+) from an added acid reacts with both the hydrogen sulfide ion and the hydroxide ion of this system, removing both from the system, and shifting the equilibrium to the right. Zinc sulfide is much more soluble in acidic solution:

$$H_3O^+(aq) + HS^-(aq) \rightleftharpoons H_2S(aq) + H_2O(l) \qquad K = 1.1 \times 10^7$$
$$H_3O^+(aq) + OH^-(aq) \rightleftharpoons 2\ H_2O(l) \qquad K = 1.0 \times 10^{14}$$
$$ZnS(s) + H_2O(l) \rightleftharpoons Zn^{2+}(aq) + HS^-(aq) + OH^-(aq) \qquad K = {\sim}1.8 \times 10^{-25}$$

$$ZnS(s) + 2\ H_3O^+(aq) \rightleftharpoons Zn^{2+}(aq) + H_2S(aq) + 2\ H_2O(l) \qquad K_{spa} = {\sim}2.0 \times 10^{-4}$$

This equilibrium is often referred to as K_{spa}—the solubility product in acidic conditions. Removal of H_2S from the solution as hydrogen sulfide gas will shift the equilibrium even further to the right.

Water is a stronger acid than HS$^-$. The HS$^-$ ion is not acidic at all in aqueous solution. In other words, the S^{2-} ion cannot exist in water.

This is analogous to saying that NH$_3$ is not acidic in water, or that the anion NH$_2^-$ cannot exist in water.

Or you can compare the behavior of S^{2-} to the behavior of oxide ions O^{2-} in water. Oxide ions react with water to produce hydroxide ions in solution.

It is perhaps misleading to say that zinc sulfide is more soluble in acidic solution. Certainly more zinc sulfide dissolves in acidic solution, but the salt is no longer zinc sulfide. If, for example, the acid used is nitric acid, the zinc in solution is zinc nitrate.

The same is true of calcium carbonate below. If nitric acid is added to calcium carbonate, the salt dissolves as calcium nitrate. The carbon dioxide bubbles out of the solution.

TABLE 46.1 Solubility constants K_{sp} for some sparingly soluble sulfide salts.

K_{sp}^* is the equilibrium constant for the hypothetical but unrealistic equilibrium:

$$ZnS(s) \rightleftharpoons Zn^{2+}(aq) + S^{2-}(aq)$$

K_{sp} is the equilibrium constant for the reaction:

$$ZnS(s) + H_2O(l) \rightleftharpoons Zn^{2+}(aq) + HS^-(aq) + OH^-(aq)$$

K_{spa} is the equilibrium constant for the reaction in acidic solution:

$$ZnS(s) + 2\,H_3O^+(aq) \rightleftharpoons Zn^{2+}(aq) + H_2S(aq) + 2\,H_2O(l)$$

The relationships are: $K_{spa} = K_{sp}^*/K_{a1}K_{a2}$, or $K_{spa} = 1.1 \times 10^{26} \times K_{sp}^*$

$K_{spa} = K_{sp}/K_wK_{a2}$, or $K_{spa} = 1.1 \times 10^{21} \times K_{sp}$

Salt		K_{sp}^*	K_{sp}	K_{spa}
Cadmium sulfide	CdS	8×10^{-33}	8×10^{-28}	8×10^{-7}
Copper(II) sulfide	CuS	6×10^{-42}	6×10^{-37}	6×10^{-16}
Iron(II) sulfide	FeS	6×10^{-24}	6×10^{-19}	6×10^{2}
Lead(II) sulfide	PbS	3×10^{-33}	3×10^{-28}	3×10^{-7}
Manganese(II) sulfide	MnS	3×10^{-19}	3×10^{-14}	3×10^{7}
Mercury(II) sulfide	HgS	2×10^{-58}	2×10^{-53}	2×10^{-32}
Silver sulfide	Ag_2S	6×10^{-56}	6×10^{-51}	6×10^{-30}
Tin(II) sulfide	SnS	1×10^{-31}	1×10^{-26}	1×10^{-5}
Zinc sulfide	ZnS	2×10^{-30}	2×10^{-25}	2×10^{-4}

Other examples of insoluble salts that dissolve when treated with a strong acid are the carbonates. Calcium carbonate, for example, dissolves completely in strong acid even though its solubility product is quite small ($K_{sp} = 8.7 \times 10^{-9}$). The reactions that occur in acidic solution are:

$CaCO_3(s) \rightleftharpoons Ca^{2+}(aq) + \cancel{CO_3^{2-}(aq)}$	$K = 3.4 \times 10^{-9}$
$\cancel{CO_3^{2-}(aq)} + H_2O(l) \rightleftharpoons HCO_3^-(aq) + \cancel{OH^-}(aq)$	$K_b = K_w/K_{a2} = 2.1 \times 10^{-4}$
$\cancel{HCO_3^-}(aq) + H_2O(l) \rightleftharpoons H_2CO_3(aq) + \cancel{OH^-}(aq)$	$K_b = K_w/K_{a1} = 2.2 \times 10^{-8}$
$2\,H_3O^+(aq) + 2\,\cancel{OH^-}(aq) \rightleftharpoons \cancel{4}^{2}H_2O(l)$	$K = 1.0 \times 10^{28}$

$CaCO_3(s) + 2\,H_3O^+(aq) \rightleftharpoons Ca^{2+}(aq) + H_2CO_3(aq) + 2\,H_2O(l)$ $K = 1.6 \times 10^8$

The equilibrium constant for the overall reaction is large and the reaction goes to completion. Because the carbonic acid H_2CO_3 is really just a solution of carbon dioxide in water, the carbon dioxide bubbles out of the solution shifting the equilibrium even further to the right. When a strong acid is added to calcium carbonate, the effervescence of carbon dioxide occurs immediately (Figure 46.2).

In addition to sulfides and carbonates, sparingly soluble metal phosphates and hydroxides are much more soluble in acidic solutions. The solubility of any salt containing an anion that is the conjugate base of a weak acid will be greater in acidic solution:

$$Ca_3(PO_4)_2(s) + 6\,H_3O^+(aq) \rightleftharpoons 3\,Ca^{2+}(aq) + 2\,H_3PO_4(aq) + 6\,H_2O(l)$$

$$Mg(OH)_2(s) + 2\,H_3O^+(aq) \rightleftharpoons Mg^{2+}(aq) + 4\,H_2O(l)$$

If the anion of the salt is the conjugate base of a strong acid (e.g. chloride Cl^-, bromide Br^-, or iodide I^-), then addition of a strong acid will not increase the

FIGURE 46.2 Addition of a strong acid (HCl) to limestone (calcium carbonate).
The effervescence of carbon dioxide by the action of a strong acid on calcium carbonate.

You may wonder if the solubility of a salt of a weak base and strong acid is increased in the presence of a strong base. The same principles would apply. However, the common weak base is ammonia and most ammonium salts are soluble, so the problem doesn't arise.

solubility. These conjugate bases are very weak and are not removed from the equilibrium by the strong acid. Moreover, if HCl is added to a chloride salt the solubility is suppressed by the common ion effect and the salt is even less soluble in the strong acid than in water.

EXAMPLE 46.2   THE EFFECT OF A STRONG ACID ON THE SOLUBILITY OF A SALT

Determine whether the addition of a strong acid will affect the solubility of the following salts:

a. Chromium(III) hydroxide $Cr(OH)_3$

b. Lead(II) iodide PbI_2

c. Calcium fluoride CaF_2

UNDERSTAND THE QUESTION

The solubility of any salt containing an anion that is the conjugate base of a weak acid will be greater in acidic solution. This occurs because the hydronium ions from the strong acid combine with the anion of the salt to produce the weak acid from which the salt is derived. This removes the anion from the system and shifts the equilibrium to the right.

PLAN THE SOLUTION

Determine the acid used to make the salt. If the acid is weak, the solubility will increase in the presence of added hydronium ion. If the acid is strong, the solubility will *not* increase in the presence of added hydronium ion.

SOLVE THE PROBLEM

a. Chromium(III) hydroxide $Cr(OH)_3$. The hydroxide ion is the conjugate base of the weak acid water—the solubility will increase.

b. Lead(II) iodide PbI_2. The iodide ion is the conjugate base of the strong acid HI. The solubility will not be affected unless the strong acid is HI—in which case the solubility will be suppressed.

c. Calcium fluoride CaF_2. The fluoride ion is the conjugate base of the weak acid HF—the solubility will increase.

PROBLEM 46.2A

Determine whether the addition of a strong acid will affect the solubility of the following salts:

a. Magnesium ammonium phosphate $MgNH_4PO_4$

b. Copper(I) iodide CuI

c. Strontium iodate $Sr(IO_3)_2$

PROBLEM 46.2B

Determine whether the addition of a strong acid will affect the solubility of the following salts:

a. Copper(II) oxalate CuC_2O_4

b. Copper(I) chloride CuCl

c. Silver bromide AgBr

46.3   Formation of Complex Ions

One of the Lewis acid-base reactions discussed in Unit 38 was the coordination of molecules or ions, possessing a lone pair of electrons, to metal cations. The metal cation is the Lewis acid and the molecule or ion with the lone pair is the Lewis base, commonly called a **ligand**. The compound that results is called a coordination compound or complex ion.

Whenever a metal ion is dissolved in water, the metal ion is hydrated—surrounded by water molecules. In this case the water molecules of the solvent are the ligands. This coordination of water molecules is implied by the symbol (aq). When a stronger ligand (a stronger Lewis base) is added, then the water molecules are displaced. For example, consider a saturated solution of silver chloride:

$$AgCl(s) \rightleftharpoons Ag^+(aq) + Cl^-(aq) \qquad K_{sp} = 1.8 \times 10^{-10}$$

If ammonia is added to this solution, the ammonia molecules coordinate to the silver ions to form the $[Ag(NH_3)_2]^+$ complex ion:

$$Ag^+(aq) + 2\ NH_3(aq) \rightleftharpoons [Ag(NH_3)_2]^+(aq) \qquad K_f = 1.6 \times 10^7$$

The equilibrium constant for the formation of the complex ion is called the **formation constant** and is given the symbol K_f. The overall equilibrium is represented by the sum of these two simultaneous equilibria:

$$\begin{aligned} AgCl(s) &\rightleftharpoons \cancel{Ag^+}(aq) + Cl^-(aq) & K_{sp} &= 1.8 \times 10^{-10} \\ \cancel{Ag^+}(aq) + 2\ NH_3(aq) &\rightleftharpoons [Ag(NH_3)_2]^+(aq) & K_f &= 1.7 \times 10^7 \\ \hline AgCl(s) + 2\ NH_3(aq) &\rightleftharpoons [Ag(NH_3)_2]^+(aq) + Cl^-(aq) & K &= 3.1 \times 10^{-3} \end{aligned}$$

Addition of the ammonia effectively removes the Ag^+ ions from the equilibrium and more silver chloride dissolves. The equilibrium constant for the overall process is much higher than K_{sp}. In general, complex ion formation increases the solubility of a sparingly soluble salt. The formation constants for some other complex ions are listed in Table 46.2.

Another example of the increased solubility of a sparingly soluble salt occurs when silver ions are complexed by the thiosulfate anion:

$$Ag^+(aq) + 2\ S_2O_3^{2-}(aq) \rightleftharpoons [Ag(S_2O_3)_2]^{3-}(aq) \qquad K_f = 4.7 \times 10^{13}$$

This is the procedure used to remove excess silver bromide from photographic film negatives after they have been exposed to light and developed. The thiosulfate is added as an aqueous solution of sodium thiosulfate, usually called 'hypo'. The silver bromide dissolves (and is therefore removed from the negative) as the hypo is added. The process is usually called 'fixing' the negative so that it does not darken further upon additional exposure to light. The overall equilibrium is:

$$AgBr(s) + 2\ S_2O_3^{2-}(aq) \rightleftharpoons [Ag(S_2O_3)_2]^{3-}(aq) + Br^-(aq) \qquad K = 25$$

This equilibrium constant is much higher than K_{sp} for silver bromide.

TABLE 46.2   Formation constants K_f for some complex ions.

The formation constants represent the equilibrium constants for the general reaction:

$$M^{n+}(aq) + xL \rightleftharpoons [ML_x]^{n+}$$

where L, the ligand, is a neutral molecule or negatively-charged ion

Complex Ion	K_f
$[Ag(CN)_2]^-$	1.0×10^{21}
$[Ag(NH_3)_2]^+$	1.7×10^7
$[Ag(S_2O_3)_2]^{3-}$	4.7×10^{13}
$[Ag(SCN)_4]^{3-}$	1.2×10^{10}
$[Al(OH)_4]^-$	3.0×10^{33}
$[Cd(NH_3)_4]^{2+}$	1.3×10^7
$[Cu(CN)_4]^{2-}$	1.0×10^{25}
$[CuCl_3]^{2-}$	5.0×10^5
$[Cu(NH_3)_4]^{2+}$	6.8×10^{12}
$[Co(NH_3)_6]^{3+}$	5.0×10^{31}
$[Fe(CN)_6]^{4-}$	2.0×10^{35}
$[Fe(CN)_6]^{3-}$	7.0×10^{42}
$[Fe(SCN)]^{2+}$	8.9×10^2
$[Ni(NH_3)_6]^{2+}$	5.6×10^8
$[Ni(CN)_4]^{2-}$	2.0×10^{31}
$[Zn(NH_3)_4]^{2+}$	2.9×10^9
$[Zn(OH)_4]^{2-}$	4.6×10^{17}

EXAMPLE 46.3 DETERMINATION OF THE CONCENTRATION OF A METAL ION IN SOLUTION IN THE PRESENCE OF A LIGAND

Solutions used for electroplating silver often contain cyanide ions. The cyanide ions complex the silver ions. This ensures that the concentration of silver ions in the solution is very low, producing a slow, uniform, and very fine electroplated finish, while maintaining a large reservoir of silver for the process. Calculate the concentration of free silver ion [Ag$^+$] in an aqueous solution of 0.10 M AgNO$_3$ containing 0.25 M KCN.

UNDERSTAND THE QUESTION

Silver ions form a complex ion with cyanide ions in solution:

$$Ag^+(aq) + 2\,CN^-(aq) \rightleftharpoons [Ag(CN)_2]^-(aq) \qquad K_f = 1.0 \times 10^{21}$$

The equilibrium constant is very large and the concentration of free silver ions in solution in the presence of excess cyanide ions will be extremely small. The problem can be solved using an ICE table such as those introduced in Unit 35.

PLAN THE SOLUTION

Follow the usual procedure for a system with a large value for the equilibrium constant. Assume that the reaction goes to completion and then backs off very slightly. Set up an ICE Table to summarize the data.

SOLVE THE PROBLEM

The ICE Table is (with concentrations in M):

$$Ag^+ + 2\,CN^- \rightleftharpoons [Ag(CN)_2]^-$$

Initial: 0.10 0.25 0

Assume the reaction goes to completion using 0.10 M Ag$^+$ (all of it) and 0.20 M CN$^-$ (leaving 0.05 M CN$^-$ unused):

0   0.05   0.10

Then backs off slightly to the left:

Change: $+ x$ $+ 2x$ $- x$

Equilibrium concentrations: x $0.05 + 2x$ $010 - x$

The equilibrium concentrations are now substituted into the expression for the equilibrium constant K_f and the value of x calculated.

$$K_f = \frac{[Ag(CN)_2^-]}{[Ag^+][CN^-]^2} = \frac{(0.10 - x)}{x(0.05 + 2x)^2} = 1.0 \times 10^{21}$$

In this case, because K_f is so large, x is a very small number compared to 0.05, and the x in (0.050 + 2x) and the x in (0.10 − x) can be ignored. So,

$$x = 4.0 \times 10^{-20}$$
$$[Ag^+] = 4.0 \times 10^{-20}\ M.$$

The concentration of free Ag$^+$ ions in solution is extremely low.

PROBLEM 46.3A

Calculate the concentration of free nickel(II) ion [Ni^{2+}] in an aqueous solution of 0.15 M Ni(NO$_3$)$_2$ containing 1.00 M NH$_3$.

$$Ni^{2+}(aq) + 6\,NH_3(aq) \rightleftharpoons [Ni(NH_3)_6]^{2+}(aq) \qquad K_f = 5.6 \times 10^8$$

PROBLEM 46.3B

Calculate the concentration of free silver ion [Ag^+] in an aqueous solution of 0.20 M $AgNO_3$ containing 1.00 M $Na_2S_2O_3$.

$$Ag^+(aq) + 2\,S_2O_3^{2-}(aq) \rightleftharpoons [Ag(S_2O_3)_2]^{3-}(aq) \qquad K_f = 4.7 \times 10^{13}$$

Let's continue with an examination of the complex formed between silver ions and cyanide ions and determine how the solubility of silver bromide is increased in the presence of cyanide ions. The overall process is represented by the equation:

$$AgBr(s) + 2\,CN^-(aq) \rightleftharpoons [Ag(CN)_2]^-(aq) + Br^-(aq) \qquad K = 5.4 \times 10^8$$

Again the formation of the complex silver ion increases the magnitude of the equilibrium constant and the solution process now is heavily product favored.

K_{sp} for AgBr	= 5.4×10^{-13}
K_f for $[Ag(CN)_2]^-$	= 1.0×10^{21}
Overall K	= 5.4×10^8

EXAMPLE 46.4   DETERMINATION OF THE SOLUBILITY OF SILVER BROMIDE IN THE PRESENCE OF CYANIDE IONS

Calculate the solubility of silver bromide in an aqueous solution containing 0.30 M KCN.

UNDERSTAND THE QUESTION

As noted above, the solubility of silver bromide is increased in the presence of the cyanide ions due to the formation of the silver cyanide complex ion.

PLAN THE SOLUTION

We'll solve the problem again using an ICE table. Always start the problem by writing the equation for the overall process.

SOLVE THE PROBLEM

The ICE Table is (with concentrations in M):

$$AgBr(s) + 2\,CN^- \rightleftharpoons [Ag(CN)_2]^- + Br^-$$

Initial:	0.30	0	0

Assume the reaction goes to completion using all the available cyanide ion:

	0	0.15	0.15

Then backs off slightly to the left:

Change:	+ 2x	– x	– x
Equilibrium concentrations:	2x	0.15 – x	0.15 – x

The equilibrium concentrations are now substituted into the expression for the equilibrium constant K_f and the value of x calculated.

$$K_f = \frac{[Ag(CN)_2^-][Br^-]}{[CN^-]^2} = \frac{(0.15 - x)^2}{(2x)^2} = 5.4 \times 10^8$$

This expression can be simplified by taking the square root of both sides:

$$(0.15 - x) = (2x) \times 2.32 \times 10^4$$

$$x = 3.2 \times 10^{-6}$$

The value of x is very small. Essentially all the cyanide ion is used in the formation of the silver complex. This might have been anticipated—the value of the equilibrium constant is very large. The concentration of the silver cyanide complex is 0.15 M—one half the concentration of the cyanide ion originally present.

The solubility of silver bromide in the presence of ammonia is not as great as in the presence of cyanide ions. This is because the formation constant for the diamminesilver(I) complex $[Ag(NH_3)_2]^+$ is only 1.7×10^7 compared to 1.0×10^{21} for the dicyanosilver(I) complex $[Ag(CN)_2]^-$. The following problem illustrates this.

PROBLEM 46.4A

Calculate the solubility of silver bromide in an aqueous solution containing 1.0 M NH_3. K_f for the formation of the $[Ag(NH_3)_2]^+$ is 1.7×10^7.

PROBLEM 46.4B

Calculate the solubility of nickel(II) iodate in an aqueous solution containing 1.0 M NH_3. Equilibrium constants are listed in Tables 45.1 and 46.2.

46.4   Amphoteric Hydroxides

Aluminum hydroxide $Al(OH)_3$ is unusual in that it is soluble in strongly acidic solution and soluble in strongly basic solution but insoluble at pHs between 4 and 10 (Figure 46.3). Similar behavior is exhibited by $Zn(OH)_2$, $Sn(OH)_2$, $Cr(OH)_3$, and $Pb(OH)_2$. These hydroxides are called **amphoteric** hydroxides. The corresponding oxides, which form the hydroxides in water, are called amphoteric oxides.

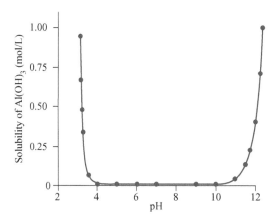

FIGURE 46.3   A chart of the solubility of aluminum hydroxide at different pH values.
$Al(OH)_3$ is virtually insoluble in water between a pH of 4 and a pH of 10 but dissolves in strong acid and strong base.

Aluminum hydroxide acts as an acid in basic solution. The high 3+ charge on the Al^{3+} ion pulls electrons away from the oxygen atom of a coordinated water molecule (*cf.* Figure 41.3). This in turn polarizes the O–H bond in the water molecule and allows a hydrogen ion to break away.

Aluminum hydroxide acts as a base in acidic solution when one of the hydroxide ions coordinated to the aluminum accepts a hydrogen ion from the acid to form a complex ion.

In acid: $[Al(H_2O)_3(OH)_3] + H_3O^+ \rightleftharpoons [Al(H_2O)_4(OH)_2]^+ + H_2O$

In base: $[Al(H_2O)_3(OH)_3] + OH^- \rightleftharpoons [Al(H_2O)_2(OH)_4]^- + H_2O$

The neutral species $[Al(H_2O)_3(OH)_3]$ is insoluble but both the protonated forms and the deprotonated forms—the charged species—are soluble (Figure 46.4). The protonated form can be protonated further to $[Al(H_2O)_5(OH)]^{2+}$ and $[Al(H_2O)_6]^{3+}$ depending upon the strength of the acid.

Species such as $[Al(H_2O)_2(OH)_4]^-$ are normally written just as $[Al(OH)_4]^-$, that is, without the coordinated water molecules.

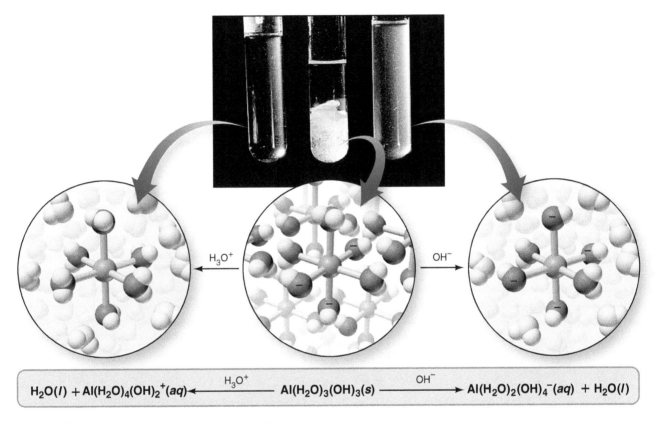

FIGURE 46.4   The amphoteric behavior of Al(OH)$_3$.
In acid the charged species $[Al(H_2O)_4(OH)_2]^+$ is soluble. In base the charged species $[Al(H_2O)_2(OH)_4]^-$ is soluble. But in neutral solution the neutral species $[Al(H_2O)_3(OH)_3]$ is insoluble.

46.5   Qualitative Analysis

The precipitation of an insoluble salt provides a means to identify the metal cations or anions present in a solution. The different solubilities of metal salts, the ability of some metal cations to form complex ions, and the dependence of the solubility on the pH of the solution provide ways to distinguish between different metals. A general scheme has been developed that allows the identification of metals present in a solution. The method is usually referred to as **qualitative analysis**.

In general, the scheme involves the precipitation of an insoluble salt, or salts, and then the separation of the precipitate and the remaining solution, called the

Cations usually included in a qualitative analysis scheme are:

Ag⁺
Al³⁺
As³⁺
Ba²⁺
Bi³⁺
Ca²⁺
Cd²⁺
Co²⁺
Cr³⁺
Cu²⁺
Fe²⁺
Fe³⁺
K⁺
Hg²⁺
Hg₂²⁺
Mg²⁺
Mn²⁺
Na⁺
NH₄⁺
Ni²⁺
Pb²⁺
Sb³⁺
Sn²⁺
Sn⁴⁺
Sr²⁺
Zn²⁺

There are, of course, other metal cations and the scheme can be modified appropriately.

supernatant liquid, in a centrifuge. The supernatant liquid is examined further for the presence of other metal cations. The precipitate is examined to determine which precipitates are present. Let's look at the ways in which various metal ions in a solution can be identified (Figure 46.5).

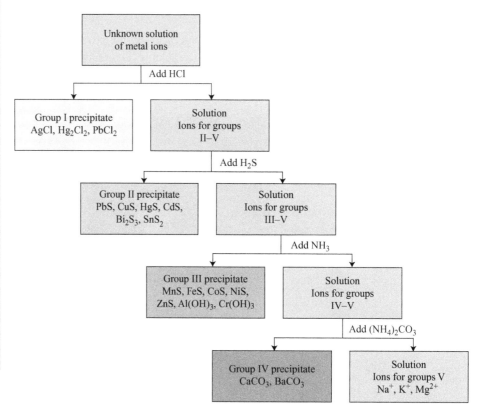

FIGURE 46.5 A general qualitative analysis scheme.
Cations are divided into five groups based upon the different solubilities of their chlorides, sulfides, hydroxides, and phosphates.

If a dilute (6 M) solution of HCl is added to a solution of metal salts, the white insoluble Ag^+, Hg_2^{2+}, and Pb^{2+} chlorides will precipitate from solution. These cations are referred to as Group 1 cations (not to be confused with Group 1A in the Periodic Table).

The supernatant liquid is acidic and is treated with H_2S. Sulfides insoluble in acidic conditions precipitate from solution. These cations are referred to as the Group 2 cations and include As^{3+}, Bi^{3+}, Cd^{2+}, Cu^{2+}, Pb^{2+} (again), Hg^{2+}, Sb^{3+}, and Sn^{4+}. Note that these cations are not always present as simple hydrated cations. For example, Bi^{3+} is present as the complex ion $BiCl_4^-$ due to the HCl added in the first step. The arsenic is present as the acid H_3AsO_3. However, the sulfides precipitate from solution. Many have different colors. For example, cadmium sulfide is yellow, tin(II) sulfide is red, and antimony(III) sulfide is bright yellow.

The precipitate is removed and the supernatant liquid made slightly basic to precipitate those sulfides insoluble in basic solution. These are the metal cations of Group 3 and include Mn^{2+}, Fe^{2+}, Co^{2+}, Ni^{2+}, and Zn^{2+}. The insoluble hydroxides $Al(OH)_3$, $Fe(OH)_3$ and $Cr(OH)_3$ also precipitate at this point.

The supernatant liquid is now treated with ammonium carbonate to precipitate the insoluble carbonates of Group 4—$CaCO_3$, $SrCO_3$, and $BaCO_3$. The magnesium carbonate does not precipitate because the carbonate concentration in the slightly basic solution is too low.

The remaining cations in solution are the alkali metals and magnesium. These are the cations of Group 5. Magnesium is identified by a white precipitate of $MgNH_4PO_4$ upon addition of $(NH_4)_2HPO_4$. Calcium, strontium, and barium will also form insoluble phosphates if they are still present in the solution. The alkali metals are identified by flame tests. Each alkali metal changes the color of a bunsen flame to a characteristic color.

Once the ions have been separated into groups, additional separations and specific tests are necessary to identify the ions present within each group. For example, in Group 1, three ions precipitate: the insoluble chlorides Ag^+, Hg_2^{2+}, and Pb^{2+}. The Pb^{2+} is more soluble than the other two—that's why it is also precipitated in Group 2. The precipitate from Group 1 is treated with hot water and the lead dissolves. Treatment with sodium chromate precipitates the yellow lead chromate $PbCrO_4$ which confirms the presence of Pb^{2+}. Of the Ag^+ and Hg_2^{2+} ions, only the silver chloride dissolves in ammonia due to the formation of the diammine complex $[Ag(NH_3)_2]^+$. The precipitates are therefore treated with dilute ammonia solution, then the precipitates are separated from the supernatant solution, and the solution treated with nitric acid to remove the ammonia. If any silver is present in the supernatant solution as the complex $[Ag(NH_3)_2]^+$, it is reprecipitated as AgCl.

Similar schemes are used to identify the ions present in the precipitates of the other groups.

Review Questions

1. Explain how the solubility of a salt, containing as an anion the conjugate base of a weak acid, can be increased by the addition of a strong acid. Is the solubility of a salt containing an anion that is the conjugate base of a strong acid affected by the addition of a strong acid?

2. Explain why the solubility of a salt is increased by complex ion formation. Describe an example.

3. Describe the meaning of the word 'amphoteric'. Explain why amphoteric hydroxides are soluble in strong acids, insoluble in neutral solution, but soluble again in strong bases.

Solutions to Problems

PROBLEM 46.1A

The two equilibria are:

$$Hg_2Cl_2(s) \rightleftharpoons Hg_2^{2+} + 2\ Cl^- \quad K_{sp} = 1.4 \times 10^{-18}$$
$$Hg_2I_2(s) \rightleftharpoons Hg_2^{2+} + 2\ I^- \quad K_{sp} = 5.2 \times 10^{-29}$$

Reverse the second equation and add to the first equation:

$$Hg_2Cl_2(s) + 2\ I^- \rightleftharpoons Hg_2I_2(s) + 2\ Cl^- \quad K = 2.7 \times 10^{10}$$

The equilibrium constant $K = [Cl^-]^2/[I^-]^2 = 2.7 \times 10^{10}$

The ratio of $[Cl^-]$ to $[I^-] = 163{,}000$

If the concentration of $[Cl^-]$ is 0.010, then $[I^-] = 6.1 \times 10^{-8}\ M$.

This answer is the same as that obtained in the solution to Problem 45.5A.

PROBLEM 46.2A

a. Magnesium ammonium phosphate $MgNH_4PO_4$. The phosphate ion is the conjugate base of the very weak acid HPO_4^{2-}—the solubility will increase.

b. Copper(I) iodide CuI. The iodide ion is the conjugate base of the strong acid HI—the solubility will not be affected (unless the strong acid is HI).

c. Strontium iodate $Sr(IO_3)_2$. The iodate ion is the conjugate base of iodic acid. This acid is weak in aqueous solution. The solubility of strontium iodate will increase when a strong acid is added.

PROBLEM 46.3A

The ICE Table is (with concentrations in M):

$$Ni^{2+}(aq) + 6\,NH_3 \rightleftharpoons [Ni(NH_3)_6]^{2+}$$

Initial: 0.15   1.00   0

Assume the reaction goes to completion using 0.15 M Ni^{2+} (all of it) and 0.90 M NH_3 (leaving 0.10 M NH_3 unused):

                  0   0.10   0.15

Then backs off slightly to the left:

Change: $+ x$ $+ 6x$ $- x$

Equilibrium
  concentrations: x   0.10 + 6x   0.15 − x

The equilibrium concentrations are now substituted into the expression for the equilibrium constant K_f and the value of x calculated.

$$K_f = \frac{[Ni(NH_3)_6^{2+}]}{[Ni^{2+}][NH_3]^6} = \frac{(0.15 - x)}{x(0.10 + 6x)^6} = 5.6 \times 10^8$$

In this case, because K_f is large, x is a comparatively small number compared to 0.15 and 0.10. So,

$$x = 2.7 \times 10^{-4}$$
$$[Ni^{2+}] = 2.7 \times 10^{-4}\ M.$$

To check that the neglect of the x in the concentration terms for $[Ni(NH_3)_6^{2+}]$ and $[NH_3]$ is justified, the value of

x can be substituted in the equilibrium constant expression and a new value calculated.

$$[Ni^{2+}] = 2.4 \times 10^{-4}\ M.$$

The iteration can be repeated until a consistent result is achieved.

PROBLEM 46.4A

The ICE Table is (with concentrations in M):

$$AgBr(s) + 2\,NH_3 \rightleftharpoons [Ag(NH_3)_2]^+ + Br^-$$

Initial: 1.0   0   0

Change: $- 2x$ $+ x$ $+ x$

Equilibrium
  concentrations: 1.0 − 2x   x   x

The equilibrium concentrations are now substituted into the expression for the equilibrium constant K and the value of x calculated.

K_{sp} for AgBr	$= 5.4 \times 10^{-13}$
K_f for $[Ag(NH_3)_2]^+$	$= 1.7 \times 10^7$
Overall K	$= 9.2 \times 10^{-6}$

$$K = \frac{[Ag(NH_3)_2^+][Br^-]}{[NH_3]^2} = \frac{x^2}{(1.0 - 2x)^2} = 9.2 \times 10^{-6}$$

This expression can be simplified by taking the square root of both sides:

$$x/(1.0 - 2x) = 3.03 \times 10^{-3}$$
$$x = 3.0 \times 10^{-3}$$

The value of x is small—the concentration of the $[Ag(NH_3)_2]^+$ complex is low ($3.0 \times 10^{-3}\ M$). However, the solubility is considerably higher than the concentration of silver ions in solution in the absence of ammonia ($7.4 \times 10^{-7}\ M$).

Answers to Review Questions

1. An anion that is the conjugate base of a weak acid hydrolyzes in solution:

$$A^-(aq) + H_2O(l) \rightleftharpoons HA(aq) + OH^-(aq) \quad K_b = K_w/K_a$$

Addition of a strong acid removes hydroxide ion OH^- from this equilibrium and the system moves to the right. This removes the A^- ion and causes more salt to dissolve. When a strong acid is added to the solution of a salt containing as an anion the conjugate base of a strong acid, nothing happens because there is no hydrolysis of the anion. If the acid contains a common ion, for example, HCl is added to a chloride salt, the solubility is suppressed by the common ion effect and the salt is even less soluble in the strong acid than in pure water.

2. If a complex ion is formed in solution the solubility of the salt will increase. For example, silver chloride is more soluble in the presence of ammonia due to the formation of the complex ion $[Ag(NH_3)_2]^+$. An overall equilibrium constant can be obtained by multiplying the K_{sp} for the solution process and the K_f for the complex ion formation.

3. An amphoteric substance, for example, aluminum hydroxide, behaves as a base in strongly acidic solution and as an acid in strongly basic solution. In neutral solution, aluminum hydroxide exists as the neutral species $[Al(H_2O)_3(OH)_3]$ and is insoluble. In acidic and basic solutions, the charged species—the protonated form $[Al(H_2O)_4(OH)_2]^+$ and the deprotonated form $[Al(H_2O)_2(OH)_4]^-$—are soluble.

End-of-Unit Problems

1. Determine the relative concentrations of bromide ion and iodide ion in a $PbBr_2(s)/PbBr_2(aq)$ system after some sodium iodide is added. Assume solid $PbBr_2$ and solid PbI_2 are present at equilibrium.

2. Determine the relative concentrations of chloride ion and iodide ion in a $AgCl(s)/AgCl(aq)$ system after some potassium iodide is added. Assume solid $AgCl$ and solid AgI are present at equilibrium.

3. Suppose that a saturated solution of calcium sulfate, with some solid calcium sulfate, is added to a system of saturated lead(II) sulfate solution and solid lead(II) sulfate. When equilibrium is reached, the system contains both solids. What is the ratio of the concentrations of the calcium and lead ions in solution?

4. Calcium and magnesium carbonate are mixed and partially dissolved. What is the ratio of the concentrations of the calcium and magnesium ions in solution at equilibrium?

5. K_{sp} for nickel(II) hydroxide $Ni(OH)_2$ is 5.48×10^{-16}. At what pH will nickel(II) hydroxide precipitate from a 0.050 M solution of nickel(II) nitrate?

6. K_{sp} for scandium(III) hydroxide $Sc(OH)_3$ is 2.22×10^{-31}. At what pH will scandium(III) hydroxide precipitate from a 0.0020 M solution of scandium(III) acetate?

7. A solution contains lead nitrate, silver nitrate, and mercury(I) nitrate, each at a concentration of 0.010 M. A solution of sodium chloride is added. In which order do the metal chlorides precipitate? What concentration of chloride is required for each metal?

8. A solution contains 0.010 M beryllium, cadmium, and lead ions. A solution of sodium hydroxide is added to the mixture. In which order do the metal hydroxides precipitate? What concentration of hydroxide is required for each metal?

   K_{sp} beryllium hydroxide $Be(OH)_2 = 6.9 \times 10^{-22}$

   K_{sp} cadmium hydroxide $Cd(OH)_2 = 7.2 \times 10^{-15}$

   K_{sp} lead hydroxide $Pb(OH)_2 = 1.4 \times 10^{-20}$

9. Determine whether the addition of a strong acid will affect the solubility of the following salts:

   a. aluminum phosphate $AlPO_4$

   b. cesium perchlorate $CsClO_4$

   c. lead(II) chloride $PbCl_2$

10. Determine whether the addition of a strong acid will affect the solubility of the following salts:

    a. magnesium carbonate $MgCO_3$

    b. mercury(I) oxalate $Hg_2C_2O_4$

    c. silver iodide AgI

11. Write equations representing

    a. the solution process of the sparingly soluble strontium fluoride SrF_2.

    b. the hydrolysis of the fluoride ion in aqueous solution.

    c. the overall process when strontium fluoride dissolves in water.

    Indicate the direction in which the system shifts when a strong acid (H_3O^+) is added to the solution. The K_{sp} for strontium fluoride is 4.3×10^{-9}. Calculate the equilibrium constant for the overall reaction described in (c).

12. Write equations representing

    a. the solution process of the sparingly soluble zinc carbonate $ZnCO_3$.

    b. the hydrolysis of the carbonate ion in aqueous solution.

    c. the overall process when zinc carbonate dissolves in water.

    Indicate the direction in which the system shifts when a strong acid (H_3O^+) is added to the solution. Calculate the equilibrium constant for the overall reaction described in (c).

13. Write equations representing

    a. the solution process of the sparingly soluble nickel(II) iodate $Ni(IO_3)_2$.

    b. the formation of the complex $[Ni(NH_3)_6]^{2+}$ with ammonia.

    c. the overall solution process when nickel(II) iodate dissolves in aqueous ammonia.

14. Write equations representing

    a. the solution process of the sparingly soluble silver cyanide $AgCN$.

    b. the formation of the complex $[Ag(CN^-)_2]^-$ with additional cyanide ions.

    c. the overall process when sodium cyanide is added to a system of $AgCN(s)/AgCN(aq)$.

15. If the formation constant for the complex ion $[Ag(CN)_2]^-$ is 1.0×10^{21}, and the K_{sp} for silver iodide AgI is 8.5×10^{-17}, write the equation for the reaction that occurs when sodium cyanide is added to a saturated solution of silver iodide in the presence of solid silver iodide and calculate the equilibrium constant for the reaction.

16. If the formation constant for the complex ion $[Cu(NH_3)_4]^{2+}$ is 6.8×10^{12}, and the K_{sp} for copper(II) oxalate CuC_2O_4 is 4.4×10^{-10}, write the equation for the reaction that occurs when ammonia is added to a saturated solution of copper(II) oxalate in the presence of solid copper(II) oxalate and calculate the equilibrium constant for the reaction.

17. Zinc hydroxide $Zn(OH)_2$ is an amphoteric hydroxide that dissolves in strongly basic solution even though the K_{sp} for $Zn(OH)_2$ is only 3.0×10^{-17}. The formation constant K_f for the tetrahydroxozincate ion $[Zn(OH)_4]^{2-}$ is 4.6×10^{17}. Write the equation for the overall reaction and the expression for the equilibrium constant. What pH is required to dissolve sufficient zinc hydroxide to make a 0.020 M solution?

18. Cobalt(II) hydroxide $Co(OH)_2$ is only sparingly soluble in neutral aqueous solution. The K_{sp} for the salt is 6.0×10^{-15}. However, the hydroxide will form the complex ion $[Co(OH)_4]^{2-}$ in strongly basic solutions. The formation constant K_f for the tetrahydroxocobaltate(II) ion $[Co(OH)_4]^{2-}$ is 5.0×10^9. Write the equation for the overall reaction and the expression for the equilibrium constant. What pH is required to dissolve sufficient cobalt(II) hydroxide to make a 1.0×10^{-5} M solution?

19. For the salt calcium fluoride CaF_2

    a. Write an equation representing the solution of CaF_2 in pure water assuming no hydrolysis.

    b. Add the equation for the hydrolysis of the fluoride ion and derive the overall equation for the solution process.

    c. Now add the equation for the autoionization of water written in reverse and obtain an equation representing the solution of CaF_2 in acidic solution.

    d. Calculate the equilibrium constant for this equation (c).

    e. Use this equation and the K you have calculated to determine the solubility of calcium fluoride in an acidic solution with a pH of 2.0.

20. For the salt silver acetate $AgCH_3CO_2$

    a. Write an equation representing the solution of $AgCH_3CO_2$ in pure water assuming no hydrolysis.

    b. Add the equation for the hydrolysis of the acetate ion and derive the overall equation for the solution process.

    c. Now add the equation for the autoionization of water written in reverse and obtain an equation representing the solution of $AgCH_3CO_2$ in acidic solution.

    d. Calculate the equilibrium constant for this equation (c).

    e. Use this equation and the K you have calculated to determine the solubility of $AgCH_3CO_2$ in an acidic solution with a pH of 3.5.

21. Suggest methods to separate the following pairs of ions:

    a. K^+ and Pb^{2+}

    b. Ag^+ and Hg_2^{2+}

    c. Mg^{2+} and K^+

22. Suggest methods to separate the following pairs of ions:

    a. Cd^{2+} and Zn^{2+}

    b. Ag^+ and Cu^{2+}

    c. Al^{3+} and As^{3+}

First Law of Thermodynamics

47.1   Introduction

We originally looked at the first law of thermodynamics in Unit 11 when we investigated the relationship between the internal energy of a system and the energy transferred between the system and its surroundings in the form of heat or work. In this unit we will examine the first law in greater detail. In particular we will examine the various processes that involve the interaction of the system with its surroundings. To begin we will review the definitions of various words and terms used in thermodynamics; we have already encountered some of these in Unit 11.

The part of the universe upon which we want to focus attention is called the **system**. The rest of the universe is called the **surroundings**. In practice, as you may recall, the surroundings need be only that part of the rest of the universe that is in thermal contact with the system.

Universe = System + Surroundings

Thermodynamic systems are classified acccording to their ability to exchange energy or matter with the surroundings:

An **open system**   —can exchange both matter and energy

A **closed system**   —can exchange energy but not matter

An **isolated system** —can exchange neither energy nor matter

The interface between a system and its surroundings, or between two systems, is called a **boundary**. A boundary may be a **wall**—an actual physical barrier—but it need not be. An example of a boundary that is *not* a wall is the surface of a liquid in a beaker on a hot plate. Walls may be rigid or movable. Examples of movable walls are balloons or pistons in cylinders.

If a wall allows the passage of energy in the form of heat it is referred to as a **diathermal** wall. If the wall is insulating, and does not allow the passage of heat, it is called **adiabatic**.

To complete this review, recall that the sign convention is such that if energy passes *into* the system, the sign is positive. If energy passes *out* of the system, the sign is negative.

47.2   The Zeroth Law of Thermodynamics

The zeroth law of thermodynamics states that if two systems are in thermal equilibrium with a third system, then the two systems must be in thermal equilibrium with each other. This is illustrated in Figure 47.1. Heat can pass through the diathermal walls between the systems A and C, and the systems B and C. So, although systems A and B are insulated from one another by the adiabatic wall, they must reach thermal equilibrium because heat can pass between A and B through the third system C.

47.3   State Functions

Review Unit 11.5.

Before we consider the first law of thermodynamics, let's review those properties of a system that are state functions and those quantities that are not.

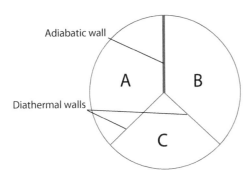

FIGURE 47.1   The Zeroth Law of Thermodynamics.
Even though separated by an adiabatic wall, the two systems A and B must be in thermal equilibrium.

A property of a system that describes the state of the system is called a **state function**. Such functions are independent of the past history of the system and what might happen to the system in the future. The property merely describes the state of the system at that particular instant. Examples are temperature, T, volume, V, pressure, P, enthalpy, H, internal energy, E, entropy, S, and free energy, G. Notice how many state functions have symbols that are upper case letters.

One important characteristic of state functions is that the change in the state function as a system moves from one state to another is independent of the path the system takes between the two. Changes in state functions, denoted by a Δ sign, are said to be **path-independent**. For example, the change in volume between two states of a system, ΔV, is simply the difference between the volumes of the two states and is independent of how the volume change takes place.

Quantites such as heat, q, and work, w, are *not* state functions—they are *not* properties of the system. Instead, they are properties of a process, how the change from one state of the system to another takes place. They are **path-dependent** functions.

The difference between heat and work is described in Unit 11.

47.4   The First Law of Thermodynamics

The first law of thermodynamics is the **law of conservation of energy**. Energy may be moved from place to place; it may change from one form into another; but it cannot be created or destroyed. The law can be written in terms of the entire universe, in which case

$$\Delta E_{univ} = \text{zero}$$

or it can be written in terms of the system as

$$\Delta E_{sys} = q + w$$

where ΔE_{sys} is the internal energy of the system, q is the heat, and w is the work. Heat and work are the means by which energy is transferred between the system and its surroundings. If no subscript is written, the ΔE invariably refers to the change in the internal energy of the system under investigation.

We will examine chemical reactions in Unit 49.

It is convenient to classify the various physical changes that can occur to a system as follows:

- A constant volume change (isochoric)
- A constant pressure change (isobaric)
- A constant temperature change (isothermal)
- A change where no heat is transferred (adiabatic)

In a constant volume process, no expansion work is done on or by the system. This means that w = zero, and the change in the internal energy of the system $\Delta E = q$. In this case the q is often given a subscript v to indicate that the heat is transferred between the system and its surroundings at constant volume.

Review Unit 11 for a description and derivation of the enthalpy change ΔH.

In a constant pressure process, some expansion work is almost always done on or by the system. Because it is sometimes difficult to determine the amount of work done, a new thermodynamic quantity called enthalpy H is used such that $\Delta H = q_p$. The subscript p on the q indicates that the heat is transferred between the system and its surroundings at constant pressure.

In summary:

$$q_v = \Delta E \text{ for a constant volume process}$$

$$q_p = \Delta H \text{ for a constant pressure process}$$

In a constant temperature process, the internal energy of the system remains the same. This means that any heat transferred between the system and its surroundings is balanced by an equivalent amount of work done on or by the system. $\Delta E = $ zero and $q = -w$.

In an adiabatic process, no heat is transferred. Any change in the internal energy of the system is a result of work done on or by the system. In this case $q = $ zero and $\Delta E = w$.

In summary:

- A constant volume change $\quad\quad w = 0 \quad\quad \therefore \Delta E = q_v$
- A constant pressure change $\quad\quad \Delta H = q_p$
- A constant temperature change $\quad\quad \Delta E = 0 \quad\quad \therefore q = -w$
- A change where no heat is transferred $\quad q = 0 \quad\quad \therefore \Delta E = w$

In any expansion, work is done by the system—the system loses energy. The amount of work done depends upon the type of expansion.

Obviously, the first of the four processes just described, where the volume is constant, is not an expansion.

We will consider three types of expansion: constant pressure, isothermal, and adiabatic, corresponding to the last three of the four processes just described. Since liquids and solids do not change in volume appreciably when the pressure or temperature is changed, we will examine the behavior of gases. Moreover, we will assume that the gas is ideal.

47.5   Constant Pressure Expansion

The amount of expansion work done by a system or on a system depends upon the pressure opposing the expansion and the change in the volume:

$$\text{work} = - \text{ pressure opposing the expansion} \times \text{change in volume}$$

$$\text{work} = - P_{ext} \times \Delta V$$

The negative sign indicates that, if the system does work, there is an increase in the volume of the system but a decrease in the internal energy of the system. If the pressure is measured in pascals, Pa, and the volume change is measured in m^3, then the work is expressed in joules. One pascal is equal to a force of one newton per square meter:

$$Work = Pa \times m^3$$
$$= N \times m^{-2} \times m^3$$
$$= N \times m$$
$$= J$$

Pressure, particularly atmospheric pressure, is often expressed in atmospheres and volumes are often expressed in liters (L). Energy, therefore, can be expressed in units of liters × atmospheres or L atm.

> The conversion between L atm and J is:
>
> 1 L atm = 101.325 J

EXAMPLE 47.1   WORK DONE DURING A CONSTANT PRESSURE EXPANSION

An ideal gas, having an initial volume of 12.7 L and temperature 310 K, expands to 25.4 L—a two-fold increase in volume. Calculate the work done by the system as it expands under a constant external pressure of 0.500 atm.

> This conversion factor is the ratio of the gas constants (*cf.* Unit 25):
>
> R = 8.314472 J K^{-1} mol^{-1}
>
> = 0.0820575 L atm K^{-1} mol^{-1}
>
> Ratio = 101.325 J L^{-1} atm^{-1}

UNDERSTAND THE QUESTION

The work done depends upon the pressure opposing the expansion and the change in the volume.

PLAN THE SOLUTION

Use the expression $w = -P\Delta V$ to determine the work done. Be careful with the units used in the calculation.

SOLVE THE PROBLEM

Change in volume = 25.4 − 12.7 L = 12.7 L

Work = −0.500 atm × 12.7 L = −6.35 L atm

= −6.35 L atm × 101.325 J $L^{-1}atm^{-1}$

= −643 J

The negative sign indicates that the system is losing energy, work is being done by the system.

PROBLEM 47.1A

A system consists of a cylinder full of gas. The gas in the cylinder expands in volume from 0.500 liters to 0.850 liters against an external pressure of 1.10 atm. At the same time the system absorbs 45 J of heat from the surroundings. Calculate the work done on or by the system. Calculate the change in the internal energy of the system.

PROBLEM 47.1B

A system consists of a moveable piston in a cylinder. The piston moves in the cylinder against an external pressure of 1.05 atm. The increase in the volume of the gas in the cylinder is 450 mL. How much work is done? Is work done by the system or on the system?

47.6   Isothermal Reversible Expansion

Boyle's Law is described in Unit 25. (Figure 25.7)

For an ideal gas at constant temperature, the pressure and the volume are inversely proportional. This is often written as PV = constant, which you may recognize as Boyle's Law. A plot of Boyle's Law shows how the pressure and the volume are related (Figure 47.2). The line on the graph is called an **isotherm**—meaning constant temperature.

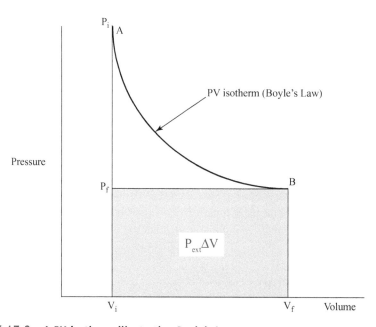

FIGURE 47.2   A PV isotherm illustrating Boyle's Law.
The plot shows the change in pressure and volume as a gas expands isothermally. The shaded area shows the work done by the system when the external pressure is constant.

The description 'reversible' means that the expansion is done so that the external pressure against which the work is done is only infinitesimally smaller than the internal pressure. In this way the external pressure is as high as possible during the expansion and the maximum amount of work is done. In other words, if work is pressure × volume, and the pressure is as high as possible, then the work will be the maximum possible. Ideally, reversible means that the internal pressure is the same as the external pressure so that an infinitesimal increase in the internal pressure causes the system to expand and an infinitesimal increase in the external pressure causes the system to contract. In this case the system is in equilibrium with its surroundings and no expansion would take place—the expansion would take an infinite length of time.

In Figure 47.2, a reversible expansion from State A to State B follows the isotherm. The rectangular blue shaded area represents the work done under constant pressure. The work done in a reversible isothermal expansion is the *total* area under the PV isotherm—which is obviously greater.

For an isothermal reversible expansion,

$$\text{work} = -\int_{V_i}^{V_f} P_{ext} dV \qquad \text{where } P_{ext} \text{ is not constant and is inside the integral}$$

Using the ideal gas law, $P = \dfrac{1}{V} nRT$

The P in this expression is the internal pressure of the system which equals the pressure against which the work is done (P_{ext}) because the process is reversible; the two pressures are equal.

$$\text{work} = -nRT\int_{V_i}^{V_f} \frac{1}{V}\, dV = -nRT \ln\left(\frac{V_f}{V_i}\right)$$

Let's work through an example and compare the result with the constant pressure expansion in Example 47.1.

EXAMPLE 47.2   WORK DONE DURING AN ISOTHERMAL REVERSIBLE EXPANSION

An ideal gas, having an initial volume of 12.7 L and temperature 310 K expands to 25.4 L—the volume doubles. Calculate the work done by the system as it expands isothermally and reversibly from an initial pressure of 1.00 atm to a final pressure of 0.500 atm.

UNDERSTAND THE QUESTION

This is the same system described in Example 47.1. The expansion in this case will follow the PV isotherm in Figure 47.2 instead of the constant pressure line at 0.500 atm.

PLAN THE SOLUTION

Use the expression $w = -nRT \ln\left(\dfrac{V_f}{V_i}\right)$ to determine the work done. We can calculate the number of moles of gas in the system using the ideal gas law. Use the appropriate values for the gas constant in the two calculations.

SOLVE THE PROBLEM

Number of moles of gas, $n = PV/RT$

$$= (1.00\ \text{atm} \times 12.7\ \text{L}) / (0.08206\ \text{L atm K}^{-1}\text{mol}^{-1} \times 310\ \text{K})$$

$$= 0.500\ \text{mol}$$

$$\text{Work} = -nRT \ln\left(\frac{V_f}{V_i}\right)$$

$$= -0.500\ \text{mol} \times 8.3145\ \text{JK}^{-1}\text{mol}^{-1} \times 310\ \text{K} \times \ln(25.4/12.7)$$

$$= -893\ \text{J}$$

Compare this to the 643 J of work done by the system in the constant pressure expansion. The difference, 250 J, is the area between the blue-shaded block and the PV curve in Figure 47.2.

PROBLEM 47.2A

A system initially at 25°C and 15.0 L expands to 25.0 L under a constant external pressure of 1.00 atm. Calculate the amount of work done in this expansion. Calculate the work done if the same system expands isothermally and reversibly from a pressure of 1.67 atm to the same final state. Compare the two results.

PROBLEM 47.2B

A system of 3.00 moles of an ideal gas at 350 K and 5.00 atm expands isothermally and reversibly until the pressure reaches 2.00 atm. How much work is done by the system during this expansion? How much heat must be taken in by the system during this expansion?

47.7   Molar Heat Capacity

Before we examine the adiabatic expansion of an ideal gas, it is useful to know a little about the molar heat capacity of an ideal gas. Then we can relate the isothermal expansion to the adiabatic expansion and examine the differences between them.

In Unit 12 we defined the specific heat of a substance as the quantity of heat necessary to raise the temperature of exactly one gram of the substance by exactly one degree Celsius. A property of a substance that is closely related to the specific heat is the molar heat capacity. This is defined as the quantity of heat necessary to raise the temperature of exactly one mole of the substance by exactly one degree Celsius.

Just like the specific heat of a system, the molar heat capacity relates the heat entering or leaving the system with the temperature change:

$$\text{Heat} = \text{molar heat capacity} \times \text{moles} \times \text{temperature change}$$

The molar heat capacity depends upon whether the heating occurs at constant pressure or constant volume. For a change occurring at constant volume, the symbol used is $\overline{C_v}$. For a change occurring at constant pressure, the symbol used is $\overline{C_p}$.

At constant volume: $q_v = n\overline{C_v}\Delta T$

At constant pressure: $q_p = n\overline{C_p}\Delta T$

The volume change when solids and liquids are heated is very small and therefore the difference between the two heat capacities $\overline{C_v}$ and $\overline{C_p}$ for solids and liquids is also very small and can usually be ignored. The volume change when gases are heated or cooled, however, is significant and the difference between $\overline{C_v}$ and $\overline{C_p}$ cannot be ignored.

In Unit 27, we determined from the Kinetic Molecular Theory that the kinetic energy for an ideal (monatomic) gas is equal to (3/2)RT per mole, or (3/2)kT per molecule. When an ideal gas is heated at constant volume, the capacity of the system to absorb the heat (the heat capacity) is due only to the ability of the molecules to move faster and increase their average kinetic energy. There is no other way to absorb the energy; there is, for example, no vibration or rotation of the molecules, and no expansion of the system.

$$\text{Heat input} = q_v = \frac{3}{2} R \, \Delta T$$

$$\text{The heat capacity is } \frac{3}{2} R \text{ per mole.}$$

When an ideal gas is heated at constant pressure, on the other hand, the capacity of the system to absorb the heat is increased because the system can expand and do work. The ideal gas law is:

$$P V = n R T$$

For a change in temperature and volume at constant pressure:

$$P \, \Delta V = n R \, \Delta T$$

$P\Delta V$ is the work done by a system heated under constant pressure conditions. A system allowed to expand under constant pressure conditions requires *more* heat for a given temperature change because energy is used in the expansion. This additional energy is P ΔV which equals n R ΔT.

Additional heat required = nR ΔT

Additional heat capacity due to expansion = nR

Therefore:

$$\underset{\substack{\text{heat capacity} \\ \text{under constant} \\ \text{pressure}}}{n\overline{C}_p} = \underset{\substack{\text{heat capacity} \\ \text{under constant} \\ \text{volume}}}{n\overline{C}_v} + \underset{\substack{\text{additional heat} \\ \text{capacity due to} \\ \text{expansion}}}{nR}$$

and for an ideal (monatomic) gas:

the heat capacity at constant volume $\overline{C}_v = \dfrac{3}{2}R$ per mole

the heat capacity at constant pressure $\overline{C}_p = \overline{C}_v + R = \dfrac{5}{2}R$ per mole

47.8 Adiabatic Reversible Expansion

The third type of expansion we will consider is an adiabatic expansion. In this expansion no heat enters or leaves the system. Because the system does work during the expansion, the system must lose energy. The temperature falls—the decrease in the temperature of the system corresponds to the decrease in the internal energy of the system as it does work.

A comparison of an isothermal expansion and an adiabatic expansion from the same initial state to the same final volume is illustrated in Figure 47.3. Again, we will assume that the adiabatic expansion is reversible so that the internal pressure equals the external pressure.

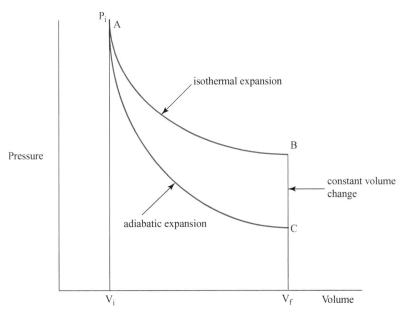

FIGURE 47.3   A comparison of an isothermal expansion and an adiabatic expansion from the same initial state to the same final volume.
The temperature, and therefore the pressure, at the end of the adiabatic expansion must be lower than that at the end of the isothermal expansion.

There are two ways to calculate the work done in the adiabatic expansion. We could integrate the adiabat to obtain the area under the curve which is the work done in the expansion. Or we can use the fact that ΔE is path-independent and compare the two routes from A to C, the route via B and the route directly down the adiabat—ΔE must be the same for both.

For the route $A \rightarrow B \rightarrow C$, ΔE for the first step $A \rightarrow B$ is zero (PV isotherm) and ΔE for the second step $B \rightarrow C$ is equal to q_v because w equals zero (constant volume). The total ΔE for this route is q_v. We learned in the last section that this equals $n\overline{C}_v\Delta T$. This expression is the easiest way to calculate the work done in an adiabatic expansion. The problem, however, is that we don't know what ΔT is. We first must calculate the temperature at point C.

We can do this by equating the two expressions for the work done:

$$w = n\overline{C}_v\Delta T$$

$$w = -\int_{V_i}^{V_f} P_{ext}dV$$

Setting these equal to each other, using the ideal gas law to substitute for P, and dividing through by T:

$$n\overline{C}_v\int_{T_i}^{T_f}\frac{1}{T}dT = -nR\int_{V_i}^{V_f}\frac{1}{V}dV$$

Integrating :

$$n\overline{C}_v\ln\frac{T_f}{T_i} = -nR\ln\frac{V_f}{V_i}$$

Substituting $\overline{C}_v = \frac{3}{2}R$ for an ideal monatomic gas, and cancelling the n and R:

$$\frac{3}{2}\ln\frac{T_f}{T_i} = -\ln\frac{V_f}{V_i}$$

$$\ln\left(\frac{T_f}{T_i}\right)^{\frac{3}{2}} = \ln\frac{V_i}{V_f}$$

Taking the antilog of both sides:

$$\left(\frac{T_f}{T_i}\right)^{\frac{3}{2}} = \frac{V_i}{V_f}$$

This is a useful expression because, as long as the initial and final volumes are known, and the initial temperature is known, then the temperature at the end of an adiabatic expansion can be calculated. Then ΔT can be determined and the work done during the expansion can be calculated. Let's look again at the system examined in Examples 47.1 and 47.2. We can then compare the work done in all three types of expansion.

Another useful relationship that allows you to calculate the final pressure after an adiabatic expansion of an ideal gas is:

$$P_f V_f^{\frac{5}{3}} = P_i V_i^{\frac{5}{3}}$$

This can be derived from

$$\left(\frac{T_f}{T_i}\right)^{\frac{3}{2}} = \frac{V_i}{V_f}$$

by substituting PV for T using the ideal gas law and multiplying through by V_f and P_i.

Alternatively, having calculated T_f and knowing V_f, use the ideal gas law to calculate P_f directly.

EXAMPLE 47.3   WORK DONE DURING AN ADIABATIC REVERSIBLE EXPANSION

An ideal gas, having an initial volume of 12.7 L, an initial pressure of 1.00 atm, and an initial temperature of 310 K expands adiabatically to 25.4 L—a two-fold increase in volume. Calculate the work done by the system as it expands.

UNDERSTAND THE QUESTION

This is the same system described in Examples 47.1 and 47.2. The expansion in this case will follow the adiabat from A to C in Figure 47.3. We've previously calculated that the number of moles in the system equals 0.50 mol.

PLAN THE SOLUTION

First calculate the final temperature, then determine ΔT, the decrease in the temperature of the system during the exansion, and then use the expression $w = n\overline{C_v}\Delta T$ to determine the work done.

SOLVE THE PROBLEM

Calculate the final temperature:

$$\left(\frac{T_f}{T_i}\right)^{\frac{3}{2}} = \frac{V_i}{V_f}$$

$$\left(\frac{T_f}{310}\right)^{\frac{3}{2}} = \left(\frac{12.7}{25.4}\right)$$

$$T_f = 195 \text{ K}$$

The temperature change $\Delta T = T_f - T_i = 195 \text{ K} - 310 \text{ K} = -115 \text{ K}$

$$\text{Work} = n\overline{C_v}\Delta T$$

$$= 0.500 \text{ mol} \times \frac{3}{2} \times 8.3145 \text{ JK}^{-1}\text{mol}^{-1} \times -115 \text{ K}$$

$$= -717 \text{ J}$$

Not surprisingly, the amount of work done during the adiabatic exansion is less than during the isothermal expansion (−893 J)—the pressure decreases more rapidly during the adiabatic expansion due to the fall in temperature.

PROBLEM 47.3A

This problem involves the same system described in Problem 47.2A. A system at 25°C, 1.67 atm, and 15.0 L in volume, expands adiabatically to 25.0 L. Calculate the amount of work done in this expansion. Compare the result with the isothermal expansion described in Problem 47.2A.

PROBLEM 47.3B

A system of 3.00 moles of an ideal gas initially at 350 K and 5.00 atm expands adiabatically and reversibly until the volume is 2.50 times the original volume. How much work is done by the system during this expansion? Compare the result with your answer to Problem 47.2B. In terms of the heat released or absorbed by the system, what is the difference between the two expansions?

Review Questions

1. The first law of thermodynamics is often described as the law of conservation of energy. Explain why this is so.

2. What is the difference between a property of a state (a state function) and a property of a process? Give an example of each.

3. What is meant by the descriptions "path-independent" and "path-dependent"?

4. Summarize the values of ΔE, q, and w for the four different processes examined in this unit: isothermal expansion, adiabatic expansion, constant volume process, and constant pressure process.

Solutions to Problems

PROBLEM 47.1A

For a constant pressure expansion:

Change in volume = 0.850 − 0.500 L = 0.350 L

Work = −1.10 atm × 0.350 L = −0.385 L atm

= −0.385 L atm × 101.325 J $L^{-1}atm^{-1}$

= −39.0 J

Heat = +45 J

Change in the internal energy of the system,
ΔE = q + w = 45 − 39 = 6.0 J

PROBLEM 47.2A

For the constant pressure expansion:

Change in volume = 25.0 − 15.0 L = 10.0 L

Work = −1.00 atm × 10.0 L = −10.0 L atm

= −10.0 L atm × 101.325 J $L^{-1}atm^{-1}$

= −1010 J

For the isothermal expansion:

Number of moles of gas, n = PV/RT

= (1.67 atm × 15.0 L) /
(0.08206 L atm $K^{-1}mol^{-1}$ ×
298 K)

= 1.02 mol

Work = $-nRT \ln\left(\dfrac{V_f}{V_i}\right)$

= −1.02 mol × 8.3145 $JK^{-1}mol^{-1}$ × 298 K ×
ln (25/15)

= −1290 J

More work is done in the isothermal reversible expansion, as expected.

PROBLEM 47.3A

This problem involves the same system described in Problem 47.2A.

Calculate the final temperature:

$$\left(\frac{T_f}{T_i}\right)^{\frac{3}{2}} = \frac{V_i}{V_f}$$

$$\left(\frac{T_f}{298}\right)^{\frac{3}{2}} = \left(\frac{15.0}{25.0}\right)$$

$$T_f = 212 \text{ K}$$

The temperature change ΔT = $T_f - T_i$ = 212 K − 298 K
= −86 K

Work = $n\overline{C_v}\Delta T$

= 1.02 mol × $\dfrac{3}{2}$ × 8.3145 $JK^{-1}mol^{-1}$ × −86 K

= −1094 J

The amount of work done during the adiabatic exansion is less than during the isothermal expansion (−1290 J).

Answers to Review Questions

1. Conservation of energy means that energy can neither be created nor destroyed. Energy may be moved from place to place; it may change from one form into another; but the total energy of the universe remains constant. This is the first law.

2. A state function is a property of a system that depends only upon the current state of the system and not upon how the system arrived at that state. Examples we have encountered in this unit are temperature, T, volume, V, pressure, P, and internal energy, E. A process function is a property that depends upon how a change in a system occurs. It depends not upon the change in the system itself but upon how the change happens. The particular property we have encountered in this unit that is a function of the process is work. The amount of work done by a system as it expands depends upon how the expansion takes place.

3. Path-independent describes a property that is not dependent upon how a change in a system occurs. Changes in state functions such as volume or temperature are path independent. Path-dependent properties depend upon how the change in a system happens. Examples are heat and work.

4.

		ΔE	q	w
Constant volume	isochoric	q	$-n\overline{C_v}\Delta T$	*zero*
Constant pressure	isobaric	q + w	$-n\overline{C_p}\Delta T$	$-P\Delta V$
Constant temperature	isothermal	*zero*	$-w$	$-nRT\ln\left(\dfrac{V_i}{V_f}\right)$
Adiabatic		w	*zero*	$-n\overline{C_v}\Delta T$

End-of-Unit Problems

1. A cylinder fitted with a movable piston absorbs 75 kJ of heat. The piston moves up as the gas expands and does 55 kJ of work on the surroundings. What is the change in the internal energy of the system?

2. A piston is pushed into a cylinder containing an ideal gas; the amount of work done on the system is 560 J. The cylinder and piston liberate 350 J of heat to the surroundings. What is the change in the internal energy of the system?

3. A system consists of a large cylinder full of gas. The gas in the cylinder is heated and expands in volume from 15 liters to 20 liters against an external pressure of 1.10 atm. The amount of heat absorbed by the system is 750 J. Calculate the work done on or by the system and calculate the change in the internal energy of the system.

4. A piston moves in a cylinder against an external pressure of 180 kPa. The increase in the volume of the gas in the cylinder is 650 mL. How much work is done by the system?

5. An ideal gas, having an initial volume of 14.0 L, an initial pressure of 3.00 atm, and a temperature of 256 K expands to 42.0 L under a constant external pressure of 1.00 atm. Calculate the work done by the system as it expands.

6. An ideal gas, having an initial volume of 17.0 L, an initial pressure of 4.60 atm, and a temperature of 381 K expands to 34.0 L under a constant external pressure of 2.30 atm. Calculate the work done by the system as it expands.

7. The same system described in Question 5 expands isothermally and reversibly from 14.0 L to 42.0 L. Calculate the work done by the system as it expands and compare your answer with the answer to Question 5.

8. The same system described in Question 6 expands isothermally and reversibly from 17.0 L to 34.0 L. Calculate the work done by the system as it expands and compare your answer with the answer to Question 6.

9. Calculate the temperature change when 1.2 moles of an ideal gas absorbs 200 J of heat
   a. at constant volume
   b. at constant pressure

10. Calculate the temperature change when 3.1 moles of an ideal gas absorbs 550 J of heat
    a. at constant volume
    b. at constant pressure

11. A sample of an ideal gas at 6.40 atm occupies 10.0 liters at 520 K.
    a. Calculate the work done by the system if it expands isothermally and reversibly until the volume is 40.0 L
    b. Calculate the final temperature and pressure if the same sample of gas expands adiabatically to the same volume (40.0 L).
    c. Calculate the work done by the system in this adiabatic expansion.
    d. Draw a PV diagram illustrating the isothermal and adiabatic expansions and summarize for each curve the values of ΔE, q, and w.

12. A sample of an ideal gas at 3.60 atm occupies 12.0 liters at 351 K.
    a. Calculate the work done by the system if it expands isothermally and reversibly until the volume is 36.0 L.

b. Calculate the final temperature and pressure if the same sample of gas expands adiabatically to the same volume (360 L).
c. Calculate the work done by the system in this adiabatic expansion.
d. Draw a PV diagram illustrating the isothermal and adiabatic expansions and summarize for each curve the values of ΔE, q, and w.

13. A sample of an ideal gas occupies 4.00 L at a pressure of 1.50 atm and a temperature of 25.0°C. Calculate the amount of work done by the system as it expands at constant pressure to 12.0 L. How much heat is released or absorbed by the system during this expansion?

14. A sample of an ideal gas occupies 12.0 L at a pressure of 2.00 atm and a temperature of 300 K. Calculate the amount of work done by the system as it expands at constant pressure to 30.0 L. How much heat is released or absorbed by the system during this expansion?

The Second Law of Thermodynamics

48.1 Introduction

In this unit and the next we return to the second law of thermodynamics we first examined in Unit 30. In particular, we will calculate the entropy changes for various physical and chemical processes. First, however, a short review of Unit 30:

All reactions and physical processes move spontaneously toward a state called **equilibrium**. Recall that the word **spontaneous** has a special meaning in thermodynamics—it describes any process that happens by itself.

The second law of thermodynamics specifies the direction of spontaneous change. In other words, in which direction, if any, will a system move to reach equilibrium? The answer is that for any spontaneous process, the **entropy** of the universe must increase.

$$\Delta S_{univ} > \text{zero}$$

In Unit 30 we investigated the meaning of entropy. In particular, we related entropy to the number of ways in which the components of a system can be arranged. We defined entropy in terms of the Boltzmann equation:

$$S = k \ln W$$

where W represents the number of microstates available to the system. All processes and reactions have a preferred direction and that direction leads to a dispersal of energy, matter, or both. The system moves to a state for which the value of W, the number of possible arrangements (microstates), is greater. In other words, the entropy increases. The reason why a gas expands to occupy the volume available is that there are more ways to arrange the molecules in the larger volume compared to the initial smaller volume. It's really just a matter of probability—there are more microstates available to a system when the components are dispersed than when they are more organized and therefore the dispersed state is more probable.

We can calculate the change in entropy during some process if we know the values of W for the initial and final states:

$$S_{init} = k \ln W_{init}$$
$$S_{final} = k \ln W_{final}$$
$$\Delta S = k \ln W_{final} - k \ln W_{init} = k \ln \left(\frac{W_{final}}{W_{init}} \right)$$

We will use this expression in a moment to determine the entropy change for the isothermal reversible expansion of an ideal gas.

As we learned in Unit 30, determining W for molecular systems can be difficult. If there are more than just a few molecules, the number of possible microstates is enormous. There is an alternative way to determine the entropy change.

Review Unit 30.

Entropy changes are related to the heat entering or leaving a system. If heat enters a system, energy is dispersed over more microstates and the entropy increases. The entropy change that occurs depends upon two factors:

- The amount of heat entering or leaving the system.
- The temperature at which the process occurs.

This dependence on heat and temperature was expressed by R. Clausius in 1865 as:

$$\Delta S = \frac{q_{rev}}{T}$$

where q_{rev} is defined as the heat entering or leaving the system reversibly. In other words, there is no temperature difference between the system and its surroundings and any change in the system takes place infinitely slowly.

Let's first look at the physical changes we encountered in the last unit. Again, we will start with gases because the behaviour of gases when the pressure or temperature is changed is more interesting than for liquids and solids. We have two expressions for the entropy change ΔS and, as we will discover, they both yield the same result.

48.2   Isothermal Reversible Expansion

An isothermal expansion follows a PV isotherm—a Boyle's Law plot. The idea is to keep the pressure as high as possible all the time, just fractionally greater than the external pressure, so that the maximum amount of work is done. The work done in a reversible isothermal expansion is the area under the PV isotherm.

We specify a reversible expansion so that the internal pressure is the same as the external pressure.

Let's first calculate the entropy change using a statistical approach, i.e. using the expression:

$$\Delta S = k \ln\left(\frac{W_{final}}{W_{init}}\right)$$

We learned in Unit 30 that the number of microstates for an ideal gas is equal to the volume raised to a power equal to the number of molecules:

$$W_{init} = V_{init}^{N}$$
$$W_{final} = V_{final}^{N}$$

Substituting this into our expression for ΔS:

$$\Delta S = k \ln\left(\frac{V_{final}^{N}}{V_{init}^{N}}\right)$$

We can take the N outside the natural log:

$$\Delta S = Nk \ln\left(\frac{V_{final}}{V_{init}}\right)$$

But N (the number of molecules) $\times$ k (the gas constant per molecule) is equal to n (the number of moles of molecules) $\times$ R (the gas constant per mole).

$$n = N/N_A$$
$$R = k \times N_A$$

So $Nk = nR$ and

$$\Delta S = nR \ln\left(\frac{V_{final}}{V_{init}}\right)$$

N_A is Avogadro's number

Now let's examine the same isothermal reversible expansion using the expression:

$$\Delta S = \frac{q_{rev}}{T}$$

We know that for an isothermal expansion, ΔE is zero, and we determined in Unit 47 that the work done is:

$$w = -nRT \ln\left(\frac{V_{final}}{V_{init}}\right)$$

Heat enters the system to keep the temperature constant as the system expands very slowly. If ΔE = zero then the heat entering the system must equal the work done by the system: $q_{rev} = -w$:

$$q_{rev} = nRT \ln\left(\frac{V_{final}}{V_{init}}\right)$$

$$\text{and} \quad \Delta S = \frac{q_{rev}}{T} = nR \ln\left(\frac{V_{final}}{V_{init}}\right)$$

which is exactly the same expression we obtained using the statistical approach.

Although we derived this expression for an isothermal reversible expansion, it applies to any expansion where the temperature at the end is the same as at the beginning. This is because entropy is a state function and therefore ΔS is path-independent. It doesn't matter how the expansion occurs, this expression will always yield the corresponding entropy change. All we need to know are the initial and final volumes.

EXAMPLE 48.1 DETERMINING THE ENTROPY CHANGE FOR THE ISOTHERMAL EXPANSION OF A GAS

An ideal gas, having an initial volume of 12.7 L expands at a constant temperature of 310 K to 25.4 L — a two-fold increase in volume. Calculate the entropy change in the system as it expands isothermally and reversibly from an initial pressure of 1.00 atm to a final pressure of 0.500 atm.

UNDERSTAND THE QUESTION

You may recognize this system as the the same one described in Example 47.2. The expansion follows the PV isotherm in Figure 47.2.

PLAN THE SOLUTION

Use the expression $\Delta S = nR \ln\left(\frac{Vf}{V_i}\right)$ to determine the entropy change. As before, we can calculate the number of moles of gas in the system using the ideal gas law. Use the appropriate values for the gas constant.

SOLVE THE PROBLEM

Number of moles of gas, n = PV/RT

$$= (1.00 \text{ atm} \times 12.7 \text{ L}) / (0.08206 \text{ L atm K}^{-1}\text{mol}^{-1} \times 310 \text{ K})$$

$$= 0.500 \text{ mol}$$

Entropy change $\Delta S = nR \ln\left(\dfrac{V_f}{V_i}\right)$

$$= 0.500 \text{ mol} \times 8.3145 \text{ JK}^{-1}\text{mol}^{-1} \times \ln(25.4/12.7)$$

$$= 2.88 \text{ JK}^{-1}$$

PROBLEM 48.1A

A system initially at 25°C and 1.67 atm expands isothermally and reversibly from 15.0 L to 25.0 L. Calculate the entropy change for this expansion. If the system, from the same initial state, is heated at constant pressure until the volume is 25.0 L, and then is cooled at constant volume until the temperature is again 25°C, what is the entropy change for this process?

PROBLEM 48.1B

A system of 3.00 moles of an ideal gas at 350 K and 5.00 atm expands isothermally and reversibly until the pressure reaches 2.00 atm. Calculate the entropy change for this expansion.

48.3   Constant Pressure and Constant Volume Changes

Processes in which either the pressure is kept constant or the volume is kept constant must involve a change in temperature. For example, if a system expands at constant pressure, the temperature must increase proportionately. Similarly, if the pressure is increased keeping the volume constant, heat must be absorbed by the system and the temperature again must increase.

In Unit 47 we derived two expressions relating heat and temperature; one for constant pressure and one for constant volume:

At constant volume: $q_v = n\overline{C_v}\Delta T$

At constant pressure: $q_p = n\overline{C_p}\Delta T$

If we know the temperature change, we can calculate the heat. If we know the heat, we can calculate the entropy change:

$$\Delta S = \frac{q_{rev}}{T}$$

The only problem is that the T in this expression changes as the system is heated. So we have to integrate. For constant volume:

$$\Delta S = \frac{q_{rev}}{T} = n\overline{C_v}\int_{T_i}^{T_f}\frac{1}{T}dT = n\overline{C_v}\ln\left(\frac{T_f}{T_i}\right)$$

Similarly, for a constant pressure change:

$$\Delta S = \frac{q_{rev}}{T} = n\overline{C_p}\int_{T_i}^{T_f}\frac{1}{T}dT = n\overline{C_p}\ln\left(\frac{T_f}{T_i}\right)$$

Let's look at the calculation of an entropy change for a system changing temperature. For a change, let's consider a system other than an ideal gas.

EXAMPLE 48.2 DETERMINING THE ENTROPY CHANGE AT CONSTANT PRESSURE OR VOLUME

Determine the entropy change that takes place when 100.0 grams of water is warmed from 22°C to its boiling point at 100°C at a constant pressure of 1.0 atm. The specific heat of water is 4.184 J K^{-1} g^{-1}.

UNDERSTAND THE QUESTION

The entropy of any substance is expected to increase if the temperature is increased.

$$\Delta S = n\overline{C}_p \ln\left(\frac{T_f}{T_i}\right)$$

In this expression, n is the number of moles and $\overline{C}_v$ is the molar heat capacity. We can just as well use the number of grams and the specific heat. Always check the units:

$$\Delta S = m\,C\ln\left(\frac{T_f}{T_i}\right)$$

PLAN THE SOLUTION

Remember to use the kelvin temperature scale.

SOLVE THE PROBLEM

$$\Delta S = 100.0\text{ g} \times 4.184\text{ JK}^{-1}\text{g}^{-1} \times \ln\left(\frac{373}{295}\right)$$

$$= 98.2\text{ JK}^{-1}$$

PROBLEM 48.2A

Calculate the entropy change when two identical 100 gram blocks of copper, one at 200°C and the other at 20.0°C, come into contact in an insulated container. The specific heat of copper is 0.385 JK^{-1}g^{-1}.

PROBLEM 48.2B

Calculate the entropy change when 500 grams of hot water at 95°C is poured into 200 grams of water at 20°C in an insulated container. The specific heat of water is 4.184 JK^{-1}g^{-1}.

48.4 Adiabatic Expansion

In an adiabatic process, no heat enters or leaves the system. The heat, q, equals zero. Since q is zero then the entropy change ΔS must be zero. Refer again to Figure 47.3 which is repeated here in Figure 48.1. Entropy is a state function and ΔS is path independent. Because the entropy change down the adiabat directly from A to C is zero, then the increase in entropy down the isotherm from A to B must be exactly balanced by a decrease in entropy for the constant volume change from B to C—so that the sum *via* that route is also zero.

The entropy change from A to B:

$$\Delta S = nR\ln\left(\frac{V_f}{V_i}\right)$$

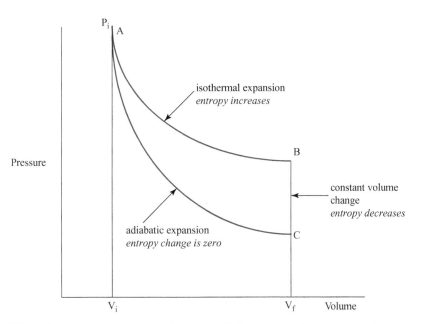

FIGURE 48.1   The entropy change down the adiabatic expansion from A to C equals zero.
The entropy change from A to C *via* B must therefore also equal zero. The entropy increases during the isothermal expansion from A to B but then decreases as the temperature decreases from B to C by exactly the same amount.

The entropy change from B to C at constant volume:

$$\Delta S = n\overline{C_v}\ln\left(\frac{T_f}{T_i}\right)$$

The sum of the two changes equals zero:

$$nR\ln\left(\frac{V_f}{V_i}\right) + n\overline{C_v}\ln\left(\frac{T_f}{T_i}\right) = 0$$

Substituting $C_v = \frac{3}{2}R$ for an ideal monatomic gas, and cancelling the n and R:

$$\ln\left(\frac{V_f}{V_i}\right) + \frac{3}{2}\ln\left(\frac{T_f}{T_i}\right) = 0$$

$$\ln\left(\frac{V_f}{V_i}\right) + \ln\left(\frac{T_f}{T_i}\right)^{\frac{3}{2}} = 0$$

Taking the antilog of both sides:

$$\left(\frac{V_f}{V_i}\right) + \left(\frac{T_f}{T_i}\right)^{\frac{3}{2}} = 0$$

or

$$\left(\frac{V_i}{V_f}\right) = \left(\frac{T_f}{T_i}\right)^{\frac{3}{2}}$$

which is the same expression we obtained in Unit 47; it allows us to calculate the final temperature after an adiabatic expansion of an ideal gas.

EXAMPLE 48.3   ENTROPY CHANGES IN A CYCLE

An ideal gas, having an initial volume of 12.7 L (Point A in Figure 48.1) expands at a constant temperature of 310 K to 25.4 L (Point B in Figure 48.1)— a two-fold increase in volume.

The gas is then cooled at constant volume until the temperature reaches 195K and the system is at Point C at the end of the adiabat.

Calculate the entropy changes in the system as

a. it expands along the isotherm from A to B

b. it expands along the adiabat from A to C

c. it cools at constant volume from B to C

Show, as a result, that entropy is a state function and that ΔS is path independent.

UNDERSTAND THE QUESTION

This system is the the same one as described in the examples in the previous unit and in Example 48.1.

PLAN THE SOLUTION

Use the expression $\Delta S = nR \ln\left(\dfrac{V_f}{V_i}\right)$ to determine the entropy change along the isotherm from A to B as before. Then

use the expression $\Delta S = n\overline{C_v} \ln\left(\dfrac{T_f}{T_i}\right)$ to determine the entropy change for the constant volume change from B to C. Use the appropriate values for the gas constant (that is, check the units).

SOLVE THE PROBLEM

As in Example 48.1, number of moles of gas, n = PV/RT

$$= (1.00 \text{ atm} \times 12.7 \text{ L}) / (0.08206 \text{ L atm K}^{-1}\text{mol}^{-1} \times 310 \text{ K})$$

$$= 0.500 \text{ mol}$$

a. Entropy change from A to B, $\Delta S = nR \ln\left(\dfrac{V_f}{V_i}\right)$

$$= 0.500 \text{ mol} \times 8.3145 \text{ JK}^{-1}\text{mol}^{-1} \times \ln(25.4/12.7)$$

$$= 2.88 \text{ JK}^{-1}\text{—this is the same calculation as Example 48.1}$$

b. Entropy change from A to C, ΔS = zero

c. Entropy change from B to C, $\Delta S = n\overline{C_v} \ln\left(\dfrac{T_f}{T_i}\right)$

$$= 0.500 \text{ mol} \times (3/2) \times 8.3145 \text{ JK}^{-1}\text{mol}^{-1} \times \ln(195/310)$$

$$= 2.88 \text{ JK}^{-1}$$

The sum of the entropy changes from A to B and from B to C equals zero, as expected.

PROBLEM 48.3A

What is the entropy change when 1.00 mol of an ideal gas expands adiabatically from a pressure of 1.00 atm and a volume of 20.0 L to a final volume of 50.0 L? What is the entropy change when the gas expands isothermally to the same 50.0 L?

PROBLEM 48.3B

What is the entropy change when 2.50 mol of an ideal gas expands isothermally from a pressure of 3.00 atm and a volume of 15.0 L to a final volume of 45.0 L? What is the entropy change when the gas expands adiabatically to the same final volume? Therefore, what is the entropy change when the gas cools at constant volume from the end of the isotherm to the end of the adiabat?

48.5 Gibbs Free Energy

In Unit 30 we learned that the change in the Gibbs free energy is a convenient way to express the second law in terms of the system rather than the entire universe. If

$$\Delta S_{sys} = \Delta S_{sys} + \Delta S_{surr} > \text{zero for a spontaneous process}$$

then either ΔS_{sys} or ΔS_{surr}, or both, must be greater than zero for the process to happen. If the system liberates heat in an exothermic process and the heat goes into the surroundings, then the entropy of the surroundings increases. So, for a spontaneous process, either the entropy of the system increases, or the process is exothermic so that the entropy of the surroundings increases, or both.

$$\Delta S_{sys} - \frac{\Delta H_{sys}}{T} > \text{zero}$$

This relationship is usually rearranged by multiplying through by $-T$:

$$\Delta H - T\Delta S < \text{zero}$$

This function $\Delta H - T\Delta S$ is the change in the Gibbs free energy of the system ΔG.

The two ways to express the second law are:

$\Delta S_{univ} > \text{zero for a spontaneous process}$

$\Delta G_{sys} < \text{zero for a spontaneous process (at constant P and T)}$

48.6 Changes of State

When a substance is at its melting point or its boiling point, the two states are in equilibrium. This means, for a substance, $\Delta G°$ is equal to zero. Therefore $\Delta H° - T\Delta S°$ must equal zero. At the melting point, for example,

$$\Delta H°_{fus} - T\Delta S°_{fus} = 0 \quad \text{and} \quad \Delta S°_{fus} = \frac{\Delta H°_{fus}}{T}$$

Likewise, for the boiling point,

$$\Delta H°_{vap} - T\Delta S°_{vap} = 0 \quad \text{and} \quad \Delta S°_{vap} = \frac{\Delta H°_{vap}}{T}$$

If the enthalpies of fusion (melting) or vaporization, and the melting or boiling points are known, then the corresponding entropies of fusion and vaporization can be calculated.

Normally, ΔG is said to be zero at equilibrium, but in this case we're dealing with a (pure) substance. At the melting point, the free energy of the (pure) liquid is the same as the free energy of the (pure) solid. So we can use $\Delta G°$. $\Delta G°$ is rarely zero for chemical reactions.

Recall Trouton's Rule described in Unit 31.4.

EXAMPLE 48.4 ENTROPY CHANGES IN CHANGES OF STATE

Calculate the entropy change when 100 g of water is heated from 25°C to its boiling point and then vaporized.

The standard enthalpy of vaporization of water, $\Delta H°_{vap}$ = +40.7 kJ mol^{-1} at its boiling point. The specific heat of water is 4.184 JK^{-1}g^{-1}.

UNDERSTAND THE QUESTION

This is a two-part question; two changes take place. First, the water is heated to increase its temperature from 25°C to 100°C. Second, the water is vaporized. The entropy increases in both stages.

PLAN THE SOLUTION

Calculate the entropy changes for the two stages separately and then add them. For the first stage, heating the water, use the expression $\Delta S = n\overline{C_p} \ln\left(\dfrac{T_f}{T_i}\right)$ or $\Delta S = mC\ln\left(\dfrac{T_f}{T_i}\right)$. For the second stage, vaporizing the water, use the relationship $\Delta S°_{vap} = \dfrac{\Delta H°_{vap}}{T}$. Note that the units must match. Use J, not kJ, and note that the temperature must be in K.

SOLVE THE PROBLEM

Heating the water:

$$\Delta S = mC\ln\left(\frac{T_f}{T_i}\right)$$
$$= 100 \text{ g} \times 4.184 \text{ JK}^{-1}\text{g}^{-1} \times \ln(373.15/298.15)$$
$$= 93.9 \text{ JK}^{-1}$$

Vaporizing the water:

$$\Delta S°_{vap} = \frac{\Delta H°_{vap}}{T}$$
$$= (40.7 \text{ kJ mol}^{-1} \times 1000 \text{ J/kJ} \times 100 \text{ g}/18.016 \text{ g mol}^{-1})/373.15 \text{ K}$$
$$= 605.4 \text{ JK}^{-1}$$

Total entropy change = 93.9 + 605.4 = 699 JK^{-1}

PROBLEM 48.4A

Calculate the entropy change when 50 g of hot water at 90°C is added to a mixture of 100 g of ice and 100 g of liquid water at 0°C in an insulated container.

Specific heat of liquid water = 4.184 JK^{-1}g^{-1}

Latent heat of fusion of ice = 333 J g^{-1}

PROBLEM 48.4B

The standard enthalpy of vaporization of hydrogen cyanide, $\Delta H°_{vap}$ (HCN) = +26.23 kJ mol^{-1} at 25°C. The standard entropy of vaporization of hydrogen cyanide, $\Delta S°_{vap}$ (HCN) = +88.94 JK^{-1} mol^{-1} at 25°C. Calculate the approximate boiling point of hydrogen cyanide from these data.

Review Question

1. Summarize the expressions used to calculate the entropy change ΔS during a

   - constant volume process
   - constant pressure process
   - constant temperature process
   - adiabatic process
   - change of state

Solutions to Problems

PROBLEM 48.1A

Number of moles of the gas = PV/RT = 1.67 × 15.0/0.08206 × 298.15 = 1.02 mol

Isothermal expansion:

$$\Delta S = nR \ln\left(\frac{V_f}{V_i}\right)$$

$$= 1.02 \times 8.3145 \times \ln(25.0/15.0)$$

$$= 4.33 \text{ JK}^{-1}$$

The final state via the alternate route is the same (25.0 L, 25°C, same number of moles, pressure must be the same). Therefore ΔS must be the same—the change in entropy is path independent.

PROBLEM 48.2A

The final temperature is (200°C + 20°C)/2 = 110°C = 383K

The entropy change for the hot block:

$$\Delta S = mC \ln\left(\frac{T_f}{T_i}\right)$$

$$= 100 \text{ g} \times 0.385 \text{ JK}^{-1}\text{g}^{-1} \times \ln(383/473)$$

$$= -8.13 \text{ JK}^{-1}$$

The entropy change for the cold block:

$$\Delta S = mC \ln\left(\frac{T_f}{T_i}\right)$$

$$= 100 \text{ g} \times 0.385 \text{ JK}^{-1}\text{g}^{-1} \times \ln(383/293)$$

$$= 10.31 \text{ JK}^{-1}$$

Total entropy change:

$$\Delta S = 10.31 - 8.13 = 2.18 \text{ JK}^{-1}$$

PROBLEM 48.3A

The entropy change for an adiabatic expansion = zero.

Isothermal expansion from 20.0 L to 50.0 L:

$$\Delta S = nR \ln(V_f/V_i) = 1.0 \times 8.3145 \times \ln(50.0/20.0)$$

$$= 7.62 \text{ JK}^{-1}$$

PROBLEM 48.4A

Heat required to melt all 100 g of the ice = 333 J g^{-1} × 100 g = 33300 J

Heat available from the hot water cooling = 4.184 JK^{-1}g^{-1} × 50 g × 90 K = 18828 J

Not all the ice melts.

It is not necessary to calculate this, but

the mass of ice that melts = 18828 J / 333 J g^{-1} = 56.5 g

ΔS for the ice melting = 18828 J / 273.15 K = 68.9 JK^{-1}

ΔS for the hot water cooling = 50 g × 4.184 JK^{-1}g^{-1} × ln (273/363) = −59.6 JK^{-1}

Total ΔS = 68.9 − 59.6 = 9.3 JK^{-1}

Answers to Review Question

1. Constant volume process:

$$\Delta S = n\overline{C_v} \ln\left(\frac{T_f}{T_i}\right)$$

Constant pressure process:

$$\Delta S = n\overline{C_p} \ln\left(\frac{T_f}{T_i}\right)$$

Constant temperature process:

$$\Delta S = nR \ln\left(\frac{V_f}{V_i}\right)$$

Adiabatic process:

$$\Delta S = \text{zero}$$

Change of state:

$$\Delta S° = \frac{\Delta H°}{T}$$

End-of-Unit Problems

1. Calculate the decrease in the entropy of a 100 gram sample of water at 0°C when it freezes. The heat of fusion of ice is 333 J g⁻¹.

2. Calculate the increase in the entropy of a 50 gram sample of water at 100°C when it completely vaporizes. The heat of vaporization of water is 2260 J g⁻¹.

3. Calculate the decrease in the entropy of a 25 gram sample of water at 25°C when it cools to 0°C and then freezes. The heat of fusion of ice is 333 J g⁻¹; the specific heat of water is 4.184 JK⁻¹g⁻¹.

4. Calculate the increase in the entropy of a 100 gram sample of water at 20°C when it is heated to 100°C and then vaporizes. The heat of vaporization of water is 2260 J g⁻¹; the specific heat of water is 4.184 JK⁻¹g⁻¹.

5. Calculate the change in entropy when a 50 gram block of copper metal at 60°C is added to a mixture of 50 g of ice and 100 g of water at 60°C. The specific heat of copper is 0.385 JK⁻¹g⁻¹; the specific heat of water is 4.184 JK⁻¹g⁻¹; and the heat of fusion of ice is 333 J g⁻¹.

6. Calculate the change in entropy when a 50 gram block of copper metal at 80°C is brought into contact with a 100 g block of copper at 20°C in an insulated container. The specific heat of copper is 0.385 JK⁻¹g⁻¹.

7. How much energy, in kJ, is required to heat to the boiling point and completely vaporize a 10 g sample of ethanol originally at 25°C? Calculate the entropy change for this process.

    The boiling point of ethanol is 78.0°C

    The enthalpy of vaporization of ethanol is 838.3 J g⁻¹

    The specific heat of ethanol is 2.44 J g⁻¹ K⁻¹

8. 1.50 mol of an ideal gas, having an initial volume of 24.0 L, expands at a constant temperature of 350 K to 60.0 L. What is the entropy change for this expansion? If the gas expands adiabatically from the same initial state to the same final volume, what is the entropy change for this expansion? What is the entropy change for the constant volume change (60.0 L) from the end of the isotherm to the end of the adiabat?

9. The heat required to vaporize phosphorus trichloride PCl_3 at 25°C is 32.7 kJ mol⁻¹. The entropy of vaporization ΔS°_{vap} is 94.60 JK⁻¹ mol⁻¹. Calculate the boiling point of phosphorus trichloride.

10. A closed system consisting of an ideal gas at 10.0 atm pressure and 487.5 K with a volume of 4.00 L (State A) expands isothermally and reversibly to a new state (State B) where the pressure is 2.50 atm. The system at State A also was able to expand adiabatically and reversibly through a State D (where the pressure is the same as at State B) to a State C (where the volume is the same as at State B).

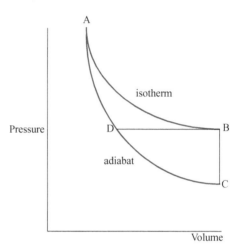

Calculate the temperatures at States D and C. What happens to the temperature of the system going down the adiabat from A to D to C?

Calculate the entropy changes

a. from State A to State B

b. from State D to State B

c. from State C to State B

What is true of these three entropy changes in the system? Why?

Thermodynamics and Chemical Reactions

49.1   Introduction

The three thermodynamic quantities associated with chemical reactions occurring under constant pressure are the change in enthalpy, $\Delta H°$, the change in entropy, $\Delta S°$, and the change in Gibb's free energy, $\Delta G°$. Of these, the change in Gibb's free energy is the most useful. It is this quantity that is related to the equilibrium constant K for the reaction and indicates whether the reaction is product–favored.

49.2   Free Energy and the Equilibrium Constant

We have already seen in Unit 35 that a reaction is spontaneous if ΔG is negative. The reaction will proceed in the direction for which ΔG is negative until ΔG becomes equal to zero. At this point the system reaches equilibrium. The free energy of a system changes as a reaction proceeds from reactants to products. The diagram is shown again below (Figure 49.1).

In this case, when the reactants are mixed, the free energy of the system is relatively high. As the reactants combine to make products, the free energy of the system decreases—the slope of the line is negative (ΔG is negative)—the free energy of the system decreases. In this region the reaction quotient Q is smaller than the equilibrium constant K.

The decrease continues until the minimum point on the curve is reached. The slope of the curve ΔG becomes zero and the system reaches equilibrium. At this point

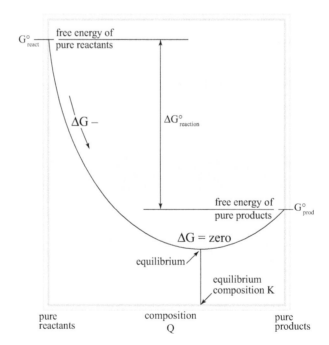

FIGURE 49.1   The variation in the free energy of a system as the composition changes.
If Q < K, the system moves toward the product side. If Q > K, the system moves toward the reactant side. In both cases ΔG is negative.

on the curve the reaction quotient Q equals the equilibrium constant K. At equilibrium the free energy of the reactants *in the reaction mixture* is the same as the free energy of the products *in the reaction mixture*.

The equilibrium can be reached equally well from the product side. As the products combine to make reactants, the free energy of the system decreases—the slope of the line is again negative (ΔG is negative). In this region the reaction quotient Q is larger than the equilibrium constant K. The decrease continues until again the minimum point on the curve is reached. Once at equilibrium, no further movement of the system toward reactant or product is possible under the same conditions.

The quantity of most interest is ΔG. It is ΔG that determines in which direction, if any, the reaction will go. Although we will not derive this expression, the value of ΔG is related to $\Delta G°$ and the reaction quotient Q:

$$\Delta G = \Delta G° + RT \ln Q \quad \text{where} \quad \text{R is the gas constant} = 8.3145 \text{ J K}^{-1} \text{ mol}^{-1}$$
$$\text{T is the temperature in K}$$

The two terms of this relationship on the right side of the equation can be interpreted as follows:

It is the $\Delta G°$ term that determines the shape of the curve and ultimately the value of K, the equilibrium constant. Three situations are illustrated in Figure 49.2. In the first diagram, $\Delta G°$ is positive; in the second diagram, $\Delta G°$ is zero; and in the third diagram, $\Delta G°$ is negative. The shape of the curve changes as $\Delta G°$ changes and K, the equilibrium constant, becomes progressively larger. The system becomes more product-favored (usually the desirable condition) as $\Delta G°$ becomes more negative.

It is the RTlnQ term that determines where the system exists on the curve. For example, if Q is small then the system exists somewhere on the left side of the curve. If Q is large then the system is on the right side of the curve.

$$\Delta G = \underset{\substack{\text{the shape}\\\text{of the curve}}}{\Delta G°} + \underset{\substack{\text{where}\\\text{on the curve}}}{RT \ln Q}$$

The special case is when the system is at equilibrium. At equilibrium, Q = K and the system is at the minimum point on the curve ($\Delta G = 0$). Substituting these conditions into the equation yields the fundamental relationship between $\Delta G°$ and K:

$$\Delta G° = -RT \ln K$$

This equation is particularly useful because it allows the calculation of equilibrium constants from thermodynamic data (for example, standard free energies of formation) and *vice versa* (*cf.* Example 35.2).

49.3   The Effect of Temperature

The equilibrium constant for a reaction is indeed constant—except if the temperature is changed. The temperature has an effect on both the value of $\Delta G°$ and the equilibrium constant K for a reaction. We learned in Unit 30 that $\Delta G°$ is equal to $\Delta H° - T\Delta S°$ and, even if $\Delta H°$ and $\Delta S°$ change only slightly with a change in temperature, the T in the expression ensures that $\Delta G°$ will change. Additionally, as we have just seen, $\Delta G°$ and K are related.

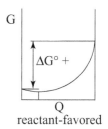

reactant-favored

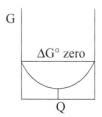

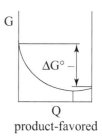

product-favored

FIGURE 49.2   The dependence of the shape of the free energy curve upon the value of $\Delta G°$.
As $\Delta G°$ becomes more negative, the system becomes more product-favored, and K becomes larger.

We have two expressions for $\Delta G°$:

$$\Delta G° = -RT \ln K$$

$$\Delta G° = \Delta H° - T\Delta S°$$

We can set these two expressions equal to one another:

$$\Delta G° = -RT \ln K = \Delta H° - T\Delta S°$$

$$\ln K = -\frac{\Delta H°}{RT} + \frac{\Delta S°}{R}$$

For two temperatures T_1 and T_2:

$$\ln K_1 = -\frac{\Delta H°}{RT_1} + \frac{\Delta S°}{R}$$

$$\ln K_2 = -\frac{\Delta H°}{RT_2} + \frac{\Delta S°}{R}$$

Subtracting the first expression from the second, and cancelling the $\Delta S°/R$ terms:

$$\ln \frac{K_2}{K_1} = \frac{\Delta H°}{R}\left(\frac{1}{T_1} - \frac{1}{T_2}\right)$$

This equation, often called the **van't Hoff equation**, can be used to calculate the value of an equilibrium constant at a different temperature. The equation assumes that both $\Delta H°$ and $\Delta S°$ do not vary significantly over the temperature range involved.

> Jacobus van't Hoff has more than one equation named for him—this is one of them.
>
> You may recognize the similarity between the van't Hoff equation and the Clausius-Clapeyron equation in Unit 31.
>
> $$\ln\frac{P_2}{P_1} = \frac{\Delta H°_{vap}}{R}\left(\frac{1}{T_1} - \frac{1}{T_2}\right)$$

EXAMPLE 49.1   THE EFFECT OF A CHANGE IN TEMPERATURE UPON AN EQUILIBRIUM

The standard enthalpy change $\Delta H°$ for the reaction:

$$2\ SO_2(g) + O_2(g) \rightleftharpoons 2\ SO_3(g)$$

is -197.8 kJ mol^{-1} and the equilibrium constant K_p at 298 K is 7.2×10^{24}. Calculate the value of the equilibrium constant at 500 K (227°C).

UNDERSTAND THE QUESTION

The van't Hoff equation can be used to calculate the value of K_p at any temperature if the standard enthalpy change for the reaction and the value of K_p at some other temperature are known.

PLAN THE SOLUTION

Write the van't Hoff equation and substitute the known values. A common error is to forget to change the units of $\Delta H°$ from kJ mol^{-1} to J mol^{-1}. The temperatures must be in K.

SOLVE THE PROBLEM

$$\ln\frac{K_2}{K_1} = \frac{\Delta H°}{R}\left(\frac{1}{T_1} - \frac{1}{T_2}\right)$$

$$\ln(K_2/7.2 \times 10^{24}) = -(197{,}800\ \text{J mol}^{-1}/8.314\ \text{JK}^{-1}\text{mol}^{-1}) \times (500 - 298)\text{K}/(500 \times 298)\text{K}^2$$

$$\ln(K_2/7.2 \times 10^{24}) = -32.25$$

$$K_2/7.2 \times 10^{24} = 9.84 \times 10^{-15}$$

$$K_2 = 7.1 \times 10^{10}$$

At the higher temperature the value of K is smaller (7.1×10^{10} *vs.* 7.2×10^{24}). There is less product at equilibrium—the system has moved to the reactant side.

PROBLEM 49.1A

The standard heat of formation of ammonia is -46.1 kJ mol^{-1}. The Haber Process for the production of ammonia from nitrogen and hydrogen is run at a high temperature to increase the rate of the reaction even though the equilibrium constant for the production is lower at a higher temperature. The equilibrium constant K_p for the equilibrium:

$$N_2(g) + 3\,H_2(g) \rightleftharpoons 2\,NH_3(g)$$

at 298 K is 6.8×10^5. Calculate the value of K_p at 500 K and show that the reaction is less product-favored at the higher temperature.

PROBLEM 49.1B

The decomposition of chlorine molecules into chlorine atoms is an endothermic process—the bond energy is 230 kJ mol^{-1}. You might anticipate therefore that the reaction would be more favored at a higher temperature. At 1000 K, the equilibrium constant K_p for the reaction:

$$Cl_2(g) \rightleftharpoons 2\,Cl(g)$$

is 1.0×10^{-5}. Calculate the value of K_p at 1500 K and show that the reaction is indeed more product-favored at the higher temperature.

49.4   The Haber Process for the Synthesis of Ammonia

In Unit 35, you were introduced to the Haber process which is used to manufacture ammonia from nitrogen and hydrogen. This process is important because plants need fixed nitrogen—not nitrogen gas, but nitrogen in the form of ammonium salts, nitrates, and other nitrogen compounds—in order to grow. The problem is that it is not particularly easy to convert nitrogen into its compounds because the triple bond between the two nitrogen atoms in the dinitrogen molecule is one of the strongest covalent bonds known and it requires considerable energy to break it.

In the years just before World War I, Fritz Haber and Carl Bosch developed a method for the manufacture of ammonia from nitrogen and hydrogen. This method is still used today to produce ammonia. The Haber process is a compromise between kinetics and thermodynamics. The reaction is exothermic:

$$N_2(g) + 3\,H_2(g) \rightleftharpoons 2\,NH_3(g) \qquad \Delta H^\circ = -92.2 \text{ kJ}$$

Application of the van't Hoff equation (*cf.* Problem 49.1A), shows that for an exothermic reaction, the product is less favored at a higher temperature. In this case, the value of K_p is 6.8×10^5 at 298 K but only 1.9×10^{-3} at 600 K. The thermodynamics of the system suggests that the reaction should be run at a low temperature.

However, the rate of the reaction is much slower at a low temperature. The equilibrium position is product-favored at low temperature but it takes a very long time to get there. Fritz Haber was able to find an appropriate catalyst, iron metal, to increase the rate at low temperatures. Current industrial plants are run at high pressures, 200 to 300 atm, at temperatures between 770 and 790 K and in the presence of an iron catalyst. The reaction mixture is cycled through a condenser, in which the ammonia liquefies (b.pt. $-33.4°C$) and is removed. The high pressure and the removal of the ammonia from the system favors the formation of more ammonia.

Review Questions

1. What is the difference between the standard free energy change $\Delta G°$ and the free energy change ΔG? In what way is ΔG related to $\Delta G°$?

2. What is the relationship between $\Delta G°$ and K_p?

3. The equilibrium constant is not constant if the temperature is changed. Describe how the equilibrium constant depends upon the temperature and the standard enthalpy change for the reaction.

Solution to Problem

PROBLEM 49.1A

The enthalpy change for the reaction is twice the standard heat of formation of ammonia (2.0 moles are formed).

$$N_2(g) + 3\,H_2(g) \rightleftharpoons 2\,NH_3(g)$$

$\Delta H° = 2\ \text{mol} \times -46.1\ \text{kJ mol}^{-1} = -92.2\ \text{kJ} = -92{,}200\ \text{J}$

$$\ln \frac{K_2}{K_1} = \frac{\Delta H°}{R}\left(\frac{1}{T_1} - \frac{1}{T_2}\right)$$

$\ln (K_2/6.8 \times 10^5) = -(92{,}200\ \text{J mol}^{-1}/8.314\ \text{JK}^{-1}\ \text{mol}^{-1}) \times (500 - 298)\text{K}/(500 \times 298)\text{K}^2$

$\ln (K_2/6.8 \times 10^5) = -15.0$

$K_2/6.8 \times 10^5 = 2.96 \times 10^{-7}$

$K_2 = 2.0 \times 10^{-1}$

The equilibrium constant is considerably lower at the higher temperature. A careful balance between the increased rate of reaction and the less favorable equilibrium condition must be determined.

Answers to Review Questions

1. $\Delta G°$ is the difference between the Gibbs free energy of the pure products and the Gibbs free energy of the pure reactants. ΔG is the change in the free energy of the system as the reactants change to products, or *vice versa*. ΔG equals zero at equilibrium. $\Delta G°$ is the same regardless of the state of the system—it doesn't matter whether the system is at equilibrium or not. ΔG is related to $\Delta G°$ by the expression $\Delta G = \Delta G° + RT \ln Q$.

2. At equilibrium $Q = K$ and $\Delta G = $ zero. Therefore $\Delta G° = -RT \ln K$.

3. The temperature dependence of the equilibrium constant is described by the van't Hoff equation. The general rule is that if $\Delta H°$ is negative (exothermic), K decreases when the temperature increases, and if $\Delta H°$ is positive, K increases when the temperature increases. This is confirmed by LeChâtelier's principle.

End-of-Unit Problems

1. Many reactions either don't go at all, that is, they are not spontaneous, or they go almost to completion. If completion is interpreted as 99.9% product, what must $\Delta G°$ be at least equal to at 25°C? How does this value compare to $\Delta G°$ for common chemical reactions?

2. Is it likely that $\Delta G°$ is equal to zero? If $\Delta G°$ is equal to zero, what is the value of the equilibrium constant K_p? For the system $N_2O_4(g) \rightleftharpoons 2\,NO_2(g)$, what could you do to make $\Delta G°$ equal to zero?

3. Calculate the value of the standard free energy change $\Delta G°$ for the reaction:

$$2\,N_2H_4(l) + N_2O_4(g) \rightleftharpoons 3\,N_2(g) + 4\,H_2O(g)$$

given

$\Delta G_f° \text{(hydrazine}(l)) = +149.3\ \text{kJ mol}^{-1}$

$\Delta G_f° \text{(dinitrogen tetroxide)} = +97.9\ \text{kJ mol}^{-1}$

$\Delta G_f° \text{(water vapor)} = -228.6\ \text{kJ mol}^{-1}$

4. Calculate the value of the standard free energy change $\Delta G°$ for the reaction:

$$2\,NO(g) + 2\,H_2(g) \rightleftharpoons N_2(g) + 2\,H_2O(g)$$

given

$\Delta G_f° \text{(nitric oxide)} = +86.6\ \text{kJ mol}^{-1}$

$\Delta G_f° \text{(water vapor)} = -228.6\ \text{kJ mol}^{-1}$

5. Calculate the equilibrium constant K_p for the system described in Question 3.

6. Calculate the equilibrium constant K_p for the system described in Question 4.

7. Calculate the standard free energy change $\Delta G°$ for the reaction:

$$H_2(g) + I_2(g) \rightleftharpoons 2\,HI(g)$$

if the equilibrium constant K_p for the system is 160 at 500 K.

8. Calculate the standard free energy change $\Delta G°$ for the reaction:

$$2\,NO(g) + O_2(g) \rightleftharpoons 2\,NO_2(g)$$

if the equilibrium constant K_p for the system is 4.2×10^{12} at 298 K.

9. Calculate the standard free energy change $\Delta G°$ for the reaction:

$$COCl_2(g) \rightleftharpoons CO(g) + Cl_2(g)$$

if the equilibrium constant K_p for the system is 8.2×10^{-4} at 360 °C.

10. Calculate the standard free energy change $\Delta G°$ for the reaction:

$$Br_2(g) + I_2(g) \rightleftharpoons 2\,IBr(g)$$

if the equilibrium constant K_p for the system is 3.2×10^2 at 75°C.

11. If ΔH_f° (hydrazine(l)) $= +50.6$ kJ mol^{-1}
ΔH_f° (dinitrogen tetroxide) $= +9.2$ kJ mol^{-1}
ΔH_f° (water vapor) $= -241.8$ kJ mol^{-1}

calculate the value of the equilibrium constant for the reaction described in Question 3 at 500 K.

12. If ΔH_f° (nitric oxide) $= +90.3$ kJ mol^{-1}
ΔH_f° (water vapor) $= -241.8$ kJ mol^{-1}

calculate the value of the equilibrium constant for the reaction described in Question 4 at 400 K.

13. Calculate the value of K_p for the reaction at 1000K, given

$$2\,CO(g) + O_2(g) \rightleftharpoons 2\,CO_2(g)$$

ΔG_f° (carbon monoxide) $= -137.2$ kJ mol^{-1}

ΔG_f° (carbon dioxide) $= -394.4$ kJ mol^{-1}

ΔH_f° (carbon monoxide) $= -110.5$ kJ mol^{-1}

ΔH_f° (carbon dioxide) $= -393.5$ kJ mol^{-1}

14. Calculate the value of K_p for the production of ammonia from nitrogen and hydrogen at 1000K, given

$$N_2(g) + 3\,H_2(g) \rightleftharpoons 2\,NH_3(g)$$

ΔG_f° (ammonia) $= -16.5$ kJ mol^{-1}

ΔH_f° (ammonia) $= -46.1$ kJ mol^{-1}

Electrochemistry

50.1 Galvanic Cells

Almost all chemical reactions liberate or absorb energy. This energy can be in the form of heat, which is the subject of **thermochemistry** (*cf.* Unit 11); the energy can be in the form of light, which is the subject of **photochemistry**; or the energy can be in the form of electricity, which is the subject of **electrochemistry**. In this unit and the next, we will examine how a chemical reaction can be used to generate electrical energy and how electrical energy can be used to drive a chemical reaction.

An **electrochemical cell** is a device in which electrical energy is either produced or used in a chemical reaction. If the cell is one in which electrical energy is produced, it is called a **galvanic** or **voltaic cell**. We will look at these cells in this unit. If the cell is one in which electrical energy is used to bring about a chemical reaction, it is called an **electrolytic cell**. We'll look at these in Unit 51.

If a piece of zinc metal is placed in a solution of copper(II) sulfate the surface of the zinc acquires a coating of copper metal which often falls off and collects at the bottom of the vessel. The zinc metal slowly disappears—it seems to dissolve—and the blue solution slowly becomes paler in color (Figure 50.1). What is happening in this reaction?

The reaction is a redox reaction (*cf.* Unit 9) in which the zinc atoms at the surface of the zinc metal give up electrons to the copper(II) ions in solution. The zinc is oxidized and the zinc(II) ions that are produced go into solution. The copper(II) ions are reduced and the copper metal that is produced adheres to the zinc or falls off to collect at the bottom. Copper(II) ions are blue in color and zinc(II) ions are colorless, so, as the reaction proceeds, the solution slowly loses its blue color.

$$Zn(s) + Cu^{2+}(aq) \rightarrow Zn^{2+}(aq) + Cu(s)$$

$$\text{blue} \qquad \text{colorless}$$

electrochemical cell

galvanic cell   electrolytic cell

chemical → electrical   electrical → chemical

reaction   energy   energy   reaction

Luigi Galvani (1737–1798) and Alessandro Volta (1774–1827) were both Italian scientists who investigated electrochemical cells. Volta built the first battery of cells in 1798. The battery was called a voltaic pile—a pile of alternating zinc and silver metal disks separated by paper soaked in a salt solution.

Humphrey Davy (1778–1829) used the newly invented voltaic piles to isolate the elements potassium, sodium, barium, strontium, and magnesium by electrolysis.

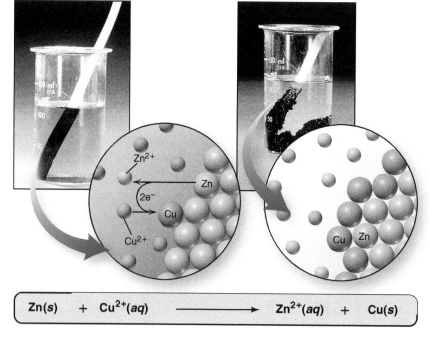

FIGURE 50.1 The oxidation of zinc and the reduction of copper(II) when zinc metal is immersed in a solution of copper(II) sulfate.

Why does this reaction happen? Why do the electrons prefer to be on the copper rather than the zinc? The electrons move to the copper because on the copper they are at a lower electrical (chemical) potential than on the zinc.

In a galvanic cell, the oxidation of the zinc metal and the reduction of the copper(II) ions are separated into two **half-cells** as shown in Figure 50.2. At the zinc **electrode**, the zinc metal is oxidized and the zinc ions go into the solution. This electrode, at which oxidation occurs, is called the **anode**. At the copper electrode, the copper(II) ions are reduced and copper metal is deposited on the electrode. This electrode, at which reduction takes place, is called the **cathode**. A wire is attached to both electrodes so that the electrons can flow from the anode, where they are released by the zinc, to the cathode, where they are used to reduce the copper(II) ions. To complete the circuit, a bridge, called a **salt bridge**, is placed between the two half-cells. Ions travel through this bridge to maintain electrical neutrality in each half of the cell. Ions, not isolated electrons, travel through the solution. Positively charged ions, the **cations**, travel toward the cathode, and negatively charged ions, the **anions**, travel toward the anode through the bridge. The salt bridge allows the passage of ions but inhibits the mixing of the solutions.

The separation of the oxidation and the reduction processes in the two half-cells means that the electrons must travel along the external wire. This flow of electrons, the electric current, can be made to do work. For example, the current may heat a filament in an incandescent light bulb or drive an electric motor. If the zinc metal is placed directly in the copper sulfate solution, the oxidation and reduction reactions will occur (as we have seen in Figure 50.1) but there would be no way to harness the available electrical energy. The energy would instead be released as heat.

The cell illustrated in Figure 50.2 is a simple version of the Daniell cell, invented by John Frederic Daniell (1790–1845) in 1836. This cell provided one of the most reliable constant-current sources of electrical energy in the mid-1800s.

Cell Potential

Electrons flow from the anode to the cathode due to the difference in the potential energy at the two electrodes. This difference in electric potential energy is called the **cell potential** and is measured in **volts (V)**. The driving force for the movement of electrons from the anode to the cathode is often referred to as the **electromotive force (emf)**—literally the force that makes electrons move. This force is the same as the cell potential measured in volts.

The movement of electrons down in potential energy from the anode to the cathode is analogous to a hydroelectric scheme (Figure 50.3). Water in a reservoir high in the mountains or behind a dam flows downhill to the power-generating plant.

The amount of energy provided by the water depends upon two factors. One is the potential energy difference between the reservoir and the power-generating plant. The other is the amount of water that flows down the pipe. The energy provided is the product of the two. The energy available in a galvanic cell similarly depends upon two factors. One is the potential energy difference between the two electrodes and the other is the amount of electrical charge that flows down the wire.

The terms, anode and cathode, anion and cation, electrode and ion, were devised by Michael Faraday (1791–1867) with the help of William Whewell (1794–1866). Faraday also developed the system of oxidation numbers.

Reduction *always* occurs at the cathode (and therefore oxidation *always* at the anode). If you have difficulty remembering this, think of a red cat (*red*uction at the *cat*hode).

John Frederic Daniell was professor of chemistry at King's College, London. Daniell's zinc-copper cell became the standard for telegraph systems in the US and Britain in the mid-1800s.

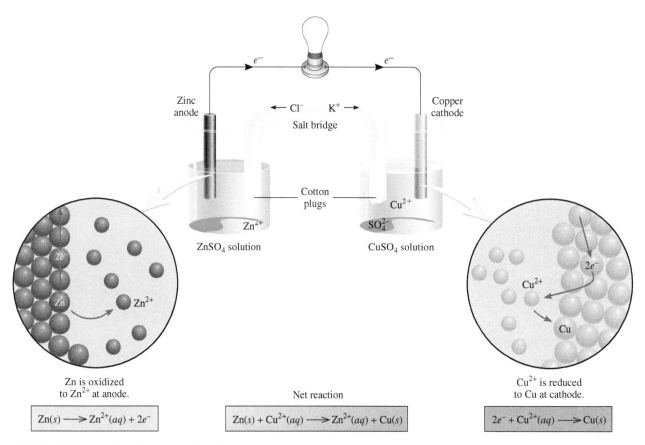

FIGURE 50.2 A galvanic (or voltaic) cell.
At the anode, zinc atoms lose electrons and enter solution as Zn^{2+} ions. At the cathode, Cu^{2+} ions are reduced to copper metal. Electrons flow through the external wire from the anode to the cathode. The inverted U-tube completes the electrical circuit. Sodium ions of the sodium sulfate in the U-tube move toward the cathode. Sulfate ions move toward the anode. Zinc ions move into the U-tube on the left and sulfate ions move into the U-tube on the right. The solutions maintain their electrical neutrality.

The amount of electrical charge is measured in **coulombs (C)**. One coulomb is the amount of electrical charge transferred when a current of **one ampere (A)** flows for one second. The cell potential is measured in volts (V).

$$\text{Energy (J)} = \text{Volts (V)} \times \text{Coulombs (C)}$$

The cell potential depends upon the identities of the materials used at the anode and the cathode and upon the concentrations of the solutions at both electrodes. It is useful to specify a set of standard conditions so that cell potentials can be compared. The standard conditions are:

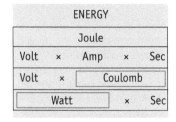

- Concentrations equal to 1 M.
- Gas pressures equal to 1 bar (often 1 atm is used).
- Temperatures equal to 25°C unless otherwise noted.

Cell potentials are usually denoted E°_{cell} or E° where the ° symbol signifies standard conditions.

The potential difference

The flow

FIGURE 50.3 **Water in a reservoir flows downhill to the power-generating plant where the water turns turbines to generate electricity. In the same way, electrons flow downhill from the anode to the cathode.**
The amount of energy provided by the water is the product of the potential energy difference between the reservoir and the power-generating plant and the amount of water that flows down the pipe. The energy available from a galvanic cell is the product of the potential energy difference between the two electrodes and the amount of electrical charge that flows down the wire.

Cell Notation

Instead of drawing the cell as shown in Figure 50.2, it is convenient to use a shorthand notation. The following conventions are used in the notation:

- The anode is placed on the left and the cathode is placed on the right. This is not a requirement but is highly recommended.

- A single vertical line | represents a boundary between two phases. For example, the zinc metal electrode and the Zn^{2+} solution in the anode of the Daniell cell is represented as: $Zn(s)|Zn^{2+}(aq)$.

- A comma separates substances in the same phase (the same solution). For example, the reduction of Fe^{3+} to Fe^{2+} in aqueous solution at a graphite electrode is represented as: $Fe^{3+}(aq),Fe^{2+}(aq)|C(graphite)$.

- A double vertical line ‖ represents a salt bridge or porous barrier between two solutions. Such barriers allow the passage of ions without allowing the solutions to mix.

The Daniell cell is represented by the notation:

phase boundary   salt bridge   phase boundary

$$Zn(s)|Zn^{2+}(aq)\,\|\,Cu^{2+}(aq)|Cu(s)$$

anode half-cell   cathode half-cell

The concentrations of the solutions are often included in the cell notation.

The advantage of writing the anode half-cell on the left and the cathode half-cell on the right is that in many cases the reaction reads from left to right. In this case, for example, the zinc is oxidized and the copper(II) is reduced:

$$Zn(s) \rightarrow Zn^{2+}(aq) \,\|\, Cu^{2+}(aq) \rightarrow Cu(s)$$

50.2   Standard Electrode Potentials

The cell potential E_{cell}° for the Daniell cell described above is 1.10 V. Note that the cell potential is a positive number. It's interesting to ask the question: what portion of this cell potential is due to the zinc electrode and what portion is due to the copper electrode? It's a question that cannot be answered.

The problem is analogous to asking: how high is a mountain? The usual answer is a height relative to sea level. But sea level is an arbitrary standard that is assigned a height of zero. The height of Cathedral Peak in the Sierra Nevada, for example, is 3326 m above sea level. Some parts of the country are below sea level—they have a negative height. The elevation of Death Valley at its lowest point is –86 m (Figure 50.4). Note that the difference in height between Death Valley and Cathedral peak is 3412 m, a difference that is always the same and independent of the zero standard chosen. The contribution that Cathedral Peak makes to this difference (3326 m) depends upon the standard chosen.

A cell potential is also a *difference*. It is the difference between the potential of the electrons at the anode and the potential of the electrons at the cathode. If we want

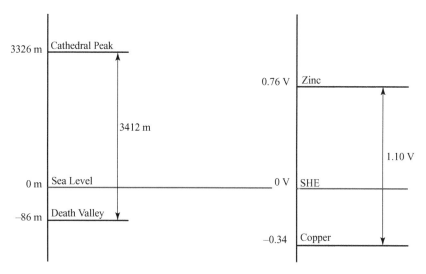

FIGURE 50.4   The arbitrary standards chosen as zero for geographical elevation and for half-cell potentials.
The difference between the elevations of two geographical locations is independent of the standard chosen. Similarly, the difference in potential between two half-cells is independent of the standard chosen.

to assign a contribution independently to the anode and cathode we need to choose an arbitrary standard for zero—just like sea level (Figure 50.4).

The standard chosen is the hydrogen electrode. The **standard hydrogen electrode (SHE)** is assigned an electrode potential of zero. In the SHE, hydrogen gas at 1.0 bar pressure is bubbled past an inert platinum electrode immersed in a 1.0 M H_3O^+ aqueous solution (Figure 50.5).

If a galvanic cell is constructed from a zinc electrode as the anode and the SHE as the cathode, the cell potential is +0.76V:

$$Zn(s) \,|\, Zn^{2+}(aq, 1M) \,\|\, H^+(aq, 1M) \,|\, H_2(g, 1\,atm) \,|\, Pt(s) \;\; E^\circ_{cell} = +0.76V$$

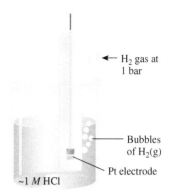

← H_2 gas at 1 bar

Bubbles of $H_2(g)$

Pt electrode

~1 M HCl

FIGURE 50.5 The standard hydrogen electrode (SHE). An inert platinum electrode immersed in a 1.0 M H_3O^+ aqueous solution with hydrogen gas at 1.0 bar bubbling through the solution.

The positive cell potential indicates that zinc metal is more easily oxidized than hydrogen gas; it loses or releases its electrons more easily. The zinc metal is a better reducing agent than hydrogen gas. In any galvanic cell, the electrode more easily oxidized is always the anode—where oxidation occurs. In this case, since the SHE is assigned an electrode potential of zero, the entire cell potential is attributed to the zinc electrode and is called the standard half-cell potential of the zinc electrode.

If another galvanic cell is constructed from a copper electrode as the cathode and the SHE as the anode, the cell potential is +0.34 V:

$$Pt(s) \,|\, H_2(g, 1\,atm) \,|\, H^+(aq, 1M) \,\|\, Cu^{2+}(aq, 1M) \,|\, Cu(s) \;\; E^\circ_{cell} = +0.34V$$

In this case the positive cell potential indicates that hydrogen gas is more easily oxidized than copper; it is a better reducing agent than copper. The cell potential is the standard half-cell potential of the copper electrode.

By international convention, the standard half-cell potential is always a reduction potential. In other words, it is the potential of a half-cell when it is the cathode in a galvanic cell. The **standard half-cell reduction potential** of copper is therefore +0.34V. The half-cell potential is written:

$$E^\circ(Cu^{2+}\,|\,Cu) = +0.34 \text{ V}$$

The direction left to right ($Cu^{2+}\,|\,Cu$) indicates the reduction process taking place.

In the galvanic cell in which zinc was compared with the SHE, the zinc electrode was the anode. The zinc is oxidized to Zn^{2+} and its half cell potential is an oxidation potential, equal to +0.76 V. In order to write this half cell potential as a *reduction* potential the sign must be reversed:

$$E^\circ(Zn^{2+}\,|\,Zn) = -0.76 \text{ V}$$

The more negative the half-cell reduction potential, the more easily the metal loses its electrons. In other words, it is more easily oxidized and is a better reducing agent.

The great advantage of the adoption of an arbitrary standard—the SHE—is that half-cell reduction potentials can be assigned to any half-cell and then the cell potential for any cell can be calculated by adding the appropriate half-cell potentials. Some standard half-cell reduction potentials are listed in Table 50.1.

Platinum is used as the electrode material because in most cases the metal is inert. It does not participate in the reaction but merely serves to conduct the electrons to or from the location where reduction or oxidation occurs.

It is interesting, however, that the use of platinum electrodes can lead to unexpected results. The discovery of the anticancer drug cisplatin resulted from the use of platinum electrodes in an experiment to determine the effect of an electric field on the cell division of E. coli.

TABLE 50.1 Some standard reduction potentials at 25°C.

Oxidized Form		Reduced Form	Potential E° (V)
$F_2(g) + 2e^-$	$\rightarrow$	$2\ F^-$	+2.87
$O_3(g) + 2H^+(aq) + 2e^-$	$\rightarrow$	$O_2(g) + H_2O(l)$	+2.08
$S_2O_8^{2-}(aq) + 2e^-$	$\rightarrow$	$SO_4^{2-}(aq)$	+2.05
$Co^{3+}(aq) + e^-$	$\rightarrow$	$Co^{2+}(aq)$	+1.82
$H_2O_2(aq) + 2H^+(aq) + 2e^-$	$\rightarrow$	$2\ H_2O(l)$	+1.76
$Au^+(aq) + e^-$	$\rightarrow$	$Au(s)$	+1.69
$PbO_2(s) + 4H^+(aq) + SO_4^{2-}(aq) + 2e^-$	$\rightarrow$	$PbSO_4(s) + 2H_2O(l)$	+1.69
$MnO_4^-(aq) + 8H^+(aq) + 5e^-$	$\rightarrow$	$Mn^{2+}(aq) + 4H_2O(l)$	+1.51
$Cl_2(g) + 2e^-$	$\rightarrow$	$2\ Cl^-$	+1.36
$Cr_2O_7^{2-}(aq) + 14H^+(aq) + 6e^-$	$\rightarrow$	$2\ Cr^{3+}(aq) + 7H_2O(l)$	+1.33
$O_2(g) + 4H^+(aq) + 4e^-$	$\rightarrow$	$2H_2O(l)$	+1.23
$2IO_3^-(aq) + 12H^+(aq) + 10e^-$	$\rightarrow$	$I_2(s) + 6H_2O(l)$	+1.20
$Br_2(g) + 2e^-$	$\rightarrow$	$2\ Br^-$	+1.09
$NO_3^-(aq) + 4H^+(aq) + 3e^-$	$\rightarrow$	$NO(g) + 2H_2O(l)$	+0.96
$Ag^+(aq) + e^-$	$\rightarrow$	$Ag(s)$	+0.80
$Fe^{3+}(aq) + e^-$	$\rightarrow$	$Fe^{2+}(aq)$	+0.77
$I_2(s) + 2e^-$	$\rightarrow$	$2\ I^-$	+0.54
$Cu^{2+}(aq) + 2e^-$	$\rightarrow$	$Cu(s)$	+0.34
$Sn^{4+}(aq) + 2e^-$	$\rightarrow$	$Sn^{2+}(aq)$	+0.14
$2H^+(aq) + 2e^-$	$\rightarrow$	$H_2(g)$	0.0
$Pb^{2+}(aq) + 2e^-$	$\rightarrow$	$Pb(s)$	−0.13
$Sn^{2+}(aq) + 2e^-$	$\rightarrow$	$Sn(s)$	−0.14
$Co^{2+}(aq) + 2e^-$	$\rightarrow$	$Co(s)$	−0.28
$Fe^{2+}(aq) + 2e^-$	$\rightarrow$	$Fe(s)$	−0.44
$Zn^{2+}(aq) + 2e^-$	$\rightarrow$	$Zn(s)$	−0.76
$2H_2O(l) + 2e^-$	$\rightarrow$	$H_2(g) + 2OH^-(aq)$	−0.83
$Al^{3+}(aq) + 3e^-$	$\rightarrow$	$Al(s)$	−1.68
$Mg^{2+}(aq) + 2e^-$	$\rightarrow$	$Mg(s)$	−2.36
$Na^+(aq) + e^-$	$\rightarrow$	$Na(s)$	−2.71
$K^+(aq) + e^-$	$\rightarrow$	$K(s)$	−2.93
$Li^+(aq) + e^-$	$\rightarrow$	$Li(s)$	−3.05

EXAMPLE 50.1   CALCULATING CELL POTENTIALS

A galvanic cell is constructed from two half-cells. In one half-cell a magnesium electrode is placed in a 1.0 M $Mg(NO_3)_2$ solution. In the other half-cell a silver electrode is placed in a 1.0 M $AgNO_3$ solution.

Standard half-cell reduction potentials are:

$$E°(Mg^{2+}\,|\,Mg) = -2.37\ V$$
$$E°(Ag^+\,|\,Ag) = +0.80\ V$$

a. Draw the cell using the shorthand cell notation.
b. Calculate the cell potential.

UNDERSTAND THE QUESTION

Any galvanic cell is made up of two parts: the half-cell in which oxidation occurs and the half-cell in which reduction occurs. The cell potential can be calculated by adding the appropriate half-cell potentials. Remember that standard half-cell potentials are reduction potentials and that the sign must be changed for the oxidation at the anode.

PLAN THE SOLUTION

The first task is to determine which half-cell is the anode and which is the cathode. The half-cell in which oxidation occurs is always the one with the more negative reduction potential. A more negative reduction potential means that the metal is more easily oxidized.

SOLVE THE PROBLEM

a. $E°(Mg^{2+}|Mg) = -2.37$ V—this is more negative, so Mg is oxidized to Mg^{2+} at the anode.

$E°(Ag^+|Ag) = +0.80$ V

The cell notation is:

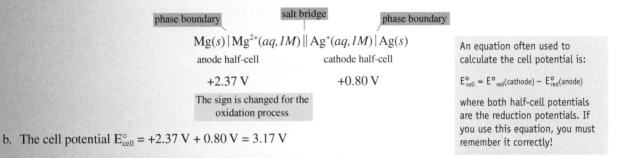

An equation often used to calculate the cell potential is:

$E°_{cell} = E°_{red}(cathode) - E°_{red}(anode)$

where both half-cell potentials are the reduction potentials. If you use this equation, you must remember it correctly!

b. The cell potential $E°_{cell} = +2.37$ V $+ 0.80$ V $= 3.17$ V

PROBLEM 50.1A

A galvanic cell is constructed from two half-cells. In one half-cell a copper electrode is placed in a 1.0 M $Cu(NO_3)_2$ solution. In the other half-cell a chromium electrode is placed in a 1.0 M $Cr(NO_3)_3$ solution.
Standard half-cell reduction potentials are:

$$E°(Cu^{2+}/Cu) = +0.34 \text{ V}$$
$$E°(Cr^{3+}/Cr) = -0.74 \text{ V}$$

a. Draw the cell using the shorthand cell notation.

b. Calculate the cell potential.

PROBLEM 50.1B

A galvanic cell is constructed from two half-cells. In one half-cell a cadmium electrode is placed in a 1.0 M $Cd(NO_3)_2$ solution. In the other half-cell a tin electrode is placed in a 1.0 M $Sn(NO_3)_2$ solution.
Standard half-cell reduction potentials are:

$$E°(Cd^{2+}|Cd) = -0.40 \text{ V}$$
$$E°(Sn^{2+}|Sn) = -0.14 \text{ V}$$

a. Draw the cell using the shorthand cell notation.

b. Calculate the cell potential.

50.3 Oxidizing and Reducing Agents

The positions of the **oxidizing** and **reducing agents** in Table 50.1 can be used to predict the result of redox reactions in aqueous solution. To use our familiar example of the reactions that occur in the Daniell cell, zinc is oxidized to zinc ions Zn^{2+} and copper ions Cu^{2+} are reduced to copper metal. This means that zinc is the reducing agent and the copper ion is the oxidizing agent. The zinc has the more negative electrode reduction potential.

Species are arranged in Table 50.1 in order of their oxidizing and reducing ability. The best oxidizing agent is listed at the top of the table on the left and the best reducing agent is listed at the bottom of the table on the right. Fluorine, at the top on the left, wants electrons. Lithium, at the bottom on the left, gives up its electrons very easily. The order is summarized in Figure 50.6, with the reductions of Zn^{2+} and Cu^{2+} included.

Any substance higher on the left will react with any substance lower on the right. In our case, the Cu^{2+} ions will react with Zn metal to produce Cu metal and Zn^{2+} ions. The Cu^{2+} ion is a better oxidizing agent than the Zn^{2+}—it is higher on the left. Similarly, Zn metal is a better reducing agent than Cu—it is lower on the right.

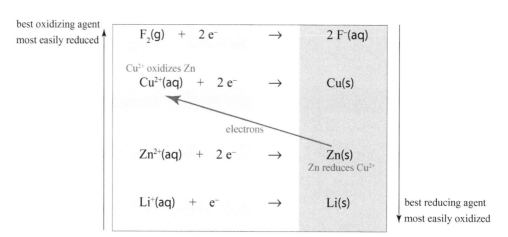

FIGURE 50.6   A diagram of standard reduction potentials and the relative oxidizing and reducing abilities of different substances.
By convention, in tables such as this the most positive value of $E°_{red}$ is at the top of the table and the most negative is at the bottom.

EXAMPLE 50.2   OXIDATION AND REDUCTION

Predict if any reaction will occur, and if so what will occur, when an acidic aqueous solution of dichromate ion is added to an aqueous solution of iodide ion.

a. Write the balanced equation for the redox reaction.

b. Using the cell notation, draw the galvanic cell that could be used to extract electrical energy from the reaction.

c. Calculate the standard cell potential.

d. Will the dichromate ion oxidize chloride ion to chlorine?

UNDERSTAND THE QUESTION

The oxidation and reduction that may occur can be predicted from the position of the substances in Table 50.1. Any substance higher on the left will oxidize any substance lower on the right. Once the probability of reaction is established, the balanced equation for the redox reaction can be written using the procedure described in Unit 9. The cell notation is written and the cell potential is calculated using the procedures described earlier.

PLAN THE SOLUTION

Find the dichromate ion $Cr_2O_7^{2-}$ in Table 50.1. It may help to realize that chromium in the dichromate ion is in a high oxidation state (+6) and is therefore a powerful oxidizing agent. It should be high on the left. If the iodide ion is lower on the right, then a reaction will occur.

SOLVE THE PROBLEM

a. The balanced equation for a similar redox reaction was derived in Problem 8.4A:

$$14 \, H^+ + Cr_2O_7^{2-} + 6 \, I^- \rightarrow 2 \, Cr^{3+} + 7 \, H_2O + 3 \, I_2$$

b. The galvanic cell is:

$$Pt(s) \, | \, I^-(aq), I_2(s) \, \| \, Cr_2O_7^{2-}(aq), Cr^{3+}(aq) \, | \, Pt(s)$$

The electrodes can be any inert substance; they do not participate in the reaction.

c. The standard half-cell reduction potentials are:

$$E°(I_2 | I^-) = +0.54 \text{ V}$$
$$E°(Cr_2O_7^{2-} | Cr^{3+}) = +1.33 \text{ V}$$

The cell potential $E°_{cell} = +1.33 \text{ V} - 0.54 \text{ V} = +0.79 \text{ V}$

The cell potential is positive and the reaction will go as indicated.

d. The standard half-cell reduction potentials in this case are:

$$E°(Cl_2 | Cl^-) = +1.36 \text{ V}$$
$$E°(Cr_2O_7^{2-} | Cr^{3+}) = +1.33 \text{ V}$$

The cell potential $E°_{cell}$ for a cell in which Cl^- is oxidized = $+1.33 \text{ V} - 1.36 \text{ V} = -0.03 \text{ V}$

The cell potential is negative and the reaction will *not* go. Examination of Table 50.1 indicates that the Cl^- is *higher* on the right than the dichromate ion on the left.

PROBLEM 50.2A

Determine whether the following reactions will occur under standard conditions:

a. $Hg^{2+}(aq) + 2 \, I^-(aq) \rightarrow Hg(l) + I_2(s)$

b. $Sn(s) + 2 \, Cu^{2+}(aq) \rightarrow Sn^{2+}(aq) + 2 \, Cu^+(aq)$

c. $Co(s) + Fe^{2+}(aq) \rightarrow Co^{2+}(aq) + Fe(s)$

PROBLEM 50.2B

Determine whether the following reactions will occur under standard conditions:

a. $Cl_2(aq) + 2 \, I^-(aq) \rightarrow I_2(aq) + 2 \, Cl^-(aq)$

b. $2 \, Al(s) + 3 \, Cu^{2+}(aq) \rightarrow 2 \, Al^{3+}(aq) + 3 \, Cu(s)$

c. $Cu^{2+}(aq) + 2 \, Ag(s) \rightarrow Cu(s) + 2 \, Ag^+(aq)$

50.4 Spontaneous Change and Equilibrium

A galvanic cell that provides electrical energy is undergoing a spontaneous change. The cell will continue to provide electrical energy until it reaches equilibrium. The cell is then said to be 'dead'. We have already noted that the energy provided by the cell, or the maximum work that the cell is able to do, is the product of the cell potential and the amount of electrical charge that flows between the anode and cathode. If the work is expressed in joules, the cell potential is expressed in volts, and the amount of charge is expressed in coulombs, then:

$$\text{Work (J)} = \text{Cell potential (V)} \times \text{Charge (C)}$$

The charge (C) is normally expressed as the number of moles of electrons transferred, n, multiplied by the charge on one mole of electrons. The charge on one mole of electrons is 96,485 coulombs, a quantity known as one faraday (F). Under standard conditions, the cell potential is $E°$. Therefore,

$$\text{Work (J)} = E°(V) \times nF(C)$$

Normally written as:

$$\text{Work} = nFE°$$

We noted in Unit 30 that the free energy of a system is the energy a system has that can be used to do work. The change in the free energy $\Delta G°$ is the maximum amount of electrical work that can be done by a galvanic cell. Therefore,

$$\Delta G° = -nFE°$$

The negative sign is present because work is done by the system and the change in the free energy is negative. The number of moles, n, is the number of moles of electrons transferred in the balanced equation for the reaction. In other words, n is the number of moles of electrons lost by the species being oxidized and the number of moles of electrons gained by the species being reduced—both are of course the same in a balanced equation.

The standard free energy change $\Delta G°$ depends upon the equation used to represent the reaction. $\Delta G°$ is an extensive property. If, for example, the coefficients in the equation are doubled, then $\Delta G°$ is also doubled. The cell potential $E°$ however is unchanged—it is an intensive property. It is the same regardless of the equation used to represent the reaction. $E°$ is proportional to $\Delta G°/n$ and if n is doubled, so is $\Delta G°$; therefore $E°$ stays the same.

You may have noticed that common alkaline cells in sizes AAA, AA, C, and D all have the same cell potential (voltage) of 1.5 V. The voltage is independent of the size. What is different is the number of coulombs the cells are able to supply—the amount of energy they have available.

For nonstandard conditions,

$$\Delta G = -nFE$$

If the reaction is spontaneous, ΔG must be negative. Since both n and F are positive, this means that for a spontaneous process, E must be positive, as we have already observed.

The faraday (F) is named after Michael Faraday (1791–1867), acknowledged to be one of the greatest of all scientists. He is best known for his discoveries in electricity and magnetism.

This is analogous to another intensive property, density, that is the ratio of mass to volume. If the mass is doubled, so is the volume; and therefore the density remains the same.

It also means that at equilibrium, when ΔG is zero, the cell potential E also equals zero—the cell is dead.

The standard free energy change for a reaction is related to the equilibrium constant K for the reaction (*cf.* Unit 35):

$$\Delta G° = -RTlnK$$

This means that all three thermodynamic quantities, $\Delta G°$, K, and E° are related to one another. The relationship is summarized in Figure 50.7. If any one of the three quantities is known, then the other two can be calculated. The measurement of cell potentials provides a very useful way to determine the equilibrium constants for reactions that go essentially to completion—when the value of K is very large. The measurement or calculation of cell potentials is also a useful way to determine very small equilibrium constants—such as solubility products. The following example illustrates a typical calculation.

If $\Delta G°$ has a large negative value, the reaction is product-favored, and E° is high, and K is large.

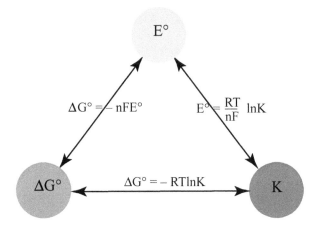

FIGURE 50.7   The relationships between the three thermodynamic quantities, $\Delta G°$, K, and E°.

EXAMPLE 50.3   THE DETERMINATION OF AN EQUILIBRIUM CONSTANT FROM A CELL POTENTIAL

For the oxidation of copper using iron(III) under standard conditions (25°C), calculate

a. the cell potential E° for a galvanic cell employing the reaction shown,

b. the standard free energy change $\Delta G°$ for the reaction,

c. the equilibrium constant K for the reaction.

$$Cu(s) + 2\ Fe^{3+}(aq) \rightarrow 2\ Fe^{2+}(aq) + Cu^{2+}(aq)$$
$$E°(Cu^{2+}|Cu) = +0.34\ V$$
$$E°(Fe^{3+}|Fe^{2+}) = +0.77\ V$$

UNDERSTAND THE QUESTION

The thermodynamic quantities, $\Delta G°$, K, and E° are related to one another. The relationships are summarized in Figure 50.7. If one can be measured or calculated, the remaining two can be determined. In this case we know the half-cell reduction potentials and can calculate the standard cell potential.

PLAN THE SOLUTION

Calculate the standard cell potential E°_{cell} and then use the relationships in Figure 50.7 to calculate ΔG° and K.

SOLVE THE PROBLEM

a. The copper is oxidized (at the anode), so change the sign of its half-cell potential (from reduction to oxidation) and add the two:

The cell potential E°_{cell} = +0.77 V – 0.34 V = +0.43 V

b. The free energy change $\Delta G^\circ = -nFE^\circ$

In the balanced equation for the reaction, n = 2,

$$\Delta G^\circ = -2 \text{ mol} \times 96{,}485 \text{ C mol}^{-1} \times 0.43 \text{ V}$$
$$= -8.3 \times 10^4 \text{ J}$$
$$= -83 \text{ kJ for the reaction as it is written.}$$

c. The equilibrium constant can be calculated from ΔG° or from E°:

From $\Delta G^\circ = -RT \ln K$: -8.3×10^4 J = -8.314 J K$^{-1} \times 298.15$ K $\times \ln$ K

$\ln$ K = 33

K = 3.5×10^{14} —the reaction goes to completion.

From $E = \dfrac{RT}{nF} \ln K$:

0.43 V = $((8.314$ J K$^{-1} \times 298.15$ K$)/(2$ mol $\times 96{,}485$ C mol$^{-1})) \ln$ K

$\ln$ K = 33 and K = 3.5×10^{14} as before.

> In general it is often convenient to omit the mol^{-1} from the units of R and refer the calculation to the reaction as it is written in the balanced equation. In other words, the calculation is for 'one mole of reaction'.
>
> Similarly, the ΔG° previously calculated refers to the free energy change for 'one mole of reaction' as it is written.

PROBLEM 50.3A

An equilibrium constant can be calculated for any reaction if appropriate half-cell reactions can be identified that add up to the overall reaction. An example is the calculation of the solubility product for silver(I) chloride. If the two half-cell reduction potentials are:

$$E^\circ(AgCl(s)|Ag(s)) = +0.22 \text{ V}$$
$$E^\circ(Ag^+(aq)|Ag(s)) = +0.80 \text{ V}$$

a. Write equations for these two half-cell reductions.

b. Show that the two half-cell equations sum to the equation for the overall reaction.

c. Calculate the cell potential.

d. Calculate the equilibrium constant K_{sp}.

PROBLEM 50.3B

Magnesium metal can be used to reduce aluminum ions to aluminum according to the equation:

$$3 \text{ Mg}(s) + 2 \text{ Al}^{3+}(aq) \rightarrow 3 \text{ Mg}^{2+}(aq) + 2 \text{ Al}(s)$$

a. Calculate the cell potential E° for a galvanic cell employing the reaction shown.

b. What is the value of n for this reaction?

c. Calculate the standard free energy change ΔG° for the reaction.

d. Calculate the equilibrium constant K for the reaction.

$$E^\circ(Mg^{2+}|Mg) = -2.36 \text{ V}$$
$$E^\circ(Al^{3+}|Al) = -1.68 \text{ V}$$

When a cell is constructed, the cell potential can be measured. If the conditions are standard, and the temperature is constant, then the same value of E° will always be obtained. As Problem 50.3A illustrates, an equilibrium constant K or a free energy change $\Delta G°$ can be calculated for any reaction if appropriate half-cell reactions can be identified that add up to the overall reaction. Usually this presents no problem. However, in some cases, different half-cell reactions can be used to derive the overall reaction and care must be taken.

An example of this occurs in disproportionation reactions—reactions in which the same element is both oxidized and reduced. Consider the disproportionation of Cu^+:

$$2\ Cu^+ \rightarrow Cu + Cu^{2+}$$

There are two ways to divide this reaction into two half-cell reactions:

$Cu^+ \rightarrow Cu$ $2\ Cu^+ \rightarrow 2\ Cu$

$\dfrac{Cu^+ \rightarrow Cu^{2+}}{2\ Cu^+ \rightarrow Cu + Cu^{2+}}$ $\dfrac{Cu \rightarrow Cu^{2+}}{2\ Cu^+ \rightarrow Cu + Cu^{2+}}$

The standard electrode reduction potentials are:

$E°(Cu^+|Cu) = +0.52$ V $E°(Cu^+|Cu) = +0.52$ V

$E°(Cu^{2+}|Cu^+) = +0.16$ V $E°(Cu^{2+}|Cu) = +0.34$ V

The cell potentials are therefore

$E° = +0.52$ V $- 0.16$ V $= + 0.36$ V $E° = +0.52$ V $- 0.34$ V $= + 0.18$ V

The cell potentials are different for the two cells—one is twice the other. But isn't the overall reaction the same in both cases? The overall reaction is indeed the same. $\Delta G°$ for the reaction can be calculated and equals -34.7 kJ.

If $\Delta G°$ is the same and E° is different, and $\Delta G° = -nFE°$, then n must be different. The cells are different. If you examine the two sets of half-reactions used, you will notice that the first set are reactions in which just one electron is lost or gained and the second set are reactions in which two electrons are lost or gained—the number of moles of electrons n is twice as great in the second set. This can also be seen if the cells are drawn using the cell notation:

In the first case the cell is:

$$Pt(s)\,|\,Cu^+(aq), Cu^{2+}(aq)\,\|\,Cu^+(aq)\,|\,Cu(s) \qquad E° = + 0.36\ V$$

In the second case the cell is:

$$Cu(s)\,|\,Cu^{2+}(aq)\,\|\,Cu^+(aq)\,|\,Cu(s) \qquad E° = + 0.18\ V$$

In the first case, the number of moles of electrons involved in the oxidation at the anode and the reduction at the cathode is 1. In the second case the number of moles of electrons involved in the oxidation at the anode and the reduction at the cathode is 2. The calculation of $\Delta G°$ yields the same answer for both cases:

$$\begin{aligned}
\Delta G° &= -nFE° \\
&= -1\ mol \times 96{,}485\ C\ mol^{-1} \times 0.36\ V \\
&= -2\ mol \times 96{,}485\ C\ mol^{-1} \times 0.18\ V \\
&= -34{,}700\ J
\end{aligned}$$

Perhaps the more logical way to think of this disproportionation reaction of Cu^+ is in terms of a one-electron oxidation to Cu^{2+} and a one-electron reduction to Cu^+, that is, the first example described (n=1), but be aware that the reaction can be divided into two different half-cell reactions that will result in different values for E° and n.

50.5 The Nernst Equation

If the concentrations of the solutions in a galvanic cell are not standard (1 *M*), then the cell potential E will not be the standard cell potential E°. We can derive an equation for the cell potential under nonstandard conditions using the relationship between $\Delta G°$ and ΔG we first encountered in Unit 35:

$$\Delta G = \Delta G° + RT \ln Q$$

$$\Delta G° = -nFE°, \text{ and similarly } \Delta G = -nFE.$$

Substitution of these expressions for $\Delta G°$ and ΔG produces the equation:

$$-nFE = -nFE° + RT \ln Q$$

Dividing through by $-nF$:

$$E = E° - \frac{RT}{nF} \ln Q$$

$$\text{At } 25°C, \frac{RT}{nF} = (8.3145 \text{ J K}^{-1} \times 298.15 \text{ K})/(n \text{ mol} \times 96,485 \text{ C mol}^{-1})$$
$$= 0.02569/n \text{ V}$$

In this equation the logarithmic function $\ln Q$ is usually expressed as a logarithm to the base 10, primarily because the pH of a solution is $\log_{10}[H^+]$, so the factor 0.02569 is multiplied by 2.3026 to give 0.0592V:

$$E = E° - (0.0592/n) \log_{10} Q \text{ volts at } 25°C$$

The value of n refers to a balanced equation for the redox reaction. It is equal to the number of electrons lost in the oxidation or the number of electrons gained in the reduction—which must be the same if the equation is properly balanced.

$$\frac{\ln Q}{\ln 10} = \log_{10} Q$$

$$\text{and } \ln 10 = 2.3026$$

This equation was derived by Walther Nernst (1864–1941) in 1889 and is referred to as the **Nernst equation**. It can be used to calculate the cell potential under nonstandard conditions if the concentrations of the electrolytes are known. And it can be used to determine the concentration of an electrolyte if the cell potential is measured. This is done most notably when the pH of a solution is measured using a pH meter.

Walther Nernst was awarded the Nobel Prize in Chemistry in 1920 for his contributions to electrochemistry and thermodynamics.

Let's return to the Daniell cell we examined earlier. As the cell is used to supply energy, the zinc anode is oxidized and the concentration of zinc ions in the anode half-cell increases. At the same time, copper(II) ions are reduced at the cathode and the concentration of copper ions in the cathode half-cell decreases. As time progresses, and more energy is supplied by the cell, the voltage drops. The voltage at any point can be calculated using the Nernst equation. The following example illustrates a typical calculation.

Concentration Cells

The Nernst equation illustrates how the cell potential depends upon the concentrations of the solutions at the anode and cathode of a galvanic cell. This suggests that a galvanic cell could be constructed using the same electrode at both the anode and cathode but with different concentrations of the electrolyte at the two electrodes. Such a cell is called a **concentration cell** because the cell potential depends upon the difference in the two concentrations.

EXAMPLE 50.4 USING THE NERNST EQUATION

The standard cell potential for a Daniell cell at 25°C is 1.10 V.

$$E°(Cu^{2+} | Cu) = +0.34 \text{ V}$$
$$E°(Zn^{2+} | Zn) = -0.76 \text{ V}$$

a. Calculate the cell potential when the concentration of Zn^{2+} ions in the anode half-cell has increased to 1.50 M and the concentration of the Cu^{2+} ions in the cathode half-cell has reduced to 0.50 M.

b. If the volume of the solutions at the anode and cathode are each 200 mL, estimate the energy supplied by the Daniell cell up to this point.

UNDERSTAND THE QUESTION

The chemical equation for the reaction in the Daniell cell is:

$$Cu^{2+}(aq) + Zn(s) \rightarrow Cu(s) + Zn^{2+}(aq)$$

The reaction quotient Q in the Nernst equation is the [product]/[reactant] ratio. The zinc and copper solids are not included in the expression for Q and therefore Q in this case is $[Zn^{2+}]/[Cu^{2+}]$. The number of moles of electrons, n, in the balanced equation is 2. The energy provided by the cell can be estimated if the average cell potential (voltage) is known and the number of coulombs of charge can be determined. The charge can be calculated if the number of moles of zinc that are oxidized (or the number of moles of copper(II) that are reduced) can be determined.

PLAN THE SOLUTION

Use the Nernst equation to calculate the cell potential E. Use the increase in the concentration of Zn^{2+} in the anode half-cell to calculate the moles of Zn^{2+} ions produced and from this calculate the number of moles of electrons provided. Then calculate the energy supplied using the relationship Energy = nFE.

SOLVE THE PROBLEM

a. The Nernst equation is $E = E° - (0.0592 \text{ V } /n) \log_{10}Q$ at 25°C

$$Q = [Zn^{2+}]/[Cu^{2+}] = (1.50/0.50) = 3.0$$

$$\log_{10}Q = 0.48$$

$$E = 1.10 \text{ V} - (0.0592/2) \times 0.48 \text{ V}$$
$$= 1.10 \text{ V} - 0.01\text{V}$$
$$= 1.09 \text{ V}$$

An interesting feature of galvanic cells is how the cell potential is maintained at a high level until the cell is near the end of its useful life. You may have noticed this using a flashlight. The flashlight maintains its brightness until close to the end of the life of the cells and then quickly dims. The reason is the logarithmic function in the Nernst equation. If the voltage of the Daniell cell is plotted against the charge supplied, a graph such as that shown in Figure 50.8 is obtained.

The number of moles of zinc oxidized = increase in concentration × volume in L

$$= 0.50 \text{ M} \times 0.200 \text{ L}$$

$$= 0.100 \text{ moles}$$

Number of moles of electrons supplied = 2 × moles of zinc oxidized

$$= 0.200 \text{ moles}$$

Charge passed

$$= nF$$

$$= 0.200 \text{ mol} \times 96,485 \text{ C mol}^{-1}$$

$$= 19,300 \text{ C}$$

Approximate voltage   = 1.09 V

Energy supplied (J)   = V × C

                                      = 1.09 V × 19,300 C

                                      = 21 kJ

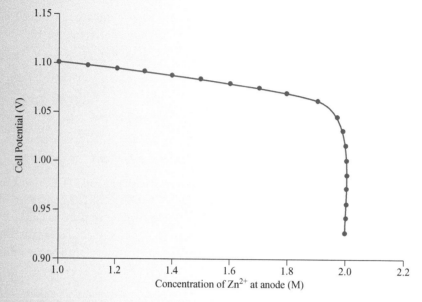

FIGURE 50.8   **The change in the cell potential of a Daniell cell during the life of the cell.**
The cell potential is calculated using the Nernst equation. Notice how the voltage is
maintained at a relatively high level until near the end of the life of the cell.

PROBLEM 50.4A

For the Daniell cell described in the preceding example 50.4,

a. Calculate the cell potential after 99.99% of the copper in the cathode half-cell has been reduced to copper.

b. Calculate the concentration of Zn^{2+} in the anode half-cell and the concentration of Cu^{2+} in the cathode half-cell when the cell reaches equilibrium (when the cell is 'dead').

c. Calculate the equilibrium constant for the reaction:

$$Cu^{2+}(aq) + Zn(s) \rightarrow Cu(s) + Zn^{2+}(aq)$$

d. Calculate $\Delta G°$ for the reaction.

PROBLEM 50.4B

When it was invented and used in telegraphy in the mid-1800s, a Daniell cell used a saturated solution of copper sulfate at the cathode. Three cells were connected in series in a battery. Suppose that the copper sulfate solution at 25°C has a molarity equal to 1.60 M and that the initial concentration of zinc sulfate in the anode compartment is 0.10 M. The standard cell potential E° equals 1.10 V.

a. Calculate the cell potential E for the Daniell cell.

b. What is the voltage across a battery of three cells?

Suppose, for example, that both the anode and the cathode are zinc metal electrodes placed in aqueous solutions of 0.10 M and 1.90 M zinc sulfate respectively. The diagram for the cell using the cell notation is:

$$Zn(s) \,|\, Zn^{2+}(aq, 0.10M) \,\|\, Zn^{2+}(aq, 1.90M) \,|\, Zn(s)$$

The cell potential can be calculated using the Nernst equation:

$$E = E° - (0.0592/n) \log_{10}Q \text{ volts at } 25°C$$

$E°$ is zero because both electrodes are the same. The cell potential depends only upon the difference in the concentrations and the value of n. It is interesting therefore that the cell potential for a concentration cell is independent of the identity of the electrode provided that the charge on the ions in solution at the electrodes is the same. For example, concentration cells based upon $Ni^{2+}\,|\,Ni$, $Zn^{2+}\,|\,Zn$, $Cu^{2+}\,|\,Cu$, $Mg^{2+}\,|\,Mg$, etc. will all result in the same cell potential.

In the case described above, the cell potential E is:

$$E = 0 - (0.0592/2) \log_{10}(0.10/1.90) \text{ V}$$
$$= 0.038 \text{ V}$$
$$= 38 \text{ mV}$$

> The anode $[Zn^{2+}]$ concentration is the product of the oxidation. The cathode $[Zn^{2+}]$ concentration is the reactant in the reduction process.

You may be familiar with the story of Luigi Galvani's experiments on the effect of an electric current on the contractions of the muscles in a frog's legs. Alessandro Volta's interpretation of the experiment was that the muscle contractions were caused by the current flowing between two dissimilar metals, brass and iron.

The muscle contractions of the human heart are caused by electrical impulses arising from a concentration cell. In this case the cardiac muscle cells have different concentrations of sodium and potassium ions inside and outside the cell. The concentration of potassium ions inside the cell is high (about 135 mM) and the concentration outside the cell wall is low—the ratio is about 30:1. The reverse is true of the sodium ions. The difference in the ion concentrations produces a potential difference across the cell wall. At body temperature (37°C) the potential across the cell membrane is about 94 mV. A regular change in the concentrations of the ions inside the cell due to the migration of ions through the cell wall leads to a regular oscillation of the potential across the cell membrane stimulating a regular beating of the cardiac muscles. The electric impulses generated are strong enough to be detected by electrodes taped to the surface of the skin and can be recorded on an ECG (electrocardiogram). An appropriate concentration of potassium ions in blood is critical to the proper operation of the cells that stimulate the beating of the heat muscles. If the concentration is too low or too high, cardiac arrest will occur.

pH Electrodes

The measurement of the hydrogen ion concentration in a solution can be achieved using a concentration cell in which the cathode half-cell contains a standard 1.0 M solution of H^+—a standard hydrogen electrode. This assumes that the unknown hydrogen ion concentration in the anode half-cell is less than 1.0 M (or it wouldn't be the anode!). The H^+ concentration of the unknown solution can be calculated using the Nernst equation for a concentration cell:

$$E = E° - (0.0592/n) \log_{10}Q \text{ volts at } 25°C$$
$$E = 0 - (0.0592/2) \log_{10}([H^+]^2/(1.0)^2) \text{ V}$$
$$E = 0.0592 \times \log_{10}[H^+] \text{ V}$$

> $\log x^2 = 2 \log x$

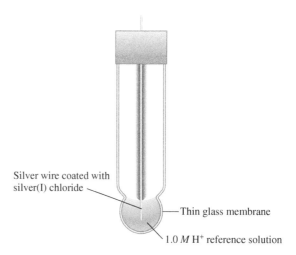

Silver wire coated with silver(I) chloride

Thin glass membrane

1.0 M H$^+$ reference solution

FIGURE 50.9 **A glass electrode used to measure the pH of a solution.**
The half-cell potential depends directly upon the difference between the pH of the solution and the pH of the reference inside the glass.

Measurement of the cell potential allows an easy computation of the [H$^+$]. In practice the hydrogen electrode is awkward to use—it requires at least a source of hydrogen gas at 1 bar pressure. Instead the electrode for the unknown solution consists of a silver wire coated with silver(I) chloride dipping into a 1.0 M solution of H$^+$ (as HCl). The electrode is contained within a thin-walled glass membrane (Figure 50.9). When the electrode is immersed in a solution containing an acidic solution with a H$^+$ concentration other than 1.0 M, a potential develops across the glass membrane.

In place of the standard hydrogen electrode, the reference used is the saturated calomel electrode. This consists of a platinum electrode dipping in calomel (mercury(I) chloride) in contact with liquid mercury and aqueous potassium chloride. The saturated calomel electrode has a precisely known half-cell potential. Both electrodes are often encased in a single unit.

Review Questions

1. Describe what happens when a strip of zinc metal is immersed in a solution of copper(II) sulfate.

2. Define the terms: electrode, cathode, anode, anion, and cation.

3. Describe what happens in the two half-cells of a galvanic cell.

4. What is a salt-bridge and why is it used?

5. What is the relationship between energy, charge, and cell potential?

6. What is the faraday and how is it related to the coulomb?

7. What is the standard hydrogen electrode? What is a standard half-cell electrode reduction potential? Why are standard half-cell reduction potentials so useful?

8. How are the standard cell potential, the standard free energy change of a reaction, and the equilibrium constant related?

9. How is the standard electrode reduction potential related to the ease with which a species is oxidized or reduced?

10. Describe the Nernst equation and what it is used for.

11. What is a concentration cell and how does it work? What are the concentrations of the electrolyte at the two electrodes when a concentration cell reaches equilibrium?

Solutions to Problems

PROBLEM 50.1A

a. The standard reduction potential $E°(Cr^{3+}|Cr)$ is more negative and therefore the chromium will be oxidized at the anode. The copper(II) will be reduced at the cathode:

$$Cr(s)|Cr^{3+}(aq,1M)||Cu^{2+}(aq,1M)|Cu(s)$$

b. $E°(Cu^{2+}|Cu) = +0.34$ V

$E°(Cr^{3+}|Cr) = -0.74$ V—change the sign for oxidation at the anode.

The cell potential $E° = +0.34$ V $+ 0.74$ V $= 1.08$ V.

PROBLEM 50.2A

a. $Hg^{2+}(aq) + 2 I^-(aq) \rightarrow Hg(l) + I_2(s)$

Hg^{2+} is reduced and I^- is oxidized.

Hg^{2+} is higher on the left than I^- on the right—the reaction will occur.

The cell potential is +0.32 V.

b. $Sn(s) + 2 Cu^{2+}(aq) \rightarrow Sn^{2+}(aq) + 2 Cu^+(aq)$

Cu^{2+} is reduced and Sn is oxidized.

Cu^{2+} is higher on the left than Sn on the right—the reaction will occur.

The cell potential is +0.30 V.

c. $Co(s) + Fe^{2+}(aq) \rightarrow Co^{2+}(aq) + Fe(s)$

Fe^{2+} is reduced and Co is oxidized.

Fe^{2+} is lower on the left than Co on the right—the reaction will *not* occur.

The cell potential for the reaction as written is -0.16 V the reaction is *not* spontaneous.

The reverse reaction will happen.

PROBLEM 50.3A

The solution process for AgCl is represented by the equation:

$$AgCl(s) \rightleftharpoons Ag^+(aq) + Cl^-(aq)$$

a. Reduction: $AgCl(s) \rightarrow Ag(s) + Cl^-(aq)$
$E°(AgCl(s)|Ag(s)) = +0.22$ V

Reduction: $Ag^+(aq) \rightarrow Ag(s)$
$E°(Ag^+(aq)|Ag(s)) = +0.80$ V

Reverse this equation for oxidation:

$Ag(s) \rightarrow Ag^+(aq)$ $E°_{oxid}(Ag(s)|Ag^+(aq)) = -0.80$ V

b. $AgCl(s) \rightarrow Ag(s) + Cl^-(aq)$
$Ag(s) \rightarrow Ag^+(aq)$
—————————————————
$AgCl(s) \rightleftharpoons Ag^+(aq) + Cl^-(aq)$

c. $E° = 0.22$ V $- 0.80$ V $= -0.58$ V.

d. $RT \ln K_{sp} = nFE°$

$\ln K_{sp} = (1$ mol $\times 96,485$ C mol^{-1}/8.3145 JK$^{-1} \times$ 298.15 K) $\times (-0.58$ V)

$\ln K_{sp} = -22.58$

$K_{sp} = 1.6 \times 10^{-10}$

This value agrees well with the value listed in Unit 45.

PROBLEM 50.4A

a. Initial concentration of copper(II) = 1.0 M

Concentration when 99.99% used = 1.0×10^{-4} M

Concentration of zinc(II) = 2.0 M

The Nernst equation is $E = E° - (0.0592/n) \log_{10}Q$ volts at 25°C

$Q = [Zn^{2+}]/[Cu^{2+}] = (2.0/1.0 \times 10^{-4}) = 2.0 \times 10^4$

$\log_{10}Q = 4.30$

$E = 1.10$ V $- (0.0592/2) \times 4.30$ V

$= 0.97$ V

b. At equilibrium, E = 0:

$E = E° - (0.0592/n) \log_{10}Q$ V at 25°C

$0 = 1.10$ V $- (0.0592/2) \log_{10}Q$ V

$\log_{10}Q = 37.16$

$Q = 1.5 \times 10^{37}$

The concentration of Zn^{2+} in the anode half-cell will be 2.0 M

The concentration of Cu^{2+} in the cathode half-cell will be essentially zero (1.3×10^{-37} M)

c. The equilibrium constant for the reaction K = Q at equilibrium = 1.5×10^{37}

d. $\Delta G°$ can be calculated from the cell potential $E°$ or from the equilibrium constant K:

$\Delta G° = -nFE° = 2$ mol $\times 96,485$ C mol$^{-1} \times 1.10$ V $= 212$ kJ for the reaction as written.

$\Delta G° = -RT \ln K = 8.314$ JK$^{-1} \times 298.15$ K $\times \ln (1.5 \times 10^{37}) = 212$ kJ for the reaction as written.

Answers to Review Questions

1. When a strip of zinc metal is immersed in a solution of copper(II) sulfate, zinc atoms at the surface of the electrode give up two electrons each to copper(II) ions in solution. The copper(II) ions are reduced to copper metal and the zinc ions go into solution. Eventually all the copper ions in solution are replaced by zinc ions.

2. An electrode is a metal conductor in contact with an electrolyte in an electrochemical cell. Sometimes the electrode is a nonmetallic conductor such as graphite. If oxidation occurs at the electrode, it is called the anode. If reduction occurs, it is called the cathode. Anions are negatively charged ions that move in solution toward the anode. Cations are positively charged ions that move in solution toward the cathode.

3. A redox reaction can always be divided into two half-reactions: one half-reaction representing the oxidation process and the other representing the reduction process. Electrochemical cells can always be divided into two halves: one half-cell in which oxidation takes place and the other in which reduction takes place.

4. A salt-bridge is a means of electrically connecting two solutions without allowing the solutions to mix. Ions can travel through the salt bridge to maintain electrical neutrality in the two half-cells of an electrochemical cell.

5. Energy (J) = potential (V) × charge (C).

6. One faraday = 96485 coulombs per mole of electrons. It is the charge carried by one mole (Avogadro's number) of electrons.

7. In the standard hydrogen electrode (SHE), hydrogen gas at 1 bar pressure is bubbled past an inert platinum electrode immersed in a 1.0 M H$^+$ solution. The SHE is assigned a half-cell potential of zero and is the half-cell to which other half-cells are compared. By convention, standard half-cell potentials are always listed as standard reduction potentials. This is the potential for the half-cell as a reduction half-cell (at the cathode) and is the cell potential when the anode is the SHE. Half-cell potentials are useful because you can calculate the potential of any cell simply by adding two half-cell potentials together (after changing the sign of $E°_{red}$ for the oxidation at the anode).

8. $\Delta G° = -nFE° = -RT \ln K$

9. In a table of standard reduction potentials, the reduction process is from left to right. An example is $E°(Zn^{2+}|Zn) = -0.76$ V.

   The more positive the reduction potential (the higher it is in the table), the more easily the species on the left is reduced. This means that it is a better oxidizing agent.

   The more negative the reduction potential (the lower it is in the table), the more easily the species on the right is oxidized. This means that it is a better reducing agent.

   For example, F$_2$ is at the top of the table and is reduced very easily to F$^-$. F$_2$ is a vigorous oxidizing agent. $E°(F_2|F^-) = +2.87$ V.

   Li$^+$ is at the bottom of the table. This means that Li (on the left) is oxidized easily and is a vigorous reducing agent. $E°(Li^+|Li) = -3.04$ V. The oxidation potential can be represented as $E°_{oxid}(Li|Li^+) = +3.04$ V—again a large positive number.

10. The Nernst equation is an equation for the cell potential E of a galvanic cell in which the concentrations are not standard. The cell potential is expressed in terms of the standard cell potential E° and the reaction quotient Q:

    E = E° – (RT/nF)lnQ where Q is the reaction quotient

    The Nernst equation is used when the conditions are not standard, for example, concentrations of electrolytes may not be 1 M, or gas pressures may not be 1 bar.

11. A concentration cell is a galvanic cell that has the same electrode at both the anode and cathode but has different concentrations of the electrolyte at the two electrodes. The cell potential depends upon the difference in the two concentrations. The oxidation at the anode and reduction at the cathode occur until the two concentrations are equal. At this point, the cell has reached equilibrium, Q = 1, and E = E° = zero.

End-of-Unit Problems

1. A galvanic cell is constructed in which one electrode is silver metal placed in a solution of silver nitrate and the other electrode is iron in a solution of iron(II) chloride. Under standard conditions,

   a. which electrode is the anode and which is the cathode?

   b. draw the cell notation

   c. what are the half-cell reduction potentials?

   d. what is the cell potential?

   e. write an equation for the cell reaction

2. A galvanic cell is constructed in which one electrode is copper metal placed in a solution of copper(II) sulfate and the other electrode is nickel metal in a solution of nickel(II) sulfate. Under standard conditions,

   a. which electrode is the anode and which is the cathode?

   b. draw the cell notation

   c. what are the half-cell reduction potentials?

   d. what is the cell potential?

   e. write an equation for the cell reaction

3. A galvanic cell is constructed that uses the following reaction:

   $$2\,Fe^{3+}(aq) + Sn(s) \rightarrow Sn^{2+}(aq) + 2\,Fe^{2+}(aq)$$

   a. write equations for the half-cell reactions

   b. which reaction occurs at the cathode?

   c. calculate the standard cell potential

4. A galvanic cell is constructed that uses the following reaction:

   $$3\,Sn^{2+}(aq) + 2\,Al(s) \rightarrow 3\,Sn(s) + 2\,Al^{3+}(aq)$$

   a. write equations for the half-cell reactions

   b. which reaction occurs at the anode?

   c. calculate the standard cell potential

5. Draw a picture of the galvanic cell that uses the following reaction between silver(I) nitrate and zinc metal to generate an electrical current. Use a salt bridge filled with potassium nitrate and assume the solution in the zinc electrode compartment is zinc nitrate.

   $$2\,Ag^{+}(aq) + Zn(s) \rightarrow 2\,Ag(s) + Zn^{2+}(aq)$$

   a. Indicate the direction in which the electrons flow between the anode and cathode.

   b. Indicate which ions flow in what direction through the salt bridge.

   c. Calculate the standard cell potential.

6. Draw a picture of the galvanic cell that uses the following reaction between copper(II) sulfate and magnesium metal to generate an electrical current. Use a salt bridge filled with sodium sulfate and assume the solution in the magnesium electrode compartment is magnesium sulfate.

   $$Cu^{2+}(aq) + Mg(s) \rightarrow Cu(s) + Mg^{2+}(aq)$$

   a. Indicate the direction in which the electrons flow between the anode and cathode.

   b. Indicate which ions flow in what direction through the salt bridge.

   c. Calculate the standard cell potential.

7. Write the half-reactions and a balanced chemical equation for the following cells. Calculate the standard cell potential for each:

   a. $Ni(s)\,|\,Ni^{2+}(aq)\,\|\,Ag^{+}(aq)\,|\,Ag(s)$

   b. $Pt(s)\,|\,Sn^{4+}(aq),\,Sn^{2+}(aq)\|I_2(s)\,|\,I^-(aq)\,|\,Pt(s)$

   c. $Ti(s)\,|\,Ti^{2+}(aq)\,\|\,Mn^{2+}(aq)\,|\,Mn(s)$

8. Write the half-reactions and a balanced chemical equation for the following cells. Calculate the standard cell potential for each:

   a. $Cu(s)\,|\,Cu^{2+}(aq)\,\|\,Cu^{+}(aq)\,|\,Cu(s)$

   b. $Sn(s)\,|\,Sn^{2+}(aq)\|Sn^{4+}(aq),\,Sn^{2+}(aq)\,|\,Pt(s)$

   c. $C(graphite)\,|\,H_2(g)\,|\,H^{+}(aq)\,\|\,Cl^-(aq)\,|\,Cl_2(g)\,|\,Pt(s)$

9. From the following half-cells construct the cell with the highest standard cell potential.

   a. Write the cell notation.

   b. Write a balanced chemical equation for the redox reaction.

   c. Calculate the cell potential.

   $$E°(Cu^{2+}|Cu) = +0.34\ V$$
   $$E°(Sn^{4+}|Sn^{2+}) = +0.14\ V$$
   $$E°(Ag^{+}|Ag) = +0.80\ V$$
   $$E°(Al^{3+}|Al) = -1.68\ V$$

10. From the following half-cells construct the cell with the highest standard cell potential.

   a. Write the cell notation.

   b. Write a balanced chemical equation for the redox reaction.

   c. Calculate the cell potential.

   $$E°(Mg^{2+}|Mg) = -2.36\ V$$
   $$E°(Zn^{2+}|Zn) = -0.76\ V$$
   $$E°(Fe^{3+}|Fe^{2+}) = +0.77\ V$$
   $$E°(Fe^{2+}|Fe) = -0.44\ V$$

11. Use data in Table 50.1 to determine if
    a. Zn will reduce Co^{2+} in aqueous solution
    b. Br_2 will oxidize Cl^- in aqueous solution
    c. Mg will reduce Sn^{2+} in aqueous solution

12. Use data in Table 50.1 to determine if
    a. Fe^{3+} will oxidize Zn in aqueous solution
    b. Cl_2 will oxidize I^- in aqueous solution
    c. MnO_4^- will oxidize Cl^- in aqueous solution

13. Under standard conditions, which one of the following pairs of species is the better reducing agent?
    a. Na or Mg
    b. Cd or Ni
    c. Sn or Pb

14. Under standard conditions, which one of the following pairs of species is the better oxidizing agent?
    a. Br_2 or Cl_2
    b. Cl_2 or MnO_4^-
    c. Fe^{3+} or Cr^{3+}

15. For the reduction of cobalt Co^{2+} using zinc Zn under standard conditions at 25°C,
    a. write the balanced equation
    b. determine the value of n
    c. calculate the cell potential E° for a galvanic cell employing the reaction
    d. calculate the standard free energy change ΔG° for the reaction,
    e. calculate the equilibrium constant K for the reaction.

16. For the oxidation of copper Cu using oxygen gas in acidic solution under standard conditions at 25°C,
    a. write the balanced equation
    b. determine the value of n
    c. calculate the cell potential E° for a galvanic cell employing the reaction
    d. calculate the standard free energy change ΔG° for the reaction,
    e. calculate the equilibrium constant K for the reaction.

17. Tin exists in two oxidation states, Sn^{2+} and Sn^{4+}. Using the appropriate standard half-cell reduction potentials, determine whether an aqueous solution of Sn^{2+} will disproportionate to Sn and Sn^{4+}.

18. Copper exists in two oxidation states, Cu^+ and Cu^{2+}. Using the appropriate standard half-cell reduction potentials, determine whether an aqueous solution of Cu^+ will disproportionate to Cu and Cu^{2+}.

19. Look up the appropriate half-cell reduction potentials and determine if the following reaction will occur if iron metal is added to a solution of iron(III):

$$Fe(s) + Fe^{3+}(aq) \rightarrow 2\ Fe^{2+}(aq)$$

20. Look up the appropriate half-cell reduction potentials and determine if the following reaction will occur in acidic solution:

$$V^{3+}(aq) + VO_2^+(aq) \rightarrow 2\ VO^{2+}(aq)$$

21. Iron metal can be used to reduce lead ions Pb^{2+} to lead according to the equation:

$$Fe(s) + Pb^{2+}(aq) \rightarrow Fe^{2+}(aq) + Pb(s)$$

    a. Calculate the cell potential E° for a galvanic cell employing this reaction
    b. What is the value of n for this reaction?
    c. Calculate the equilibrium constant K for the reaction.

22. Aluminum metal can be used to reduce silver ions Ag^+ to silver according to the following equation. This reaction is useful in removing tarnish from silver.

$$Al(s) + Ag^+(aq) \rightarrow Al^{3+}(aq) + Ag(s)$$

    a. Calculate the cell potential E° for a galvanic cell employing this reaction
    b. What is the value of n for this reaction?
    c. Calculate the equilibrium constant K for the reaction.

23. Calculate the cell potential for a Daniell cell in which the concentration of Zn^{2+} is 0.25 M and the concentration of Cu^{2+} is 1.80 M. Assume all other conditions are standard.

24. A galvanic cell is constructed as illustrated:

$$Mg(s)\,|\,Mg^{2+}(aq)\,\|\,Sn^{2+}(aq)\,|\,Sn(s)$$

Calculate the cell potential if the concentration of Mg^{2+} is 0.50 M and the concentration of Sn^{2+} is 1.25 M. Assume all other conditions are standard.

25. A galvanic cell is constructed as illustrated:

$$Zn(s)\,|\,Zn^{2+}(aq)\,\|\,H^+(aq)\,|\,H_2(g)\,|\,Pt(s)$$

Calculate the pH of the solution in the cathode half-cell if the cell potential is +0.62 V and all other conditions are standard.

26. A galvanic cell is constructed as illustrated:

$$Pt(s)\,|\,H_2(g)\,|\,H^+(aq)\,\|\,Cu^{2+}(aq)\,|\,Cu(s)$$

Calculate the pH of the solution in the anode half-cell if the cell potential is +0.40 V and all other conditions are standard.

27. A concentration cell is made using copper electrodes. In the anode compartment, the Cu^{2+} concentration is 0.075 M. In the cathode compartment, the Cu^{2+} concentration is 1.35 M.

$$Cu(s)\,|\,Cu^{2+}(aq,0.075M)\,\|\,Cu^{2+}(aq,1.35M)\,|\,Cu(s)$$

Calculate the cell potential at 25°C.

28. A concentration cell is made using tin electrodes. In the anode compartment, the Sn^{2+} concentration is 0.123 M. In the cathode compartment, the Sn^{2+} concentration is 1.55 M.

$$Sn(s)\,|\,Sn^{2+}(aq,0.123M)\,\|\,Sn^{2+}(aq,1.55M)\,|\,Sn(s)$$

Calculate the cell potential at 25°C.

Batteries, Corrosion, and Electrolysis

51.1 Batteries

It is difficult to imagine life without batteries. The ability to carry a portable source of electrical energy is essential to many aspects of modern life—whether it's in an automobile or an iPod™, in a cell phone or a pacemaker to regulate heartbeat. We begin this unit by examining the wide variety of commercially available cells.

A **battery** is a collection of cells in series although colloquially the term is often used for a single cell. When cells are connected in series, the overall voltage of the battery is the sum of the individual cell potentials. A common 9V battery is a collection of six cells in series (Figure 51.1).

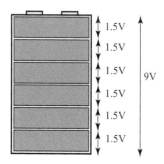

FIGURE 51.1 **The construction of a 9V battery.**
Six cells are connected in series.

The **Daniell cell** in its day was very successful. It provided a reliable source of electricity at a constant current. The Daniell cell is however a wet cell—it contains liquid electrolytes and is inconvenient to transport and handle. The first commercial dry cell was invented by Georges Leclanché in 1866 and the basic design is still used today. The electrolyte in a **Leclanché cell** is a moist paste of manganese(IV) oxide, ammonium chloride, and powdered carbon. The carbon improves the conductivity of the paste. The ammonia of the ammonium chloride complexes with the Zn^{2+} ions as the zinc ions are produced. The anode is a zinc pot that serves as the container for the cell and the cathode is a carbon rod (Figure 51.2).

Leclanché's actual cell was a glass jar containing the moist NH_4Cl electrolyte. The carbon cathode was surrounded by MnO_2 in a porous pot. The anode was a rod of zinc. Both the porous pot and the anode were immersed in the NH_4Cl electrolyte.

The cell reaction can be represented by the cell notation:

$$Zn(s)\,|\,ZnCl_2(aq),\ NH_4Cl(aq)\,|\,MnO(OH)(s)\,|\,MnO_2(s)\,|\,C(graphite) \quad E^\circ = 1.5\ V$$

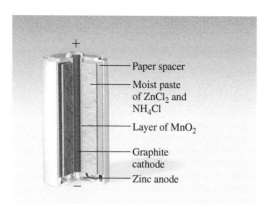

FIGURE 51.2 A Leclanché dry cell.

The paste in the Leclanché cell is acidic due to the presence of the NH_4Cl and the zinc anode reacts with the paste even when the cell is not in use. You may have noticed how dry cells leak as they age due to the buildup of gas inside—their shelf-life is limited. Another disadvantage of the Leclanché cell is the drop-off in the cell voltage under high current drain due to the formation of gases at the electrodes that increases the internal resistance to the flow of current through the cell.

An alkaline cell (Figure 51.3), although more expensive, has a longer shelf-life due to the alkaline conditions at the zinc electrode. The electrolyte paste consists of manganese dioxide (MnO_2) and potassium hydroxide (KOH) and the gas formation is avoided. The cell withstands a high current drain much better and lasts longer than a similarly sized Leclanché cell—there's more room for the MnO_2 since the NH_4Cl is not present. In addition, powdered zinc is used in place of the zinc can to increase the amount of zinc available for oxidation. The container is steel. The cell notation is:

$$Zn(s)\,|\,ZnO(s)\,|\,OH^-(aq)\,|\,Mn(OH)_2(s)\,|\,MnO_2(s)\,|\,C(graphite) \quad E° = 1.5\ V$$

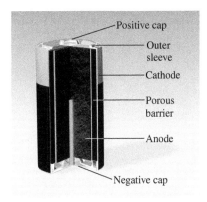

FIGURE 51.3 An alkaline cell.

The small cells often used in watches, calculators, and cameras are based on the reduction of silver or mercury at the cathode. The anode is again zinc. In the mercury cell, mercury(II) oxide is reduced to mercury. In the silver cell, silver(I) oxide is reduced to silver. Both cells use a steel cathode (Figure 51.4). The cell notations are:

$$Zn(s)\,|\,ZnO(s)\,|\,OH^-(aq)\,|\,HgO(s)\,|\,Hg(l)\,|\,Steel(s) \qquad E° = 1.3\ V$$
$$Zn(s)\,|\,ZnO(s)\,|\,OH^-(aq)\,|\,Ag_2O(s)\,|\,Ag(s)\,|\,Steel(s) \qquad E° = 1.6\ V$$

The migration of hydroxide ions from the mercury (or silver) electrode to the zinc electrode carries the current through the cell. The concentration of hydroxide remains constant and the voltage is therefore constant. The current output is steady and reliable and the cells can be made very small. Mercury, however, is toxic and silver is expensive; if possible, the cells should be recycled after use.

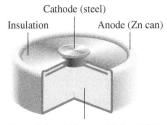

FIGURE 51.4 A mercury cell.

Replacing the zinc with lithium in a dry cell has two benefits. The cell potential is increased (compare $E°_{zinc} = -0.74\ V$ and $E°_{lithium} = -3.04\ V$) and lithium weighs considerably less than zinc.

The cells described so far are referred to as **primary cells**. Once used, that is, once the systems have reached equilibrium, they cannot be recharged. **Secondary cells** *can* be recharged. The batteries used in automobiles, hybrid vehicles, portable computers and cell phones are secondary cells. Once run down, the cells are recharged by applying an external source of electrical current to reverse the cell reaction.

The **lead-acid battery** is a common example of a rechargeable battery. Each cell in a lead-acid battery supplies 2.0 V, so a 12 V battery is a set of six cells connected in series. You may recall that there are six individual cells to look at when checking the acid levels in a car battery. The anode in a lead-acid cell is made of lead, usually as an alloy with 2.5 to 3.0% antimony and a trace of arsenic to inhibit gas formation when the battery is recharged. The anode is a grid filled with spongy lead with a large surface area. The large surface area means that the cell can deliver a high current—essential for turning over car engines. The cathode is also made of the lead alloy, in this case packed with lead oxide. The electrolyte is approximately 4.5 M sulfuric acid (Figure 51.5).

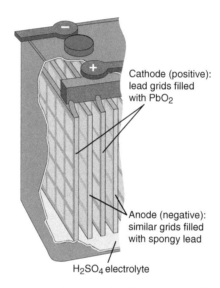

Cathode (positive): lead grids filled with PbO_2

Anode (negative): similar grids filled with spongy lead

H_2SO_4 electrolyte

FIGURE 51.5   The design of a cell of a lead-acid rechargeable battery illustrating the lead alloy grids used for the anode and cathode.

Lead is oxidized at the anode to produce lead sulfate. Lead oxide is reduced at the cathode to produce lead sulfate—the same product. The cell notation is:

$$Pb(s)\,|\,PbSO_4(s)\,|\,H^+(aq),\,HSO_4^-(aq)\,|\,PbO_2(s)\,|\,PbSO_4(s)\,|\,Pb(s) \quad E° = 2.0 \text{ V}$$

Why then is this cell rechargeable compared to the primary cells described earlier? The lead(II) sulfate formed in the oxidation and reduction adheres to the respective electrodes. When a reverse potential, typically 13 to 15 V (higher than 12 V), is applied to the battery, the reactions at the electrodes are reversed. Automobile lead-acid batteries are discharged to some extent every time you start your car. The alternator then recharges the battery once the engine is running. For the recharging to take place successfully, the lead(II) sulfate must remain attached to the electrode. If it falls off then the reverse reaction cannot take place. The batteries have a long life if treated carefully but rough roads will reduce the life of the battery. Similarly, if allowed to stand unused for more than a few weeks, the lead sulfate crystallizes on the electrodes and again tends to fall off, prohibiting a recharge.

It's interesting that the discharge of the battery reduces the sulfuric acid in the electrolyte—the sulfate ions are used to produce lead sulfate. The charging process increases the sulfuric acid concentration. One method used to determine the state of a lead-acid battery is to measure the density of the electrolyte and therefore the strength of the acid.

Rechargeable cells must involve reactions that are reversible at the electrodes. The reduced species must remain in contact with the cathode and the oxidized species must remain in contact with the anode.

Another rechargeable battery frequently encountered is the **nickel-cadmium battery** (**nicad**) invented in 1899 but not manufactured in its current sealed form until 1947. In a cell of this battery the anode is cadmium and the cathode is a nickel(III) oxyhydroxide NiO(OH) supported on nickel metal. The electrolyte is a basic paste of potassium hydroxide. The oxidation of the cadmium at the anode produces cadmium hydroxide and the reduction at the cathode produces nickel(II) hydroxide:

$$Cd(s) \,|\, Cd(OH)_2(s) \,|\, OH^-(aq) \,|\, NiO(OH)(s) \,|\, Ni(OH)_2(s) \,|\, Ni(s) \quad E° = 1.25 \text{ V}$$

The metal hydroxides remain in contact with the electrodes and the reaction can be reversed by the application of a reverse potential. The battery is rugged and can be recharged many times. It is often used in cordless power tools. A great disadvantage of nicad batteries is their disposal—cadmium is highly toxic and millions of nicad cells are disposed of improperly every year.

An improved rechargeable battery, replacing the nicad in cordless power tools, is the **nickel metal hydride battery** (**NiMH**) (Figure 51.6). This cell can be recharged more than a 1000 times and lasts three times longer than a nicad. The reaction at the cathode is the same as in the nicad but the anode is made of an alloy (for example LaNi$_5$ or ZrNi$_2$) able to absorb hydrogen gas. The reaction at the anode is the oxidation of the hydrogen to H$^+$, which then combines with the OH$^-$ to produce water. Both oxidation and reduction processes are reversible:

$$AlloyH(s) \,|\, H_2O(aq) \,|\, OH^-(aq) \,|\, NiO(OH)(s) \,|\, Ni(OH)_2(s) \,|\, Ni(s) \quad E° = 1.2 \text{ V}$$

You may be familiar with the term *memory* applied to a rechargeable battery. The term describes the inability of a secondary cell to accept a recharge—the cell reaction becomes irreversible. This is usually due to the formation of crystals at the electrodes (as described for the lead-acid battery). Nicad cells work better when used regularly (to avoid memory) and charged quickly.

NiMH cells also need exercising (charging and discharging) but not as often as Nicad cells.

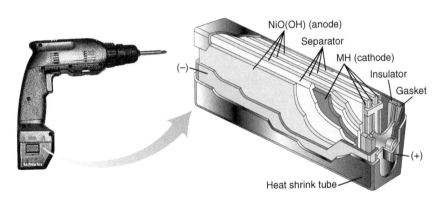

FIGURE 51.6 A NiMH battery.

The rechargeable batteries used in portable computers, cell phones, and video cameras are often **lithium-ion batteries**. Their great advantage is their light weight and high cell potential. Not only does lithium have the highest E° of any metal but it is also the metal with the smallest molar mass—6.94 g of lithium will supply one mole of electrons. Compare that to 32.7 grams of zinc, 56.2 grams of cadmium, or a 104 grams of lead. They are however more expensive than the nicad and NiMH

Aluminum has promise as an anode material. One mole of aluminum (27 g) supplies 3 moles of electrons. Therefore, 9 g of aluminum supplies as many electrons as 7 g of lithium.

batteries. The anode is lithium metal absorbed between the layers of graphite. The cathode is a lithium metal oxide such as $LiMn_2O_4$ or $LiCoO_2$. The electrolyte is a lithium salt such as $LiClO_4$ in an organic polymer such as polypropylene. The lithium ions migrate from anode to cathode during use and then back from the cathode to the anode during recharge. The cell can be written:

$$Li(\textit{in graphite}) \,|\, Li^+ \,|\, CoO_2(s) \,|\, LiCoO_2(s) \quad E° = 3.8 \text{ V}$$

51.2 Fuel Cells

Much of the world's economy is based upon the combustion of fossil fuels. The way in which the chemical energy of the fuel is converted into useful energy varies considerably in efficiency. Early steam engines of the 1800s were notoriously inefficient—only about 5% of the chemical energy was converted into work. Modern steam turbines such as those used in nuclear power plants achieve up to 30% efficiency. Early internal combustion engines were equally inefficient at about 4% although current automobile engines reach 28% efficiency. This efficiency is not particularly good—72% of the available energy in the fuel is *not* used to do work. Diesel-electric engines reach about 45% efficiency and modern electrical generation power plants reach up to 57% efficiency.

The first fuel cell was invented by William Grove in 1839.

In **fuel cells**, the chemical energy of the fuel is converted directly to electricity. Instead of burning the fuel to create steam to drive a generator, the conversion is direct and therefore more efficient. Typical efficiencies are 70% and with thermal recovery (collecting the heat generated as well) the efficiencies can reach 85%.

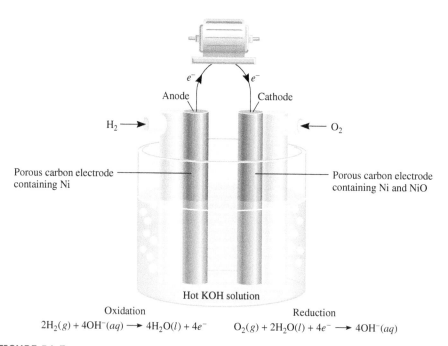

FIGURE 51.7 A cross-section illustration of a hydrogen–oxygen fuel cell.

Unlike a battery in which the chemical reactants are used as the cells discharge, a fuel cell is continually supplied with reactants—both a fuel that is oxidized and an oxidizing agent that is reduced. Possibly the only disadvantage of fuel cells is their inability to store energy—the fuels must be continuously supplied. However, the fuel cell is highly efficient, nonpolluting, and reliable. A typical fuel cell consists of two electrodes separated by an electrolyte such as potassium hydroxide just as in a galvanic cell. In a hydrogen fuel cell, hydrogen is fed to the anode where it is oxidized to hydrogen ions. Oxygen is fed to the cathode where it is reduced to hydroxide ions. The hydrogen ions and the hydroxide ions combine to form water (Figure 51.7).

Other fuel cells are based upon the combustion of methane gas, methanol, or larger hydrocarbons. The electrolyte can be potassium hydroxide in an alkaline fuel cell (as described above), or phosphoric acid in an acidic fuel cell. Currently most fuel cells are used as stationary electrical generators where the waste heat is also used for hot water or for heating buildings.

51.3 Corrosion

The spontaneous oxidation of metals in galvanic cells is desirable—the cells would not otherwise produce electrical energy. However, there are situations in which the oxidation of metals is not desirable and great lengths are taken to prevent it. Iron is used to a huge extent in the construction of automobiles, ships, bridges, and buildings, and iron rusts. The damage to iron and steel structures due to rusting costs billions of dollars every year. In fact, 20 to 25% of all steel produced in the US is used simply to replace iron or steel that has corroded.

Given the correct conditions, iron combines with oxygen to produce rust $Fe_2O_3 \cdot nH_2O$. The reaction has a complicated mechanism. For example, both oxygen and water must be present. Iron will not rust in water without oxygen and it will not rust in oxygen without water. The reaction occurs when an electrochemical cell is created on the surface of the iron (Figure 51.8).

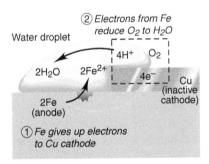

FIGURE 51.8 The mechanism of rusting.
A water droplet on the surface of iron forms a miniature galvanic cell. Notice that the oxidation of the iron may occur at some distance from where the rust is formed.

At the anode area, typically where there is some strain or damage to the iron surface, iron is oxidized to Fe^{2+}:

$$Fe(s) \rightarrow Fe^{2+}(aq) + 2 e^- \qquad\qquad E^{\circ}_{red} = -0.44 \text{ V}$$

Electrons move through the metal to another area where oxygen is in contact with the water. Here the electrons reduce the oxygen to water:

$$O_2(g) + 4\,H^+ + 4\,e^- \rightarrow 2H_2O(l) \qquad\qquad E^\circ_{red} = +1.23\text{ V}$$

The oxidation process is made easier if the concentration of H^+ ions in the solution is high (low pH). The process is also facilitated by the presence of salt which improves the conductivity of the solution. The overall process is represented by the equation:

$$2\,Fe(s) + O_2(g) + 4\,H^+ \rightarrow 2\,Fe^{2+}(aq) + 2\,H_2O(l) \qquad E^\circ = +1.67\text{ V}$$

The Fe^{2+} ions move through the water and are eventually oxidized to Fe^{3+} by oxygen. The Fe^{3+} forms as rust $Fe_2O_3 \cdot nH_2O$ which deposits on the metal surface. The reaction replenishes the hydrogen ions used in the first redox reaction:

$$2\,Fe^{2+}(aq) + (2+n)\,H_2O(l) + \tfrac{1}{2}\,O_2(g) \rightarrow Fe_2O_3 \cdot nH_2O + 4\,H^+(aq)$$

It is interesting that the formation of the rust can occur at some distance from the area at which the iron is oxidized. All that is required is some means of transporting the Fe^{2+} ions.

Corrosion Prevention

Perhaps the easiest way to protect iron from rusting is to paint the surface. However, the smallest scratch will allow rusting to begin and the reaction will spread underneath the adjacent painted surface. A better protection is achieved by **galvanizing** the iron. This involves coating the surface in a more active metal (usually zinc). Zinc is more easily oxidized than iron and acts as a **sacrificial anode** even when the surface is scratched. Electrically connecting a more active metal to the iron, either by galvanizing with zinc or attaching a block of a metal such as magnesium, is called **cathodic protection** (because iron becomes the cathode rather than the anode). The idea is that it is much easier to replace a block of magnesium than it is to replace the entire iron structure (Figure 51.9).

Iron is by no means the only metal that is easily oxidized. Most metals are oxidized by oxygen. The half-cell reduction potentials $E^\circ_{red}(M^{n+}|M)$ for most metals are below $E^\circ_{red}(O_2|H_2O)$ in the table of standard electrode reduction potentials. Aluminum, for example, should be oxidized more readily than iron. However, when aluminum reacts with oxygen in the air it acquires a very thin layer of impervious aluminum oxide that protects the aluminum from further oxidation. Other metals such as magnesium, titanium, and chromium acquire similar protective oxide coatings. The acquisition of an inert protective layer on the surface of a metal is referred to as **passivation**. Usually the layer is an oxide but the term is also used for the formation of other compounds. An example is the passivation of nickel metal by fluorine.

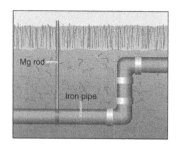

FIGURE 51.9 Cathodic protection of one metal by another more active metal.

51.4 Electrolysis

Just as chemical reactions absorb and release heat in endothermic and exothermic reactions, reactions can absorb or release electrical energy. In our study of electrochemistry so far we have been concerned only with the production of electrical energy in galvanic cells. In galvanic cells, chemical energy is converted into electrical energy.

In an **electrolytic cell**, electrical energy is converted into chemical energy. The process of converting electrical energy into chemical energy is called **electrolysis**.

The combination of hydrogen and oxygen to form water is a spontaneous process. The reaction is used to produce electrical energy in a fuel cell. The reverse reaction is not spontaneous—water does not decompose spontaneously to form hydrogen and oxygen.

$$2\ H_2(g) + O_2(g) \rightarrow 2\ H_2O(l) \qquad\qquad \Delta G^\circ = -474.4\ kJ$$

This value of ΔG° corresponds to a standard cell potential 1.229 V. If a potential greater than 1.229 V is applied to the electrodes of an electrolytic cell containing a dilute solution of sulfuric acid, hydrogen gas is produced at the cathode and oxygen gas is produced at the anode. The reaction is forced to go in the opposite direction (Figure 51.10).

$$\Delta G^\circ = -nFE^\circ$$

The reaction at the cathode is:

$$2\ H^+(aq) + 2\ e^- \rightarrow H_2(g) \qquad\qquad E^\circ_{red} = 0\ V$$

The reaction at the anode is:

$$2\ H_2O(l) \rightarrow O_2(g) + 4H^+(aq) + 4\ e^- \qquad\qquad E^\circ_{oxid} = -1.229\ V$$

The overall reaction is (multiply the first reaction by 2 and add):

$$2\ H_2O(l) \rightarrow 2\ H_2(g) + O_2(g) \qquad\qquad E^\circ_{oxid} = -1.229\ V$$

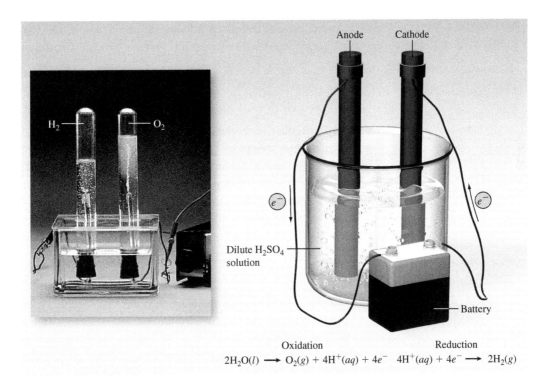

FIGURE 51.10   The electrolysis of water.
The electrolyte is a dilute solution of sulfuric acid. The volume of hydrogen formed at the cathode is twice the volume of oxygen formed at the anode.

Note that in an electrolytic cell, reduction occurs at the cathode (just as in a galvanic cell). Electrons are pushed by the external supply down the cathode to reduce the water. Electrons are withdrawn from the anode where the oxidation occurs.

Dilute sulfuric acid is used as the electrolyte, rather than pure water, to supply a sufficient concentration of ions to conduct the electrical current through the solution. In practice, a potential in excess of 1.23 V is required to overcome a phenomenon referred to as overpotential. **Overpotential** is a kinetic effect, an additional potential required to overcome the activation energy for electron transfer at the electrode. Overpotentials are particularly high for electrode reactions involving gases.

Electrolysis of Aqueous Sodium Chloride

In determining the products of the electrolysis of an aqueous solution of a salt it is necessary to examine which species present in solution might be oxidized or reduced. This includes the oxidation and reduction of the solvent itself. For example, in the electrolysis of an aqueous solution of sodium chloride what species are present in the solution that might be reduced at the cathode? One possibility is the reduction of sodium ions to sodium metal. Another possibility is the reduction of water to hydrogen gas:

$$Na^+(aq) + e^- \rightarrow Na(s) \qquad\qquad E^\circ_{red} = -2.71 \text{ V}$$
$$2\,H_2O(l) + 2\,e^- \rightarrow H_2(g) + 2\,OH^-(aq) \qquad\qquad E^\circ_{red} = -0.83 \text{ V}$$

> You may know that sodium metal reacts with water to produce sodium hydroxide and hydrogen gas. So it seems logical that hydrogen would be produced in preference.

The half-cell reduction potential for water is much lower than for the sodium ion—the value is less negative. This means that a lower potential is required for the reduction of water. Hydrogen, not sodium, is produced at the cathode.

What species are present that might be oxidized at the anode? One possibility is the oxidation of chloride ions to chlorine gas and another possibility is the oxidation of water to oxygen gas:

$$2\,Cl^-(aq) \rightarrow Cl_2(g) + 2\,e^- \qquad\qquad E^\circ_{red} = +1.36 \text{ V}$$
$$2\,H_2O(l) \rightarrow O_2(g) + 4H^+(aq) + 4\,e^- \qquad\qquad E^\circ_{red} = +1.23 \text{ V}$$

Based upon the reduction potentials for the possible reactions at the anode, it might seem that oxygen should be produced. The half-cell reduction potential is less positive, or, in other words, the oxidation potential is less negative. The idea is to choose the less negative reduction potential for the cathode reaction and the less negative oxidation potential for the anode reaction so that added together the lowest negative total is achieved. In general, it is the reaction that requires the lowest applied potential that occurs. The overall cell potential is determined by adding the two half-cell potentials:

> The reduction half-cell potential is reversed in sign for the oxidation at the anode.

The cell potential $E^\circ_{cell} = -0.83 \text{ V} - 1.23 \text{ V} = -2.06 \text{ V}$

The negative result indicates that the reaction is not spontaneous. A potential of 2.06 V must be applied across the cell to drive the reaction. However, in practice, if a potential of 2.06 V is applied to the cell, nothing happens! If the applied potential is increased, hydrogen gas is produced at the cathode as predicted but chlorine gas, not oxygen gas, is produced at the anode.

The problem is the overpotential required to overcome the activation energy for the reactions at the electrodes. The applied potential required in practice always exceeds the calculated potential, especially when the products at the electrodes are gases. At the cathode, the production of hydrogen has a low overpotential. At the anode, the overpotential for oxygen is much larger than the overpotential for chlorine and chlorine is produced in preference. Theoretically, the minimum potential required is:

$$E^{\circ}_{cell} = -0.83 \text{ V} - 1.36 \text{ V} = -2.19 \text{ V}$$

Any overpotential must be added to this cell potential.

The reaction that occurs in an electrolytic cell depends also upon the concentration of the electrolyte. Standard electrode potentials were used in the preceding discussion—it was assumed that the concentration of the salt was 1.0 M and that the concentration of H^+ was 1.0 M. This, of course, is not necessarily the case. However, in the electrolysis of aqueous sodium chloride, the concentration of the salt must be very dilute before oxygen is produced in preference to chlorine at the anode.

> The production of oxygen is favored thermodynamically. Kinetically the chlorine is produced at a much faster rate due to the overpotential. This is a process under kinetic control, not thermodynamic control (*cf.* Unit 34).

> There is no way to predict the magnitude of an overpotential. They can be determined experimentally. In general, overpotentials for the oxidation or deposition of solids are quite low. Overpotentials for electrode reactions involving gases can be quite large—as high as 1 or 2 V.

EXAMPLE 51.1   PREDICTING THE RESULTS OF ELECTROLYSIS

If a 1.0 M solution of potassium iodide in an aqueous solution at a pH of zero is electrolyzed, what reactions occur at the electrodes and what are the products of the electrolysis? What is the minimum applied potential required for the electrolysis?

UNDERSTAND THE QUESTION

What species are present in the aqueous solution that might be oxidized and reduced? This includes water itself. As mentioned earlier, the idea is to choose the less negative reduction potential for the cathode reaction and the less negative oxidation potential for the anode reaction so that added together the lowest negative total is achieved. The reaction that requires the lowest applied potential usually occurs.

> In answering questions such as these, overpotentials can be ignored. In reality, as we have seen, they can make a difference.

PLAN THE SOLUTION

Determine the possible reductions at the cathode and the possible oxidations at the anode. Write the half-cell reactions and look up the half-cell reduction potentials. Determine which combination leads to the lowest (least negative) cell potential.

SOLVE THE PROBLEM

Reduction at the cathode:

$$K^+(aq) + e^- \rightarrow K(s) \qquad\qquad E^{\circ}_{red} = -2.92 \text{ V}$$
$$2 H_2O(l) + 2 e^- \rightarrow H_2(g) + 2 OH^-(aq) \qquad E^{\circ}_{red} = -0.83 \text{ V}$$

Oxidation at the anode:

$$2 I^-(aq) \rightarrow I_2(s) + 2 e^- \qquad\qquad E^{\circ}_{red} = +0.54 \text{ V}$$
$$2 H_2O(l) \rightarrow O_2(g) + 4H^+(aq) + 4 e^- \qquad E^{\circ}_{red} = +1.23 \text{ V}$$

The less negative reduction potential for the reduction at the cathode is for the reduction of water. In other words, hydrogen is produced in preference to potassium (as you might have expected). The less negative oxidation potential (less positive reduction potential) for the oxidation at the anode is for the oxidation of the iodide ion. The required applied potential for the electrolysis is:

$$E^{\circ}_{cell} = -0.83 \text{ V} - 0.54 \text{ V} = -1.37 \text{ V plus any overpotential}$$

PROBLEM 51.1A

If a 1.0 M solution of magnesium bromide in an aqueous solution at a pH of zero is electrolyzed, what reactions occur at the electrodes and what are the products of the electrolysis? What is the minimum applied potential required for the electrolysis?

PROBLEM 51.1B

If a 1.0 M solution of aluminum sulfate in an aqueous solution at a pH of zero is electrolyzed, what reactions occur at the electrodes and what are the products of the electrolysis? What is the minimum applied potential required for the electrolysis?

51.5   Electrolysis in Industry

Electrolysis is used extensively in the chemical industry to isolate and purify elements. We will look at a few important applications.

Electrolysis of Molten Sodium Chloride

The commercial production of sodium metal is achieved on a huge scale by the electrolysis of a molten mixture of sodium chloride and calcium chloride in a **Downs cell** (Figure 51.11).

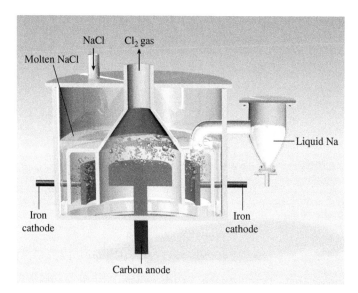

FIGURE 51.11   The Downs cell used for the commercial production of sodium metal and chlorine gas.

Calcium chloride is mixed with the sodium chloride to lower the melting point. The reduction potential for Ca^{2+} is more negative than that for Na^+ so the sodium Na^+ is reduced preferentially.

Molten sodium is produced at the cathode where it floats on the molten salt mixture and is drawn off as it is produced. Chlorine gas is produced at the graphite anode. An iron screen prevents the sodium and chlorine from coming into contact and reforming sodium chloride. Low voltages (7 to 8 V) are used but the currents are high (typically 30,000 A).

Recall the depression of the freezing point by increasing the entropy of the liquid state discussed in Unit 33.

Electrolysis of Aqueous Sodium Chloride

The manufacture of sodium hydroxide and chlorine by the electrolysis of aqueous sodium chloride is the basis of the **chlor-alkali industry**. Current production of chlorine and sodium hydroxide in the United States amounts to over 10 million tons of each per year, generating billions of dollars in sales annually. The largest use of chlorine is in the manufacture of chloro-organic compounds such as vinyl chloride (used to make PVC) and chlorinated hydrocarbon solvents. Other uses include water treatment and bleaching. Sodium hydroxide is used in the pulp and paper industry, in the chemical industry for the production of other chemicals, for making soaps and detergents, and in the textile industry.

As we have seen, electrolysis of an aqueous solution of sodium chloride produces hydrogen gas at the cathode and chlorine gas at the anode. There are three principal types of electrolysis cells used to achieve this: the diaphragm cell, the mercury cell, and the membrane cell. The diaphragm cell, developed in 1885 is illustrated in Figure 51.12. The diaphragm is the essential part of the cell because the chlorine gas must

A useful by-product is hydrogen gas, which can be used onsite in the Haber process to make ammonia or in various hydrogenation processes.

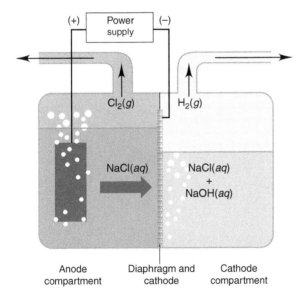

FIGURE 51.12 A schematic of the diaphragm cell for the electrolysis of aqueous sodium chloride.
The anode is constructed of titanium metal. The cathode is combined with the diaphragm and is constructed of a steel mesh covered with asbestos. The difference in the heights of the electrolytes ensures that sodium chloride solution moves through the diaphragm during the electrolysis.

be kept separate from the sodium hydroxide and the hydrogen gas. The diaphragm is constructed from asbestos covered steel mesh. To avoid the use of asbestos and because of greater economy, the diaphragm cell is being replaced by the membrane cell. The overall reaction is:

$$2\,Na^+(aq) + 2\,Cl^-(aq) + 2H_2O(l) \rightarrow 2\,Na^+(aq) + 2\,OH^-(aq) + H_2(g) + Cl_2(g)$$

The mercury cell produces a purer product than the diaphragm cell but is more expensive both to install and to operate. Moreover, mercury is toxic. The first commercially successful mercury cell was the **Castner-Kellner cell**, patented by Castner in 1892. In this cell the cathode is mercury. At a mercury cathode, sodium is produced in preference to hydrogen due to the high overpotential for hydrogen gas. The sodium forms an amalgam with the mercury which then is brought into contact with water to produce sodium hydroxide and hydrogen. In the original Castner-Kellner cell, the cell was rocked back and forth to bring the mercury amalgam into contact with water in a separate compartment. In current versions of the mercury cell, the amalgam is pumped through a separate chamber where it reacts with water before returning to the electrolysis cell. The schematic is illustrated in Figure 51.13.

Hamilton Castner (1858–1899) was an American who developed many industrial chemical processes. Unable to get financial backing in the US for a process to make sodium he moved to the UK. There, with an Austrian, Carl Kellner, he founded the Castner-Kellner Alkali Co. which later became part of ICI, the predominant chemical manufacturing company in the UK.

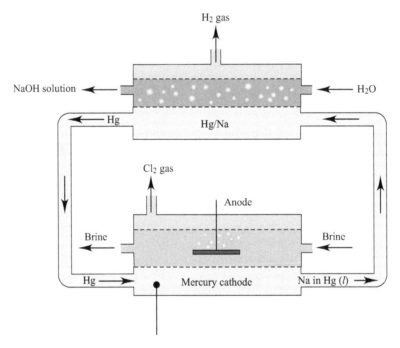

FIGURE 51.13 A schematic of the mercury cell for the electrolysis of aqueous sodium chloride.

The membrane cell was developed in 1970. A fluorine-based polymeric ion-exchange membrane is used to separate the sodium and chloride ions. The cell is illustrated in Figure 51.14.

The Hall-Héroult Process for the Production of Aluminum

In the mid 1800s Hamilton Castner developed an improved manufacturing process for sodium metal for the sole purpose of reducing alumina (Al_2O_3) to aluminum. As a result the price of aluminum dropped to 5% of its previous cost. Unfortunately for

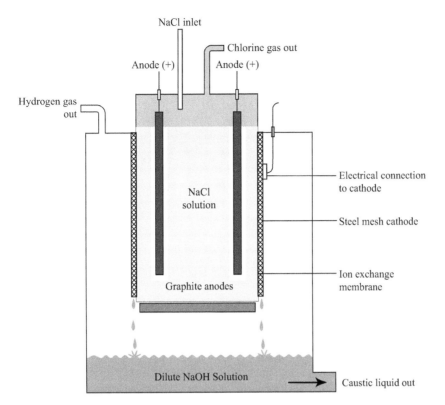

FIGURE 51.14 The membrane cell for the electrolysis of aqueous sodium chloride.

Castner, two years later in 1888 the commercial application of a new process invented by Charles Hall in the US and Paul Héroult in France in 1886 made the sodium reduction of alumina redundant.

In the **Hall-Héroult process**, alumina (Al_2O_3) is dissolved in molten cryolite (Na_3AlF_6). The temperature required is about 950°C—much lower than the melting point of alumina itself (2050°C). The cell used in the Hall-Héroult process is illustrated in Figure 51.15. Enormous currents, in the range of 50,000 to 100,000 A are used. The voltage is a mere 5 to 6 V.

Electrorefining and Electroplating

Metals such as copper and silver that have been extracted from their ores often contain impurities that have to be removed before the metals are sufficiently pure for their intended purposes. The purification is done by electrolysis and the process is called **electrorefining**.

Copper metal must be very pure if it is to conduct electricity efficiently. The purification is achieved by electrolysis. The crude metal is cast into large slabs that are used as the anodes in an electrolytic cell. Thin sheets of pure copper are used as the cathodes. Alternating anodes and cathodes are arranged in an array of electrolysis cells (Figure 51.16). The electrolyte is a solution of copper(II) sulfate and sulfuric acid. A high current, which depends upon the size of the cell, is passed for two to four weeks. Copper, and impurities that are more easily oxidized, are oxidized at the anode. Metals less easily oxidized fall to the bottom of the cell beneath the anodes. This **anode**

Charles Hall was a student at Oberlin College in Ohio when his chemistry professor, Frank Jewett, mentioned that anyone who could devise a cheap method of manufacturing aluminum would make a fortune. Hall decided to try. After much experimentation and with considerable help from Frank Jewett, he discovered that molten cryolite (Na_3AlF_6) would dissolve alumina and permit the electrolysis. Hall founded a company that would become the Aluminum Company of America (Alcoa) and indeed made a fortune.

About 2 billion tons of aluminum is manufactured worldwide every year.

It is curious that Charles Hall and Paul Héroult were both born in 1863 and both died in 1914. They both independently invented their process for electrolytically reducing alumina within a few weeks of each other in 1886.

The production of aluminum using the Hall-Héroult process is the single largest consumer of electricity in the US (about 5%). The second largest is the electrolysis of sodium chloride.

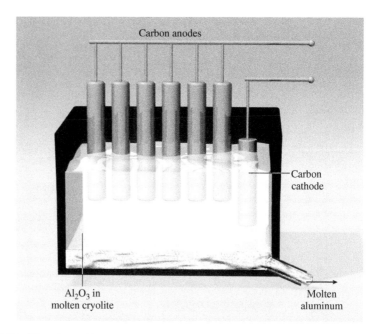

FIGURE 51.15 **The Hall-Héroult process for the electrolysis of alumina (Al₂O₃) dissolved in molten cryolite (Na₃AlF₆).**
Molten aluminum is more dense than the electrolyte and it settles to the bottom of the cell, where it is periodically drawn off. The carbon anodes are oxidized and must be periodically replaced.

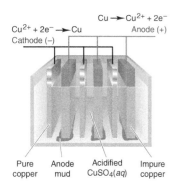

FIGURE 51.16
Electrorefining copper.

Approximately one-eighth of the gold and one-quarter of the silver produced each year in the US is extracted from the anode sludge from copper refining.

sludge is a valuable source of silver, gold, platinum, and other precious metals. Copper is reduced at the cathode. The cell voltage is carefully chosen to prevent the reduction of the impurities such as zinc and nickel in solution. The copper produced is at least 99.95% pure.

Electroplating uses electrolysis to produce a thin layer of one metal on another. Silver may be plated on copper, for example, or nickel may be plated on steel. This may be done to improve the appearance of an object or to increase its resistance to corrosion. Chromium, for example, is plated on steel automobile and motorcycle parts for both reasons.

51.6 Faraday's Laws of Electrolysis

The amount of metal oxidized at the anode or reduced at the cathode in electrolysis depends upon the amount of charge passed through the cell. The laws that determine the quantitative aspects of electrolysis were established by Michael Faraday in the early 1800s. His two laws of electrolysis are:

- The amount of a substance liberated or deposited at an electrode is directly proportional to the quantity of electrical charge passed though the cell.
- For a given quantity of electrical charge, the amount of any metal deposited is proportional to its equivalent mass.

As we learned earlier, the charge in coulombs is the product of the current in amperes and the time in seconds:

Charge (C) = current (A) × time (s)

The charge on one mole of electrons is 96485 C, equal to one faraday.

One faraday = 96485 coulombs

> Equivalent mass is not a concept used in this text although, before atomic masses were properly established in the late 1800s, the idea was very useful. The equivalent mass is the molar mass divided by the number of electrons lost or gained.

EXAMPLE 51.2   FARADAY'S LAWS

What current would deposit 404 mg of copper metal at the cathode of an electrolytic cell if passed through the cell for 5.0 hours?

UNDERSTAND THE QUESTION

The amount of metal deposited on the cathode depends upon the amount of charge passed through the cell. The charge is the product of the current and the time.

PLAN THE SOLUTION

In a problem such as this always start by writing the information given. Then manipulate this information using dimensional analysis to achieve the answer required. The relationship between the current and time, the charge in coulombs, the moles of electrons and the moles of substance reduced or oxidized is illustrated in the margin. Appropriate factors are used to move up or down this sequence, cancelling the current units and progressing toward the units of the desired answer.

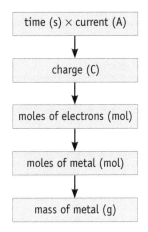

SOLVE THE PROBLEM

Two pieces of information are given: the mass of copper and the time. Let's start with the mass of copper. We divide by 1000 mg g^{-1} to convert to grams and then divide by the molar mass to convert to moles of copper. Each mole of copper requires two moles of electrons. One mole of electrons is one faraday and one faraday is 96485 coulombs. One coulomb is one ampere second.

$$404 \text{ mg Cu} \times \left(\frac{1 \text{ g}}{1000 \text{ mg}} \right) \times \left(\frac{1 \text{ mol Cu}}{63.55 \text{ g}} \right) \times \left(\frac{2 \text{ mol e}^-}{1 \text{ mol Cu}} \right) \times \left(\frac{1 \text{ faraday}}{1 \text{ mol e}^-} \right)$$

$$\times \left(\frac{96485 \text{ C}}{1 \text{ faraday}} \right) \times \left(\frac{1 \text{ A s}}{1 \text{ C}} \right)$$

We now have units of A s, and continue the series of factors by dividing by 3600 to convert seconds to hours and finally dividing by the time provided in the question (5 hours):

$$\times \left(\frac{1 \text{ hr}}{3600 \text{ s}} \right) \times \left(\frac{1}{5 \text{ hr}} \right)$$

The units are now A, the units of the desired answer:

Current = 0.068 A or 68 mA.

PROBLEM 51.2A

Two cells are connected in series and the same current passed through both. At the cathode of one cell, 550 mg of silver was deposited from a solution of silver(I) nitrate. The other cell contained nickel(II) sulfate. What mass of nickel was deposited on the cathode of this cell?

PROBLEM 51.2B

Brine (salt water) is electrolyzed at a potential of 5.0 V and a current of 240,000 A.

a. How long does it take to produce 500 kg of chlorine gas at the anode?

b. How much sodium hydroxide is produced at the cathode?

c. Approximately how much energy is used by the cell?

Review Questions

1. Describe the difference between a Leclanché cell and an alkaline cell.

2. What is the difference between a primary cell and a secondary cell?

3. How does a fuel cell differ from an ordinary alkaline cell?

4. Describe ways in which a metal can be protected against corrosion.

5. In what way does an electrolytic cell differ from a galvanic cell? Are the anodes, and the cathodes, the same in both?

6. How can you determine which reactions will occur at the electrodes when an aqueous solution of a salt is electrolyzed in an electrolytic cell?

7. Describe Faraday's laws of electrolysis.

Solutions to Problems

PROBLEM 51.1A

Reduction at the cathode:

$Mg^{2+}(aq) + 2\ e^- \rightarrow Mg(s)$ $E°_{red} = -2.36\ V$

$2\ H_2O(l) + 2\ e^- \rightarrow H_2(g) + 2\ OH^-(aq)$ $E°_{red} = -0.83\ V$

Oxidation at the anode:

$2\ Br^-(aq) \rightarrow Br_2(s) + 2\ e^-$ $E°_{red} = +1.07\ V$

$2\ H_2O(l) \rightarrow O_2(g) + 4H^+(aq) + 4\ e^-$ $E°_{red} = +1.23\ V$

The less negative reduction potential for the reduction at the cathode is for the reduction of water. Hydrogen is produced in preference to magnesium. The less negative oxidation potential (less positive reduction potential) for the oxidation at the anode is for the oxidation of the bromide ion. The required applied potential for the electrolysis is:

$E°_{cell} = -0.83\ V - 1.07\ V = -1.90\ V$ plus any overpotential

PROBLEM 51.2A

$$550\ mg\ Ag \times \left(\frac{1\ g}{1000\ mg}\right) \times \left(\frac{1\ mol\ Ag}{107.9\ g}\right)$$

$$\times \left(\frac{1\ mol\ e^-}{1\ mol\ Ag}\right) \times \left(\frac{1\ mol\ Ni}{2\ mol\ e^-}\right)$$

$$\times \left(\frac{58.69\ g}{1\ mol\ Ni}\right) \times \left(\frac{1000\ mg}{1\ g}\right)$$

$$= 150\ mg\ Ni$$

An answer of this approximate value is expected because nickel requires twice as many electrons and has approximately half the molar mass compared to silver. The answer should be approximately one-quarter of 550 mg.

Answers to Review Questions

1. Both the Leclanché cell and the alkaline cell are dry cells, but the Leclanché cell has an acidic electrolyte (NH_4Cl) and the alkaline cell has an alkaline electrolyte (KOH). The acidic electrolyte of the Leclanché cell corrodes the zinc anode even when not in use, which reduces the shelf-life of the cell. The alkaline cell has a much longer shelf life and can deliver a larger current.

2. A primary cell cannot be recharged—the reactions at the electrodes are not reversible. Once the cell has reached equilibrium no further electrical energy can be obtained. Examples are the Lechanché dry cell and the alkaline cell. A secondary cell can be recharged. Applying a reverse potential across the cell reverses the reactions at the electrodes. Examples are the lead-acid battery, the nicad battery, and the lithium metal hydride battery.

3. A fuel cell is an electrochemical cell in which the reactants for the reaction taking place are supplied continuously and the products of the reaction are removed continuously. Unlike an alkaline cell, the fuel cell does not store electrical energy. It will not operate without fuel. However, a fuel cell never reaches equilibrium and will continue to supply electrical energy as long as fuel is supplied.

4. A metal can be painted, galvanized, or plated. These are ways in which water and oxygen are kept away from the metal surface. Galvanizing (coating with zinc) provides cathodic protection because zinc is preferentially oxidized—it is a sacrificial anode. Other forms of cathodic protection involve attaching a block of an active metal (e.g. magnesium) to the metal to be protected.

5. In a galvanic cell a chemical reaction (a redox reaction) provides electrical energy. In an electrolytic cell electrical is used to drive a chemical reaction. In both cells, the cathode is the electrode where reduction takes place.

6. In general, if an external potential is applied to an electrolytic cell, the reaction that occurs is the one with the smallest negative cell potential (the least negative sum of half-cell potentials). The species most easily reduced at the cathode is reduced and the species most easily oxidized at the anode is oxidized. However, nonstandard concentrations and kinetic surface effects (overpotentials) at the electrodes often influence which products are formed.

7. Faraday's laws of electrolysis relate the charge passed through a cell to the amount of metal oxidized at the anode and the amount of metal (or other substance) deposited at the cathode. The charge (C) can be calculated from the current (A) and time (s). The charge is related to the moles of electrons transferred ($C = nF$), which in turn is related to the number of moles of the element deposited at the cathode or removed from the anode.

End-of-Unit Problems

1. Draw a picture of a galvanic cell that employs the oxidation of zinc by nickel Ni^{2+}. Use 1.0 M solutions of the nitrate salts for the electrolytes and incorporate a salt bridge containing sodium nitrate. On the diagram,

   a. label the anode and the cathode.

   b. indicate the direction of electron flow at the anode and the cathode.

   c. illustrate the the movement of ions through the cell.

   d. write equations for the reactions at each half-cell.

   e. write the representation of the cell using the standard cell notation.

   f. write an overall equation for the reaction that occurs in the cell.

   g. calculate the cell potential and comment on the significance of the sign.

   Now draw an electrolytic cell based upon the same system in which a reverse potential is applied to the cell. Determine what reactions occur at the anode and the cathode of the cell. Answer again questions (a) through (g).

2. Draw a picture of a galvanic cell that employs the oxidation of copper by silver Ag^+. Draw an electrolytic cell that drives the oxidation of silver by copper Cu^{2+} (the reverse reaction). Use 1.0 M solutions of the nitrate salts for the electrolytes and incorporate a salt bridge containing sodium nitrate. On each diagram,

   a. label the anode and the cathode.

   b. indicate the direction of electron flow at the anode and the cathode.

   c. illustrate the movement of ions through the cell.

   d. write equations for the reactions at each half-cell.

e. write the representation of the cell using the standard cell notation.

f. write an overall equation for the reaction that occurs in the cell.

g. calculate the cell potential and comment on the significance of the sign.

3. One of the experiments tried by Charles Hall in his attempts to produce aluminum metal was the electrolysis of aqueous solutions of aluminum salts. Explain why this method was doomed to failure.

4. Explain why it is impossible to produce fluorine gas by the electrolysis of an aqueous solution of a fluoride salt.

5. Tin cans for food are made from steel coated with a thin layer of tin. Does the tin protect the steel from oxidation in the same way as zinc? If not, why use tin?

6. Explain why blocks of magnesium are often attached to underground iron pipes.

7. A common kitchen remedy for tarnished silver is to place the tarnished item in an aluminum dish filled with an aqueous solution of baking soda (sodium bicarbonate). Explain what happens in the reaction.

8. Examination of iron supports for a railroad trestle bridge across a river revealed that the iron rusted rapidly at the waterline but at a much lower rate above the waterline and at some distance below the waterline. Explain why this happened.

9. In an experiment to electrolyze water, a salt is added to the water to improve the conductivity. Sodium sulfate was chosen in preference to sodium chloride. Why?

10. In the mercury cell for the electrolysis of aqueous sodium chloride, sodium is reduced at the mercury cathode, not water. Why is this?

11. In the electrolysis of fused (molten salts), mixtures of salts are often used. For example, in the electrolysis of molten sodium chloride, calcium chloride is added to the sodium chloride.

   a. Why is this done?

   b. Why isn't calcium metal produced at the cathode?

12. In the electrolysis of alumina,

   a. the success of the method developed by Charles Hall depended upon finding a salt in which alumina would dissolve. Why wasn't the alumina used in a pure molten state by itself?

   b. the charge (current × time) required is about three times greater for the production of aluminum than that required for the same mass of sodium. Why is this?

13. Two cells are connected in series and the same current passed through both. At the cathode of one cell, 435 mg of copper was deposited from a solution of copper(II) nitrate. The other cell contained silver(I) nitrate. What mass of silver was deposited on the cathode of this cell?

14. Two cells are connected in series and the same current passed through both. At the cathode of one cell, 1.290 g of tin was deposited from a solution of tin(II) nitrate. The other cell contained potassium iodide. What mass of iodine I_2 was produced at the anode of this cell?

15. 10 amps of current is passed through an electrolysis cell. If the cell contains potassium dichromate in acidic solution, how long does it take to plate out 500 mg of chromium metal?

16. 12.5 amps of current is passed through an electrolysis cell. If the cell contains silver nitrate in an aqueous cyanide solution, how long does it take to plate out 2.00 grams of silver metal?

17. In the production of aluminum by the electrolysis of alumina in molten cryolite, 75,000 A are passed through the cell for 15.00 hours. How much aluminum is produced?

18. In the refining of copper by the electrolysis of a copper sulfate/sulfuric acid solution, 30,000 A are passed through the cell for 2.0 weeks. How much copper is deposited at the cathode?

19. In an alkaline fuel cell, hydrogen gas and oxygen gas combine to form water. Assuming 75% efficiency in converting the chemical energy into work, how much work is done when 150 liters of hydrogen gas at a pressure of 300 atm and a temperature of 22°C are used in the fuel cell?

20. In a NiMH battery, the reaction at the cathode is the reduction of NiO(OH) to Ni(OH)$_2$.

   This reduction is reversed when the battery is recharged. If a NiMH battery is recharged at a current of 350 mA for 90 min, how much Ni(OH)$_2$ is oxidized to NiO(OH)?

21. The current supplied by a 12 V lead-acid automobile battery to the starter motor is 6.0 A. Suppose that the starter runs for 8.0 seconds to start the engine. How much lead is oxidized to lead(II) sul-

fate at the anode of each cell in the battery? How much lead(IV) oxide is reduced to lead(II) sulfate at the cathode of each cell?

22. If the alternator of a car supplies 350 mA to recharge the 12 V lead-acid battery, how long does it take to convert 1.00 g of lead(II) sulfate back to lead at the electrode of one of the cells?

23. A method once used to measure the amount of charge passed through an electrolytic cell was to place a silver coulometer in series within the circuit. The coulometer is named as such because it measures the number of coulombs passing through the circuit. In the coulometer a silver cathode is placed in a solution of silver nitrate and the electrode is weighed before and after the experiment. In one experiment lasting 45.0 minutes, the cathode increased in mass by 4.132 grams. What charge passed through the circuit?

24. Thomas Edison was a proponent of direct current, as opposed to the alternating current now used. The amount of electricity used by customers of his direct current supply was determined by passing the current through a coulometer based upon the reduction of zinc ions Zn^{2+} to zinc metal at the cathode and the oxidation of zinc metal to Zn^{2+} at the anode.

a. If the mass of zinc deposited at the cathode, and oxidized at the anode, was 12.78 g, what charge in C was supplied to the customer?

b. If the voltage was 48 V, what energy was supplied?

c. Currently, electrical consumption is measured in kWh. Convert the answer to (b) to kWh.

Hydrogen and the Alkali Metals

52.1   Hydrogen

Hydrogen is by far the most abundant element in the universe and is the tenth most abundant element by mass in the earth's crust, although it accounts for 15% of all the atoms present. The element was identified by Henry Cavendish in 1766 and shown to be a constituent element of water by Lavoisier in 1784. Experiments by Cavendish led him to the same conclusion at much the same time but unfortunately he interpreted his results in terms of the **phlogiston theory**. Through his work on acids such as HCl, Humphry Davy showed that hydrogen, not oxygen, was the essential element present in acids.

The placement of hydrogen in the Periodic Table presents a problem. You will often find it above lithium at the top of Group 1A because its valence shell configuration is $1s^1$. Like the alkali metals it forms an ion with a single positive charge although its ionization energy is considerably higher (1312 kJ mol^{-1} compared to lithium 520 kJ mol^{-1}). It is sometimes placed in Group 7A above fluorine because, like the halogens, it is one electron short of a complete valence shell, it forms a negative ion (H^-), and it exists as a diatomic molecule (H_2). Occasionally you will find hydrogen placed at the top of both groups, 1A and 7A. Perhaps the best place for hydrogen is by itself at the top of the table.

The element occurs as three isotopes: **protium** ^1H, **deuterium** ^2H, and **tritium** ^3H (radioactive). Naturally occurring hydrogen is 99.985% ^1H and 0.015% ^2H. Deuterium has twice the mass of protium and substitution of protium by deuterium in compounds has a significant effect. For example, deuterium oxide, D_2O, is known as heavy water because its density is 20/18 times that of ordinary water (the ratio of their molar masses). The melting and boiling points of D_2O are 3.81°C and 101.42°C respectively—slightly higher than for H_2O.

Hydrogen exists as a diatomic molecule with a relatively high dissociation energy—the bond strength is 436 kJ mol^{-1}. In comparison, the strength of a F—F bond is only 159 kJ mol^{-1}. Normally a gas, it has the lowest m.pt. (13.96K) and b.pt (20.39K) of any molecule. Most of the hydrogen on earth exists in combination with oxygen as water but it is also found in combination with carbon in fossil fuels (coal, oil, and natural gas).

Industrial Production and Uses

The predominant industrial preparation of hydrogen is the **steam-hydrocarbon reforming** process in which a hydrocarbon (for example, propane C_3H_8) and steam are passed over a nickel catalyst at 900°C:

$$C_3H_8(g) + 3\ H_2O(g) \rightarrow 3\ CO(g) + 7\ H_2(g)$$

The mixture of carbon monoxide and hydrogen is called **synthesis gas**. This gas is cooled to 350°C and reacts with more steam over a copper/iron catalyst to produce carbon dioxide and more hydrogen in the **shift reaction**:

$$CO(g) + H_2O(g) \rightarrow CO_2(g) + H_2(g)$$

Most hydrogen is made from petrochemicals in this way. A similar reaction of coke (C) and steam produces **water gas** which again undergoes the shift reaction to produce more hydrogen:

$$C(s) + H_2O(g) \rightarrow CO(g) + H_2(g)$$

Cavendish regarded hydrogen as water saturated with phlogiston. He considered oxygen (dephlogisticated air) to be water minus phlogiston so that, as he reported in 1784, the combination of the two produced water. The phlogiston theory was remarkably tenacious.

It was Lavoisier who named hydrogen (water-former) and oxygen (acid-former).

The nuclei of the hydrogen isotopes:

Protium

Deuterium

Tritium

The blue circles represent protons and the gray circles represent neutrons.

Only monatomic helium has a lower m.pt and b.pt than hydrogen.

Both synthesis gas and water gas are mixtures of carbon monoxide and hydrogen. Water gas is a 1:1 stoichiometric mixture. Synthesis gas has a composition appropriate for the production (synthesis) of alcohols. For example, using a cobalt catalyst:

$CO(g) + 2\ H_2(g) \rightarrow CH_3OH(g)$

Other sources of hydrogen include the electrolysis of brine (*cf.* Unit 51) and cracking petroleum. Small quantities of hydrogen can be made in the laboratory by the reaction of an acid on an active metal such as zinc (Figure 52.1).

$$Zn(s) + HCl(aq) \rightarrow Zn(OH)_2(aq) + H_2(g)$$

Most manufactured hydrogen is used in the production of ammonia using the **Haber-Bosch process**. Other uses include the hydrogenation of liquid vegetable oils to make margarine. Considerable hydrogen is used in the reduction of copper and other metals with a positive half-cell reduction potential (*cf.* Unit 50). The oxide or sulfide ore is dissolved in acid and then the metal ions are reduced by bubbling hydrogen through the solution. Only metals with a positive half-cell reduction potential $E°$ can be reduced in this way.

As petroleum and other fossil fuel reserves are depleted, an alternative fuel will eventually have to be found. Hydrogen has been proposed as the ideal nonpolluting fuel—for use either in a fuel cell or in an internal combustion engine. The challenge is to find a way to extract hydrogen from water economically—since no more energy can be obtained from burning hydrogen than was originally supplied in extracting it from water. The ideal solution would be the direct use of solar energy in a catalyzed water-splitting reaction. Hydrogen gas can be transported either in liquid form or absorbed on metal. The solubility of hydrogen in palladium has been known since 1866 and the alloy $LaNi_5$, for example, can absorb so much hydrogen at room temperature and 2.5 atm that the hydrogen density is *twice* that of liquid hydrogen.

52.2 Compounds of Hydrogen

Hydrogen is colorless, odorless, and relatively unreactive due to its high bond strength. It is unique in that the loss of an electron to form a positive ion yields a species with *no* electrons at all. The hydrogen ion H^+, therefore, is extremely small and is therefore a highly polarizing cation—the charge density is very high. In water and other solvents it always attaches itself to other molecules and forms a covalent bond—for example in water it forms the hydronium ion H_3O^+.

Hydrogen can also accept an electron to form a hydride ion H^- (configuration $1s^2$). The hydride ion is comparatively large with an atomic radius 154 pm.

The electronegativity of hydrogen is 2.1 on the Pauling scale. It therefore forms **covalent molecular compounds** with the nonmetals and **ionic hydrides** with electropositive metals. In this respect hydrogen behaves like other elements with electronegativities above 2.0—for example, carbon and chlorine. Typical molecular binary compounds of hydrogen and carbon are methane CH_4, ethane C_2H_6, acetylene C_2H_2, benzene C_6H_6 and hundreds of related hydrocarbons—we will examine these organic molecules in Units 63 and 64. Binary hydrogen compounds of the elements in Groups 5A through 7A are ammonia NH_3 and phosphine PH_3, water H_2O and hydrogen sulfide H_2S, and hydrogen fluoride HF and hydrogen chloride HCl. The strengths of the bonds between hydrogen and the nonmetals are strong. The C–H bond strength, for example, is 413 kJ mol^{-1}, and the H–F bond strength is 565 kJ mol^{-1}. Others are listed in Table 24.4.

Typical ionic hydrides are sodium hydride NaH and calcium hydride CaH_2, often referred to as **saline hydrides** due to their salt-like structure. They are prepared by heating the metal in hydrogen gas:

$$2\,Na(s) + H_2(g) \rightarrow 2\,NaH(s)$$

FIGURE 52.1 The reaction of zinc with hydrochloric acid to produce hydrogen gas.

Hydrogen for the manufacture of ammonia is usually produced specifically for that purpose in the ammonia production process.

Palladium can absorb up to 950 times its own volume of hydrogen gas. One problem is getting the hydrogen out of the metal once it has been absorbed.

Carbon nanotubes have the ability to store hydrogen gas and are being investigated as a possible means of transporting the fuel.

Probably the most important hydrogen compound is water H_2O—we'll examine some of the properties of water in Unit 56.

The alkali metal hydrides have the same crystalline structure as sodium chloride (*cf.* Unit 29).

acid	pK$_a$
HF	+3
HCl	−7
HBr	−9
HI	−10

Recall that acids with a pK$_a$ less than 0 are strong and are completely ionized in dilute aqueous solution.

The ionic hydrides are strong reducing agents. They will reduce oxygen to water and they react with water to produce basic solutions. The hydride ion H⁻ is a stronger base than hydroxide OH⁻ and the reaction goes to completion. The net ionic equation is:

$$\overset{\displaystyle \overset{\text{H}^+}{\longrightarrow}}{\underset{\substack{\text{base}\\\text{stronger}}}{\text{H}^-}} + \underset{\substack{\text{acid}\\\text{stronger}}}{\text{H}_2\text{O}} \rightleftharpoons \overset{\displaystyle \overset{\text{H}^+}{\longrightarrow}}{\underset{\substack{\text{base}\\\text{weaker}}}{\text{OH}^-}} + \underset{\substack{\text{acid}\\\text{weaker}}}{\text{H}_2}$$

The covalent binary hydrogen compounds increase in acidity down any group. For example, the halogen acids increase in acidity down Group 7A. Similarly, phosphine PH$_3$ is more acidic than ammonia NH$_3$ (ammonia is more basic), and hydrogen sulfide H$_2$S is more acidic than water.

Between the saline hydrides of the elements on the left side of the Periodic Table and the covalent hydrogen compounds of the elements on the right side of the Periodic Table, there is a gradual change in the character of the binary hydrogen compounds. Although beryllium is less electronegative (1.5) than hydrogen (2.1), beryllium hydride BeH$_2$ is covalent in character (Figure 53.10). Similarly, boron and hydrogen form many different compounds that are covalent in character. In both the beryllium and boron hydrides the structures are **electron deficient**—short of electrons—and this leads to some interesting structures (*cf.* Unit 53).

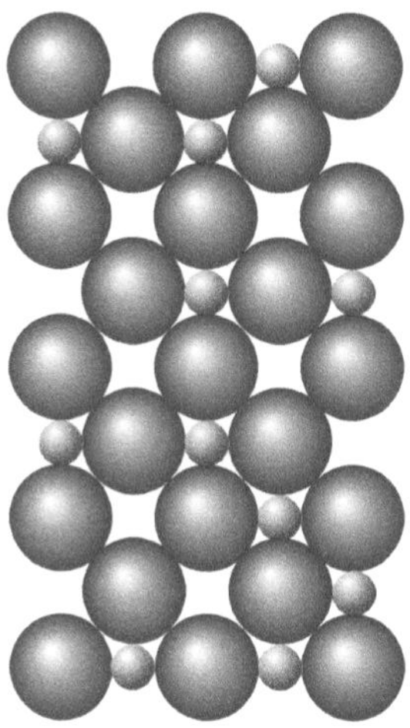

Further to the right in the Periodic Table at the beginning of the transition series, some metals such as titanium and zirconium form **metallic hydrides** with hydrogen. These are nonstoichiometric compounds sometimes described as solutions of hydrogen in the metal. They are also called **interstitial hydrides** because the hydrogen atoms and molecules occupy the spaces (or interstices) in the metallic lattice (Figure 52.2). It is interesting that metals in the center of the transition series (in the Mn, Fe, and Co groups) have no tendency to form hydrogen compounds. As noted earlier, palladium has the ability to absorb an enormous amount of hydrogen.

One of the more remarkable characteristics of the hydrogen compounds of nitrogen, oxygen, and fluorine is their ability to form hydrogen bonds. This strong attraction between a hydrogen atom attached to N, O, or F and a lone pair of electrons on N, O, or F has a profound effect upon the properties of molecules containing N—H and O—H groups of atoms and is particularly important in biochemistry (*cf.* Unit 66).

FIGURE 52.2 A typical interstitial structure.
The metal atoms form a face-centered cubic lattice and the hydrogen atoms fill some fraction of the holes between the metal atoms.

Hydrogen bonds were described in Unit 28.4.

EXAMPLE 52.1   CLASSIFICATION OF HYDRIDES

Classify the following hydrides as molecular (covalent), saline (ionic), or metallic:

  a. PH$_3$

  b. TiH$_2$

  c. CaH$_2$

UNDERSTAND THE QUESTION

The type of hydride formed depends primarily upon the electronegativity of the other element involved. Hydrogen has an electronegativity of 2.1 and if the electronegativity of the other element is approximately 2.1 or higher (a non-metal), then the compound is molecular (covalent). If the electronegativity of the element is low (alkali or alkaline earth metal), then the hydrogen compound is a saline hydride. Some transition metals form interstitial metallic hydrides. The general scheme is illustrated in Figure 52.3.

PLAN THE SOLUTION

Determine the position of the element involved in the Periodic Table and deduce the type of hydrogen compound formed.

SOLVE THE PROBLEM

a. Phosphorus is a nonmetal; PH_3 is a molecule.

b. Titanium is a transition metal; the hydride is metallic.

c. Calcium is an alkaline earth metal; the hydride formed is a saline hydride.

PROBLEM 52.1A

a. A nonmetallic element X from Period 3 forms a hydride XH_2. What is the element X?

b. The alkaline earth metal Sr forms a saline hydride. What is its formula?

PROBLEM 52.1B

Classify the following hydrides as molecular, ionic (saline), or metallic:

a. HCl

b. KH

c. H_2O

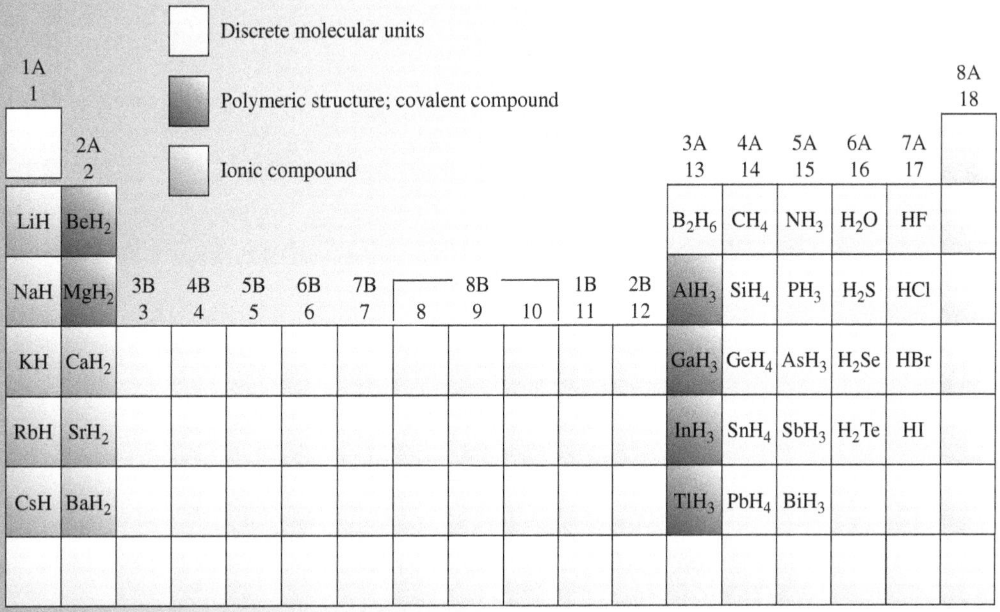

FIGURE 52.3 **Binary hydrides of the elements.**
The representative elements form ionic (saline) or covalent (molecular or polymeric) hydrides. Many transition metals form metallic (interstitial) hydrides.

52.3 The Alkali Metals

The name potassium is derived from *potash*, which is the name for potassium carbonate isolated from the ashes of wood fires used for cooking. *Caustic potash* is potassium hydroxide. Similarly, *soda ash* is sodium carbonate, and *caustic soda* is sodium hydroxide. Sodium carbonate was once used in laundry (before detergents were developed) and is still sometimes called *washing soda*. Sodium bicarbonate is *baking soda*.

Rubidium (deep red) and cesium (blue) were identified spectroscopically by Bunsen and Kirchoff using their newly-invented spectroscope.

Only two other metals are colored—copper and gold.

Lithium has the lowest density of all known metals.

Sodium (2.27%) and potassium (1.84%) are the seventh and eighth most abundant elements by mass in the earth's crust. Huge deposits of sodium chloride (rock salt), sodium carbonate and sodium bicarbonate (trona), sodium nitrate (Chile saltpetre), and sodium sulfate (mirabilite) occur in nature due to the evaporation of ancient seas. Sodium is also present in an enormous amount as sodium chloride in the oceans of the world. Potassium occurs naturally as potassium nitrate (saltpetre) and potassium chloride (sylvite). Lithium, rubidium, and cesium compounds are present in much lower quantities.

When he was only 29 years old (in 1807), Humphry Davy isolated potassium and sodium by the electrolysis of molten KOH and NaOH respectively. He used the relatively new voltaic piles of Volta as his source of electrical energy. Lithium was discovered in 1817 and isolated by Davy in 1818. Rubidium and cesium were discovered spectroscopically in 1861 and named for the colors they emitted. Francium was identified by Marguerite Perey in 1939. It is intensely radioactive, decaying by β emission with a half-life of only 21.8 minutes.

The Group 1A elements are all soft metals with relatively low melting points (Table 52.1). Most are silver-gray in color; cesium is silvery-yellow in color (Figure 52.4). The valence shell electron configuration is ns^1—a single electron that is loosely held and easily lost. This characteristic governs the physical and chemical properties of the elements. For example, the bonding in the solid state is relatively

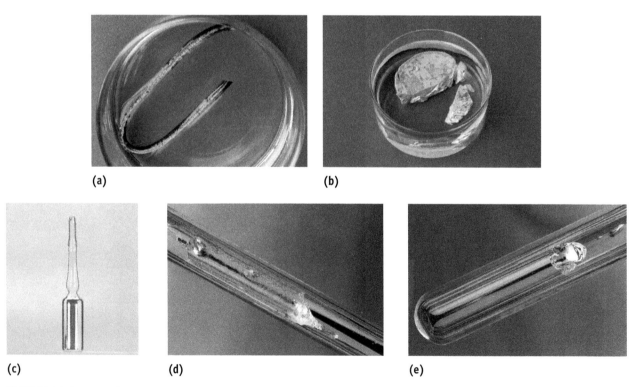

(a) (b)

(c) (d) (e)

FIGURE 52.4 The alkali metals.
(a) lithium; (b) sodium; (c) potassium; (d) rubidium; (e) cesium

weak and the metals are soft, the crystalline structure is bcc rather than close-packed, the densities are low, and the melting points and boiling points are low. The metals are very reactive, very easily oxidized, and are therefore excellent reducing agents. For this reason they are never found in the elemental state in nature—they form compounds so readily. The size of the alkali metal decreases dramatically when the ns^1 valence electron is lost (Table 52.1).

TABLE 52.1 The Alkali metals.

Name	Symbol	Melting Point °C	Boiling Point °C	ΔH°_{fus} @ m.pt. kJ mol^{-1}	Density g cm^{-3}	Ionization Energy kJ mol^{-1}	Metallic Radius pm	Ionic M$^+$ Radius pm
Lithium	Li	181	1347	3.0	0.53	520	152	76
Sodium	Na	98	881	2.6	0.97	496	186	102
Potassium	K	63	766	2.3	0.86	419	227	138
Rubidium	Rb	39	688	2.2	1.53	403	248	152
Cesium	Cs	28	705	2.1	1.87	376	265	167

EXAMPLE 52.2 PROPERTIES OF THE ALKALI METALS

Select from the alkali metals, Li, Na, K, Rb, and Cs,

 a. the one with the lowest electronegativity.
 b. the one with the lowest melting point.

UNDERSTAND THE QUESTION

The properties of the elements vary in a systematic way throughout the Periodic Table because the properties of the elements depend upon their electron configurations.

PLAN THE SOLUTION

This question concerns elements in a single column (Group 1A). Examine how the property in question varies from the top to the bottom of the table.

SOLVE THE PROBLEM

 a. Electronegativity decreases down any group. Cesium has the lowest electronegativity.
 b. The melting point depends upon the strength of the bonding between the atoms. Cesium, with the most loosely held valence electrons of the elements in the group, would be expected to be the softest element with the lowest melting point.

PROBLEM 52.2A

Select from the alkali metals, Li, Na, K, Rb, and Cs,

 a. the one with the highest ionization energy.
 b. the one that would react most vigorously with chlorine gas.

Industrial Production and Uses

More sodium chloride is used in the chemical industry than any other material. Almost half of the rock salt mined is used as the raw material in the electrolysis of brine or the fused salt as described in Unit 51. About one quarter is used in the salting of roads and the remaining quarter is used in a variety of processes, including food preparation, animal feed, and the paper and textile industry.

Sodium chloride is essential in animal diet. About 2.4 g per day is required but this is usually exceeded by 200% in a typical Western diet. In earlier times salt was a valuable commodity. Roman soldiers were paid in part with a salt allowance—hence the word salary.

Vast quantities of sodium carbonate are mined in Wyoming as the mineral trona, $Na_3(HCO_3)CO_3 \cdot 2H_2O$ which is heated to produce Na_2CO_3. Overseas, most sodium carbonate is produced by the **Solvay Process** in which sodium carbonate is produced in a series of reactions from sodium chloride and calcium carbonate (limestone). The overall reaction is:

$$CaCO_3 + 2\,NaCl \rightarrow Na_2CO_3 + CaCl_2$$

Most of the sodium carbonate is used in glass manufacture and in water softening.

Potassium is essential for plant growth and 95% of all potassium chloride mined is used in fertilizers. Potassium nitrate would be a better fertilizer because of its nitrogen content but it is much more expensive. The other predominant use of potassium chloride is in the production of potassium hydroxide which in turn is used for soaps, detergents, and other products.

A significant use of lithium carbonate is in the treatment of manic-depressive disorders.

Lithium is 1000 times less abundant than sodium in the earth's crust. Ores such as the aluminosilicate spodumene $LiAlSi_2O_6$ contain only 3% to 4% lithium. A considerable amount of lithium is used as lithium stearate in the formulation of lithium greases for the lubrication of automobiles. In fact, approximately half of the grease now used in automobiles is lithium-based because of its wide useful temperature range and water-repelling quality. Lithium is also used in various lightweight aluminum and magnesium alloys. The use of lithium in lightweight batteries was described in Unit 51.

Rubidium and cesium are less abundant than lithium and are available principally as a by-product of the lithium production.

Potassium, rubidium, and cesium metals are produced by the sodium or calcium reduction of their chlorides:

$$KCl(l) + Na(l) \rightleftharpoons K(g) + NaCl(l)$$

$$2\,RbCl(l) + Ca(l) \rightleftharpoons 2\,Rb(g) + CaCl_2(l)$$

800°C is higher than the b.pt. of K but lower than the b.pt. of Na.

As reducing agents, sodium and calcium metals are theoretically not strong enough to reduce K^+, Rb^+, or Cs^+, but at the high temperatures (~800°C) used, the volatile metals distill from the reaction mixture and shift the equilibria continually to the product side of the equation. Sodium is also used as a reducing agent in the isolation of several metals (for example, titanium) from their ores.

52.4 Compounds of the Alkali Metals

In almost all their reactions, the alkali metals form salts of the monopositive ions. The energy required for the removal of a second electron is prohibitive. With the halogens, for example, the alkali metals M form halides with a stoichiometry MX:

$$\text{Li}(s) + \tfrac{1}{2}\,\text{Br}_2(g) \rightarrow \text{LiBr}(s) \qquad \text{very slow burn}$$
$$\text{Na}(s) + \tfrac{1}{2}\,\text{Cl}_2(g) \rightarrow \text{NaCl}(s) \qquad \text{slow burn}$$
$$\text{K}(s) + \tfrac{1}{2}\,\text{Br}_2(g) \rightarrow \text{KBr}(s) \qquad \text{explosive}$$

In general, the intensity of the reaction increases down the group of alkali metals. Reactions involving cesium are dangerously explosive.

As noted earlier in this unit, all the alkali metals reduce hydrogen gas to form the ionic hydrides MH. The reaction is slow and heat is required. Only lithium reacts with nitrogen to from the reddish-brown nitride Li_3N and in this lithium behaves similarly to magnesium. The small size of the lithium ion allows the formation of a stable crystalline lattice with the nitride ion. The lattice energy must be sufficiently high to compensate for the energy required to break the strong N_2 triple bond. All the alkali metals form phosphides $M_3\text{P}$.

When heated with carbon, lithium and sodium from acetylides $M_2\text{C}_2$. When heated with graphite, the heavier alkali metals form **intercalation compounds**—these are compounds in which the metal atoms squeeze in between the layers of the graphite structure. We'll look at these compounds in Unit 54.

When the alkali metals are burned in air, the oxide formed depends upon the alkali metal. Lithium forms the oxide Li_2O, sodium forms the peroxide Na_2O_2, and potassium, rubidium, and cesium form the superoxide KO_2:

$$2\,\text{Li}(s) + \tfrac{1}{2}\,\text{O}_2(g) \rightarrow \text{Li}_2\text{O}(s)$$
$$2\text{Na}(s) + \text{O}_2(g) \rightarrow \text{Na}_2\text{O}_2(s)$$
$$\text{K}(s) + \text{O}_2(g) \rightarrow \text{KO}_2(s)$$

Thermodynamically the preference for one oxide over another is due to the difference in the sizes of the alkali metal ions and the different lattice energies of the products. For example, the superoxide is more stable in the presence of the larger cations. Oxides, peroxides, and superoxides of all the alkali metals can be prepared by changing the conditions of the reactions. The oxides become more colored down the group: Li_2O and Na_2O are white, K_2O is pale yellow, Rb_2O is bright yellow, and Cs_2O is orange. Sodium peroxide is a widely used bleaching agent and has been used to replace carbon dioxide in air with oxygen—in submarines and spacecraft for example:

$$\text{Na}_2\text{O}_2(s) + \text{CO}_2(g) \rightarrow \text{Na}_2\text{CO}_3(s) + \tfrac{1}{2}\text{O}_2(g)$$

The orange potassium superoxide behaves similarly, producing 50% more oxygen than carbon dioxide used:

$$2\,\text{KO}_2(s) + \text{CO}_2(g) \rightarrow \text{K}_2\text{CO}_3(s) + 3/2\,\text{O}_2(g)$$

All the alkali metals react with water to produce alkaline solutions—hence their name. This is another example of the reducing ability of the alkali metals. The intensity of the reaction increases down the group. Lithium reacts with a rapid bubbling of hydrogen. The reaction with sodium is more vigorous—the sodium metal usually

In a closed-system breathing apparatus such as that used by firemen, the superoxide reacts with water to produce the hydroxide, releasing oxygen gas. The hydroxide absorbs carbon dioxide to form the hydrogen carbonate (*cf.* Problem 52.3B).

FIGURE 52.5 The reaction of potassium with water.

This blue color was first noticed by Humphry Davy in 1807.

melts and skates across the surface of the water. Potassium liberates enough heat to immediately ignite the hydrogen gas released (Figure 52.5). Rubidium and cesium react explosively:

$$Na(s) + H_2O(l) \rightarrow NaOH(aq) + \tfrac{1}{2}H_2(g)$$

Reaction with Ammonia

The reaction of the alkali metals with ammonia is fascinating. At low temperatures ($-33°C$), the alkali metals dissolve in liquid ammonia to produce a beautiful blue color. In liquid ammonia, the alkali metal loses its valence electron which is then held in a cavity (radius about 300 pm) formed by the ammonia molecules. The blue color is due to the absorption of light by this solvated electron. The solution is less dense than the liquid ammonia itself due to the formation of the cavities in solution.

If the solution is made more concentrated the color changes from blue to a bronze color and the conductivity of the solution approaches that of a liquid metal. These ammonia solutions are unstable at higher temperatures and form the alkali metal amide with the liberation of hydrogen:

$$Na(s) + NH_3(l) \rightarrow NaNH_2(aq) + \tfrac{1}{2}H_2(g)$$

Covalent Bonding

This was discussed in Unit 19. The degree of covalent character becomes more evident in Groups 2A and 3A.

The lithium ion Li^+ is very small and is therefore a highly polarizing cation—the charge density is high. When a lithium ion is adjacent to an anion with polarizable electron cloud, some distortion of the electron cloud might be expected. The more the distortion, the greater the degree of covalent character in the bond (Figure 52.6). Of all the alkali metals, lithium can form bonds that are predominantly covalent. Compounds containing lithium–carbon bonds are referred to as **organometallic compounds** and they find great use in organic chemistry. In this respect they are similar to organomagnesium compounds called **Grignard reagents**. A typical reagent is n-butyllithium, $CH_3CH_2CH_2CH_2Li$, where the lithium takes the place of a hydrogen atom in a butane molecule.

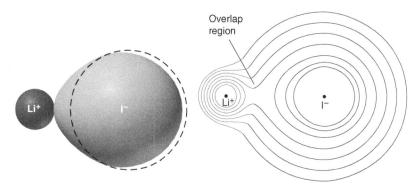

FIGURE 52.6 The polarization of a neighboring electron cloud by a lithium ion and the subsequent covalent character of the bond.

Solvation

All alkali metal cations are strongly solvated in aqueous solution. The small sizes of the ions leads to a large charge density (the ratio charge/size) and the ions attract the solvent water molecules strongly. It is this large solvation energy, with the increase in entropy associated with the break up of the ionic lattice, that results in the high solubilities of the alkali metal salts.

The attraction of the solvent molecules is greatest for the smallest ion, lithium Li^+. Each lithium ion is associated with about 25 water molecules in solution—this number is called the **hydration number**. The number decreases down the group as the charge density of the cation decreases. It is interesting therefore that as the size of the cation increases, the size of the hydration sphere decreases, the hydration energy decreases, and the mobility of the ions in solution increases (Table 52.2).

The mobility of ions has units of velocity (m s^{-1}) in an electrical field of 1 volt per meter.

TABLE 52.2 The hydration of the alkali metal ions in aqueous solution.

	Li$^+$	Na$^+$	K$^+$	Rb$^+$	Cs$^+$
Ionic radius (pm)	76	102	138	152	167
Hydrated radius (pm)	340	276	232	228	228
Hydration number	25	17	11	10	10
Hydration energy (kJ mol^{-1})	519	406	322	301	276
Mobility of the ions (10^{-8} m^2 V^{-1} s^{-1})	4.01	5.19	7.62	7.92	8.01

In 1967, C. J. Pedersen synthesized several cyclic polyethers, commonly called **crown ethers**, which are able to complex alkali metal cations. The interaction between the oxygen atoms of the polyether and the alkali metal cation mirrors the hydration of the cations in aqueous solution. The alkali metal cation preferred by a crown ether depends upon the space available inside the ring and different crown ethers can be designed to selectively complex different cations. The potassium ion seems to be a perfect fit for the 18-crown-6 ether shown in Figure 52.7.

Pedersen shared the 1987 Nobel Prize in Chemistry for this work.

The naming scheme for crown ethers is simple: the 18 indicates the number of atoms in the ring and the 6 indicates the number of coordinating oxygen atoms.

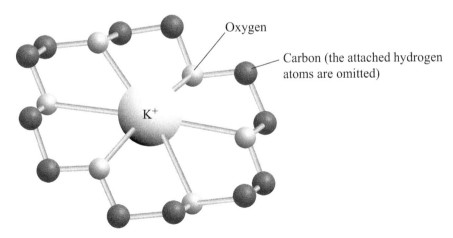

FIGURE 52.7 The structure of the potassium complex of 18-crown-6.

The interesting property of the crown ether complex is that they are hydrophobic and dissolve in organic solvents such as benzene. For example, the strong oxidizing agent potassium permanganate is insoluble in benzene but in the presence of 18-crown-6, the salt dissolves very well because the potassium ion is complexed by the crown ether. Note that the active ion of the salt, the permanganate ion, is not complexed and remains free to undertake its task of oxidizing whatever needs to be oxidized in the organic medium.

In water: $[K(H_2O)_n^+][MnO_4^-]$

In benzene: $[K(18\text{-crown-}6)^+][MnO_4^-]$

The idea was taken a step further by J-M. Lehn who prepared bicyclic structures he called **cryptands**. These ligands can be made very cation-specific, able to differentiate between the cations Na^+ and K^+ by a factor of 10^5. The thermodynamic stability of the encapsulated sodium ion is so large that crystalline salts of sodium *anions* (**sodides**) can be prepared (in ethylamine). The structure of the golden-yellow crypt–222 complexed sodium sodide is shown in Figure 52.8.

$$2\,Na + crypt\text{–}222 \rightarrow [Na(crypt\text{–}222)]^+\,Na^-$$

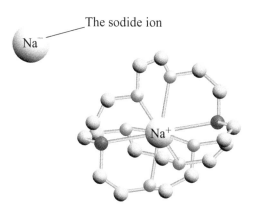

The sodide ion

Na^-

Na^+

FIGURE 52.8   The structure of $[Na(crypt\text{-}222)]^+Na^-$.

The autoionization of the sodium is thermodynamically driven by the formation of the complex. Potassides, rubidides, and cesides can also be prepared. If the stoichiometric ratio of cryptand to metal is increased, then electride salts such as $[Cs(crypt\text{–}222)_2]^+\,e^-$ can be prepared. In this case the electrons released by the cesium atoms exist in cavities between the cryptand molecules—similar to the behavior of electrons in liquid ammonia.

J. L. Dye, who first prepared the sodium sodide salt in 1974, recently prepared a sodium hydride (actually hydrogen sodide) in which the charges on the ions are reversed: $Na^-\,H^+$. This was achieved by encapsulating the hydrogen ion in an adamanzane ligand (Figure 52.9) and further illustrates the thermodynamic stability of an encapsulated ion. In this case the encapsulation of the H^+ is essentially irreversible—the protonated adamanzane is both kinetically and thermodynamically resistant to deprotonation.

J-M. Lehn shared the 1987 Nobel Prize in Chemistry with C. J. Pedersen.

The 222 indicates the number of oxygen atoms in each chain between the two nitrogen atoms. The radius of the cavity in the crypt–222 is 140 pm.

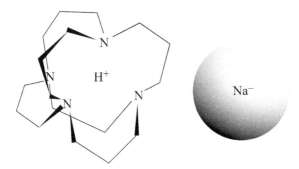

FIGURE 52.9 The H⁺Na⁻ adamanzane salt.

EXAMPLE 52.3   CHEMICAL PROPERTIES OF THE ALKALI METALS

Write equations representing the following reactions:

  a. The reaction of potassium and oxygen to form potassium superoxide.

  b. The burning of lithium in nitrogen to form lithium nitride.

  c. The explosive reaction of cesium and bromine.

What characteristic behavior of the alkali metal is common to all these reactions?

UNDERSTAND THE QUESTION

The alkali metals are very reactive, they easily lose their single valence electron, and are therefore excellent reducing agents. The results of their reactions are often predictable on this basis.

PLAN THE SOLUTION

Write the formulas for the reactants and products (if given) and balance the equation. If the product is not provided, predict the probable result.

SOLVE THE PROBLEM

  a. $K(s) + O_2(g) \rightarrow KO_2(s)$

  b. $6\,Li(s) + N_2(g) \rightarrow 2\,Li_3N(s)$

  c. $2\,Cs(s) + Br_2(g) \rightarrow 2\,CsBr(s)$

In all three reactions, the alkali metal is oxidized to the positive ion. The other participant in the reaction is reduced.

PROBLEM 52.3A

Write equations representing the following reactions:

  a. The reaction of potassium superoxide with carbon dioxide.

  b. The reaction of lithium hydride with water.

  c. The formation of potassium iodide from hydroiodic acid and potassium hydroxide.

  d. The formation of potassium phosphide from its constituent elements.

PROBLEM 52.3B

Write equations representing the reaction of potassium superoxide with water to produce potassium hydroxide and oxygen gas, and the subsequent reaction of potassium hydroxide with carbon dioxide to produce potassium hydrogen carbonate. How many moles of oxygen gas are produced for every mole of carbon dioxide absorbed?

Review Questions

1. Describe the principal means of manufacturing hydrogen gas. What is most of the gas used for?

2. Describe the classification of the binary hydrides? How do they differ?

3. What are major sources of the alkali metals? Which alkali metal is produced more than any other?

4. What are the principal uses of the alkali metals?

5. In the great majority of their reactions, the alkali metals behave in the same way. What way is this?

6. Of all the alkali metals, lithium is the only one able to form bonds that are predominantly covalent in character. Why is this?

Solutions to Problems

PROBLEM 52.1A

a. For a stoichiometry XH_2, where X is a nonmetallic element, the group must be Group 6A. In Period 3, the element is sulfur.

b. Sr is Sr^{2+} in all its compounds. The stoichiometry must be SrH_2.

PROBLEM 52.2A

a. The valence electrons of lithium are held more tightly than those of elements further down the group. Lithium has the highest ionization energy.

b. The reactivity of cesium is greater than any other element in the group (excluding Francium). Its valence electrons are farthest from the nucleus, most loosely held, and most easily lost in a reaction.

PROBLEM 52.3A

a. $2 KO_2(s) + CO_2(g) \rightarrow K_2CO_3(s) + 3/2\ O_2(g)$

b. $LiH(s) + H_2O(l) \rightarrow LiOH(s) + H_2(g)$

c. $HI(aq) + KOH(aq) \rightarrow KI(aq) + H_2O(l)$

d. $12 K(s) + P_4(s) \rightarrow 4 K_3P(s)$

Answers to Review Questions

1. The predominant industrial preparation of hydrogen is from hydrocarbons by the steam-hydrocarbon reforming process. The synthesis gas that results is often mixed with more steam and passed over a copper/iron catalyst to produce carbon dioxide and more hydrogen in the shift reaction. Most manufactured hydrogen is used in the production of ammonia.

2. There three types of binary hydride: saline, covalent, and metallic. The saline hydrides occur only with highly electropositive metals and are salts of the hydride ion. Covalent hydrides are molecules and occur with nonmetals. Usually the electronegativity of the nonmetal exceeds that of hydrogen—thus hydrogen has a +1 oxidation state. In a few instances, the electronegativity is less than that of hydrogen (e.g. Be and B) but the bonds are still predominantly covalent. Metallic hydrides occur with some elements at the left end of the transition metal block. These are hydrides in which the hydrogen occupies the spaces, holes, or interstices within the metallic lattice.

3. Major sources of sodium and potassium are vast natural deposits of NaCl, KCl, and other salts. Lithium, rubidium, and cesium are less abundant. A significant lithium mineral is spodumene. Rubidium and cesium are produced largely as by-products of lithium production. More sodium is produced than any other alkali metal—largely as a result of the chlor-alkali industry.

4. Most sodium chloride is used in the chlor-alkali industry. Some is used in the salting of roads, food preparation, the paper industry, and in chemical manufacture. Almost all the potassium chloride (and other potassium salts) mined are used in fertilizers. A significant use of lithium is in the production of lithium-based greases.

5. The common characteristic of almost all the reactions of the alkali metals is the loss of their single valence electron. The metal is oxidized and the other participant in the reaction is reduced. In virtually all their compounds, the alkali metals are present as the monopositive ions.

6. Lithium is the smallest of the alkali metals. The lithium ion Li^+ is very small and highly polarizing (*cf.* Figure 52.6). As a result the electron clouds on neighboring atoms are polarized to such an extent that the bonds are largely covalent in character.

End-of-Unit Problems

1. Describe briefly how the following elements are made commercially:

   a. sodium

   b. hydrogen

   c. potassium

2. Describe some of the principle uses of the following elements:

   a. hydrogen

   b. sodium

   c. lithium

3. The nuclear charge of a hydrogen nucleus is +1 and that of a lithium nucleus is +3. However, the ionization energy of hydrogen exceeds that of lithium. Why?

4. The ionization energy of cesium is considerably less than that of lithium. Why?

5. The ionic radius of the hydride ion is 152 pm in cesium hydride. The ionic radius of the fluoride ion in most fluoride salts is 133 pm. The fluoride ion has a complete valence shell of eight electrons and the hydride ion has only two electrons. Why is the hydride ion larger?

6. The hydride ion varies considerably in size—it depends upon the particular salt. In CsH, the size is 152 pm. In LiH, the size is 137 pm. Why does the size vary so much?

7. Predict the trends in the following properties of the elements in Group 1A.

   a. atomic size.

   b. density.

   c. the strength of the metallic bond.

8. Predict the trends in the following properties of the alkali metals.

   a. the size of the M^+ ion.

   b. hydration of the M^+ ion in aqueous solution.

   c. electronegativity.

9. Classify each of the following hydrogen compounds as an ionic (saline), covalent, or interstitial hydride:

   a. B_2H_6

   b. LiH

10. Classify each of the following hydrogen compounds as an ionic (saline), covalent, or interstitial hydride:

   a. SiH_4

   b. PdH_n

11. Write equations representing the reaction of hydrogen with

   a. chlorine

   b. magnesium

12. Write equations representing the reaction of hydrogen with

   a. phosphorus

   b. sodium

13. Explain why lithium, in some respects, behaves differently from the other members of Group 1A. Give an example of the chemical behavior of lithium that distinguishes it from the other alkali metals.

14. Lithium is said to resemble magnesium in many respects. What is the basis of this resemblance? Give an example of the chemical behavior of lithium in which it resembles magnesium.

15. Write equations representing the reaction of

   a. lithium and nitrogen

   b. potassium and water

   c. potassium superoxide and carbon dioxide

16. Write equations representing the reaction of

   a. sodium and phosphorus

   b. rubidium and chlorine

   c. potassium superoxide and water

17. Write equations for the reactions of lithium, sodium, and potassium with oxygen. Which metal forms an oxide, which forms a peroxide, and which forms a superoxide?

18. The intensity of the reaction of the alkali metals with the halogens depends upon the identity of both the alkali metal and the halogen. What trends are evident in this series of reactions?

19. Sodium metal is produced commercially in a Downs cell (*cf.* Figure 51.11). The electrolyte is molten sodium chloride. If the cell operates at a voltage of 7.5 V and a current of 30,000 amps, what mass of sodium can be produced in 24 hours.

20. Chlorine is produced in a diaphragm cell (*cf.* Figure 51.12). If the applied cell potential is 4.8 V and the current passed through the cell is 250,000 amps, what mass of sodium hydroxide is produced, and what mass of chlorine is produced, per hour?

Alkaline Earth and Group 3A Elements

53.1   The Alkaline Earth Metals

Calcium and magnesium are the fifth (4.66%) and sixth (2.76%) most abundant elements by mass in the earth's crust. Beryllium, like lithium in Group 1A, is relatively scarce. Strontium (0.0384%) and barium (0.0390%) are listed 15 and 14 on the abundance scale.

Calcium is essential to animal life. The human body contains about 1 kg of calcium—almost all of it as hydroxyapatite in bones and teeth. In plant life, magnesium is the metal at the center of the chlorophyll molecule without which **photosynthesis**, and all life higher in the food chain, would not occur.

Humphry Davy isolated the four alkaline earth metals magnesium, calcium, strontium, and barium in 1808 using electrolytic methods. Beryllium was isolated by Friedrich Wöhler in 1828 by reducing beryllium chloride with potassium. Very small amounts of the highly radioactive radium were isolated from tons of the uranium ore pitchblende by Marie and Pierre Curie in 1898. Beryllium and magnesium are silvery gray metals. Calcium, strontium, and barium have a slight yellow tinge (Figure 53.1).

The properties of the Group 2A elements parallel those of the Group 1A elements. The melting points and boiling points are however much higher and the metals are somewhat harder because there are twice as many valence electrons (ns^2) and the metallic bonding is stronger. Physical properties of the elements are listed in Table 53.1. The chemical properties of the alkaline earth metals are governed predominantly by the loss of the two valence electrons and the formation of ionic compounds. Generally, because their reactions involve the loss of two electrons, the alkaline earth metals are less reactive that the alkali metals. Nevertheless, like the alkali metals, the alkaline earth metals are never found naturally in an uncombined state.

> Historically, a metal *earth* is the insoluble oxide of the metal.

> Radium only occurs in uranium ores. About 10 tons of pitchblende must be processed to obtain 1 g of radium.

> Marie Curie received the Nobel Prize in Chemistry in 1911 for her discovery of the elements radium and polonium, and for the isolation of radium.

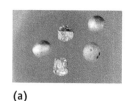
(a)

(b)

(c)

(d)

(e)

FIGURE 53.1   **The alkaline earth metals.**
(a) beryllium; (b) magnesium; (c) calcium; (d) strontium; (e) barium.

TABLE 53.1   The Alkaline Earth metals.

Name	Symbol	Melting Point °C	Boiling Point °C	ΔH°_{fus} @ m.pt. kJ mol^{-1}	Density g cm^{-3}	Ionization Energies kJ mol^{-1}		Metallic Radius pm	Ionic M^{2+} Radius pm
Beryllium	Be	1287	2472	7.9	1.85	899	1757	112	27
Magnesium	Mg	649	1105	8.5	1.74	738	1451	160	72
Calcium	Ca	839	1494	8.5	1.55	590	1145	197	100
Strontium	Sr	768	1381	7.4	2.54	549	1064	215	118
Barium	Ba	727	1805	7.1	3.51	503	965	222	135

Industrial Production and Uses

Supplies of magnesium are virtually limitless—0.13% of the world's oceans consists of magnesium. In addition, there are huge deposits of dolomitic limestone $MgCa(CO_3)_2$ on land. Other minerals are magnesite ($MgCO_3$) and epsomite ($MgSO_4$). Calcium occurs as the sedimentary calcium carbonate derived from the fossilized remains of ancient marine life. Limestone, marble, chalk and coral are all calcium carbonate. Other minerals are gypsum ($CaSO_4 \cdot 2H_2O$), fluorite (CaF_2), and apatite $Ca_5(PO_4)_3F$. Strontium occurs as the minerals celestite ($SrSO_4$) and strontianite ($SrCO_3$) and barium as the mineral baryte ($BaSO_4$). Beryllium occurs in the mineral beryl $Be_3Al_2[Si_6O_{18}]$—an aluminosilicate.

Beryllium is produced by the electrolysis of molten beryllium chloride. A major use of the metal is in the manufacture of copper and nickel alloys. Addition of small amounts of beryllium (2%) hardens copper without reducing its conductivity. The strength of the alloy is six times that of pure copper. These hard alloys do not create sparks when struck and are used to make tools for use in the petroleum industry, in grain elevators, and in other situations where explosions are possible.

Magnesium metal is produced on a large scale either by electrolysis of molten magnesium chloride or by reduction of a mixed calcium magnesium oxide. In the former method, impure magnesium chloride is obtained from seawater and the magnesium is precipitated as $Mg(OH)_2$ by adding slaked lime ($Ca(OH)_2$). The precipitate is treated with hydrochloric acid to produce the magnesium chloride. In the reduction process, dolomitic limestone is heated to obtain $CaO \cdot MgO$. This is then heated at 1200°C with FeSi (an alloy of iron and silicon). At the high temperature of the reaction, the magnesium immediately vaporizes and is removed and condensed.

$$2\ CaO \cdot MgO + FeSi \rightarrow 2Mg + Fe + Ca_2SiO_4$$

The white cliffs of Dover on the south east coast of England are calcium carbonate (Figure 53.2).

The precious stones emerald and aquamarine are aluminosilicates of beryllium with impurities (Figure 53.3).

FIGURE 53.2 The white cliffs of Dover are composed of chalk (calcium carbonate).

FIGURE 53.3 Emerald is beryl with about 2% chromium incorporated into the crystalline lattice.

Mortar is a mixture of lime, sand, and water. The mixture absorbs CO_2 from the atmosphere to form a rigid mass of $CaCO_3$. Roman cement was a mixture of mortar and aggregate such as gravel. The Romans used mortar with great success to build structures that are still standing today. Modern mortar includes cement in the mixture.

Modern **Cement** is a mixture of calcium oxide, silicates, and aluminates.

Concrete is cement mixed with a filler such as gravel or a lightweight water-soluble polymer.

The aluminate ion in $Ca_3Al_2O_6$ is $Al_6O_{18}^{18-}$:

FIGURE 53.4 The reaction of calcium metal with cold water.

Magnesium is a lightweight metal ideal for fabricating structures where weight is of some importance. Magnesium alloys equal in strength to steel weigh only one-quarter as much. Such alloys consist of more than 90% magnesium, between 2 and 9% aluminum, with some zinc and manganese. Some magnesium is added to most aluminum alloys to harden them and to improve their resistance to corrosion.

Limestone is the most available source of calcium carbonate and is mined on a huge scale. It is the starting material in the production of quicklime (CaO) and slaked lime ($Ca(OH)_2$). A hundred million tons of limestone are used annually in the production of Portland cement which is made by roasting (1500°C) a mixture of limestone ($CaCO_3$), sand and clay (silicates and aluminosilicates), and iron oxide. The cement is composed principally of calcium oxide, silicates, and aluminates such as Ca_2SiO_4, Ca_3SiO_5 and $Ca_3Al_2O_6$. Water reacts with cement to form a rigid three-dimensional network of silicates.

Enormous amounts of limestone are used in the production of iron (*cf.* Unit 58). At the temperature of the furnace the limestone decomposes to quicklime and carbon dioxide. The quicklime reacts with the silica impurity in the iron oxide ore to form calcium silicate—a compound called **slag**:

$$CaO(s) + SiO_2(s) \rightarrow CaSiO_3(l)$$

Considerable amounts of lime are used for the treatment of water supplies and waste water. It is also used whenever a cheap source of base is required. For example it is spread on soils to adjust the pH and it is used to remove sulfur dioxide from the emissions of power generating plants that burn fossil fuels—a process called **scrubbing**. Calcium carbonate is used in the glass industry and the papermaking industry.

The metals strontium and barium are produced by the reduction of their oxides at high temperatures using aluminum as the reducing agent. This is a reaction similar to the thermite reaction (*cf.* Figure 13.3).

The variation in the chemical reactivity of the alkaline earth metals can be illustrated by their reaction with water. Beryllium does not react, magnesium reacts with steam or hot water, calcium, strontium, and barium react with cold water (Figure 53.4).

EXAMPLE 53.1 QUICKLIME AND SLAKED LIME

Quicklime and slaked lime are produced and used in large quantities—they are relatively cheap. Write equations representing the following uses of these two compounds:

a. The removal of SO_2 from combustion products of coal by slaked lime.

b. The precipitation of magnesium hydroxide from seawater by slaked lime.

c. The reaction of sodium carbonate and quicklime to produce calcium carbonate and sodium hydroxide.

UNDERSTAND THE QUESTION

Quicklime and slaked lime are CaO and $Ca(OH)_2$ respectively. They are both easily produced from natural sources of $CaCO_3$. Both are bases and they will react with acids, or acidic oxides, to produce salts.

PLAN THE SOLUTION

Write the formulas of the substances involved and then balance the equations.

SOLVE THE PROBLEM

a. $Ca(OH)_2(aq) + SO_2(g) \rightarrow CaSO_3(aq) + H_2O(l)$

b. $MgCl_2(aq) + Ca(OH)_2(aq) \rightarrow Mg(OH)_2(s) + CaCl_2(aq)$

c. $Na_2CO_3(aq) + CaO(aq) + H_2O(l) \rightarrow CaCO_3(s) + 2\,NaOH(aq)$

PROBLEM 53.1A

Calcium hypochlorite "bleaching powder," used for general bleaching and disinfecting, is $Ca(OCl)_2 \cdot CaCl_2 \cdot Ca(OH)_2 \cdot 2H_2O$. It is obtained by the reaction of chlorine and slaked lime. Write an equation representing this reaction.

PROBLEM 53.1B

The bleaching solution used in the paper industry is much more powerful than ordinary household bleach. Household bleach is a dilute alkaline solution of sodium hypochlorite. Bleaching solutions for the paper industry are concentrated mixtures of calcium hypochlorite and calcium chloride. Write an equation representing the production of this solution from chlorine and slaked lime.

53.2   Compounds of the Alkaline Earth Metals

In almost all their reactions, the alkaline earth metals, except beryllium, form salts of their divalent ions. The additional energy required to remove a third electron far exceeds any return expected through bond formation. For example, the first and second ionization energies for magnesium are 738 and 1451 kJ mol^{-1}. The third ionization energy is 7733 kJ mol^{-1}. Removal of electrons from the valence shells of the alkali and alkaline earth metals is relatively easy but removal of electrons from the core is always much more difficult—the electrons are tightly held by the nucleus. It's perhaps interesting that the alkaline earth metals always lose two electrons and not just one. The additional lattice energy for the 2+ ion more than compensates for the second ionization energy required. Lattice structures of a monopositive metal ion would be thermodynamically stable—it's just that the lattice structures of the dipositive ion are more stable. A salt of the monopositive ion would disproportionate.

The chemical behavior of beryllium is different from the other members of the group. Many compounds of beryllium are covalent in character. We will return to this characteristic later in this unit.

FIGURE 53.5 When burned in air, magnesium metal produces MgO and Mg_3N_2 with the emission of a brilliant white light.

The reactions of the alkaline earth metals with the nonmetals are predictable. All the Group 2A metals form halides, sulfides, oxides, nitrides, phosphides, and carbides. The oxide formed depends upon the metal. Beryllium, magnesium, and calcium form the normal oxide but strontium and barium form the peroxide. Beryllium is unreactive at low temperatures but burns in air to form BeO and Be_3N_2 above 600°C. Higher temperatures are required to form the sulfide, and higher still (1700°C) to form the carbide. Metals lower in the group react more readily. Magnesium burns in air with a brilliant white emission to form magnesium oxide MgO and some nitride Mg_3N_2 (Figure 53.5). Some representative reactions are:

$$Mg(s) + Cl_2(g) \rightarrow MgCl_2(s)$$
$$Ca(s) + \tfrac{1}{2} O_2(g) \rightarrow CaO(s)$$
$$Ba(s) + O_2(g) \rightarrow BaO_2(s)$$
$$Ca(s) + S(s) \rightarrow CaS(s)$$
$$Mg(s) + N_2(g) \rightarrow Mg_3N_2(s)$$
$$2\,Be(s) + C(s) \rightarrow Be_2C(s)$$
$$Mg(s) + 2C(s) \rightarrow MgC_2(s)$$

Magnesium oxide dissolves only slightly in water. The small Mg^{2+} ion and the oxide ion O^{2-} form a lattice with strong electrostatic attraction between the ions. The lattice energy is high and the energy returned by solvation of the ions is insufficient. For the same reason, magnesium oxide has a high melting point (2800°C) and it is used as a **refractory** material. Magnesium hydroxide is only sparingly soluble in water and an emulsion (milk of magnesia) is often used as an antacid.

A refractory material is a material able to withstand high temperatures.

As we noted earlier, magnesium is the metal ion at the center of the chlorophyll molecule. In this molecule, the magnesium ion is surrounded by four nitrogen atoms in a macrocyclic ring called a porphyrin (*cf*. Figure 38.3). The nitrogen atoms donate electron pairs to the magnesium ion at the center. Chlorophyll is the green pigment in plants that captures radiant energy from the sun. The energy is used in photosynthesis—a process in which carbon dioxide and water are combined to form carbohydrates.

Another important porphyrin is heme, responsible for the transport and storage of oxygen.

Chlorophyll absorbs violet and red light in the visible region which is why the leaves of plants appear green.

An important alkaline earth fluoride is calcium fluoride (fluorspar) CaF_2, which is a valuable source of the element fluorine. The crystalline structure of fluorspar is illustrated in Figure 53.6.

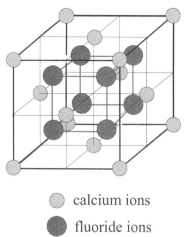

○ calcium ions

● fluoride ions

FIGURE 53.6   The crystalline fluorite structure.
The calcium ions form a fcc array and the fluoride ions fill all the tetrahedral holes (*cf*. Unit 29).

Calcium carbide CaC_2 reacts with water to form acetylene C_2H_2. In fact the hydrocarbon formed when a carbide reacts with water indicates the structure of the carbide ion. In calcium carbide the anion is the acetylide anion C_2^{2-}. We will examine this further in Unit 54.

Like the alkali metals, the more active alkaline earth metals calcium, strontium, and barium dissolve in liquid ammonia to produce deep blue solutions.

As noted earlier, calcium, strontium, and barium react with water to produce hydrogen gas at room temperature. Magnesium reacts with steam:

$$Ba(s) + H_2O(l) \rightarrow Ba(OH)_2(aq) + \tfrac{1}{2}H_2(g)$$
$$Mg(s) + H_2O(g) \rightarrow MgO(s) + H_2(g)$$

The more active alkaline earth metals are good reducing agents. For example, magnesium will burn in carbon dioxide to produce magnesium oxide and carbon (Figure 53.7), and magnesium will reduce sand (SiO_2) to produce magnesium oxide and magnesium silicide:

$$2\,Mg(s) + CO_2(s) \rightarrow 2\,MgO(s) + C(s)$$
$$4\,Mg(s) + SiO_2(s) \rightarrow 2\,MgO(s) + Mg_2Si(s)$$

Calcium carbide is used as a convenient source of acetylene gas. It was once used in miners' lamps and automobile lights in which the acetylene was burned to provide light.

FIGURE 53.7 Magnesium burning in solid carbon dioxide.

The Diagonal Relationship

The covalent character of the compounds of the elements in Groups 1A through 4A is related to the polarizing power of the cation. We noted earlier that lithium has the ability to form covalent bonds in compounds such as *n*-butyllithium. In these compounds the lithium ion Li^+ polarizes the electrons in the valence orbitals of the adjacent atom to such an extent that the bond between them is more covalent than ionic in character. There is a transfer of electron density from the 'anion' to the lithium 'cation' so that the lithium cation no longer exists as such (*cf.* Figure 52.8).

The polarizing power of a cation depends upon its charge density—the ratio of the charge on the ion to the size of the ion. Horizontally, from Group 1A through Group 4A, the charge on the cation increases from +1 to +4. The size increases down each group (Figure 53.8).

This means that in a diagonal direction from top left to bottom right, the charge to size ratio is approximately constant—the increase in the size of the ion compensates for the increase in the charge on the ion. As a result, lithium and magnesium behave similarly—we have already noted the similarity of the organometallic compounds of lithium and magnesium. Beryllium and aluminum are alike in many respects—they form the same sorts of compounds. Historically, this similarity of beryllium and aluminum led to considerable confusion about the placement of beryllium in the Periodic Table. The fact that beryllium forms compounds analogous to compounds of aluminum, with its valency of 3, implied an atomic mass of 13.5 for beryllium. It wasn't until Mendeleev's placement of beryllium in Group 2A that the confusion of more than 50 years was finally resolved.

The blue line in Figure 53.8, perpendicular to the black lines, indicates an increasing trend toward covalent behavior. Whereas compounds of potassium are best characterized as ionic, compounds of boron are covalent. Magnesium is on the borderline between the two. There are no compounds of beryllium in which the bonding is predominantly ionic.

> A similar diagonal relationship exists between boron and silicon. We will examine this further in Unit 54.

> Suppose beryllium chloride is analyzed and the composition is 11.28% Be and 88.72% Cl.
>
> 88.72 g /35.45 g mol^{-1} = 2.5 mol Cl, implying, if Be has a valency of 3 like Al, that 11.28 g is 0.83 mol Be—a molar mass of 13.5 g mol^{-1}.

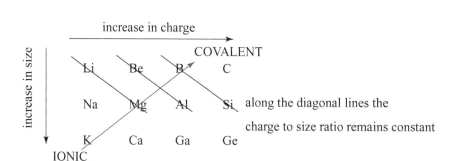

FIGURE 53.8 The diagonal relationship.

Compounds of Beryllium

Beryllium chloride is not an ionic compound like sodium chloride. It consists in the solid state as a chain of $BeCl_2$ units in which lone pairs of electrons on the chlorine atoms are donated into empty p orbitals on adjacent beryllium atoms (Figure 53.9). In this interaction, the chlorine atoms act as Lewis bases and the beryllium atoms act as Lewis acids. The chain is broken up by the action of stronger Lewis bases

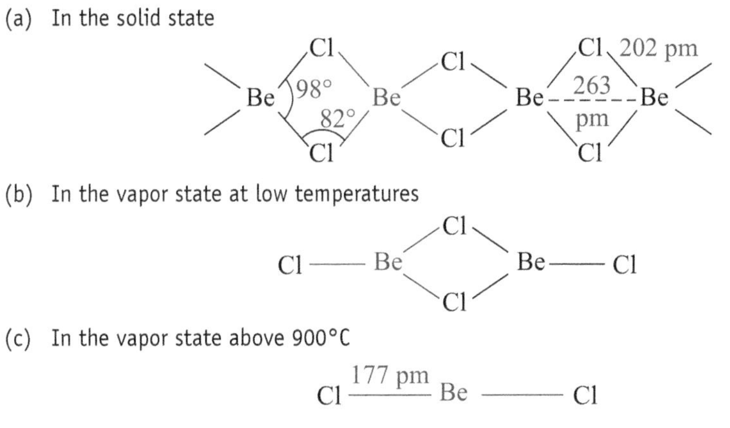

(a) In the solid state

Be $\overset{98°}{\underset{82°}{\diagdown}}$ Cl, Be, Cl, Be — — — Be Cl 202 pm 263 pm Cl

(b) In the vapor state at low temperatures

Cl —— Be $\diagdown$ Cl $\diagdown$ Be —— Cl

(c) In the vapor state above 900°C

Cl $\overset{177\ pm}{\text{———}}$ Be ——— Cl

FIGURE 53.9   The structure of beryllium chloride in the solid state and in the vapor state.

such as ammonia. The ammonia molecules form a complex ion $[Be(NH_3)_4]^{2+}$ with the beryllium. In the vapor state above 900°C the beryllium chloride exists as linear $BeCl_2$ molecules. At lower temperatures, these molecules dimerize to form Be_2Cl_4 molecules. In this dimer, two chlorine atoms bridge the two beryllium atoms as they do in the solid state.

Beryllium forms organometallic compounds involving beryllium–carbon bonds. Because the beryllium–carbon bond is stronger than the lithium–carbon bond, a convenient method of synthesis is from the corresponding lithium compound. For example:

$$2\ LiCH_3 + BeCl_2 \xrightarrow{\text{dry ether}} Be(CH_3)_2 + 2\ LiCl$$

The diethylether solvent (dry ether) is a weak Lewis base and coordinates to the dimethylberyllium molecule to complete the valence shell of the beryllium. When prepared free of the diethylether solvent, the dimethylberyllium has a chain structure similar to that of $BeCl_2$ (Figure 53.9). However, the bonding in the chain is quite different. In $BeCl_2$, the links between the $BeCl_2$ units are achieved by the donation of nonbonding pairs of electrons on the chlorine atoms to the adjacent beryllium atoms. All the Be—Cl bonds are two electron (2e) bonds. In $Be(CH_3)_2$, there are no nonbonding electron pairs available and the two electrons in the Be—CH_3 bond are shared by three atoms: one C and two Be. In valence bond theory, such a bond is often called a three center–two electron (3c—2e) bond (Figure 53.10). **Multicenter bonding** such as

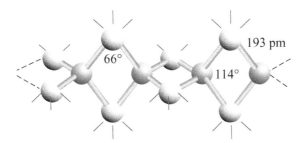

FIGURE 53.10   The structure of dimethylberyllium.
The Be—CH_3—Be bonds are 3c—2e bonds in which one pair of electrons are shared by three atoms. Beryllium hydride has a similar structure.

this is a common feature of the electron deficient covalent compounds of the elements of Groups 1A, 2A, and 3A. For example, beryllium hydride has a chain structure similar to dimethylberyllium involving Be—H—Be 3c—2e bonds.

Grignard Reagents

Victor Grignard (1871–1935) received the Nobel Prize in Chemistry in 1912 for his work in developing organomagnesium reagents—now called Grignard reagents.

The most important organometallic compounds of magnesium are **Grignard reagents** which are used to great effect in organic synthesis. A Grignard reagent is prepared by adding an organic halide (often iodide) to a mixture of dry diethylether and magnesium metal turnings. Water and air must be excluded. It is remarkable when you observe this reaction for the first time to see the magnesium metal apparently dissolving in the organic solvent. What is happening is the formation of the ether–soluble alkyl magnesium iodide. Again the weak Lewis base diethylether coordinates to the magnesium to satisfy its electron deficiency:

$$\overset{\text{dry ether}}{C_2H_5I + Mg \rightarrow C_2H_5MgI}$$

Other species, such as a bridged structure analogous to the beryllium chloride structure shown in Figure 53.9(b) are also present, particularly in more concentrated solutions.

EXAMPLE 53.2 STRUCTURE OF GRIGNARD REAGENT IN SOLUTION.

Draw the structure of ethylmagnesium iodide C_2H_5MgI

a. in a diethylether $(C_2H_5)_2O$ solution in which the diethylether is abundant.

b. in a concentrated diethylether solution (in which the amount of diethylether solvent is limited).

UNDERSTAND THE QUESTION

In solution, the weak Lewis base diethylether coordinates to the magnesium of the Grignard reagent to satisfy its electron deficiency. A lone pair of electrons on the O atom of the diethylether molecule is donated to the magnesium atom in the formation of a coordinate bond. The magnesium needs two lone pairs to satisfy its deficiency. If there is not enough diethylether available, then the ethylmagnesium iodide polymerizes, using lone pairs of electrons on the iodine atoms of adjacent molecules instead to satisfy the deficiency of electrons around the magnesium.

PLAN THE SOLUTION

Draw the structure of the ethylmagnesium iodide and then add the solvent molecules. A two-dimensional Lewis structure is adequate but keep in mind that the arrangement of the four electron pairs around the magnesium atom is tetrahedral.

SOLVE THE PROBLEM

The diethylether $(C_2H_5)_2O$ molecule is abbreviated Et_2O.

a.

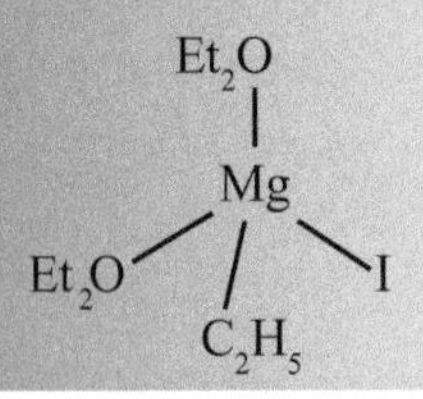

$$Et_2O$$
$$|$$
$$Mg$$
$$Et_2O \diagup \; | \; \diagdown I$$
$$C_2H_5$$

b. The molecule will polymerize; the first stage will be the formation of a dimer:

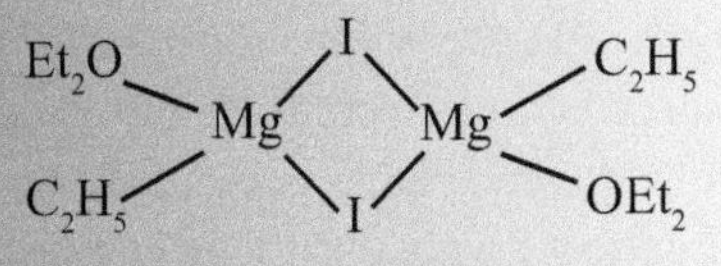

The molecule $MgAl_2(CH_3)_8$ has an interesting structure involving bridging CH_3 groups and 3c–2e bonds. Assuming the molecule is symmetrical, draw a possible structure.

From your knowledge of the structure of dimethylberyllium (Figure 53.9) predict the structure of dimethylmagnesium $(CH_3)_2Mg$. Would you expect the C—Mg bond length to be shorter or longer than the C—Be bond length (193 pm)?

53.3 Boron

Boron is at the top of Group 3A and is the only nonmetal in the group. As a result, its properties are unique within the group. Its small size and high ionization energy result in covalent rather than metallic bonding in boron itself and its compounds are covalent rather than ionic. However, boron has only three valence electrons with which to form covalent bonds and most of its compounds are electron-deficient. This electron deficiency profoundly affects the chemistry of boron. Boron has a diagonal relationship with silicon and some of its compounds are similar. For example, the borates and silicates have similar properties and the boranes and silanes are similar in reactivity .

Borax, a compound of boron $Na_2B_4O_5(OH)_4·8H_2O$, has been used since ancient times to manufacture glasses and pottery glazes but the pure element was not isolated until 1892 when Henri Moissan reduced B_2O_3 using magnesium metal. The properties of boron are contrasted with those of the other elements in Group 3A in Table 53.2. Note that the ionic radius of boron B^{3+} is a hypothetical number because there are no compounds in which boron exists as the B^{3+} ion. Note also the high melting and boiling points and the high heat of fusion of boron compared to those of the other elements in the group. This illustrates the difference between the covalent bonding in boron and the metallic bonding in the other elements of the group.

TABLE 53.2 The Group 3A elements.

Name	Symbol	Melting Point °C	Boiling Point °C	ΔH°_{fus} @ m.pt. kJ mol^{-1}	Density g cm^{-3}	Ionization Energies kJ mol^{-1}			Covalent Radius pm	Metallic Radius pm	Ionic Radius pm
						1st	2nd	3rd			
Boron	B	2092	4002	50.2	2.35	801	2427	3660	88	—	27
Aluminum	Al	660	2520	10.7	2.70	578	1817	2745	130	143	54
Gallium	Ga	29.8	2205	5.6	5.90	579	1979	2963	122	153	62
Indium	In	157	2073	3.3	7.31	558	1821	2704	150	167	80
Thallium	Tl	304	1473	4.1	11.85	589	1971	2878	155	171	89

Industrial Production and Uses

The world's largest single deposit of boron occurs at the eponymous Boron in the Mojave desert in California. The deposit consists of hydrated sodium tetraborates such as borax, $Na_2B_4O_5(OH)_4 \cdot 8H_2O$. Larger but more scattered sources occur in Turkey. The isolation of boron from the mineral involves treatment with sulfuric acid to produce boric acid H_2BO_3, followed by heating to produce boric oxide, and then the reduction of the boric oxide by magnesium to produce magnesium oxide and boron. Pure boron can be prepared by the reduction of BBr_3 vapor with hydrogen gas.

Most boron (60% in the US) is used in the manufacture of the heat-resistant borosilicate glasses (e.g. Pyrex™). The advantage of borosilicate glass over ordinary glass is its low coefficient of expansion. This means that it can be heated or cooled rapidly without breaking. In the past, considerable quantities of borax were used in borate-based washing agents. Such use has diminished but sodium peroxoborate $Na_2B_2O_4(OH)_4$ is still used to some extent in Europe. The perborate ion produces hydrogen peroxide in hot water which acts as a bleach. Boron fibers, like carbon fibers, are used in increasing amounts to reinforce composite materials.

Boron exists in many different allotropic forms although in each allotrope the basic structural unit is a B_{12} icosahedron (Figure 53.11). In the α–rhombohedral allotrope, these B_{12} icosahedra form an approximate cubic close packed (ccp) array. The space between the icosahedra is relatively large (the packing is relatively loose) and the density of the solid is low.

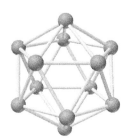

FIGURE 53.11 The B$_{12}$ icosahedron that is the basic structural unit of the allotropes of boron.
Note that the lines indicate the shape of the icosahedron and not bonds between the atoms.

53.4 Compounds of Boron

As already mentioned, the small size and high ionization energy results in covalent bonding in the compounds of boron. The electron deficiency leads to Lewis acid behavior and multicenter bonding.

Boranes

Boranes are boron-hydrogen compounds. The simplest borane is a dimer of BH_3 called diborane–6 (Figure 53.12). This is a colorless gas (b.pt. –92.6°C) readily decomposed by water and explosive in contact with oxygen. The compound can be prepared by the reaction of sodium borohydride with boron trifluoride in an ether solvent:

$$3\,NaBH_4 + 4\,BF_3 \rightarrow 3\,NaBF_4 + 2\,B_2H_6$$

The dissociation of diborane–6 to borane BH_3 requires 150 kJ mol^{-1}.

In diborane–6 two of the hydrogen atoms bridge the two boron atoms. In a valence bond approach to the bonding, two electrons are shared by the three B—H—B atoms in a three center—two electron (3c–2e) bond. There are therefore four B—H bonds and two B—H—B bonds that account for the twelve valence electrons available. Diborane–6 is the first of a series of boranes called *nido*–boranes with the general formula B_nH_{n+4}. Another example is pentaborane–9, B_5H_9, which has a square pyramidal structure (Figure 53.13). Other series are the *closo*–boranes with the general formula $B_nH_n^{2-}$ and the *arachno*–boranes with the general formula B_nH_{n+6}.

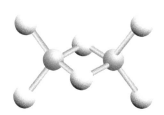

FIGURE 53.12 The structure of diborane–6.

The di– prefix indicates the number of boron atoms in the molecule. The suffix –6 indicates the number of hydrogen atoms in the molecule.

In the valence bond description of the bonding in boranes, the number of 3c—2e bonds always equals the number of boron atoms.

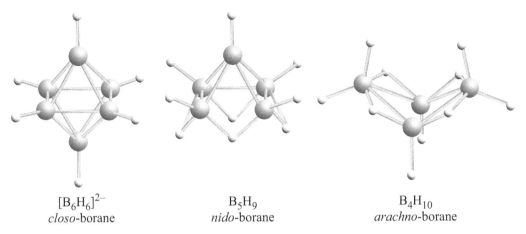

$[B_6H_6]^{2-}$
closo-borane

B_5H_9
nido-borane

B_4H_{10}
arachno-borane

FIGURE 53.13   Three series of boranes: closo $B_nH_n^{2-}$, nido B_nH_{n+4}, and arachno B_nH_{n+6}.
The stability decreases along the series as the structures become more open.
Note that some lines indicate the structures and not bonds between the atoms.

Examples are shown in Figure 53.13. The *closo*–boranes are very stable but the stability decreases along the series *closo*–, *nido*–, and *arachno*– as the structures become more open. The *arachno*–boranes are often spontaneously flammable in air.

Sodium borohydride $NaBH_4$, like lithium aluminum hydride $LiAlH_4$, is a particularly useful reducing agent in the synthesis of organic molecules.

Borides

Metal **borides** are hard, inert substances with high melting points, often used in situations where high temperatures and high stresses are likely. Titanium boride TiB_2 and other borides are used in the nose cones and nozzles of rockets, in ballistic armor, in jet turbine blades, and have been proposed as replacements for the tiles used on the surface of reentry vehicles such as the space shuttle.

There are many different boride structures—the boron may be present as single atoms, pairs or chains or atoms, linked chains of atoms, sheets of atoms, or linked polyhedra of atoms. Titanium boride, for example, incorporates huge two-dimensional sheets of boron atoms in a hexagonal pattern. Zirconium boride ZrB_{12} consists of B_{12} clusters and zirconium atoms arranged in a sodium chloride lattice structure—the B_{12} units form a ccp lattice and the zirconium atoms fill all the octahedral holes.

Borates and Boric Acids

Orthoboric acid $B(OH)_3$ is obtained by treating borax with sulfuric acid:

$$Na_2B_4O_5(OH)_4 \cdot 8H_2O(s) + H_2SO_4(aq) \rightarrow 4\,B(OH)_3(aq) + Na_2SO_4(s) + 5\,H_2O(l)$$

Heating orthoboric acid converts it to the condensed acid metaboric acid $B_3O_3(OH)_3$ which contains a six-membered B_3O_3 ring typical of borates (Figure 53.14). Both acids produce H^+ ions by abstracting OH^- ions from water (rather than releasing an H^+ from the $B(OH)_3$ molecule):

$$B(OH)_3(aq) + 2\,H_2O(l) \rightarrow B(OH)_4^-(aq) + H_3O^+(aq) \quad pK_a = 9.1 \text{ (weak)}$$

This zirconium boride-based material can be heated to temperatures above 2000°C.

The B_{12} cluster in ZrB_{12} is not an icosahedron. It has a cubo-octahedral structure—a cube with triangular facets at each corner.

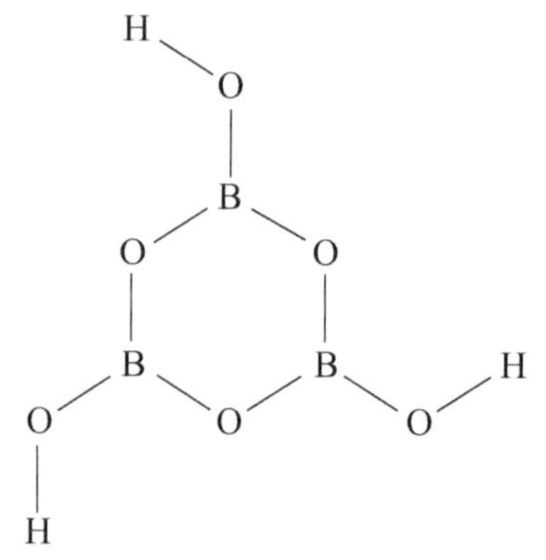

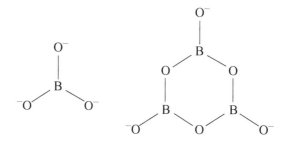

FIGURE 53.14   The six-membered ring of *meta*boric acid.

There are two principal types of borate anions, anhydrous and hydrated. For example, two anhydrous borate anions derived from orthoboric acid and metaboric acid are BO_3^{3-} and $B_3O_6^{3-}$ (Figure 53.15).

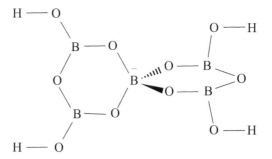

FIGURE 53.15   The borate anions of *ortho*boric acid and *meta*boric acid.

The structures of the hydrated borates contain both trigonal BO_3 units and tetrahedral BO_4^- units and the number of the BO_4^- units equals the charge on the ion. The B atoms and O atoms always alternate and more often than not form six membered rings. The arrangement of the BO_3 and BO_4^- units tends to be symmetrical and the structure can often be deduced. For example potassium pentaborate $KB_5O_6(OH)_4 \cdot 2H_2O$ has the structure illustrated in Figure 53.16. The ordinary formula for the salt $KB_5O_8 \cdot 4H_2O$ is a poorer representation of the structure.

FIGURE 53.16   The structure of the hydrated borate anion in potassium pentaborate $KB_5O_6(OH)_4$.

EXAMPLE 53.3   STRUCTURES OF HYDRATED BORATES

Deduce the structure of sodium tetraborate $Na_2B_4O_5(OH)_4 \cdot 8H_2O$ (borax) from the charge on the anion, the alternating —B—O—B—O— sequence of atoms, the preference for six-membered rings, and the general symmetry of such structures.

UNDERSTAND THE QUESTION

The structures of hydrated borates can often be deduced using the principles listed in the question.

PLAN THE SOLUTION

Determine the charge on the anion and hence the number of tetrahedral BO_4^- units. Calculate the number of trigonal BO_3 units by difference. Arrange the BO_4^- and BO_3 units symmetrically, always alternating B and O atoms, and if possible form six-membered rings.

SOLVE THE PROBLEM

There are two Na^+ ions so the charge on the anion must be 2–

The number of BO_4^- units = 2

Therefore, because there are 4 B in the anion, the number of BO_3 units = 2

An initial arrangement with the BO_3 units and the BO_4^- units alternating:

Add the terminal H atoms:

Check that the structure matches the formula $Na_2B_4O_5(OH)_4 \cdot 8H_2O$

PROBLEM 53.3A

Deduce the structure of calcium triborate $CaB_3O_3(OH)_5 \cdot H_2O$ from the charge on the anion, the alternating —B—O—B—O— sequence of atoms, the preference for six-membered rings, and the general symmetry of such structures.

PROBLEM 53.3B

Deduce the structure of magnesium diborate $MgB_2O(OH)_6$ using the method illustrated in Example 53.3.

Other Compounds of Boron

Boron–nitrogen compounds are interesting because the B–N unit is isoelectronic with a C—C unit. Although they are not easy to produce, it perhaps is not surprising that boron nitride BN exists in two forms that are structurally analogous to graphite and diamond (Figure 53.17). The graphite-like BN is slightly different from graphite in that the successive layers line up so that each B atom is directly above a N atom in the adjacent layer and *vice versa*. In graphite, as we will see in Unit 54, the successive layers are staggered.

A fullerene analog, with five-membered rings, is impossible if the B and N atoms are to alternate.

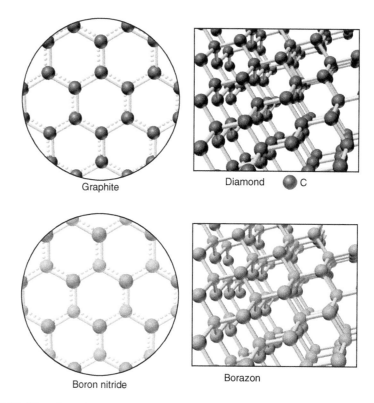

FIGURE 53.17   The polymorphs of boron nitride analogous to diamond and graphite.

Benzene (C_6H_6)

Borazine ($B_3N_3H_6$)

FIGURE 53.18   Borazine $B_3N_3H_6$, a boron nitrogen analog of benzene C_6H_6. The molecular orbitals are analogous to those of benzene illustrated in Figure 23.13. The bonding molecular orbitals are more N in character than B—reflecting the fact that the electrons are more probably found around the N than the B atoms. The antibonding orbitals are proportionately more B in character than N.

There are many other boron–nitrogen compounds analogous to compounds of carbon. An example is borazine $B_3N_3H_6$ which has structural and physical properties very like benzene C_6H_6 (Figure 53.18). The chemical properties of borazine, however, are quite different—in general it is much more reactive due to the uneven electron distribution around the ring.

Boron–halogen compounds BX_3 are known for all halogens. They are trigonal planar in shape, electron deficient in character, and act as Lewis acids. Both BF_3 and BCl_3 are used as catalysts—a catalytic activity due to their behavior as Lewis acids.

Boron trifluoride can be prepared by the action of calcium fluoride and sulfuric acid on boron oxide or borax. For example:

$$B_2O_3(s) + 3\ CaF_2(s) + 3\ H_2SO_4(l) \rightarrow 2\ BF_3(g) + 3\ CaSO_4(s) + 3\ H_2O(l)$$

Alternatively, it can be produced in better yields by the action of HF and then sulfuric acid on sodium tetraborate.

The halides are volatile (BF$_3$ b.pt. −100°C) and highly reactive. It is interesting that BF$_3$ is less acidic than BCl$_3$, even though the higher electronegativity of F would tend to withdraw electrons from the B atom more strongly. This is attributed to a π interaction between the B atom and the F atoms that tends to alleviate the electron deficiency (Figure 53.19). The π bonding is more effective with the second-period fluorine atom than the larger third-period chlorine atom—the sideways overlap of the p$_π$ orbitals is more effective. The strength of the B—F bond is unusually high (646 kJ mol^{-1}) for a single bond which implies some π contribution. For the same reason B$_2$F$_4$ is more stable than the analogous B$_2$Cl$_4$.

The analogous AlCl$_3$ is used as the traditional catalyst in the Freidel-Crafts reaction for the same reason. BF$_3$, BeCl$_2$, and all similar Lewis acids act as catalysts for Freidel-Crafts reactions.

53.5   Aluminum and Other Metals in Group 3A

Aluminum is the most abundant metal in the earth's crust (8.3%) and is present predominantly as aluminosilicates in igneous rocks, micas, and clays. The only elements present in greater abundance in the earth's crust are oxygen (46%) and silicon (27%). The remaining elements in Group 3A, gallium, indium, and thallium, are much less abundant.

Samples of impure aluminum were first obtained by H. C. Oersted and H. Wöhler in the 1820s by the reaction of aluminum chloride and potassium amalgam or potassium metal. The commercial production of aluminum was achieved in 1854 using sodium as the reducing agent but the process was expensive. The Hall-Héroult process, still used today, was invented in 1886 and started production in 1888.

Gallium was one of the elements unknown when Mendeleev devised his first Periodic Table in 1871. However, Mendeleev left a vacant space in the table for the element and predicted not only its existence but also its properties. He called it *eka-*aluminum. The element was discovered by the Frenchman P. E. Lecoq de Boisbaudran in 1875 and called gallium in honor of France. The observed properties of the element were very close to those predicted by Mendeleev (Table 53.3). Indium and thallium were discovered spectroscopically in 1863 and 1862.

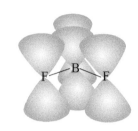

FIGURE 53.19   The delocalization of electrons through π bonding in boron trifluoride BF$_3$.
The electron deficiency of the boron is partially mitigated by sharing the p$_π$ electrons of the fluorine atoms.

Only in North America is aluminum called aluminum. Elsewhere in the world it is called aluminium.

TABLE 53.3   Properties of *eka*-aluminum predicted by Mendeleev.

	eka-Aluminum (M)	Gallium (Ga)
atomic mass	~68	69.72
density	5.9 g cm^{-3}	5.9 g cm^{-3}
m. pt.	low	29.77°C
valence	3	3
oxide	M$_2$O$_3$ density 5.5 g cm^{-3}	Ga$_2$O$_3$ density 5.9 g cm^{-3}
reaction with acids and bases	should dissolve slowly in both	dissolves slowly in both
hydroxide	M(OH)$_3$ should dissolve in both acids and bases	Ga(OH)$_3$ dissolves in both acids and bases

In general, the metallic character of the Group 3A elements increases, the size increases, and the ionization energy decreases down the group. However, gallium is anomalous (Table 53.2). It has an unusually low melting point (29.8°C) and a wide liquid range—the boiling point is 2205°C. It is also smaller than might have been anticipated from the general trend. The reason for these anomalous properties is the

The tip of the Washington monument is made of 2.8 kg of aluminum. When the monument was constructed in 1884, aluminum was an expensive precious metal.

filling of the first transition series as described in Unit 18. The strong attraction of the $4s^2 4p^1$ electrons by the additional 10+ charge on the nucleus, poorly shielded by the electrons in the d subshell, means that the $4s^2 4p^1$ electrons are held tightly by the nucleus, reducing the size of the atom and making the electrons reluctant to participate in bonding.

The other interesting feature of the elements in the group is the increasing stability of the +1 oxidation state going down the group. For aluminum, gallium, and indium, the preferred oxidation state is +3, but for thallium the preferred state is +1. This reduction by two in the preferred oxidation state at the bottom of the group occurs in other groups as well and is sometimes referred to as the **inert pair effect**. The two valence s electrons become less available for bonding down the group—the separation in energy between the s and p orbitals increases down the group. The ionization energies for the loss of the electrons of thallium are no greater than for gallium (Table 53.2) but the bonds, ionic or covalent, that would be formed would be longer and much weaker. The Tl(III) compounds are thermodynamically unstable with respect to the Tl(I).

Mercury, with a $d^{10}s^2$ electron configuration is reluctant to share these two s electrons in bonding. As a result, mercury is a liquid at room temperature.

Industrial Production and Uses

Bauxite (a mixed aluminum oxide and hydroxide) is the mineral from which aluminum is produced. Large deposits exist in Australia which is currently the largest producer of alumina. The mineral cryolite (Na_3AlF_6) is used as the solvent for the electrolysis of alumina by the Hall-Héroult process described in Unit 51 but naturally-occurring cryolite is scarce and most is manufactured specifically for the purpose.

Only iron (and steel) is made in greater quantities than aluminum. Once a precious metal, aluminum has many manufacturing and industrial uses—particularly in the packaging, construction, and aircraft industries. Weight for weight, it is a better conductor than copper. It is readily cast, forged, and machined and it resists corrosion due to the formation of a tightly bound thin layer of oxide on its surface. Aluminum is almost always alloyed with other elements such as copper, zinc, magnesium, manganese, and silicon to improve its mechanical strength.

The production of aluminum first involves the mining of the bauxite mineral and its purification. This is done by the **Bayer Process** which makes use of the amphoteric properties of aluminum oxide described in Unit 46 (Figure 46.4). The impurities are largely silica SiO_2 and iron(III) oxide Fe_2O_3. Silica is an acidic oxide and dissolves with the alumina in hot sodium hydroxide, leaving the Fe_2O_3 to be removed. The solution is then made weakly acidic with CO_2 and the alumina precipitates out of the solution. The alumina is then dissolved in cryolite and electrolyzed as described previously. Note that approximately one-third of all aluminum produced in the US is from recycled aluminum products.

Other elements in Group 3A are gallium, indium, and thallium. Gallium is a by-product of aluminum production and is used primarily in the semiconductor industry. Gallium arsenide, for example, is used in laser diodes. Indium and thallium occur naturally as sulfides and are obtained, again as a by-product, during the production of other metals such as zinc and lead from their sulfide ores. Indium is also used in the manufacture of semiconducting devices.

53.6 Compounds of Aluminum

Aluminum has a diagonal relationship with beryllium, and like beryllium, is on the borderline between ionic and covalent character. Beryllium lies more on the covalent side whereas aluminum is more on the ionic side. As described in Unit 19, aluminum chloride in the solid state has a typical six-coordinate ionic lattice structure but with considerable covalent character in the Al—Cl bonds (Figure 19.9). In the vapor state or in an inert solvent aluminum chloride exists as a covalently bonded dimer Al_2Cl_6 (Figure 53.20).

FIGURE 53.20 The dimeric structure of aluminum chloride in the vapor state.

Alumina, or aluminum oxide, is a particularly hard material. One crystalline form, α–alumina, called **corundum**, is used in a fine powder as an effective abrasive called **emery**. Emery paper is paper coated with the powdered corundum. Sometimes, corundum occurs naturally with impurities that make the mineral highly desirable. For example, ruby is α–alumina with Cr^{3+} ions replacing some Al^{3+} ions in the crystal and blue sapphire has both Fe^{3+} and Ti^{4+} impurities (Figure 53.21).

Al_2Br_6 and Al_2I_6 are dimeric and four coordinate in the solid state—the bromide and iodide ions are larger, and more polarizable, than the chloride ion.

The α–alumina consists of a hcp array of O^{2-} ions with the aluminum cations occupying 2/3 of the octahedral holes (*cf.* Unit 29).

FIGURE 53.21 Ruby and sapphire.
Ruby is alumina contaminated by chromium Cr^{3+}.
Blue Sapphire is alumina contaminated by iron Fe^{3+} and titanium Ti^{4+}.

EXAMPLE 53.4   THE HALIDES OF THE GROUP 3A ELEMENTS

Describe the structures of the three iodides BI_3, AlI_3, and TlI_3 and explain the differences between them.

UNDERSTAND THE QUESTION

The structures of the three iodides are quite different from each other. It's not usually necessary to memorize structures such as these—they can always be looked up in reference texts. It is more important to be able to suggest why the structures differ.

PLAN THE SOLUTION

The structures of the three iodides are illustrated in the margin. Think about what might cause the structures to be different.

SOLVE THE PROBLEM

BI_3 is a planar trigonal molecule with no tendency to dimerize. It's a solid with a melting point of 50°C.

Aluminum triiodide is a dimer Al_2I_6 in the solid state.

Thallium triiodide is actually a salt of the triiodide ion I_3^- and has the same structure as CsI_3. The thallium therefore is present as Tl^+, not Tl^{3+}.

The boron trihalides have no tendency to dimerize. This is attributed to the ability of the boron to accept electrons through a π interaction with appropriate orbitals on the halogen atoms—particularly fluorine. The π interaction is very limited in the trichloride, tribromide, and triiodide and the B—X bond strengths decrease down the series: 646 kJ mol^{-1} > 444 kJ mol^{-1} > 368 kJ mol^{-1} > 267 kJ mol^{-1}. For the larger halogens, the large size of the bromine or iodine atoms crowded around the small boron atom tends to discourage dimerization.

As noted on the previous page, aluminum triiodide has the same dimeric molecular structure in the solid state as it does in the vapor state. The electron deficiency of the aluminum is satisfied by the donation of an electron pair from the iodine atom of a neighboring molecule to form the dimer.

Thallium triiodide has the Tl in the +1 oxidation state. This is not surprising—the +1 oxidation state is preferred for Tl (the inert pair effect). The iodide is present as the linear triiodide ion I_3^-.

trigonal planar structure of BI_3

dimeric structure of AlI_3

ionic structure of TlI_3

PROBLEM 53.4A

The boiling points of aluminum iodide, aluminum bromide, and aluminum chloride decrease as anticipated from 382°C > 255°C > 180°C. The melting points, however, vary as follows: 188°C > 97.5°C but then 193°C for $AlCl_3$ (under pressure). Suggest why the melting point of $AlCl_3$ is higher than the trend would lead you to expect.

Aluminum chloride ordinarily sublimes.

PROBLEM 53.4B

B_2F_4 has a planar structure in the gas phase with π bonding between all the atoms but B_2Cl_4 has a staggered configuration of atoms (see below) in which the BCl_2 groups are in planes at right angles top each other. Suggest why.

Review Questions

1. Contrast the physical and chemical properties of the alkali metals and the alkaline earth metals.

2. In what way is the behavior of beryllium different from the behavior of the other elements in the group?

3. Describe the diagonal relationship between elements in the second and third periods.

4. In the valence bond description of the hydrogen compounds of boron, three-center—two-electron (3c—2e) bonds are used. Why is this necessary?

5. Describe the inert pair effect and its influence on the chemistry of the element at the bottom of the group.

Solutions to Problems

PROBLEM 53.1A

$$3 Ca(OH)_2(aq) + 2 Cl_2(g) \rightarrow$$
$$Ca(OCl)_2 \cdot CaCl_2 \cdot Ca(OH)_2 \cdot 2H_2O$$

PROBLEM 53.2A

The arrangement of electron pairs around each metal atom is tetrahedral.

PROBLEM 53.3A

There is one Ca^{2+} ion so the charge on the anion must be 2–

The number of BO_4^- units = 2

Therefore, because there are 3 B in the anion, the number of BO_3 units = 1

The three B atoms, one in the BO_3 unit and two in the BO_4^- units are probably arranged in a six-membered ring:

PROBLEM 53.4A

The structures of the aluminum iodide and aluminum bromide are the same in the liquid and solid states—a dimeric Al_2X_6 molecule. Aluminum chloride has the dimeric Al_2Cl_6 in the liquid state but a much denser, more ionic six-coordinate structure in the solid state. The volume of Al_2Cl_6 almost doubles when melted. The melting point is higher than anticipated for Al_2Cl_6 because the structure changes, from six-coordinate to four-coordinate. If nothing else, more bonds need to be broken for aluminum chloride.

Answers to Review Questions

1. The elements in Groups 1A and 2A are electropositive metals and in many respects their properties are similar. The alkaline earth metals have two valence electrons (ns^2) compared to the one valence electron (ns^1) of the alkali metals. As a result, the metallic bonding is stronger, the melting points and boiling points are higher, and the metals are harder. Like the alkali metals, the chemical properties of the alkaline earth metals is governed predominantly by the loss of the valence electrons and the formation of ionic compounds. However, the alkaline earth metals are less reactive than the alkali metals.

2. There are no compounds of beryllium in which the bonding is predominantly ionic. For example, beryllium chloride is not an ionic compound like calcium chloride and beryllium forms organometallic compounds involving covalent beryllium–carbon bonds. This is due to the high polarizing power of the hypothetical Be^{2+} cation which distorts the electron clouds of neighboring atoms to such an extent that the bonding is more covalent than ionic in character.

Magnesium, below beryllium in the group, forms some organometallic compounds but they are less stable than the beryllium compounds. The compounds of the remaining elements below magnesium in the group are essentially ionic in character.

3. For elements in Periods 2 and 3, in a diagonal direction from upper left to lower right, the charge to size ratio is more or less constant—the increase in the size of the ion compensates for the increase in the charge on the ion. As a result, pairs of elements on the diagonal have similar polarizing power and behave similarly—they form the same sorts of compounds. Examples are lithium and magnesium, beryllium and aluminum, and boron and silicon.

4. Boron is electron deficient—it doesn't have enough electrons to form four valence bonds. As a result, boron compounds are very often Lewis acids. In the absence of any suitable electron-pair donor, boron compounds alleviate the electron deficiency through multicenter bonding. In such bonding two electrons

are shared by more than two atoms. In a valence bond description, a convenient approach is to introduce three-center—two-electron (3c—2e) bonds. The number of 3c—2e bonds required equals the number of boron atoms in the molecule because each 3c—2e bond provides an 'additional' pair of electrons.

5. In general, the two s valence electrons become less available for bonding toward the bottom of the groups of the representative elements. They are held comparatively strongly by the nucleus (due to the penetration effect) and although the ionization energy isn't any greater than for elements higher in the group, the return expected through bond formation becomes progressively less down the group. As a result, the tendency *not* to participate in bonding increases. In Group 3A, thallium tends to exhibit a valency of 1. In Group 4A, lead prefers a valency of 2 rather than 4. Tin, higher in the group, exhibits valencies of both 2 and 4. In Group 5A, bismuth is most commonly found with a valency of 3 rather than 5.

End-of-Unit Problems

1. Compare the reactions of the alkaline earth elements with water to those of the elements in Group 1A.

2. Describe how the alkaline earth metals vary in their reaction with water. Explain the variation down the group.

3. Describe the diagonal relationship between lithium and magnesium and give an example of compounds of the two elements that are similar.

4. Describe the diagonal relationship between beryllium and aluminum. Describe the carbides of each and write equations illustrating the reactions of the carbides with water.

5. Describe the commercial production of magnesium. What is the primary use for magnesium metal? What is the property of magnesium that makes it so useful?

6. Beryllium is made commercially for use in the production of alloys. How is beryllium produced? What properties do beryllium alloys of copper and nickel have that are desirable?

7. More aluminum is made than any other metal except iron and steel. Describe the process by which aluminum is produced. What are the principle uses of aluminum metal?

8. Boron is produced from the mineral borax. Describe the process briefly. For what purpose is boron primarily used?

9. Write equations for the reactions of
   a. magnesium and nitrogen.
   b. barium oxide and aluminum.

10. Write equations for the reactions of
    a. beryllium and hydrogen.
    b. calcium hydroxide and hydrochloric acid.

11. In its behavior with aqueous sodium hydroxide, beryllium behaves in the same way as aluminum and forms the beryllate ion $Be(OH)_4^{2-}$. Write an equation for this reaction. Write a similar equation for the reaction of aluminum with aqueous sodium hydroxide. In what respect are the equations different?

12. Compare the structure of beryllium chloride in the vapor state with the structure of aluminum chloride in the vapor state. Describe briefly the ways in which the structures are the same and the ways in which they are different.

13. Gallium and aluminum chloride are both dimeric in the vapor state but their structures in the solid state are different. Explain why gallium has a four-coordinate structure in the solid state but aluminum has a six-coordinate structure.

14. Even though gallium is lower in Group 3A, it is smaller in size than aluminum. Why is this?

15. Although the structures of beryllium hydride and beryllium chloride in the solid state look superficially the same, the bonding involved is quite different. Describe the bonding in both structures.

16. Beryllium and magnesium are adjacent in the same group in the Periodic Table and yet their chlorides are quite different in character. Describe and explain this difference.

17. How does the structure and bonding in the diborane molecule B_2H_6 differ from that of ethane C_2H_6? Why are the structures different? Which of the two molecules would you expect to be more reactive?

18. Compare borazine $B_3N_3H_6$ to benzene C_6H_6. In what ways are the two compounds similar and in what way are they different?

19. Write equations for the reactions of

    a. slaked lime with sulfur dioxide.

    b. the production of quicklime from limestone.

20. Write equations for the reactions of

    a. the reaction between quicklime and silica SiO_2 in a blast furnace

    b. the reaction between quicklime in mortar with carbon dioxide in the air

21. Examination of the first, second, and third ionization energies for gallium and thallium shows that for both gallium and thallium the ionization energies are higher than for aluminum. This is contrary to the usual decrease in ionization energy down a group. Suggest why this is so.

22. The melting point and boiling point of boron are considerably higher than for the other elements in the group. Why is this?

23. The standard enthalpy of formation of diborane—6 is +36 kJ mol^{-1}. The standard enthalpy of formation of borane itself (BH_3) is +93 kJ mol^{-1}. Calculate the enthalpy change for the decomposition of one mole of diborane–6 into two moles of borane BH_3.

24. If the B—H bond enthalpy is 381 kJ mol^{-1}, use the answer to the previous question to calculate the bond enthalpy of a B—H—B 3c–2e bond.

Carbon, Silicon, and the Group 4A Elements

54.1 The Group 4A Elements

Carbon and silicon are the two elements at the top of Group 4A. Their chemistry, however is hugely different. Whereas carbon atoms constitute the backbones of the thousands of organic molecules that are essential to life on earth, silicon is one of the predominant elements (27%) found in the inanimate material making up the earth's crust. Carbon occurs in nature as the free element (graphite, diamond, and the fullerenes), in compounds such as the carbonates of sodium, calcium, and magnesium, and in fossil fuels—coal, oil, and natural gas. Silicon is always found in combination with oxygen.

We will review organic chemistry in Units 63 and 64.

Silicon was isolated by Berzelius in 1823 by the reduction of K_2SiF_6 using molten potassium. The name silicon was derived from silica (SiO_2) to emphasize its relationship to boron and carbon—the only two elements other than the noble gases with names ending in -on.

Like the elements in Group 3A, the character of the elements in Group 4A changes from nonmetallic to metallic down the group. Carbon is a nonmetal, silicon and germanium are borderline in character and are often called **semimetals**, and tin and lead are metals. The diagonal line separating metals and nonmetals in the Periodic Table passes between silicon and germanium. The stability of the +2 oxidation state increases down the group. Tin is common in both the +4 and the +2 oxidation states but lead much prefers the +2 state. Physical properties of the elements in Group 4A are listed in Table 54.1.

TABLE 54.1 The Group 4A elements.

Name	Symbol	Melting Point °C	Boiling Point °C	ΔH°_{fus} @ m.pt. kJ mol⁻¹	Density g cm⁻³	Ionization Energies kJ mol⁻¹				Covalent Radius pm	Metallic Radius pm	Ionic Radius M⁴⁺ pm
						1st	2nd	3rd	4th			
Carbon	C	>3550	4827	104.6	2.35	1086	2353	4620	6223	77	—	—
Silicon	Si	1414	2355	50.2	2.70	787	1577	3232	4356	118	—	—
Germanium	Ge	938	2833	36.9	5.90	762	1537	3302	4411	122	—	53
Tin	Sn	232	2260	7.0	7.31	709	1412	2943	3930	140	158	74
Lead	Pb	327	1749	4.8	11.85	716	1450	3081	4083	154	175	78

One of the more remarkable properties of carbon is its tendency to bond to itself to form molecules with chains of carbon atoms—a property called **catenation**. Few elements exhibit this property but it is essential for the construction of the complex molecules that form the basis of life. The strength of the C—C bond and its kinetic resistance to reaction contribute to the ability of carbon to catenate. Carbon is often referred to as **electron perfect**—the number of valence electrons equals the number of valence orbitals. There are no lone pairs of electrons on the carbon atoms to weaken the C—C bond (Figure 54.1).

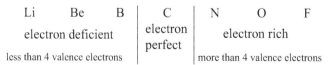

FIGURE 54.1 Carbon is often described as electron-perfect, with neither too many nor too few electrons.
It is able to form four bonds with the four valence electrons in the four valence orbitals.

Another particular property of carbon is its ability to form multiple bonds involving p_π—p_π π bonds. Although elements in periods below the second period can be coerced into multiple bonding using p_π orbitals, such multiple bonding is really only important for C, N, and O. The sideways overlap of the p_π orbitals on adjacent third and fourth period elements is minimal (Figure 54.2).

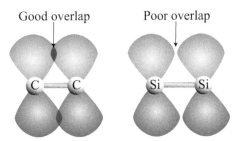

Good overlap   Poor overlap

FIGURE 54.2   Multiple π bonding using p_π orbitals is significant only for second period elements.
The sideways overlap of the π–bonding p orbitals is much poorer for the elements in Period 3 and below.

As mentioned earlier, carbon occurs naturally in three allotropic forms and in some amorphous forms. The allotropes diamond and graphite have been known for a long time but the third allotropic form, the molecular **fullerenes**, was discovered quite recently in 1985 (Figure 54.3). The C_{60} molecule is the most common fullerene but there are others, for example C_{70}, C_{76}, C_{78}, C_{82}, and C_{84}.

In diamond, each carbon atom is sp^3 hybridized and is surrounded by four other carbon atoms at a distance of 154.5 pm. In graphite, each carbon atom is sp^2 hybridized and the C—C bond length is 142 pm. A delocalized π network extends over each layer. The bonding between the layers is a weak van der Waals interaction and the distance between the layers is 335 pm. As a result, the layers of carbon atoms slip fairly easily over one another and graphite is sometimes used as a lubricant.

Robert F. Curl, Harold Kroto, and Richard E. Smalley were awarded the 1996 Nobel prize in Chemistry for their discovery of the fullerenes.

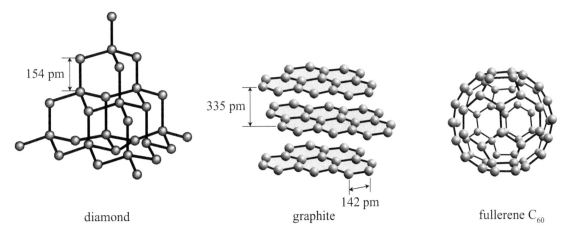

154 pm

335 pm

142 pm

diamond   graphite   fullerene C_{60}

FIGURE 54.3   The allotropes of carbon.

A form of carbon closely related to the fullerenes consists of long fibrous tubes of carbon called **nanotubes** (because of their size). The tubes are capped by a hemisphere of fullerene (Figure 54.4). The tubes can be regarded as tiny rolls of graphite with the carbon atoms arranged in a hexagonal pattern. Typically, a carbon nanotube consists of several concentric tubes. The tubes are very strong and conduct electricity due to the extended π network (like graphite). The tubes have a large surface area and have promise as a material in which to store hydrogen gas for use in fuel cells.

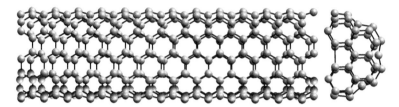

FIGURE 54.4   A carbon nanotube—a rolled-up graphite sheet capped by part of a fullerene sphere.
The cylinder contains hexagonal rings of carbon atoms but the cap must incorporate five-membered rings.

Germanium was another of the elements missing from Mendeleev's Periodic Table and the properties of which he accurately predicted. The element was not discovered until 1886 by C. A. Winkler.

Tin and lead are two metals that have been known for thousands of years. The Romans used lead extensively in plumbing and this use has continued to the present day. The extensive use of lead caused serious lead poisoning. Lead was intentionally added to wine and other foods to prevent spoilage (it poisoned the microorganisms that spoiled the wine). The lead was added in the form of sapa, a syrup that was made by boiling grape juice in lead pots. The sapa contained lead acetate which has a sweet taste and made the food or wine taste better. Unfortunately lead acetate is highly toxic causing sterility, kidney failure, and mental disorder.

In more recent times the additive TEL (tetraethyllead $(C_2H_5)_4Pb$) was added to gasoline to improve its octane rating. About 3 g of TEL was added to every gallon of gasoline. Hundreds of thousands of tons of the additive were added to gasoline every year. The release of the lead into the environment caused serious lead contamination and exposure particularly in urban areas and alongside highways. The addition of TEL to gasoline is now prohibited in many countries.

Tin is an interesting element that has two common allotropes: a metallic allotrope that is stable above 13°C and a gray nonmetallic allotrope with the same structure as diamond that is stable below 13°C. The transition from the metallic to the less dense nonmetallic form at the low temperatures in medieval cathedrals was a problem for organ pipes constructed of tin when they crumbled into powder. The transition is facilitated when the metallic tin is in contact with the nonmetallic allotrope and was referred to as **tin disease** because the crumbling of the metal seemed to spread like a disease.

Industrial Production and Uses

Diamond is the hardest material known and is useful as a cutting agent. Diamonds can be made from graphite although the pressures and temperatures required are very high

Boron nitride forms similar tubes but cannot be capped using an alternating B—N sequence of atoms.

Lead was used in the Middle East as long ago as 7000 BC. Tin was first isolated about 3500 BC.

The old name for lead acetate is *sugar of lead*.

The removal of lead from gasoline was mandated because it poisoned the precious metal catalysts in the catalytic converters required as a result of the Clean Air Act of 1970.

High quality organ pipes are often made from an alloy containing 90–95% tin, with the remainder being lead and other elements.

Diamond is more dense than graphite (3.51 g cm^{-3} vs. 2.25 g cm^{-1}), so the conversion from graphite to diamond is favored by high pressures.

FIGURE 54.5 A synthetic diamond and the graphite from which it is made.

(approximately 2000 K and 100,000 atm). Even so, many of the diamonds required for industrial cutting tools are made in this way (Figure 54.5).

Graphite is used in refractory materials, lubricants, brushes in electric motors, and pencils. It is also used for the electrodes in electrochemical cells and in the construction of the cells themselves (*cf.* Hall-Héroult process, Unit 51).

As noted earlier, silicon does not occur naturally in its elemental state. It is always found in combination with oxygen. The element can be produced by reducing silica (quartzite) with carbon in an electric arc furnace. Silicon is the basic material used in the fabrication of semiconductors but it must have an extremely high purity for this application. The crude silicon is converted to the tetrachloride by reaction with chlorine gas. The $SiCl_4$ is distilled and then reduced to silicon with pure zinc or magnesium. The silicon is then **zone-refined**. This involves passing molten zones repeatedly down the column of solid silicon. The silicon is melted and recrystallized over and over again and the impurities gradually move to the end of the column (Figure 54.6). Often the silicon is drawn into large single crystals for fabricating the intricate modern microprocessor chips.

> Silicon with less than 1 atom in 10,000,000,000 impurity is required for the fabrication of semiconductors.

Like indium, the major source of germanium is as a by-product of the production of other metals such as zinc from sulfide ores.

Tin alloyed with copper forms **bronze** and this discovery initiated the bronze age. The principal ore of tin is cassiterite (SnO_2) which is reduced by carbon in a furnace at 1200°C. The principal lead ore is galena (PbS). This is roasted in air to produce the oxide which is then reduced by carbon (coke) in a furnace. Purification of both metals is done electrolytically.

> The bronze age in Britain lasted from about 2200 BC to 700 BC. Cornwall was a major source of tin. Copper was available in North Wales.
>
> **Bronze** is an alloy of copper that contains 10–20% tin and a small amount of zinc or lead.
>
> **Brass** is an alloy of copper that contains up to 40% zinc.
>
> **Pewter** is 90–95% tin, up to 8% antimony, and up to 3% copper.

$$2\,PbS(s) + 3\,O_2(g) \rightarrow 2\,PbO(s) + SO_2(g)$$
$$PbO(s) + C(s) \rightarrow Pb(s) + CO(g)$$

The major use of lead is in the manufacture of lead-acid batteries for automobiles. The recycling of car batteries and other lead products is such that 75% of manufactured lead comes recycled products. Tin is resistant to corrosion and has been used for many years to plate steel in the manufacture of tin cans. The other principal use of tin is in the manufacture of solders.

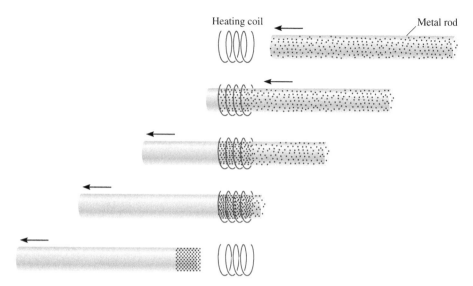

FIGURE 54.6 **Zone-refining of silicon.**
The impure metal is moved through a heating coil (or vice versa). The pure metal crystallizes from the molten zone as the heating coil moves along. The impurities remain in solution. Repeated passages through the coil produces a very pure metal.

EXAMPLE 54.1   THE GROUP 4A ELEMENTS

Which of the Group 4A elements

a. is commonly found in the +2 oxidation state?

b. readily forms double and triple bonds?

c. is present in the greatest abundance in animals?

UNDERSTAND THE QUESTION

The chemical and physical properties within a group vary in a consistent manner. To a large extent, these trends are common across all the groups of the representative elements. For example, only Period 2 elements participate readily in multiple bonding. As we have already seen, the common oxidation states decrease by 2 at the bottom of Groups 3A, 4A, and 5A. However, some properties are specific to a particular element—such as the answer to part (c).

PLAN THE SOLUTION

With reference to a Periodic Table, deduce, or look up, the answers to the questions.

SOLVE THE PROBLEM

a. The element at the bottom of the group—lead.

b. The element in Period 2—carbon.

c. Carbon.

Which of the Group 4A elements

 a. is the most electronegative?

 b. is found in nature combined with oxygen?

Which of the Group 4A elements

 a. is commonly used to fabricate semiconducting devices?

 b. is the one most able to catenate?

54.2   Compounds of Carbon

The organic chemistry of carbon will be described in Units 63 and 64. In this section we will examine some other significant compounds of carbon.

Graphite Intercalation Compounds

It is possible to insert various substances between the layers of graphite. Indeed the slippery nature of graphite is due in part to the absorption of gas molecules between the carbon layers. If graphite is treated with potassium vapor at 300°C, potassium atoms enter the space between the carbon layers and form the bronze-colored **intercalation compound** C_8K. The potassium atoms are regularly spaced in an hexagonal array between the layers (Figure 54.7) so that each K atom is surrounded by twelve

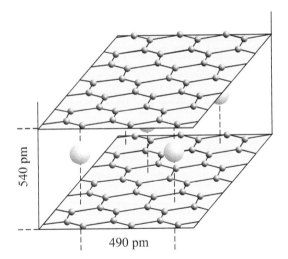

540 pm

490 pm

FIGURE 54.7   The crystal lattice of C_8K, a graphite intercalation compound.
The potassium atoms are arranged in a very regular hexagonal pattern, each surrounded by 12 carbon atoms. Unlike in graphite itself, the carbon atoms in the graphite layers line up vertically.

carbon atoms. The carbon atoms in the graphite layers now line up vertically and the distance between adjacent layers is 540 pm (an increase from 335 pm). Heating the C_8K above 300°C removes entire layers of potassium atoms to form the compounds $C_{24}K$, $C_{36}K$, $C_{48}K$, etc. Rubidium and cesium behave similarly. The intercalation compounds conduct electricity better than graphite itself suggesting that electrons are transferred from the alkali metals to the conduction band of the graphite.

Treatment of graphite with sulfuric acid produces the blue graphitic bisulfate with a stoichiometry approximately $C_8H_2SO_4$ and a structure similar to that of C_8K. In this case the graphite layers are positively charged and the conductivity increases due to the absence of electrons in the valence band (*cf.* Unit 23.7).

Carbides

FIGURE 54.8 The reaction of calcium carbide with water to produce acetylene gas.

Elements more electropositive than carbon form binary compounds called **carbides** with carbon. In general, the carbides are prepared at high temperatures (approx. 2000°C) by heating the element or its oxide with carbon. As described in Unit 53, beryllium, and aluminum (note the diagonal relationship), form salt-like carbides containing the C^{4-} anion. These carbides react with water to produce methane gas:

$$Be_2C + 4\,H_2O \rightarrow 2\,Be(OH)_2 + CH_4$$

Several carbides containing the C_2^{2-} diatomic anion are known. Probably the most familiar is calcium carbide CaC_2 (Figure 54.8). The alkali metals, other alkaline earth metals, and copper, silver, and gold form similar salts. The latter salts are explosive and the alkali metal salts react violently with water:

$$Na_2C_2 + 2\,H_2O \rightarrow 2\,NaOH + C_2H_2$$

Calcium carbide is produced on a large scale as a convenient source of acetylene gas. The gas produced when carbides react with water indicates the structure of the carbide anion. Thus C^{4-} salts produce methane CH_4 and C_2^{2-} salts produce acetylene C_2H_2. Other carbides containing the linear C_3^{4-} ion are known, for example Li_4C_3 and Mg_2C_3 (note the diagonal relationship). These salts produce propyne C_3H_4 when treated with water:

$$Li_4C_3 + 4\,H_2O \rightarrow 4\,LiOH + CH_3\text{—}C\,CH$$

The metals in the lanthanide and actinide series (the f block) form **interstitial carbides**. These are compounds in which the carbon atoms occupy the octahedral holes within the metallic lattice. They are generally hard substances with high melting points. The carbides of the early transition metals have similar structures. Tungsten carbide, WC, has a structure in which all the octahedral holes in the metallic lattice are filled with carbon atoms. This is an extremely hard material often used for cutting tools.

Silicon carbide was prepared accidentally by E. G. Acheson in 1891. He called the compound carborundum—from *carbon* and *corundum* because it wasn't quite as hard as diamond but was harder than corundum (Al_2O_3).

Silicon carbide has two principal crystalline forms: α–SiC and β–SiC. The α–SiC has the same hexagonal structure as wurtzite (ZnS) and the β-SiC has the same cubic structure as diamond. The Si—C bonds are very strong and silicon carbide is a very hard abrasive material with sharp edges.

Other Compounds of Carbon

The most significant oxides of carbon are carbon monoxide CO and carbon dioxide CO_2. Carbon monoxide is an odorless gas, virtually insoluble in water, and is highly toxic. The bond between the C and the O is a very strong triple bond (1074 kJ mol^{-1})

and as a result the molecule, like N_2, tends to be unreactive. The molecule is a Lewis base. As we will see in Unit 59, the molecule forms strong bonds with transition metals. For example, the CO molecule forms a strong bond with the iron(II) atom of hemoglobin to form a bright red complex that prevents the hemoglobin from carrying oxygen. The hemoglobin molecule preferentially bonds with the CO and concentrations as low as 0.10% result in death within a few hours.

As described in Unit 52, carbon monoxide is manufactured by heating hydrocarbons or coke with steam. The mixture of CO and H_2 is called synthesis gas and is used in the manufacture of methanol at 250–400°C and high pressures in the presence of a catalyst.

$$CO(g) + 2\,H_2(g) \rightarrow CH_3OH(g)$$

Carbon dioxide is also an odorless gas but is nontoxic. It is one of the combustion products when carbon-containing compounds, for example gasoline, are burned in air. It is produced commercially as a by-product in the fermentation of sugar to produce ethanol. Solid carbon dioxide (dry ice) is a convenient refrigerant because the solid sublimes to the vapor state at −78°C and the gas produced is nontoxic. Carbon dioxide is also commonly used in fire extinguishers because the CO_2 gas is more dense than air and smothers the fire. Supercritical CO_2 is a useful solvent in industrial applications and is used for example to extract caffeine from coffee in the production of decaffeinated coffee.

Carbon dioxide dissolves in water to produce an acidic solution referred to as carbonic acid H_2CO_3. The molecule H_2CO_3 itself cannot be isolated although salts of its two conjugate bases, the carbonate ion CO_3^{2-} and the hydrogen carbonate ion HCO_3^- are well known. The acid exists predominantly as a solution of CO_2 in water in equilibrium with small amounts of H_2CO_3, HCO_3^- and a very small concentration of CO_3^{2-}. Carbonated drinks are produced under a high partial pressure of CO_2 and when the bottle cap is removed, or the can is opened, the CO_2 gas is released and the drink effervesces.

CF_2Cl_2
(Freon-12)

$$CO_2 + H_2O \rightleftharpoons H_2CO_3$$
$$H_2CO_3 + H_2O \rightleftharpoons H_3O^+ + HCO_3^- \qquad K_{a1} = 4.3 \times 10^{-7}$$
$$HCO_3^- + H_2O \rightleftharpoons H_3O^+ + CO_3^{2-} \qquad K_{a2} = 4.8 \times 10^{-11}$$

Carbon suboxide C_3O_2 is a much less common carbon oxide (b.pt. 6.7°C) that has the linear structure:

$$O = C = C = C = O$$

$CFCl_3$
(Freon-11)

The simple halides of carbon are tetrahedral molecules CX_4. Carbon tetrachloride CCl_4 was once used extensively as a laboratory solvent but its use has declined because of its carcinogenicity. CBr_4 (m.pt. 90.1°C) and CI_4 (decomposes at 171°C) are solids less thermally stable than CCl_4 due to the large size of the halogen atoms crowded around the small carbon atom. Carbon tetrafluoride, CF_4 (b.pt. −128.5°C) is a gas. The C—F bond is strong (515 kJ mol⁻¹) and fluorocarbon compounds are generally unreactive. For example tetrafluoroethylene C_2F_4 can be polymerized to the inert nonstick polymer polytetrafluoroethylene (PTFE) used in machine bearings and kitchen pots and pans (*cf.* Unit 65).

$C_2F_3Cl_3$
(Freon-113)

Freons are mixed halogen carbon compounds such as $CFCl_3$, CF_2Cl_2, etc. (Figure 54.9). They are non toxic, generally inert (stable) compounds with low boiling

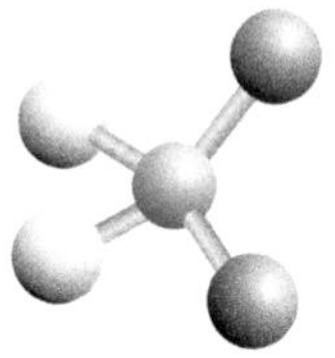

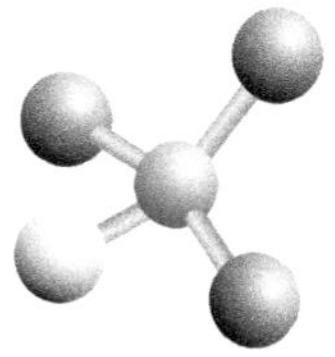

FIGURE 54.9   The structures of some Freons.

points and low viscosities ideal for use as refrigerants and propellants. Unfortunately the very properties that make them ideal for uses such as these are also responsible for their role in the serious depletion of ozone in the upper atmosphere.

EXAMPLE 54.2   COMPOUNDS OF CARBON

Write equations representing the reactions of aluminum carbide Al_4C_3 and magnesium carbide Mg_2C_3 with water.

UNDERSTAND THE QUESTION

Ionic carbides, such as Al_4C_3 and Mg_2C_3 react with water to produce hydrocarbons that reflect the nature of the carbide ion present in the salt.

PLAN THE SOLUTION

Determine the carbide ion present in the Al_4C_3 and Mg_2C_3 from the stoichiometry and therefore deduce the hydrocarbon formed in the reaction with water. Then write the equation.

SOLVE THE PROBLEM

The four Al^{3+} ions in Al_4C_3 means that the three C atoms each have a 4– charge. Each is present as a C^{4-} ion. This means that the gas produced will be methane CH_4:

$$Al_4C_3 + 12\,H_2O \rightarrow 4\,Al(OH)_3 + 3\,CH_4$$

The two Mg^{2+} ions in Mg_2C_3 means that the three C atoms have a total charge of 4–. The carbide ion present is C_3^{4-} ion. This means that the gas produced will be propyne CH_3CCH (add one H for each – charge on the ion).

$$Mg_2C_3 + 4\,H_2O \rightarrow 2\,Mg(OH)_2 + CH_3C \equiv CH$$

PROBLEM 54.2A

The crystal structure of a carbide is illustrated in the figure. The darker circle represents a metal ion; the lighter circle represents a carbon atom.

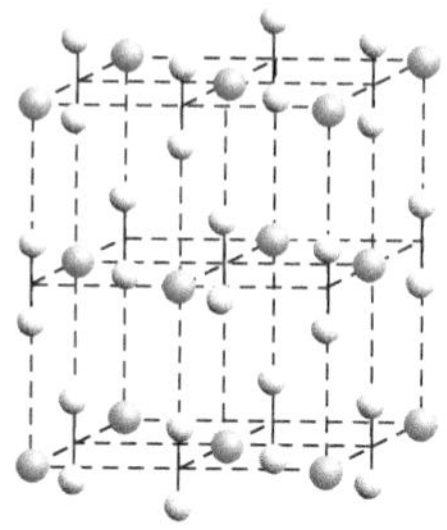

a. Describe the lattice of the metal ions.

b. To which crystal system does this cell belong?

c. What is the stoichiometry of the salt?

d. What is a possible identity of the metal?

PROBLEM 54.2B

Potassium forms a carbide containing the same carbide ion present in calcium carbide CaC_2. Write the formula of potassium carbide and an equation representing its reaction with water.

54.3   Compounds of Silicon

Silicon in the solid state is unreactive due to the formation of a very thin protective layer of SiO_2 at the surface, just like aluminum. In the molten state, however, it is very reactive. It has a high affinity for oxygen due to the strength of the Si—O bond and will reduce most oxides.

It is interesting to compare the bond strengths of carbon and silicon listed in Table 54.2.

TABLE 54.2   Bond strengths of carbon and silicon (kJ mol^{-1}).

Carbon		Silicon	
C—C	368	Si—Si	226
C—H	435	Si—H	323
C—O	358	Si—O	452

As might have been expected because of the larger size of the silicon atom compared to carbon, the Si—H and Si—Si bonds are weaker than the corresponding C—H and C—C bonds. Note however that the Si—O bond is stronger than the C—O bond. This larger than expected strength of the Si—O bond is attributed to a π interaction between a p$_\pi$ orbital of the oxygen and a d$_\pi$ orbital of the silicon.

Unlike carbon, silicon does not readily form multiple p$_\pi$–p$_\pi$ bonds. The sideways overlap between the p$_\pi$ orbitals is poor (*cf.* Figure 54.2). As a result, when silicon combines with oxygen, more energy is released in the formation of four Si—O bonds than in the formation of two Si=O bonds. The opposite is true for carbon, for which the formation of two C=O bonds is favored over four C—O bonds. Therefore CO_2 exists as a molecule with double bonds and SiO_2 exists as a covalent network solid with single bonds.

Silicon is a larger atom than carbon and has d orbitals available that can accept electron pairs from electron-rich reactants. This provides a kinetic pathway for reaction that carbon does not have. Silane SiH_4, for example, immediately ignites in air. The analogous carbon compound, methane CH_4, must be ignited. Both reactions are spontaneous.

There are several forms of crystalline silica, SiO_2, including quartz. Heated above 1713°C, the silica loses its ordered arrangement and becomes amorphous. When cooled without crystallization, the disorder is retained and a **glass** is formed. A glass does not have the long-range order found in crystalline solids; it does not have a precise melting point but becomes softer and melts over a range of temperatures. Silica is the basic ingredient of the glass industry. For example, ordinary window glass (soda-lime glass) is made by heating 12–15% sodium carbonate (soda ash), 10–12% calcium oxide (quicklime), and 70–74% silica (sand) at about 1500°C. As noted previously, partially replacing the soda ash and lime with boric oxide produces **borosilicate glass**, commonly known as Pyrex^{TM}.

Silicates

Most of the earth's crust—the soil, clays, sand, and rocks—is composed of silica, **silicates** and **aluminosilicates**. In all of these substances the silicon is surrounded by four oxygen atoms. The parent silicate is the *ortho*silicate ion SiO_4^{4-} that occurs in zircon $ZrSiO_4$ (cubic zirconia), phenacite $BeSiO_4$, and olivine $(Fe,Mg)SiO_4$ (Figure 54.10). This basic SiO_4 unit is often represented by a simple pyramid (blue) shown in the figure.

The basic SiO_4 units can be built up into chains and rings. For example two SiO_4 units that share an oxygen atom form the *pyro*silicate ion $Si_2O_7^{6-}$ that occurs in thortveitite $Sc_2Si_2O_7$ and hardystonite $Ca_2ZnSi_2O_7$ (Figure 54.11). Note that the charge on the silicate ion equals the number of terminal oxygen atoms. This equals the total charge of all the cations present.

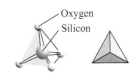

FIGURE 54.10   The orthosilicate ion SiO_4^{4-}. The blue triangle is used to represent the tetrahedral SiO_4 unit.

FIGURE 54.11   The pyrosilicate ion $Si_2O_7^{6-}$. Two SiO_4 tetrahedra linked at an oxygen atom.

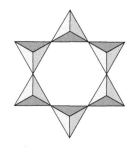

FIGURE 54.12 Two cyclic metasilicates $Si_3O_9^{6-}$ and $Si_6O_{18}^{12-}$.

The SiO_4 tetrahedra can link to form rings, called *meta*silicates, of which two of the more important are $Si_3O_9^{6-}$ and $Si_6O_{18}^{12-}$ (Figure 54.12). The former occurs in benitoite $BeTiSi_3O_9$ and the latter in beryl $Be_3Al_2Si_6O_{18}$. The gemstone emerald is beryl with some Cr^{3+} impurity (about 2%) and blue aquamarine is beryl with some Fe^{2+} impurity.

The nature of the silicate anion in silicate minerals can be determined from the Si:O ratio. The *ortho*silicates have a ratio 1:4, the *pyro*silicates have a ratio 1:3.5, and the *meta*silicates have a ratio 1:3. Other *meta*silicates, called **pyroxenes**, have a chain structure. For example, spodumene, a valuable source of lithium, is $LiAlSi_2O_6$ (Figure 54.13). Jade has a similar structure $NaAlSi_2O_6$. Different conformations of the tetrahedra in the chains can lead to a wide variety of structures. The pyroxenes such as spodumene are the most common.

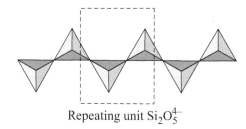

Repeating unit $Si_2O_5^{4-}$

FIGURE 54.13 A pyroxene, a metasilicate with a chain structure.

The chains of SiO_4 tetrahedra can link sideways to form double chains. Examples of these are the **amphibole** asbestos minerals (Figure 54.14). Tremolite $Ca_2Mg_5(Si_4O_{11})_2(OH)_2$ is an amphibole—two pyroxene chains joined sideways. It is the long fibrous nature of the asbestos minerals (Figure 54.15) that causes asbestosis— damage to lung tissue—when asbestos dust is inhaled. The relatively uncommon blue asbestos crocidolite is an amphibole and is responsible for severe asbestosis and lung cancer. Another type of asbestos, referred to as serpentine, is chrysotile $Mg_3(Si_2O_5)$ $(OH)_4$. This asbestos is by far the most common form of asbestos and is noncarcinogenic. It is used in reinforced concrete for roofing and other weatherproof structures. It is also used in vinyl floor tiles, brake linings, fire-fighting clothing and other applications where good thermal insulation is required.

The serpentine structure of chrysotile is closely related to that of kaolin. The sheets are rolled into thin fibers (Figure 54.21).

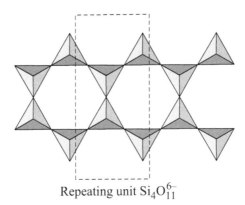

Repeating unit $Si_4O_{11}^{6-}$

FIGURE 54.14 An amphibole, a double chain of silicate units found in some asbestos minerals.

A layered structure results if the sideways linking of the SiO_4 tetrahedra is extended indefinitely (Figure 54.16). Examples are clays, vermiculite, micas, and talc. The silicate now has the stoichiometry $Si_4O_{10}^{4-}$, a Si:O ratio of 1:2.5.

For example, pyrophyllite (Figure 54.17) is a layered silicate $Al_2(Si_4O_{10})(OH)_2$. The pyrophyllite is composed of three layers; a layer of octahedral aluminum-oxygen units sandwiched between two silicate layers. The isomorphous magnesium analogue (three Mg^{2+} in place of two Al^{3+}) is talc $Mg_3(Si_4O_{10})(OH)_2$ (Figure 54.18).

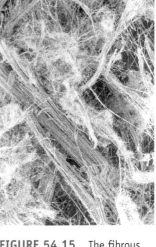

FIGURE 54.15 The fibrous nature of an asbestos mineral.

The name pyrophyllite is derived from the Greek words for fire and leaf. When the mineral is heated, it forms a mass of flaky leaves of silicate sheets.

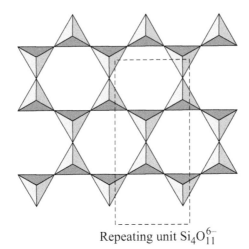

Repeating unit $Si_4O_{11}^{6-}$

FIGURE 54.16 A two-dimensional sheet of silicate units such as that found in micas and clays.

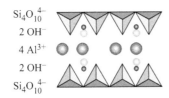

$Si_4O_{10}^{4-}$
$2\ OH^-$
$4\ Al^{3+}$
$2\ OH^-$
$Si_4O_{10}^{4-}$

FIGURE 54.17 A schematic of the mineral pyrophyllite structure.
The unit illustrated has the composition $Al_4(Si_4O_{10})_2(OH)_4$. Each Al^{3+} ion is surrounded by 6 O atoms in an octahedral arrangement (not illustrated) sandwiched between two silicate layers.

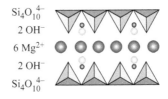

$Si_4O_{10}^{4-}$
$2\ OH^-$
$6\ Mg^{2+}$
$2\ OH^-$
$Si_4O_{10}^{4-}$

FIGURE 54.18 A schematic of the structure of talc.
The unit illustrated has the composition $Mg_6(Si_4O_{10})_2(OH)_4$. Three Mg^{2+} ions take the place of two Al^{3+} ions.

In micas, one quarter of the silicon atoms are replaced by aluminum and the additional charge is balanced by K^+. The result is an aluminosilicate. For example, muscovite (white mica) is $KAl_2(Si_3AlO_{10})(OH)_2$. The formula written in this way indicates that there are two different locations for the aluminum atoms. One aluminum atom replaces a silicon atom in the silicate structure. The other two aluminum atoms exist as ions between the silicate layers just as in pyrophyllite (Figure 54.19).

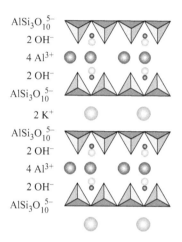

$AlSi_3O_{10}^{5-}$
2 OH⁻
4 Al³⁺
2 OH⁻
$AlSi_3O_{10}^{5-}$
2 K⁺
$AlSi_3O_{10}^{5-}$
2 OH⁻
4 Al³⁺
2 OH⁻
$AlSi_3O_{10}^{5-}$

FIGURE 54.19 A schematic of the structure of mica.
The two units illustrated each have the composition $K_2Al_4(Si_3AlO_{10})_2(OH)_4$. One quarter of the Si atoms are replaced by Al atoms and the additional charge is balanced by potassium ions K^+ between the layers. The potassium ions hold the layers together.

FIGURE 54.20 Thin flakes of mica cleaved from the mineral.

Talc is slippery because the silicate layers slide easily over one another—the layers are held together by weak van der Waals forces only (as in graphite). In mica the aluminosilicate layers are held together by an ionic attraction to the potassium ions and they do not slide over one another. However, mica can be cleaved into very thin sheets (Figure 54.20). These thin transparent sheets of mica have a very high melting point and are used for the windows of high temperature furnaces.

Clays are minerals with structures related to the micas and talc. If one silicate layer is removed from the pyrophyllite structure and the open positions are filled by —OH groups, the result is kaolinite $Al_2(Si_2O_5)(OH)_4$ which is china clay (Figure 54.21). Clays such as this readily absorb water molecules which infiltrate between the silicate sheets. This causes the clay to swell and become plastic. The clay can be molded and then fired which drives off the water and produces porcelain. When the

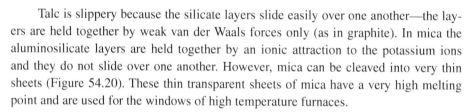

6 OH⁻
4 Al³⁺
2 OH⁻
$Si_4O_{10}^{4-}$

FIGURE 54.21 A schematic of the structure of kaolinite.
The unit illustrated has the composition $Al_4(Si_4O_{10})(OH)_8$. One layer of Si_4O_{10} is removed and the open positions are occupied by OH⁻ ions.

water is driven out, the layers of clay bond together and form a hard, tough, but brittle material called a **ceramic**. Mixing the clay with bone ash before firing produces bone china. The bone ash acts as a binder which strengthens the product. Ordinary clay can be fired to make tiles, bricks, and pots. Most china clay is used in the paper industry for filling or coating paper to produce a smooth surface.

> We will examine ceramics further in Unit 65.

The asbestos chrysotile is closely related to that of kaolin. The two aluminum ions are replaced by three magnesium ions (Figure 54.22). Thus the asbestos chrysotile bears the same relation to kaolinite as talc does to pyrophyllite.

> Much of the earth's crust is feldspar—there are many different kinds. Granite is a mixture of feldspar, mica, and quartz. Clays result from the long term weathering of feldspars.

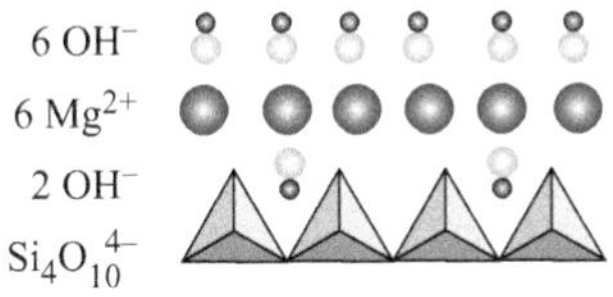

$$6\ OH^-$$
$$6\ Mg^{2+}$$
$$2\ OH^-$$
$$Si_4O_{10}{}^{4-}$$

FIGURE 54.22   A schematic of the asbestos chrysotile.
The unit illustrated has the composition $Mg_6(Si_4O_{10})(OH)_8$. Three Mg^{2+} ions take the place of two Al^{3+} ions in kaolinite.

If the linking of the SiO_4 tetrahedra is extended in the third dimension, using the last remaining corner of the SiO_4 tetrahedron, the result is the three-dimensional SiO_2 (quartz). If some silicon atoms are replaced by aluminum atoms, each aluminum atom contributes a negative charge to the three-dimensional aluminosilicate structure. The negative charges are balanced by alkali or alkaline earth metal ions. Naturally occurring three-dimensional aluminosilicates are feldspars.

Zeolites are aluminosilicates with a more open structure. They are made up of linked cubo-octahedral aluminosilicate units (Figure 54.23). The large cavities in the structure can absorb small molecules such as water and the structures are often called **molecular sieves**. They are so useful that zeolites are manufactured with specific pore sizes for different applications. Synthetic zeolites have found particular use as catalysts. For example, they are used in the separation of hydrocarbons in the production of high octane gasoline. They are used as porous supports for other catalysts in chemical processes. One application is the removal of sulfur from petroleum fuels.

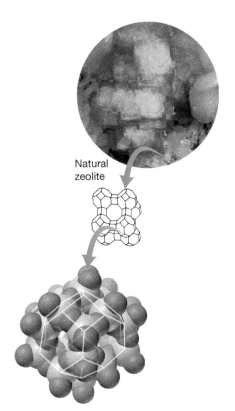

Natural zeolite

FIGURE 54.23   The open structure of the three-dimensional zeolite.

EXAMPLE 54.3 SILICATE AND ALUMINOSILICATE STRUCTURES

Deduce the probable structure of the silicate ions in the following silicates:

a. thortveitite $Sc_2Si_2O_7$

b. α–wollanstonite $Ca_3Si_3O_9$

c. the aluminosilicate orthoclase $KAlSi_3O_8$

UNDERSTAND THE QUESTION

The structures of the silicate and aluminosilicate ions can often be deduced from the ratio of silicon (and aluminum) to oxygen and the charge on the ion. The charge on the ion can be determined from the number and identity of the cations present.

PLAN THE SOLUTION

Determine the charge on the ion, and therefore the number of terminal Si—O groups in the structure. The ratio of Si (and Al) to O indicates the degree of condensation in the structure.

SOLVE THE PROBLEM

a. thortveitite $Sc_2Si_2O_7$

Two Sc ions, each 3+, so the charge on the silicate must be 6–.

There are therefore 6 terminal Si—O groups and therefore one bridging —O— atom.

The Si to O ratio is 1 : 3.5 and the silicate is a pyrosilicate.

b. α–wollanstonite $Ca_3Si_3O_9$

Three Ca ions, each 2+, so the charge on the silicate must be 6–.

There are therefore 6 terminal Si—O groups and therefore three bridging —O— atoms.

Each Si must be surrounded by four O, so the structure is cyclic:

The Si to O ratio is 1 : 3 and the silicate is a metasilicate.

c. orthoclase $KAlSi_3O_8$

This is an aluminosilicate. Each Al in the structure contributes –1 to the charge. The –1 charge is balanced by the presence of the cation K^+.

The ratio of silicon and aluminum to oxygen is 1 : 2 and therefore the structure is an infinite three-dimensional lattice.

PROBLEM 54.3A

The following diagrams represent silicate structures, where the blue pyramid represents an SiO_4 structural unit. Determine the formula and charge for each ion.

a. a synthetic potassium silicate

b. the mineral murite

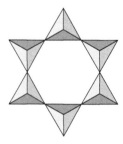

PROBLEM 54.3B

Deduce the probable structure of the silicate ions in the following silicates:

a. beryl $Be_3Al_2Si_6O_{18}$ where the aluminum is not part of an aluminosilicate network.

b. diopside $CaMgSi_2O_6$

c. phenacite Be_2SiO_4

Other Compounds of Silicon

When silicon is treated with methyl chloride at 300°C in the presence of copper powder, the compound $(CH_3)_2SiCl_2$ is formed, along with smaller amounts of CH_3SiCl_3 and $(CH_3)_3SiCl$. The $(CH_3)_2SiCl_2$ reacts with water to produce $(CH_3)_2Si(OH)_2$ which immediately condenses to form a silicone chain called polydimethylsiloxane:

$$(CH_3)_2SiCl_2 + 2\,H_2O \rightarrow (CH_3)_2Si(OH)_2 + 2\,HCl$$

$$n\,(CH_3)_2Si(OH)_2 + 2\,H_2O \rightarrow -[(CH_3)_2SiO]_n- + n\,H_2O$$

The **silicone** polymer is strong due to the strength of the individual Si—C and Si—O bonds. Therefore the polymers have good thermal and chemical stability and can be made as oils, greases, rubbers, and resins depending upon the length of the polymer chain, the substituents on the silicon atoms, and the extent of cross-linking between the chains. Chemically, the silicone oils are more stable than the corresponding hydrocarbon oils. They are also hydrophobic and do not absorb water. The viscosity of silicone oils and rubbers changes little with change in temperature whereas the viscosity of hydrocarbon-based oils changes considerably.

The structure of the polydimethylsiloxane is analogous to pyroxenes in which the terminal —O⁻ atoms are replaced by methyl —CH_3 groups. Cyclic dimethylsiloxanes can be made that are analogous to the cyclic *meta*silicates. The silicone resins are analogous in structure to the three-dimensional aluminosilicates.

The structure of the trisilylamine molecule $(SiH_3)_3N$ is interesting because it is significantly different from the structure of the analogous trimethylamine $(CH_3)_3N$. Trimethylamine has the same trigonal pyramidal shape as ammonia as might have been expected (Figure 54.24). Trisilylamine is trigonal planar. The reason is the

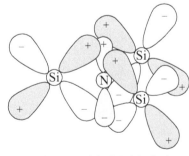

The planar trisilylamine $(SiH_3)_3N$ (the hydrogen atoms are not shown). The overlap of the d orbitals on the Si and the p orbital on the N to form a π molecular orbital requires that the molecule be planar. The N is sp^2 hybridized.

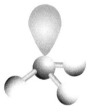

The pyramidal trimethylamine (the hydrogen atoms are not shown). The N is sp^3 hybridized.

FIGURE 54.24   The structure of trisilylamine compared with trimethylamine.

formation of a π bond extending over the trisilylamine molecule much like the π bonding in the nitrate ion or the carbonate ion except that the orbitals used on the silicon atoms are the 3d orbitals. This type of π bonding is referred to as p_π–d_π bonding. The overlap of the p_π orbital on the nitrogen atom and the d_π orbitals on the silicon atoms is sufficient to stabilize the planar structure. The trisilylamine is not basic like the trimethylamine due to the unavailability of the lone pair of electrons on the nitrogen atom. The analogous trisilylphosphine molecule $(SiH_3)_3P$ is trigonal pyramidal—the overlap of the π bonding orbitals is negligible and no p_π–d_π bonding is evident.

As we learned earlier, the multiple p_π–d_π bonding that silicon is capable of is responsible for the strength of the Si—O bond. It is also responsible for the fact that silanols are more acidic in character than the corresponding alcohols. For example, trimethylsilanol is much more acidic than ^{t}butanol (Figure 54.25). The sodium salt of trimethylsilanol is easily formed when the silanol is treated with concentrated aqueous NaOH. The negative charge on the oxygen of the anion is delocalized through the p_π–d_π bonding in the silanol and therefore is more stable. This cannot happen in the alcohol.

$$
\begin{array}{ccc}
& CH_3 & \\
& | & \\
CH_3\!-\!Si\!-\!O\!-\!H & & \\
& | & \\
& CH_3 &
\end{array}
\qquad
\begin{array}{ccc}
& CH_3 & \\
& | & \\
CH_3\!-\!C\!-\!O\!-\!H & & \\
& | & \\
& CH_3 &
\end{array}
$$

FIGURE 54.25 Trimethylsilanol and t-butanol.

Review Questions

1. Describe what is meant by the description 'electron perfect' and the effect that this has upon the chemistry of carbon.

2. Effective p_π–p_π bonding is restricted to relatively few elements in the Periodic Table. Which elements are these and why is this bonding effective for only these?

3. Compare the chemistry of carbon and silicon.

4. Review the structures of the silicates and summarize how the structures of silicates can be deduced.

Solutions to Problems

PROBLEM 54.1A

a. The most electronegative element is the one highest in the group: carbon.

b. Silicon is found in nature combined with oxygen, in silicates and aluminosilicates.

PROBLEM 54.2A

a. The lattice of the metal ions is face-centered cubic.

b. Crystal system: tetragonal.

c. MC_2.

d. An alkaline earth metal such as calcium.

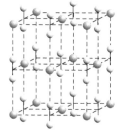

PROBLEM 54.3A

a. The cyclic ion in this case is composed of 4 SiO_4 units.

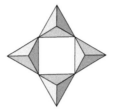

Each unit shares two oxygen atoms with its neighbors in the ring and has two terminal –O atoms. The charge on the ion must be $4 \times 2 \times -1 = -8$. The formula is $[Si_4O_{12}]^{8-}$.

b. The cyclic ion in this case is composed of 8 SiO_4 units.

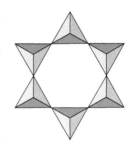

This ring is twice the size of the example in (a). You might expect the formula to be $[Si_8O_{24}]^{16-}$.

Count the number of terminal oxygen atoms = 8 = charge on the ion. Each unit shares two oxygen atoms with its neighbors in the ring and has two terminal –O atoms. The charge on the ion must be $8 \times 2 \times -1 = -16$. The formula is $[Si_8O_{24}]^{16-}$.

Answers to Review Questions

1. The number of valence electrons equals the number of valence orbitals. This means that there are no lone pairs of electrons on the carbon atoms. This in turn means that there is no repulsion weakening the C—C bond such as that between the atoms in N—N, O—O, and F—F bonds. The strength of the C—C bond and its kinetic resistance to reaction (the lack of reaction pathways provided by vacant orbitals or lone pairs of electrons) contribute to the ability of carbon to catenate. Catenation of carbon is essential for the construction of the complex molecules that form the basis of life.

2. Multiple p_π–p_π bonding is really only important for C, N, and O. The sideways overlap of the p_π orbitals on adjacent third and fourth period elements is minimal (Figure 54.2). Elements to the left of carbon in Period 2 have too few electrons. Fluorine to the right of oxygen has too many. Elements in Period 3 below C, N, and O can be coerced into multiple bonding using p_π orbitals but the bonding is not particularly effective. Elements in Period 3 are able to use d orbitals in π bonding.

3. Silicon is larger than carbon; it has d orbitals available; and it does not form multiple p_π–p_π bonds. Single bonds to silicon are weaker than single bonds to carbon. Silicon compounds therefore tend to be more reactive, thermodynamically because the

bonds are weaker and kinetically because the larger size and available d orbitals provide pathways for reaction. Silicon–oxygen bonds are strong due to a π bonding component using the silicon d orbitals. More energy is released in the formation of four Si—O bonds than in the formation of two Si=O bonds. For carbon, the formation of two C=O bonds is favored over four C—O bonds. Therefore CO_2 exists as a molecule with double bonds and SiO_2 exists as a covalent network solid with single bonds.

4. There are many silicate structure that vary in the degree of condensation between the tetrahedral orthosilicate units. They may dimerize, form chains, rings, double chains, sheets, or three-dimensional structures. The Si:O ratio in each structure is different. In the orthosilicate the ratio is 1:4. In the three dimensional silica, the ratio is 1:2. In between these, the ratio decreases as the degree of condensation increases. The number of terminal O atoms in the structure determines the number of cations required to balance the charges. For example, zircon is an orthosilicate SiO_4^{4-}, and therefore one Zr^{4+} cation is required. In the aluminosilicates, Al^- substitutes for Si and cations are required to balance the additional negative charge. Compare, for example, pyrophyllite or talc and mica (Figures 54.17, 54.18, and 54.19).

End-of-Unit Problems

1. Predict the trends in the following properties of the elements in Group 4A.

   a. ionization energy.

   b. density.

   c. strength of the bond between atoms of the element.

2. Predict the trends in the following properties of the elements in Group 4A.

   a. atomic size.

   b. metallic character.

   c. electronegativity.

3. Nitrogen in Group 5A and oxygen in Group 6A exist as diatomic molecules. Why doesn't carbon?

4. Carbon is commonly found bonded with itself, for example in the carbon chains —C—C—C— that make up the backbones of living organisms. Silicon, on the other hand, is commonly found bonded with oxygen in chains of alternating atoms —Si—O—Si—O—. Explain why.

5. The effect of filling the first transition series (3d) on the properties of the following elements is paralleled by a similar effect of filling the lanthanide series (4f) on the properties of the elements following that series. Explain why, and how, the filling of the 3d orbitals, and the filling of the 4f orbitals, affects the properties of the elements following each series. Use ionization energy as an example.

6. Explain why the preferred oxidation state of silicon is +4 but the preferred oxidation state of lead is +2.

7. There are three allotropes of carbon. Describe them and how their properties differ.

8. Tin occurs as two allotropes. The two allotropes are quite different in their structures and properties. Describe them.

9. Nanotubes are called nanotubes because the tubes are approximately 1 nm in diameter. If the hexagonal rings of the carbon network are lined up as shown in Figure 54.4, and the C–C bond length is 142 pm, how many hexagonal rings are required to fit around the circumference of a nanotube 2 nm in diameter?

10. Fullerene C_{60} has an arrangement of hexagons and pentagons the same as that on a soccer ball (Figure 54.3). The C—C bond lengths are not all the same: those between two hexagonal rings are 139 pm whereas those between a hexagonal ring and a pentagonal ring are 145 pm. Assuming an average bond length of 142 pm, what is the diameter and volume of a C_{60} molecule?

11. When carbon forms a multiple bond, what orbitals on the carbon atoms are used? What is the maximum number of electron pairs that can be shared between two carbon atoms?

12. Silicon does not form double bonds like carbon. The orbitals that are used for C—C multiple bonding cannot be used for silicon. Why? The Si—O bond is often described as having some double bond character. What orbital on the silicon could be used in a multiple bond between silicon and oxygen?

13. Germanium and silicon are used as semiconductors in the electronics industry. The compounds zinc sulfide, cadmium selenide, aluminum phosphide, and gallium arsenide all have semiconducting properties. What is significant about all these compounds?

14. Carbon monoxide CO, the cyanide ion CN⁻, the acetylide dianion C_2^{2-}, and dinitrogen N_2, are all isoelectronic. Are their Lewis structures different? In what way, if any, are their molecular orbitals different?

15. Explain why there is no silicon allotrope analogous to the graphite allotrope of carbon.

16. Explain why there is no boron nitride allotrope analogous to the fullerene allotrope of carbon.

17. There are two cyclic silicate anions, one with three SiO_4 tetrahedra in a ring and the other with six SiO_4 tetrahedra in a ring. Draw the structures of both, determine their formulas and the charges on the ions.

18. In order for a three-dimensional silicate structure to possess a charge, some fraction of the silicon atoms must be replaced by aluminum atoms. Why is this? Both mica and talc contain a sheet-like silicate structure. What is the difference between them?

19. Explain why aluminum phosphate $AlPO_4$ has polymorphs that are entirely analogous in structure to the polymorphs of silica SiO_2. Not only does aluminum phosphate exist in forms analogous to quartz, tridymite, and cristobalite, but the transformations between them take place in the same sequence as the temperature is raised.

20. Beryllium oxide BeO has a wurtzite structure which is similar to the structure of diamond except that it is based upon a hexagonal close packing rather than a cubic close packing. Discuss the possibility of beryllium oxide existing in forms analogous to the other allotropes of carbon.

Nitrogen, Phosphorus, and the Group 5A Elements

55.1   The Group 5A Elements

Nitrogen gas makes up 76% of the earth's atmosphere by mass (78% by volume) and is the most abundant naturally occurring element. It was discovered in 1772 by Daniel Rutherford although Cavendish isolated the element at about the same time. The name given to the gas was derived from the name for nitric acid and its salts, the nitrates. Principal minerals of nitrogen are saltpeter (KNO_3) and Chile saltpeter ($NaNO_3$)—these minerals were once a major source of fixed nitrogen for agricultural fertilizer and the manufacture of explosives.

Phosphorus was first isolated by Hennig Brandt in 1669 from urine. The name is derived from the Greek meaning 'light-bringing' because the element glowed when exposed to air. The principal source of phosphorus is the orthophosphate ion present in apatite minerals such as fluorapatite $Ca_5(PO_4)_3F$ and hydroxyapatite $Ca_5(PO_4)_3OH$. Both nitrogen and phosphorus are elements essential to life on earth.

Arsenic, antimony, and bismuth were all known long before the discovery of nitrogen and phosphorus. All three elements occur principally as sulfide ores, for example, realgar As_4S_4 and arsenopyrite FeAsS, stibnite Sb_2S_3, and bismuthinite Bi_2S_3, although the oxides also occur. Arsenic and its compounds have a long history as poisons. The element antimony has been known for thousands of years and was called stibium by the Romans—hence its symbol Sb. Bismuth was used to make alloys for the type in early printing presses in the 15th century, a use that continues to this day.

Nitrogen exists as a diatomic molecule N_2 in which the bond between the two N atoms is a strong triple bond. As a result, N_2 is relatively inert at room temperature. In contrast, phosphorus (and the other elements in the group) cannot so readily form the two p_p—p_p π bonds of a triple bond (*cf.* Figure 54.2) and phosphorus exists in the gas state under ordinary conditions as tetrahedral P_4 molecules, P—P bond length 221 pm (Figure 55.1). At high temperatures (800°C), a diatomic P_2 species is formed with a P—P bond length equal to 189.5 pm—indicating some multiple bonding between the P atoms. The P_4 and P_2 molecules exist in an equilibrium in which the proportion of P_2 increases as the temperature is increased. Dissociation of the diatomic P_2 molecules into single atoms occurs at still higher temperatures. The breakup of the P_4 molecules at high temperatures is endothermic and entropy-driven.

In the liquid state phosphorus exists as P_4 molecules and when the liquid solidifies (m.pt 44.1°C), a yellow-white waxy solid of the molecules is formed. The bond angles in the P_4 molecule are 60° and the molecule is strained—compare 60° with the angle (109.5°) between four pairs of electrons equally spaced around an atom. When heated in the absence of air, one of the bonds in the P_4 tetrahedron breaks to partially relieve the strain and the phosphorus atoms form chains (Figure 55.2). This amorphous allotrope is called red phosphorus. Red phosphorus is much less reactive than white

Paul Ehrlich, awarded the Nobel Prize in Medicine in 1908, developed an arsenic-based drug for the treatment of syphilis in 1909. It was the 606th arsenic compound he tested and it was called '606' or Salvarsan. The idea was to poison the bacterium but not the patient. The treatment was painful and sometimes fatal. If the syphilis was advanced the arsenic exacerbated the problem and killed the patient. Ultimately, penicillin became the treatment of choice.

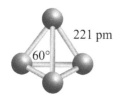

FIGURE 55.1   The tetrahedral structure of white phosphorus P_4.

FIGURE 55.2   The structure of red phosphorus.

phosphorus and has a higher melting point (~600°C). Various red crystalline allotropes can be prepared from the amorphous form. Other allotropes of phosphorus are Hittorf's violet allotrope and several black allotropes made by heating white phosphorus under high pressure. The black allotropes are the most stable form of phosphorus—the bonds are still approximately 221 pm in length but the angles are much less strained.

Like phosphorus, arsenic, antimony, and bismuth exist in several allotropic forms. The common α form of arsenic consists of sheets of covalently-bonded arsenic atoms. Antimony and bismuth have similar structures. In the vapor state arsenic and antimony exist as tetrahedral molecules As_4 and Sb_4. Samples of white and red phosphorus, arsenic, antimony, and bismuth are shown in Figure 55.3.

Trends down the group parallel those in Groups 3A and 4A already discussed. There is an increase in the metallic character down the group—nitrogen and phosphorus are nonmetals, arsenic and antimony are semimetallic, and bismuth is the only metal in the group. The properties of the elements are compared in Table 55.1.

The difference in the behavior of nitrogen and phosphorus results from the smaller size of the nitrogen atom, the unavailability of d orbitals, and the ability of nitrogen to form multiple p_π–p_π bonds. This same difference between the elements of the second period and the elements of the third period is also evident in Groups 4A and 6A.

Bismuth has the curious property (like water) of expanding when the molten metal freezes. The only other elements that act like this are gallium and germanium.

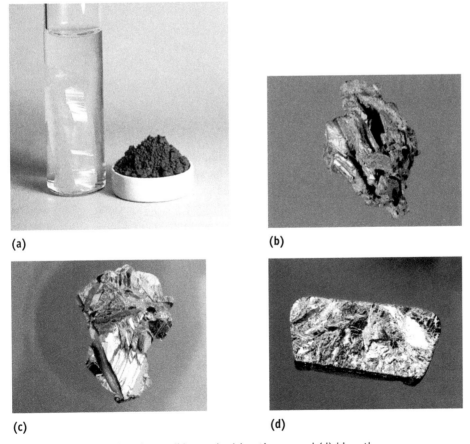

(a)

(b)

(c)

(d)

FIGURE 55.3   (a) Phosphorus, (b) arsenic, (c) antimony, and (d) bismuth.

TABLE 55.1 The Group 5A elements.

Name	Symbol	Melting Point °C	Boiling Point °C	ΔH°_{fus} @ m.pt. kJ mol^{-1}	Density g cm^{-3}	Ionization Energies kJ mol^{-1}					Covalent Radius pm	Metallic Radius pm	Ionic Radius pm
						1st	2nd	3rd	4th	5th			
Nitrogen	N	−210	−196	0.71	0.81(*l*)	1402	2856	4577	7475	9445	75	—	171(3−)
Phosphorus	P	44.1	281	0.66	1.82	1012	1903	2910	4964	6274	110	143	—
Arsenic	As	615s	—	24.4	5.78	947	1798	2736	4837	6043	122	153	58(3+)
Antimony	Sb	631	1753	19.9	6.68	834	1595	2443	4260	5400	143	167	76(3+)
Bismuth	Bi	271	1564	11.3	9.81	703	1610	2466	4370	5400	152	182	103(3+)

s = sublimes

The single, double, and triple bonds for nitrogen and carbon differ in their relative strengths (Table 55.2). Most remarkable is the difference in the strengths of the single bonds. The weakness of the N—N bond (and the O—O and F—F bonds) is attributed to repulsion between the lone pairs of electrons on the two atoms. There are no lone pairs on the carbon atoms. The weakness of the N—N single bond means that N_2 is thermodynamically stable with respect to a series of N—N single bonds whereas the opposite is true of carbon—acetylene is thermodynamically unstable with respect to structures containing C—C single bonds.

TABLE 55.2 Relative strengths of C—C and N—N bonds (kJ mol^{-1}).

Bond	Strength	Bond	Strength
C—C	346	N—N	160
C=C	598	N=N	400
C≡C	813	N≡N	946

Industrial Production and Uses

Nitrogen is obtained on a large scale by the liquefaction and subsequent **fractional distillation** of air. Other gases obtained at the same time are oxygen, neon, argon, krypton and xenon. Most nitrogen is supplied to consumers as the gas, but approximately one-third is available as liquid N_2. Nitrogen provides an atmosphere without oxygen for situations where undesirable oxidation might occur. Liquid nitrogen is also a useful coolant.

Huge amounts of nitrogen are used in the Haber-Bosch process for the production of ammonia but the process uses air rather than pure nitrogen. The series of reactions includes the production of hydrogen from methane (natural gas):

$$CH_4 + H_2O \rightleftharpoons CO + 3\,H_2 \qquad \text{steam-hydrocarbon reforming reaction}$$
$$H_2 + air \rightarrow H_2O + 2\,N_2$$
$$CO + H_2O \rightleftharpoons CO_2 + H_2 \qquad \text{shift reaction}$$

The CO_2 is removed by dissolving it in K_2CO_3 and the gas mixture now contains hydrogen and nitrogen with small amounts of methane, argon and carbon monoxide, ready for the Haber-Bosch conversion to ammonia. Between 15 and 20 million tons of ammonia are manufactured every year in the US alone of which at least 85% is used as agricultural fertilizer in various forms (ammonia itself, urea, ammonium nitrate, and ammonium phosphates). Worldwide production is approximately 120 million tons per annum. The sequence of reactions by which nitrogen is converted into different nitrogen-containing compounds via ammonia is illustrated in Figure 55.4.

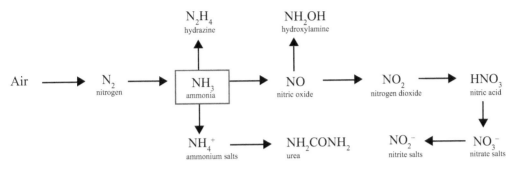

FIGURE 55.4 The sequence of reactions by which nitrogen is converted into different nitrogen-containing compounds.

Phosphorus is obtained from phosphate rock by heating the rock with sand and coke:

$$2\ Ca_3(PO_4)_2 + 6\ SiO_2 + 10\ C \rightarrow 6\ CaSiO_3 + 10\ CO + P_4$$

Most phosphate rock, however, is destined to be used in the production of phosphate fertilizers. The phosphate rock is treated with sulfuric acid to produce phosphoric acid (approximately 12 billion kg per annum in the US) or superphosphate. Representative reactions are, for example:

$$Ca_5(PO_4)_3F + 5\ H_2SO_4 \rightarrow 3\ H_3PO_4 + 5\ CaSO_4 + HF$$
$$2\ Ca_5(PO_4)_3F + 7\ H_2SO_4 + H_2O \rightarrow 3\ Ca(H_2PO_4)_2 \cdot H_2O + 7\ CaSO_4 + 2\ HF$$
superphosphate

The principal source of arsenic is FeAsS from which arsenic sublimes when the ore is heated. Arsenic oxide As_2O_3 is also obtained from the processing of copper and zinc ores. The oxide is reduced by carbon to produce arsenic. Antimony is obtained from stibnite by conversion to the oxide and subsequent carbon reduction. The same process is used for bismuth.

The principal use of arsenic and antimony is in the production of alloys. For example, the lead used in automobile lead storage batteries contains about 3% Sb and a very small amount of As to inhibit the formation of gases at the electrodes. Both antimony and arsenic are used in the semiconductor industry. Bismuth is used primarily in the formation of alloys with low melting points.

55.2 Compounds of Nitrogen

Nitrogen exhibits a wide range of oxidation states forming compounds in which its oxidation state varies from −3 to +5. Some examples are listed in Table 55.3. It is a typical nonmetal with a relatively high electronegativity. In fact only F, O, and Cl have higher electronegativities. Therefore only with these elements does nitrogen exhibit a positive oxidation state.

> Phosphate rock is a general term for minerals containing calcium phosphate (fluorapatite, hydroxyapatite, calcium phosphate itself, etc.)

> Carbon, discussed in Unit 54, also exhibits a wide range of oxidation states—from −4 (CH_4) to +4 (CO_2). Typically, the nonmetals have oxidation states that range from the Group number to the Group number minus 8.

TABLE 55.3 Compounds of nitrogen in various oxidation states.

Oxidation State	Compounds		
+5	HNO_3	$NaNO_3$	N_2O_5
+4	NO_2	N_2O_4	
+3	HNO_2	KNO_2	NCl_3
+2	NO		
+1	$H_2N_2O_2$	N_2O	
0	N_2		
−1	NH_2OH	NH_2F	
−2	N_2H_4	CH_3NHNH_2	
−3	NH_3	NH_4Cl	$NaNH_2$

Nitrogen forms binary compounds with most elements in the Periodic Table and in this its behavior is similar to hydrogen and carbon. Like the binary compounds of these elements, the nitrides are classified as saline (salt-like), covalent, and interstitial. For example, lithium and magnesium form salt-like nitrides Li_3N and Mg_3N_2 by heating the metal in nitrogen at high temperature. Covalent nitrogen compounds include compounds such as S_4N_4 and P_3N_5. The interstitial metallic nitrides are compounds in which the nitrogen atoms occupy the spaces between the atoms of a close-packed metallic lattice. These nitrides, like similar carbides, are very hard, inert, high melting point (refractory) materials.

The explosive decomposition of sodium azide is initiated electrically in automobile air bags. The decomposition releases a large amount of nitrogen gas.

Azides contain the linear N_3^- ion (Figure 55.5). Sodium azide NaN_3 and potassium azide KN_3 are quite stable and decompose quickly but smoothly when heated. Other azides, such as lead azide $Pb(N_3)_2$ or silver azide AgN_3 tend to be shock-sensitive and explosive. The parent acid, hydrogen azide HN_3, is a colorless, highly toxic liquid that tends to explode. An aqueous solution of hydrogen azide, called hydrazoic acid, is a weak acid ($pK_a = 4.77$).

FIGURE 55.5 The structure of the azide ion N_3^- and hydrogen azide HN_3.

In many respects, the most important compound of nitrogen is ammonia NH_3 because ammonia is the means by which nitrogen is fixed—both naturally by the enzyme nitrogenase for use in living organisms and industrially by the Haber process. As indicated in Figure 55.4, ammonia is the gateway to most other compounds of nitrogen. Ammonia is a colorless gas with a characteristic sharp odor and is very soluble in water to produce a basic solution.

Hydrazine NH_2NH_2 is another binary hydrogen compound of nitrogen. It is prepared by the reaction between hypochlorite and ammonia developed by F. Raschig in 1907:

$$OCl^- + 2\,NH_3 \rightarrow N_2H_4 + Cl^- + H_2O$$

Hydrazine is usually transported as a 64% solution in water. The major use of hydrazine, and its derivatives such as methylhydrazine CH_3NHNH_2 and dimethylhydrazine $(CH_3)_2NNH_2$ is in rocket fuels. Hydrazine and its derivatives have positive enthalpies of formation, energy that is made available when the compounds are oxidized. Another use of hydrazine is in the treatment of the water used in water boilers for steam turbines. The hydrazine reacts with dissolved oxygen gas to produce water and nitrogen.

EXAMPLE 55.1   REACTIONS OF NITROGEN COMPOUNDS

When methylhydrazine CH_3NHNH_2 reacts with dinitrogen tetroxide N_2O_4 in a space vehicle propulsion system, the products of the reaction are carbon dioxide, water vapor and nitrogen gas.

   a. Write an equation for the reaction.

   b. Determine the number of moles of gas produced for one mole of methylhydrazine.

   c. Calculate the enthalpy change per mole of methylhydrazine from the heats of formation.

   $\Delta H_f^\circ (CH_3NHNH_2(l)) = +54 \text{ kJ mol}^{-1}$

   $\Delta H_f^\circ (N_2O_4(g)) = +9 \text{ kJ mol}^{-1}$

   $\Delta H_f^\circ (CO_2(g)) = -394 \text{ kJ mol}^{-1}$

   $\Delta H_f^\circ (H_2O(g)) = -242 \text{ kJ mol}^{-1}$

UNDERSTAND THE QUESTION

This is a standard enthalpy calculation from the enthalpies of formation of the products and the enthalpies of formation of the reactants.

PLAN THE SOLUTION

Write the equation for the reaction. Count the number of moles of gas produced from each mole of methylhydrazine. Then list the enthalpies of formation, multiply by the coefficients, and calculate the difference (products – reactants).

SOLVE THE PROBLEM

   a. $4 \text{ CH}_3NHNH_2(l) + 5 \text{ N}_2O_4(g) \rightarrow 4 \text{ CO}_2(g) + 9 \text{ N}_2(g) + 12 \text{ H}_2O(g)$

   b. Four moles of methylhydrazine produce 25 moles of gas. One mole of hydrazine will produce 25/4 (= 6.25) moles of gas.

   c. $\Delta H_f^\circ \text{ (products)} = 4 \times \Delta H_f^\circ (CO_2) + 9 \times \Delta H_f^\circ (N_2) + 12 \times \Delta H_f^\circ (H_2O)$

   $\qquad\qquad\qquad = (4 \times -394) + (\text{zero}) + (12 \times -242)$

   $\qquad\qquad\qquad = -4480 \text{ kJ}$

   $\Delta H_f^\circ \text{ (reactants)} = 4 \times \Delta H_f^\circ (CH_3NHNH_2) + 5 \times \Delta H_f^\circ (N_2O_4)$

   $\qquad\qquad\qquad = (4 \times +54) + (5 \times +9)$

   $\qquad\qquad\qquad = +261 \text{ kJ}$

   $\Delta H^\circ \text{(reaction)} = \Delta H_f^\circ \text{ (products)} - \Delta H_f^\circ \text{ (reactants)} = -4480 \text{ kJ} - 261 \text{ kJ} = -4741 \text{ kJ}$

   Per mole of methylhydrazine, the enthalpy change = $-4741/4$ kJ = -1185 kJ

Hydrazine is added to boiler water to remove dissolved oxygen that causes corrosion. The hydrazine reacts with the oxygen to produce nitrogen gas and water.

a. Write a balanced equation for the reaction.

b. Calculate the enthalpy change for the reaction represented by the equation you have written.

$\Delta H_f^\circ (N_2H_4) = +50.6 \text{ kJ mol}^{-1}$

$\Delta H_f^\circ (H_2O(l)) = -285.8 \text{ kJ mol}^{-1}$

Hydrogen azide, HN_3, has a very endothermic heat of formation—it is not surprising that it tends to explode.

a. Write a balanced equation for the decomposition of hydrogen azide into its constituent elements.

b. Calculate the enthalpy change for the decomposition.

$\Delta H_f^\circ (HN_3) = +294.1 \text{ kJ mol}^{-1}$

The Nitrogen Oxides and Oxoacids

Nitrogen forms oxides in which its oxidation state ranges from +1 to +5. In all the compounds, p_π–p_π π bonding between the nitrogen atoms and the oxygen atoms is important and the structures tend to be planar to facilitate this. These planar structures can be contrasted with the three-dimensional structures of the oxides of the other elements in the group.

Dinitrogen monoxide N_2O is a nontoxic gas (b.pt. $-88°C$) often called laughing gas and used as a general anesthetic. Its linear structure is illustrated in Figure 55.6.

Nitric oxide (nitrogen monoxide) NO is a molecule with an odd electron. In other words, it is a **radical**. It is made industrially by the catalytic (Pt) oxidation of ammonia at 850°C:

$$4 NH_3 + 5 O_2 \rightarrow 4 NO + 6 H_2O$$

This is the first step in the production of nitric acid from ammonia by the **Ostwald process**. Nitric oxide immediately combines with oxygen when exposed to air to form nitrogen dioxide. As soon as it is produced, the nitrogen dioxide is dissolved in water to produce nitric acid according to the reactions:

$$3 NO_2 + H_2O \rightarrow 2 HNO_3 + NO \qquad \text{—the NO is recycled}$$
$$2 NO_2 + H_2O \rightarrow HNO_3 + HNO_2$$
$$2 HNO_2 \rightarrow NO + NO_2 + H_2O \qquad \text{—the NO and } NO_2 \text{ are recycled}$$

These reactions are disproportion reactions—the oxidation number of the nitrogen increases *and* decreases in the reactions.

Nitric oxide has been found to play an important role in biological systems as a messenger molecule in neurotransmission.

Dinitrogen trioxide N_2O_3 is a blue liquid produced when an NO and an NO_2 molecule (both odd-electron molecules) combine at low temperatures. Rather than a molecule containing N is an oxidation state +3, it is better pictured perhaps as a molecule

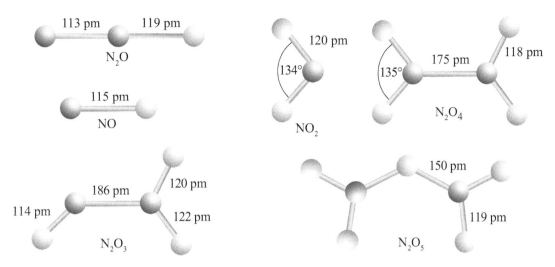

FIGURE 55.6   The structures of the nitrogen oxides.

with one N in an oxidation state +2 and the other in an oxidation state +4. The molecule readily dissociates into NO and NO_2 and dissolves in water to produce nitrous acid HNO_2.

Nitrogen dioxide NO_2 is a brown toxic gas that dimerizes readily to form the colorless dinitrogen tetroxide N_2O_4. At room temperature for example, the gas contains only 15% NO_2, the remainder being N_2O_4. Both NO_2 and N_2O_4 dissolve in water to produce a mixture of nitrous acid and nitric acid, HNO_2.

Dinitrogen pentoxide N_2O_5 is the acid anhydride of nitric acid HNO_3 and contains nitrogen in a +5 oxidation state. It is therefore a powerful oxidizing agent. It exists as a molecule in the vapor state (Figure 55.6) but as $[NO_2]^+[NO_3]^-$ in the solid state. The nitryl cation NO_2^+ is isoelectronic with carbon dioxide.

There are two common oxoacids of nitrogen: nitrous acid HNO_2 and nitric acid HNO_3. An unstable hyponitrous acid $H_2N_2O_2$ can be prepared in diethylether solution but it decomposes spontaneously into N_2O and H_2O. Nitrous acid HNO_2 is also not particularly stable; it disproportionates in aqueous solution to NO and HNO_3. For this reason it is usually prepared *in situ* when required in a reaction—from the reaction of sodium nitrite and hydrochloric acid. Nitrites such as sodium nitrite $NaNO_2$ are used as an additive to preserve meat—particularly ham and bacon. The nitrite inhibits bacterial growth and preserves the flavor and color of the meat.

Nitric acid is manufactured on a large scale by the Ostwald process and most of the acid is used to produce fertilizer—particularly ammonium nitrate. Other uses are in the manufacture of explosives (Figure 55.7) and in the plastics industry.

A bottle of nitric acid (68% HNO_3 in water) is usually slightly yellow in color due to some decomposition to NO_2 and O_2. The acid should be kept in a refrigerator if this decomposition is to be prevented. Nitric acid is both a strong acid and a strong oxidizing agent. It oxidizes many metals, an example being the reaction with copper in the presence of water:

$$3 \text{ Cu}(s) + 8 \text{ HNO}_3(aq) \rightarrow 3 \text{ Cu(NO}_3)_2(aq) + 2 \text{ NO}(g) + 4 \text{ H}_2\text{O}(l)$$

It also oxidizes nonmetals such as sulfur and phosphorus to the corresponding oxoacids H_2SO_4 and H_3PO_4.

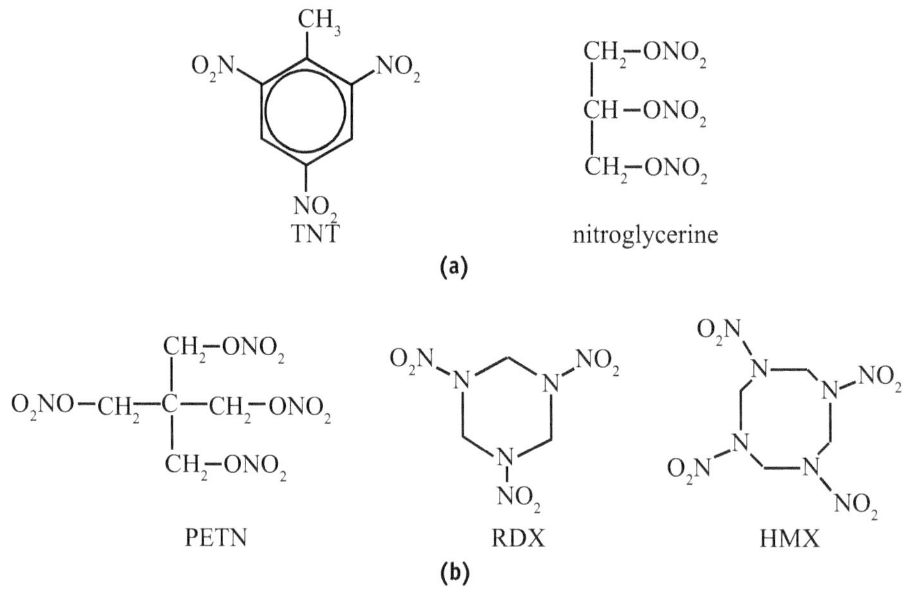

CH₃ ... (molecular structures)

TNT

nitroglycerine

(a)

PETN   RDX   HMX

(b)

FIGURE 55.7 (a) Explosives are usually organic molecules that contain —NO₂ or —ONO₂ groups. Two common examples are TNT (trinitrotoluene) and nitroglycerine. Because it is so sensitive to shock, nitroglycerine is usually absorbed on cellulose to form dynamite. It was Alfred Nobel's discovery of this way to stabilize nitroglycerine that made his fortune. (b) PETN is pentaerythritol tetranitrate, a very strong, shock sensitive high explosive used, for example, in detonating cord. Two nitrated amines are RDX and HMX. Other than TNT, military explosives are usually based upon RDX. It is not often used by itself; it can be mixed with a plasticizer such as dioctyl sebacate and a binder such as polyisobutylene to form the plastic explosive C-4, or it can be mixed with PETN and a plasticizer and binder to form Semtex.

55.3   Compounds of Phosphorus

Phosphorus trifluoride is highly toxic because it forms a complex with hemoglobin.

The pentaiodide PI_5 (or $[PI_4]^+I^-$) has not been prepared.

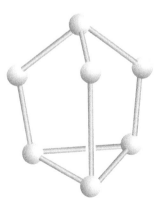

FIGURE 55.8   The structure of the P_7^{3-} ion.

Phosphine PH_3, the analogue of ammonia, is a toxic gas much less soluble in water than ammonia. Phosphine, unlike ammonia, does not form hydrogen bonds with water molecules.

Many metals form binary phosphides. The alkali metals form the salt-like M_3P compounds containing the P^{3-} ion. They also form phosphides that contain groups, chains, or layers of phosphorus atoms. For example, Li_3P_7 contains the P_7^{3-} ion illustrated in Figure 55.8.

Phosphorus forms the trihalides PX_3 and the pentahalides PX_5. All four trihalides PF_3 (m.pt. −152°C), PCl_3 (m.pt. −94°C), PBr_3 (m.pt. −42°C), and PI_3 (m.pt. 61°C) are reactive compounds. For example, all except PF_3 react vigorously with water to produce phosphorous acid. Phosphorus trichloride PCl_3 is manufactured in large quantities for use in making organophosphorus compounds.

Phosphorus pentachloride exists as a PCl_5 molecule in the gas state and as the ionic $[PCl_4]^+[PCl_6]^-$ in the solid state. The ions form a cesium chloride type lattice with coordination numbers of 8. The pentabromide exists as a PBr_5 molecule in the gas state but as $[PBr_4]^+Br^-$ in the solid state—presumably because of the larger size of the bromide ion. Mixed pentahalides such as $[PCl_4]^+[PF_6]^-$ are known. Phosphorus pentachloride PCl_5 is made from PCl_3 on an industrial scale for use as a chlorinating agent. All pentahalides react vigorously with water to produce phosphoric acid.

EXAMPLE 55.2   SHAPES OF NITROGEN AND PHOSPHORUS COMPOUNDS

Use valence shell electron pair repulsion theory (VSEPR) to determine the shapes of the following nitrogen and phosphorus molecules or ions.

a. $[PF_6]^-$

b. NO_2^+

c. NO_2^-

UNDERSTAND THE QUESTION

Valence shell electron pair repulsion theory (VSEPR) can be used to determine the shapes of most small molecules and polyatomic ions. The procedure was described in Unit 21.

PLAN THE SOLUTION

Use the procedure described in Unit 21. It's not necessary to draw Lewis structures first although you might like to do so.

SOLVE THE PROBLEM

a. $[PF_6]^-$: Phosphorus is the central atom.

   The number of valence electrons is 5 (for P) + 42 (for six F) + 1 (for the − charge) = 48.

   This is exactly 6 × 8. There are eight electrons (4 pairs) around each F, with no electrons remaining to place on the P as lone pairs.

   Therefore there are 6 bonding pairs total around the phosphorus.

   The arrangement is octahedral and the shape of the molecule is octahedral.

b. NO_2^+: Nitrogen is the central atom.

   The number of valence electrons is 5 (for N) + 12 (for two O) − 1 (for the + charge) = 16.

   This is exactly 2 × 8. There are eight electrons (4 pairs) around each O, with no electrons remaining to place on the N as lone pairs.

   Therefore there are 2 bonding pairs total around the nitrogen.

   The arrangement is linear and the shape of the molecule is linear.

c. NO_2^-: Nitrogen is the central atom.

   The number of valence electrons is 5 (for N) + 12 (for two O) + 1 (for the − charge) = 18.

   Two sets of 8 electrons are around each oxygen atom, leaving two electrons (one pair) as a lone pair on the nitrogen.

   Therefore there are 2 bonding pairs and 1 nonbonding pair around the nitrogen.

   The arrangement is trigonal planar and the shape of the molecule is bent.

PROBLEM 55.2A

Use valence shell electron pair repulsion theory (VSEPR) to determine the shapes of the following nitrogen and phosphorus molecules or ions.

a. $[PBr_4]^+$

b. PCl_3F_2

c. N_3^-

Use valence shell electron pair repulsion theory (VSEPR) to determine the shapes of the following nitrogen and phosphorus molecules or ions.

a. PCl_5

b. NO_3^-

c. $[PCl_4F_2]^-$

The Phosphorus Oxides and Oxoacids

> When phosphorus is oxidized in air to form P_4O_{10}, the phosphorus is produced in an electronically excited state. When the electrons fall to a lower energy level, visible light is emitted. This is called **phosphorescence**, from which the name phosphorus is derived.

The two important oxides of phosphorus are P_4O_6 and P_4O_{10} (Figure 55.9). Other mixed oxides can be prepared with varying numbers of terminal P=O groups. The phosphorus(III) oxide is prepared by burning phosphorus in a limited supply of oxygen. The phosphorus(V) oxide can be made directly from P_4 or via P_4O_6.

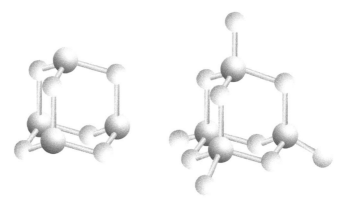

FIGURE 55.9   The structures of the two principal oxides of phosphorus.

> Phosphorus, like nitrogen, is an essential nutrient for plant growth. Most phosphate rock that is mined is used in the production of phosphate fertilizers. The insoluble phosphate rock is treated with sulfuric acid to produce **superphosphate** that consists of soluble $Ca(H_2PO_4)_2$ mixed with $CaSO_4$. If the super-phosphate is treated with phosphoric acid, the $CaSO_4$ is removed and the $Ca(H_2PO_4)_2$ is called **triple superphosphate** — it has three times the available phosphorus.

Three oxoacids, corresponding to the oxidation numbers +1, +3, and +5, can be prepared. Hypophosphorous acid H_3PO_2 is a weak monoprotic acid ($pK_a = 1.24$) in which two of the hydrogen atoms are attached directly to the phosphorus atom and are therefore not acidic. Phosphorous acid (or phosphonic acid) H_3PO_3 is the acid corresponding to the oxide P_4O_6 and can be obtained from P_4O_6 or PCl_3 by the addition of cold water. It is a weak diprotic acid ($pK_{a1} = 2.00$; $pK_{a2} = 6.59$) with one hydrogen atom connected directly to the phosphorus atom (Figure 55.10).

Phosphoric acid H_3PO_4 (*ortho*phosphoric acid) is made from phosphate rock on a huge scale by the action of sulfuric acid. In fact most sulfuric acid is manufactured specifically for this purpose.

$$Ca_3(PO_4)_2 + 3\ H_2SO_4 \rightarrow 2\ H_3PO_4 + 3CaSO_4$$

FIGURE 55.10   The structure of the diprotic acid phosphorous acid H_3PO_3.
One hydrogen atom is bonded directly to the phosphorus atom and is not acidic.

The acid is triprotic but weak ($pK_{a1} = 2.21$; $pK_{a2} = 7.21$; $pK_{a3} = 12.67$). It is commercially available as an 85% solution in water—a viscous liquid due to extensive hydrogen bonding between the phosphoric acid and water molecules. When phosphoric acid is heated, it condenses with the elimination of water to produce *pyro*phosphoric acid (or diphosphoric acid):

$$2\ H_3PO_4 \rightarrow H_4P_2O_7 + H_2O$$

Additional heating produces triphosphoric acid $H_5P_3O_{10}$:

$$H_3PO_4 + H_4P_2O_7 \rightarrow H_5P_3O_{10} + H_2O$$

Sodium triphosphate $Na_5P_3O_{10}$ (Figure 55.11) is used in detergents to bind to metal ions such as calcium that would interfere with the surfactant. *Meta*phosphoric acid $H_3P_3O_6$ exists as a chain or cyclic structure analogous to the silicate structures examined earlier.

Triphosphoric acid ($pK_{a1} \sim 0$) is stronger than *pyrophoric* acid (pK_{a1}=0.85) and *pyrophoric* acid is stronger than *ortho*phosphoric acid (pK_{a1}=2.21).

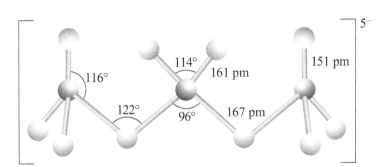

FIGURE 55.11   Sodium triphosphate $Na_5P_3O_{10}$.

Phosphate structures are important in the biological systems of plants and animals. Both DNA (deoxyribonucleic acid) and RNA (ribonucleic acid) are phosphate esters—the phosphate groups link the sugar molecules and form the backbones of the two helices making up the double helix (*cf.* Unit 66). Phosphate groups also play an essential role in storing energy in biological cells. As noted earlier in Unit 30.7, adenosine triphosphate (ATP) contains a chain of three phosphate groups. The conversion (hydrolysis) of ATP into ADP (adenosine diphosphate) releases 31 kJ mol^{-1}—energy which is used for cell growth, muscle movement, and other biochemical reactions (*cf.* Figure 30.6).

Phosphazenes

The reaction of PCl_5 with NH_4Cl in nonaqueous solution produces an interesting series of compounds with the general formula $(NPCl_2)_n$ by the condensation of HCl. The most abundant products are $(NPCl_2)_3$ and $(NPCl_2)_4$:

$$3\ PCl_5 + 3\ NH_4Cl \rightarrow (NPCl_2)_3 + 12\ HCl$$

The reaction is analogous to the reaction of PCl_5 with water to produce phosphoryl trichloride $POCl_3$ except that in that case further condensation cannot occur (there are no hydrogen atoms left). Using ammonia instead of ammonium chloride produces high molecular mass polymers. The structure of $(NPCl_2)_3$ is illustrated in Figure 55.12. The ring is an almost perfect hexagon with a P—N bond length 158 pm. This bond length is significantly shorter than a typical P—N single bond (177 pm) which suggests multiple P—N bonding.

A simple molecule involving multiple bonding between P and N is $PF_2N(CH_3)_2$ (Figure 55.13). The N is sp^2 hybridized and the P—N bond length is 163 pm. A popular explanation of the multiple bonding involves π bonding between the p_π orbital on the nitrogen and a d_π orbital on the phosphorus. However, there is much disagreement concerning the availability of the d orbitals on the phosphorus in terms of the energy of the orbitals and the extent of the π overlap.

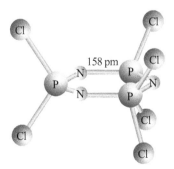

FIGURE 55.12   The structure of $(NPCl_2)_3$.
The short bond length of the P—N bond indicates some multiple bonding between the two atoms.

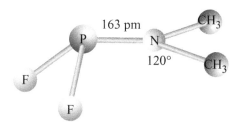

FIGURE 55.13 **The structure of PF$_2$N(CH$_3$)$_2$.**
The planar arrangement of bonds around the N (sp^2) indicates the use of the remaining p orbital in π bonding between the N and the P.

55.4 Arsenic, Antimony, and Bismuth

The pentabromides and pentaiodides are unknown.

Arsenic forms all the halides AsX$_3$ and the fluorides and chlorides AsX$_5$. It forms oxides As$_4$O$_6$ and As$_4$O$_{10}$ that have the same structures as P$_4$O$_6$ and P$_4$O$_{10}$ (Figure 55.9). However, like the other elements in the p block following the first transition series, arsenic has a reluctance to exhibit its highest oxidation state. For example, arsenic pentachloride AsCl$_5$ was not prepared until 1976 and it decomposes at temperatures above $-50°C$. This reluctance to exist in a +5 oxidation state is because of the additional 10+ charge on the nucleus with the poor shielding afforded by the 10 electrons in the 3d orbitals. The 4s electrons are tightly held. For the same reason, As$_4$O$_{10}$ and its acid H$_3$AsO$_4$ are good oxidizing agents.

Antimony is less reactive than arsenic. It is more stable toward oxidation in air but forms both antimony(III) and antimony(V) oxides on heating. Whereas the nitrogen and phosphorus oxides are acidic, those of arsenic and antimony are amphoteric, and Bi$_2$O$_3$ is basic. Bismuth oxide has a typical metallic oxide structure. This parallels the change in the character of the elements from nonmetallic, through semimetallic, to metallic down the group.

EXAMPLE 55.3 THE OXIDES OF THE GROUP 5A ELEMENTS

Explain why the structures of phosphorus(III) oxide P$_4$O$_6$ and nitrogen(III) oxide N$_2$O$_3$ are different. Why isn't the formula of phosphorus(III) oxide written P$_2$O$_3$? What structure would you anticipate for arsenic(III) oxide?

UNDERSTAND THE QUESTION

What are the principal differences in behavior between the elements in Period 2 and the elements in Period 3? In the formation of their compounds, what is it that Period 2 elements can do that Period 3 elements don't do? And what can Period 3 elements do that Period 2 elements cannot do?

PLAN THE SOLUTION

The difference in the behavior of nitrogen and phosphorus results from the smaller size of the nitrogen atom, the unavailability of d orbitals, the impossibility of any 'expansion of the valence shell', and the ability of nitrogen to form multiple p$_\pi$—p$_\pi$ bonds.

SOLVE THE PROBLEM

The particular difference between nitrogen and phosphorus that we are concerned with here is the ability of nitrogen to form multiple bonds using p$_\pi$ orbitals. In order to form p$_\pi$—p$_\pi$ bonds, the arrangement of oxygen atoms around each nitrogen atom in the nitrogen oxides is planar. The nitrogen atoms are sp^2 hybridized reserving one p orbital for the π bonding. In the phosphorus oxides, the hybridization of the phosphorus orbitals is sp^3. All the valence s and p orbitals are used to form σ bonds and the arrangement around each phosphorus atom is tetrahedral.

The formula P_4O_6 is the molecular formula of phosphorus(III) oxide. N_2O_3 is the molecular formula of nitrogen (III) oxide.

In the gas phase As_4O_6 has the same structure as P_4O_6.

PROBLEM 55.3A

Dinitrogen pentoxide N_2O_5 is an acidic oxide, whereas the analogous arsenic and antimony oxides As_2O_3 and Sb_2O_3 are amphoteric, and Bi_2O_3 is basic. Why does the acid-base character of the oxide change going down the group?

PROBLEM 55.3B

The structures of the phosphorus oxides are based upon the tetrahedral P_4 unit. What structures would you predict for the compounds P_4S_{10} and $P_4O_6S_4$?

Review Questions

1. Review the differences between nitrogen and phosphorus and their compounds.

2. Why does white phosphorus convert to red phosphorus when heated in the absence of air? What would happen if air was present?

3. Explosives (*cf.* Figure 55.7) often contain —NO_2 or —ONO_2 groups. Suggest why.

4. Explain why phosphorous acid H_3PO_3 is only diprotic—even though it has three H atoms.

5. Suppose that you prepared a compound with the stoichiometry NF_5 (nitrogen surrounded by five fluorine atoms?). What could be a possible structure? The existence of the compound PI_5 is in some doubt. Why is its existence so doubted?

Solutions to Problems

PROBLEM 55.1A

a. $N_2H_4 + O_2 \rightarrow N_2 + 2 H_2O$

b. $\Delta H°(\text{reaction}) = \Delta H°_f (\text{products}) - \Delta H°_f (\text{reactants})$

$= 2 \times \Delta H°_f (H_2O(l)) - \Delta H°_f (N_2H_4)$

$= 2 \times -285.8 \text{ kJ mol}^{-1} - 50.6 \text{ kJ mol}^{-1}$

$= -622.2 \text{ kJ mol}^{-1}$

PROBLEM 55.2A

Use valence shell electron pair repulsion theory (VSEPR) to determine the shapes of the following nitrogen and phosphorus molecules or ions.

a. $[PBr_4]^+$: Phosphorus is the central atom.

The number of valence electrons is 5 (for P) + 28 (for four Br) – 1 (for the + charge) = 32.

This is exactly 4×8. There are eight electrons (4 pairs) around each Br, with no electrons remaining to place on the P as lone pairs.

Therefore there are 4 bonding pairs total around the phosphorus.

The arrangement is tetrahedral and the shape of the molecule is tetrahedral.

b. PCl_3F_2: Phosphorus is the central atom.

The number of valence electrons is 5 (for P) + 21 (for three Cl) + 14 (for two F) = 40.

This is exactly 5×8. There are eight electrons (4 pairs) around each halogen, with no electrons remaining to place on the P as lone pairs.

Therefore there are 5 bonding pairs total around the nitrogen.

The arrangement is trigonal bipyramid and the shape of the molecule is trigonal bipyramid.

c. N_3^-: Nitrogen is the central atom.

The number of valence electrons is 15 (for three N) + 1 (for the – charge) = 16.

This is exactly 2 × 8. There are two sets of 8 electrons around each terminal nitrogen atom, leaving no electrons as lone pairs on the nitrogen.

Therefore there are 2 bonding pairs only around the nitrogen.

The arrangement is linear and the shape of the molecule is also linear.

PROBLEM 55.3A

The acidity or basicity of an oxide depends upon the electronegativity of the element and the electron distribution in the compound. Electronegative elements (nonmetals) have oxides that are molecular (covalent) in character (SO_3, NO_2, P_4O_{10}, etc.) and these are generally acidic in solution (some are insoluble). Electropositive elements form ionic oxides (Na_2O, CaO, etc.) and these are basic in solution. Elements of intermediate electronegativity are amphoteric in character. The electronegativity decreases down the group and the character of the oxide changes accordingly (*cf.* Figure 56.13).

Answers to Review Questions

1. The difference in the behavior of nitrogen and phosphorus results from the smaller size of the nitrogen atom, the unavailability of d orbitals, and the ability of nitrogen to form multiple p_π—p_π bonds. For example, nitrogen exists as a diatomic molecule N_2 and is normally a gas. Phosphorus exists as a three-dimensional molecule P_4 and is normally a solid. Nitrogen oxides are planar about the nitrogen atom and involve π bonding. Phosphorus oxides are three dimensional with no multiple p_π—p_π bonds.

2. The P_4 molecule in white phosphorus is very strained. When heated, one of the bonds in the P_4 tetrahedron breaks to partially relieve the strain. If exposed to air, white phosphorus immediately burns to form P_4O_{10}—no heat is necessary!

3. Nitrate ions, nitro groups, and nitric acid are all good oxidizing agents. The nitrogen is in a high oxidation state. The products formed in the explosion are all gases (CO_2, H_2O, N_2, etc.) and the rapid expansion due to the gas formation causes the detonation.

4. One of the H atoms is not acidic because it is attached to the P, not an O atom (*cf.* Figure 55.10).

5. The maximum number of bonds possible around nitrogen in a molecule is four. There are only four orbitals available in which to accommodate electron pairs. If a compound with a stoichiometry such as NF_5 was prepared, it would most likely be an ionic compound $[NF_4]^+F^-$ or an adduct of the type $NF_3 \cdot F_2$.

Iodine atoms are large and the bonds between iodine atoms and other atoms tend to be weak. A molecular PI_5 would be very sterically strained. Nitrogen triiodide NI_3, for example, explodes at the slightest of provocations. An alternative structure might be $[PI_4]^+I^-$ but the steric crowding around the P is still high. The analogous compound PBr_5 exists as $[PBr_4]^+Br^-$ but this dissociates to PBr_3 and Br_2 in the vapor state.

End-of-Unit Problems

1. Predict the trends in the following properties of the elements in Group 5A.
   a. metallic character.
   b. electronegativity.
   c. size of the anion M^{3-}.

2. Predict the trends in the following properties of the elements in Group 5A.
   a. atomic size.
   b. electron affinity.
   c. melting point.

3. Describe the two principal allotropes of phosphorus. Which is more reactive? Which is more stable? Why?

4. Nitrogen is an unreactive element which is why the fixation of nitrogen (and conversion to ammonia) is so significant. Why is nitrogen so unreactive?

5. a. Why does PCl_5 exist but NCl_5 does not?
   b. Why is NCl_3 dangerously explosive whereas PCl_3 is not?
   c. Why is the melting point of red phosphorus so much higher (600°C) than the melting point of white phosphorus (44°C).

6. a. Why does ammonia NH_3 have a much higher boiling point than PH_3?
   b. Why are the oxides of nitrogen planar whereas the oxides of the other elements in the group are three-dimensional?

7. The elements in Group 5A have a maximum oxidation state of +5. Of the elements in this oxidation state, nitrogen, arsenic, and bismuth are the strongest oxidizing agents, and phosphorus and antimony are not so strong. Explain why the oxidizing ability should alternate like this down the group.

8. Arsenic compounds in a +5 oxidation state are relatively difficult to prepare. Why?

9. Identify the Group 5A element or elements, or their compounds:

   a. A binary hydrogen compound manufactured in enormous quantities.

   b. An element used to make type for printing presses.

   c. Two elements found in agricultural fertilizers.

   d. An element that spontaneously ignites in air.

10. Identify the Group 5A element or elements, or their compounds:

    a. A binary hydrogen compound used as a rocket fuel.

    b. A sodium salt used in automobile air bags.

    c. The element used in Paul Erhlich's 'magic bullet'.

    d. The element found in the mineral apatite.

11. Describe the industrial production of nitrogen. What other products are obtained at the same time?

12. Describe the industrial production of ammonia. What is most of the ammonia used for?

13. There are two methods for the production of phosphoric acid. About 90% is made directly from the mineral apatite. What is this phosphoric acid used for? The phosphoric acid used in foods is made from white phosphorus. Describe this process. Why is the phosphoric acid made directly from apatite not suitable for use in foods?

14. What is the oxidation state of nitrogen in the following compounds:

    a. dimethylhydrazine

    b. nitric acid

    c. the ammonium ion

15. What is the oxidation state of nitrogen in the following compounds:

    a. the nitrite ion

    b. nitrogen dioxide

    c. magnesium nitride

16. Write the formulas and draw the structures of the following oxoacids of phosphorus and nitrogen:

    a. nitrous acid

    b. pyrophosphoric acid

    c. phosphorous acid

17. Write the formulas and draw the structures of the following oxoacids of phosphorus and nitrogen:

    a. phosphoric acid

    b. cyclic metaphosphoric acid

    c. triphosphoric acid

18. The pyrophosphate ion $P_4O_7^{4-}$ results from the condensation of two phosphoric acid molecules and the loss of the remaining four hydrogen ions. Draw the structure and derive the formula of the polyphosphate ion that results when three phosphoric acid molecules condense to form a chain and then lose their hydrogen ions.

19. Three phosphoric acid molecules can condense to form a six-membered ring. Draw the structure of this condensed triphosphoric acid and the corresponding polyphosphae ion.

20. The two liquids, dimethylhydrazine $(CH_3)_2NNH_2$ and dinitrogen tetroxide N_2O_4 ignite on contact and are used to fuel the rockets that steer the space shuttle. The products are nitrogen, carbon dioxide, and water. Write a balanced chemical equation for this reaction. What ratio by mass of the two components is required according to the equation?

21. The formation of nitric acid from nitrogen, oxygen, and water can be calculated from the heats of formation of nitric acid and water. Write the equation for the reaction and calculate enthalpy of reaction.

$$\Delta H_f^\circ (HNO_3(aq)) = -207.4 \text{ kJ mol}^{-1}$$
$$\Delta H_f^\circ (H_2O(l)) = -285.8 \text{ kJ mol}^{-1}$$

22. When white phosphorus P_4 is treated with potassium hydroxide KOH, the products are phosphine gas PH_3 and potassium dihydrogen phosphate KH_2PO_4. Write the equation for this reaction.

23. Phosphorus(V) oxide has a high affinity for water and is frequently used in desiccators to absorb water. One mole of P_4O_{10} reacts with six moles of water. Write the equation for the reaction and identify the product.

24. When PCl_5 condenses from a gas to a solid, the compound changes from the molecular PCl_5 to the ionic $[PCl_4]^+[PCl_6]^-$. Describe what is happening in this process in terms of Lewis acid-base theory.

25. When SbF_5 reacts with AsF_3, the compound produced is $[AsF_2]^+[SbF_6]^-$. Describe what is happening in this reaction in terms of Lewis acid-base theory.

Oxygen, Sulfur, and the Group 6A Elements

56.1 Group 6A Elements

Oxygen (dioxygen O_2) makes up 23% of the earth's atmosphere by mass and 46% of the material (other than water) in the earth's crust. Oxygen is present in silicates and aluminosilicates, and in the many minerals that contain the common polyatomic oxoanions such as sulfate, nitrate, carbonate, and phosphate, etc. In addition it is, of course, the major constituent (86%) of the oceans of our planet.

Sulfur occurs in the native state in vast underground deposits and at volcanos, hot springs and other vents. It occurs in the naturally occurring sulfides of metals such as iron, lead, zinc, mercury, arsenic, and antimony. In comparison, selenium and tellurium are relatively rare elements that often occur in association with sulfur and sulfide ores.

The discovery of oxygen is usually credited to C. W. Scheele and J. Priestley as a result of their independent work in 1773 and 1774. Determination of the role of oxygen in combustion and the recognition that oxygen is an element is attributed to Lavoisier—who gave oxygen its name.

Like nitrogen in the preceding group, oxygen exists as a diatomic molecule. It is, however, more reactive than nitrogen and readily forms compounds with almost every element. Although the bond energy of the dioxygen molecule is quite high (493 kJ mol^{-1}), most combustion reactions are exothermic due to the higher bond energies of the combustion products. Because of this, combustion reactions usually continue rapidly once initiated.

The dioxygen molecule is paramagnetic (*cf.* Unit 23) due to the two unpaired electrons in the π^* antibonding orbitals. It condenses to a pale blue liquid at $-183°C$. The blue color is due the absorption of light when oxygen molecules are excited to a state in which the two odd electrons become paired.

Another allotrope of oxygen is **ozone** O_3, the structure of which is shown in Figure 56.2. Sometimes drawn as a Lewis structure with one double bond and one single bond, the π bond extends over all three oxygen atoms so that the π bonding pair of electrons is delocalized over the entire molecule.

Ozone is a toxic, irritating gas that is a component of photochemical smog. Although the gas is essential in the stratosphere, it is highly undesirable at sea level and causes both health problems and damage to materials such as rubber and plastics—ozone is a more powerful oxidizing agent than dioxygen. It readily decomposes to dioxygen and, when required for a chemical reaction, it is usually prepared on site by passing a high voltage electrical discharge through oxygen gas.

The most important property of ozone is its ability to absorb UV radiation. The layer of ozone in the stratosphere protects the surface of the earth from the deleterious effects of high energy ultraviolet radiation.

Differences in the behavior of oxygen and sulfur parallel the differences between nitrogen and phosphorus, and carbon and silicon, in the preceding groups. Oxygen exists as a diatomic molecule with multiple bonding but sulfur exists predominantly as an eight-membered ring of singly-bonded sulfur atoms (Figure 56.3).

The most common allotrope of sulfur S_8 is the yellow orthorhombic form (Figure 56.4). The other principal allotrope is the monoclinic form which also contains

FIGURE 56.1 Some important sulfide minerals are: Pyrite FeS_2 (shown), Sphalerite ZnS, Cinnabar HgS, Galena PbS, Realgar As_4S_4, Stibnite Sb_2S_3.

Sulfur is a constituent of gunpowder (10% by mass), known since the 11th century in China and the 13th century in Europe. The other two constituents are KNO_3 (75%) and charcoal (15%).

128 pm   128 pm
117°

FIGURE 56.2 The structure of ozone.

FIGURE 56.3 The ring structure of sulfur S_8—the principal form of sulfur.

S_8 rings but is stable at higher temperatures; the transition from rhombic sulfur to monoclinic sulfur at 1 atm pressure occurs at 95°C (*cf.* phase diagram Figure 31.14). There are many other allotropes containing rings of anywhere between 6 and 20 sulfur atoms. In addition, sulfur exists in several amorphous forms involving long chains of S atoms that can be made by rapidly cooling liquid sulfur. These amorphous plastic allotropes slowly crystallize to the more stable crystalline allotropes over time.

Several allotropes of selenium are known, some of which consist of Se_8 rings like sulfur. The most stable form of selenium consists of long helical chains of Se atoms (Figure 56.5). Tellurium has a similar helical chain structure. It's interesting that polonium is the only element known to crystallize in a simple cubic lattice under ordinary conditions.

The properties of the elements in Group 6A are compared in Table 56.1.

Industrial Production and Uses

Oxygen gas is obtained on a huge scale by the fractional distillation of liquid air. More oxygen is produced than any other chemical except sodium chloride, sulfuric acid, and nitrogen. The major use of oxygen is in the **Bessemer process** for making steel. Other uses include applications where a high temperature flame is required—its use in an oxyacetylene torch is an example.

Sulfur is obtained in its native state from underground deposits by the **Frasch process** (Figure 56.6). A superheated water-steam mixture at about 160°C and 16 atm is pumped underground to melt the sulfur in the sulfur-bearing strata. The sulfur is more dense than the water and forms a liquid pool at the bottom of the well. The molten sulfur is forced up the inside pipe by the water pressure and compressed air pumped down the central of the three concentric pipes aerates the liquid sulfur and carries it to the surface. The sulfur is obtained with a purity of better than 99.5%. Currently large amounts of sulfur are obtained from petroleum refining and the purification of natural gas.

Almost 90% of all sulfur is used to manufacture sulfuric acid by the **contact process**. Approximately 45 million tons of sulfuric acid is produced annually in the US alone. The sulfur is first burned to produce sulfur dioxide which is oxidized further

FIGURE 56.4 Orthorhombic sulfur.

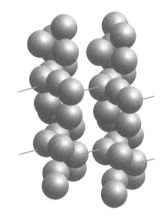

FIGURE 56.5 Segments of the long helical chains of Se atoms in the solid state. A weak van der Walls interaction (gray lines) holds the chains together.

TABLE 56.1 The Group 6A elements.

Name	Symbol	Melting Point °C	Boiling Point °C	ΔH°_{fus} @ m.pt. kJ mol⁻¹	Density g cm⁻³	Ionization Energy kJ mol⁻¹	Covalent Radius pm	Ionic (2−) Radius pm
Oxygen	O	−219	−183	0.44	1.14(*l*)	1314	73	140
Sulfur	S	115	445	1.72	2.0*	1000	103	184
Selenium	Se	219	685	6.69	4.29*	941	117	198
Tellurium	Te	452	990	17.5	6.25	869	135	211
Polonium	Po	254	962		9.25*	812	—	—

* = depends upon the allotrope

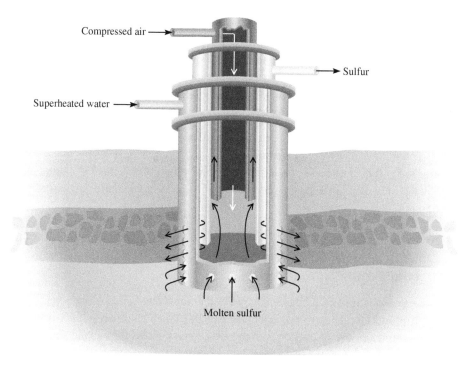

FIGURE 56.6 The Frasch process for the mining of sulfur.

to sulfur trioxide over a vanadium(V) oxide catalyst. The sulfur trioxide is dissolved in sulfuric acid to produce a viscous solution called **oleum** (a mixture of sulfuric acid H_2SO_4 and *pyro*sulfuric acid $H_2S_2O_7$):

$$SO_3(g) + H_2SO_4(l) \rightarrow H_2S_2O_7(l)$$

The oleum is added to water to produce sulfuric acid:

$$H_2S_2O_7(l) + H_2O(l) \rightarrow 2\ H_2SO_4(l)$$

The sulfur trioxide could be added directly to water to produce the sulfuric acid but it reacts very exothermically with water to create a mist of water droplets in which more SO_3 dissolves. This corrosive mist of H_2SO_4 is very persistent and difficult to deal with.

Several uses of sulfuric acid have been described already. About 60% is used in the manufacture of agricultural fertilizers and the remaining 40% is used in the chemical industry. It is used in so many chemical processes that the amount of sulfuric acid produced and used per annum is often used as an indicator of the industrial strength of a nation.

For example, addition of cadmium selenide CdSe to glass makes the color of the glass deep red. Such glass has been used in traffic lights.

Selenium is used in glass manufacture and has been used extensively in photocopying. Amorphous selenium is a photoreceptor and the photocopying process works as follows. A thin layer of selenium on an aluminum drum is electrostatically charged and then exposed to the image to be copied. Where light hits the selenium surface, the electrostatic charge is reduced—the selenium conducts the charge away to the aluminum underneath. This is called **photoconduction**. As a result an electrostatic image of the original is produced on the drum. This image is developed by toner—the particles of toner are attracted to the charged areas of the electrostatic image. The image is then transferred to a sheet of paper and fixed by heating the paper. The image on the selenium drum is removed by flooding the surface with bright light to conduct away the electrostatic charge. Typically, the drums have a lifetime of 100,000 photocopies.

Over the last ten to twelve years, photoconductive organic compounds have largely replaced selenium and arsenic-selenium compounds as photoreceptors in xerography.

EXAMPLE 56.1   REACTION ENTHALPIES

Calculate the energy required or absorbed when sulfur is burned in air to produce sulfur dioxide. Then calculate the enthalpy change when the sulfur dioxide is oxidized to sulfur trioxide over a V_2O_5 catalyst.

The enthalpies of formation are:

$$\Delta H_f^\circ(SO_2) = -296.8 \text{ kJ mol}^{-1}$$
$$\Delta H_f^\circ(SO_3) = -395.7 \text{ kJ mol}^{-1}$$

UNDERSTAND THE QUESTION

This question involves enthalpy calculations of the type first introduced in Unit 13. The enthalpy change for a reaction can be calculated from the difference between the enthalpies of formation of the products and the enthalpies of formation of the reactants.

PLAN THE SOLUTION

Write the equation for the reaction. An enthalpy of reaction is extensive—it applies to the equation as it is written. List the enthalpies of formation, multiply by any coefficients if necessary, and then calculate the difference (products—reactants).

SOLVE THE PROBLEM

$$S(s) + O_2(g) \rightarrow SO_2(g)$$

The reactants are elements in their standard states, with enthalpies of formation equal to zero. The enthalpy change for the reaction is the heat of formation of sulfur dioxide.

The standard state of sulfur is rhombic sulfur S_8. However, in equations, sulfur is often represented simply as S.

$\Delta H^\circ(\text{reaction}) = -296.8 \text{ kJ}$

$$SO_2(s) + \tfrac{1}{2} O_2(g) \rightarrow SO_3(g)$$

$\Delta H^\circ(\text{reaction}) = \Delta H_f^\circ(SO_3) - \Delta H_f^\circ(SO_2) = -395.7 \text{ kJ mol}^{-1} - (-296.8 \text{ kJ mol}^{-1})$

$\Delta H^\circ(\text{reaction}) = -98.9 \text{ kJ}$

PROBLEM 56.1A

The reaction between SO_3 and water is known to be exothermic. Calculate the enthalpy change when one mole of SO_3 reacts with one mole of water to produce one mole of sulfuric acid.

$\Delta H_f^\circ(SO_3) = -395.7 \text{ kJ mol}^{-1}$
$\Delta H_f^\circ(H_2O(l)) = -285.8 \text{ kJ mol}^{-1}$
$\Delta H_f^\circ(H_2SO_4(l)) = -814.0 \text{ kJ mol}^{-1}$

PROBLEM 56.1B

The answer calculated for Problem 56.1A does not tell the complete story because more heat is released when the sulfuric acid is diluted. Calculate the enthalpy change for the reaction shown below. Why is the ΔH_f° for the hydronium ion in aqueous solution equal to the ΔH_f° for water?

$$H_2SO_4(l) + H_2O(l) \rightarrow H_3O^+(aq) + HSO_4^-(aq)$$

$\Delta H_f^\circ(H_2SO_4(l)) = -814.0 \text{ kJ mol}^{-1}$

$\Delta H_f^\circ(H_2O(l)) = -285.8 \text{ kJ mol}^{-1}$

$\Delta H_f^\circ(H_3O^+(aq)) = -285.8 \text{ kJ mol}^{-1}$

$\Delta H_f^\circ(HSO_4^-(aq)) = -887.3 \text{ kJ mol}^{-1}$

56.2   Compounds of Oxygen

As mentioned earlier, oxygen forms compounds with almost every other element. Of these, by far the most important is water H_2O.

Water

Seventy percent of the earth's surface is covered with water. In fact 97% of the water on the planet is present in the oceans. Less than 3% is available as fresh water and most of this exists as ice at the polar icecaps. Less than 0.01% of all available water is present in fresh water lakes and rivers. Considerable effort and resources are devoted to the purification and recycling of water, particularly in areas of the world where fresh water is in limited supply. Desalination of sea water by reverse osmosis (*cf*. Unit 33.4) or distillation provides fresh water in arid regions where rainfall is inadequate.

Water is a curious compound with many seemingly incongruous properties. It is one of the few substances for which the solid state is less dense than the liquid state at the melting point (*cf*. Figure 28.8). It is also a liquid at room temperature, unlike the analogous hydrogen compounds of all the elements surrounding oxygen in the Periodic Table which are gases. These properties are attributable to the strong intermolecular hydrogen bonding (*cf*. Unit 28.4). Compared to the strength of an average covalent bond, a hydrogen bond is not particularly strong—approximately 20 kJ mol⁻¹—but this is considerably stronger than other forces of attraction between molecules. It is this strong hydrogen bonding that is responsible for the high enthalpy of vaporization of water ($\Delta H_{vap}^\circ = 40.7 \text{ kJ mol}^{-1}$), the high specific heat of water (4.184 JK⁻¹g⁻¹), and other unusual properties of water.

Hydrogen Peroxide

Hydrogen peroxide H_2O_2 is a syrupy liquid with a melting point very near that of water (–0.4°C) and a boiling point of 151°C although it decomposes before boiling. As in liquid water, the intermolecular forces are strong hydrogen bonds and the molecule is miscible in all proportions with water. It is commercially available as a 30% solution in water and is usually refrigerated to inhibit decomposition. The solution sold in pharmacies is 3% by mass and is intended for use as an antiseptic. Major uses of hydrogen peroxide are in water purification and as a bleach. Pure hydrogen peroxide has been used as the oxidant in rocket engines.

The structure of H_2O_2 depends to some extent on its environment (Figure 56.7). In the gas phase, the angle between the two O–H bonds is 111° but in the solid state the angle reduces to 90°. In various compounds, such as $Na_2C_2O_4 \cdot H_2O_2$, the angle can be anywhere between 90° and 180°.

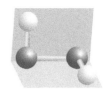

The oxidation state of the oxygen in H_2O_2 is –1 and hydrogen peroxide can act as an oxidizing agent (and be reduced to H_2O) or as a reducing agent (and be oxidized to O_2):

$$2H^+(aq) + H_2O_2(aq) + 2e^- \rightarrow 2H_2O(l) \qquad E^\circ_{red} = +1.78 \text{ V}$$
$$H_2O_2(aq) \rightarrow O_2(g) + 2H^+(aq) + 2e^- \qquad E^\circ_{oxid} = -0.68 \text{ V}$$

FIGURE 56.7 **The structure of hydrogen peroxide H_2O_2.** The angle between the O—H bonds is 90° in the solid state.

The half-cell potentials indicate that hydrogen peroxide disproportionates spontaneously to O_2 and H_2O. Adding the two equations above, the overall process is:

$$2H_2O_2(aq) \rightarrow 2H_2O(l) + O_2(g) \qquad E^\circ = +1.10 \text{ V}$$

This potential corresponds to a free energy change $\Delta G^\circ = -212$ kJ. In reality, the decomposition is slow unless a suitable catalyst is present. For example, the addition of small amounts of potassium iodide KI or manganese dioxide MnO_2 causes a rapid decomposition of H_2O_2 (Figure 56.8).

Oxides

In all compounds except those with fluorine, oxygen has a negative oxidation state. Its usual oxidation state is –2. The exceptions are oxidation numbers of –1 in peroxides and –½ in superoxides.

The character of the bonding in the oxides varies with the position in the Periodic Table of the element involved (Figure 56.9).

FIGURE 56.8 **The catalysed decomposition of hydrogen peroxide H_2O_2.** Addition of potassium iodide causes the immediate exothermic release of oxygen.

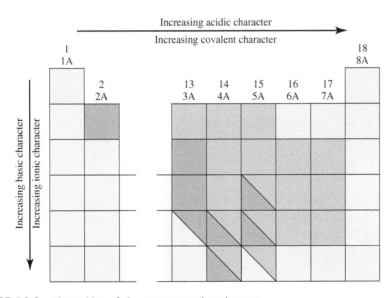

FIGURE 56.9 **The oxides of the representative elements.** The basic oxides of the electropositive metals are shown in light blue. The acidic oxides of the nonmetals are shown in dark gray. The amphoteric oxides are shown in dark blue. Note that the acid or base character of an oxide depends upon the oxidation state of the element. The higher the oxidation state, the more covalent the bonding, and the more acidic the oxide. For example, SnO is amphoteric but SnO_2, while insoluble in water, reacts only with bases and is therefore considered acidic. Both are shown on the diagram.

With the electropositive metals on the left side of the Periodic Table, the bonding is ionic and the oxides dissolve in water to produce basic solutions. A typical example is sodium oxide:

$$2 \, NaO(aq) + H_2O(l) \rightarrow 2 \, NaOH(aq)$$

This is analogous to the behavior of S^{2-} in aqueous solution.

Oxide ions cannot exist in water. As soon as they dissolve they react with water to produce hydroxide ions. This reaction has an extremely large equilibrium constant ($>10^{22}$). In other words, the oxide ion is a very strong base.

$$O^{2-}(aq) + H_2O(l) \rightarrow 2 \, OH^-(aq)$$

Note that even if a metal oxide is not very soluble in water it will act as a base in its reactions with acids.

With the electronegative nonmetallic elements on the right side of the Periodic Table, the bonding is covalent. The oxides are usually small molecules that dissolve in water to produce acidic solutions. A typical example is sulfur trioxide:

$$SO_3(g) + H_2O(l) \rightarrow H_2SO_4(aq)$$

Some nonmetal oxides do not react with water, especially those with lower oxidation numbers. For example, NO_2 dissolves but NO and N_2O do not; and CO_2 dissolves but CO does not. Other oxides are polymeric—an example is SiO_2—and do not react with water.

Aluminum, beryllium, zinc, and a few other oxides are **amphoteric**—they behave as acids in basic solution and as bases in acidic solution. In acids, for example, aluminum oxide forms hydrated aluminum(III) ions. In basic solution aluminum forms hydrated aluminum hydroxide complex ions (*cf.* Unit 46.3).

EXAMPLE 56.2   HYDROGEN PEROXIDE AS A REDUCING AGENT OR OXIDIZING AGENT

Write an equation for the reaction between dichlorine heptoxide Cl_2O_7 and hydrogen peroxide H_2O_2 to form the chlorite ion and oxygen gas in basic solution. Is the hydrogen peroxide acting as a reducing agent or as an oxidizing agent in this reaction?

UNDERSTAND THE QUESTION

Redox reactions were discussed in Unit 9 and a procedure was established for writing balanced equations for redox reactions.

PLAN THE SOLUTION

Write the equation for the reaction; divide into two half reactions; and balance each half reaction according to the procedures established in Unit 9. Recall that acidic conditions can be assumed until the last step, when hydroxide ions can be added to each side to establish basic conditions.

SOLVE THE PROBLEM

The equation for the reaction is:

$$Cl_2O_7(aq) + H_2O_2(aq) \rightarrow ClO_2^-(aq) + O_2(g)$$

Divide the equation into two half-reactions:

oxidation: $H_2O_2 \rightarrow O_2$

reduction: $Cl_2O_7 \rightarrow ClO_2^-$

Balance these half-reactions. First balance the elements other than O and H:

oxidation: $H_2O_2 \rightarrow O_2$

reduction: $Cl_2O_7 \rightarrow 2ClO_2^-$

Balance the O by adding H_2O to the appropriate side:

oxidation: $H_2O_2 \rightarrow O_2$

reduction: $Cl_2O_7 \rightarrow 2ClO_2^- + 3H_2O$

Now balance the H by adding H^+ to the appropriate side:

oxidation: $H_2O_2 \rightarrow O_2 + 2H^+$

reduction: $Cl_2O_7 + 6H^+ \rightarrow 2ClO_2^- + 3H_2O$

The charges now need to be balanced:

oxidation: $H_2O_2 \rightarrow O_2 + 2H^+ + 2e^-$

reduction: $Cl_2O_7 + 6H^+ + 8e^- \rightarrow 2ClO_2^- + 3H_2O$

The number of electrons lost (2) in the oxidation process is the same as the change in the oxidation number of the element that is oxidized ($2 \times +1$) and the number of electrons gained (8) in the reduction process is the same as the change in the oxidation number of the element that is reduced (2×-4).

The two half-reactions must now be matched. Multiply the first reaction by 4:

oxidation: $4H_2O_2 \rightarrow 4O_2 + 8H^+ + 8e^-$

reduction: $Cl_2O_7 + 6H^+ + 8e^- \rightarrow 2ClO_2^- + 3H_2O$

The equations for the two half-reactions are now added together. The electrons cancel from both sides:

$$4H_2O_2 + Cl_2O_7 \rightarrow 4O_2 + 2H^+ + 2ClO_2^- + 3H_2O$$

The solution must be made basic. This is done by adding 2 OH^- ions to both sides of the equation. The H^+ and OH^- combine to form water:

$$4H_2O_2 + Cl_2O_7 + 2OH^- \rightarrow 4O_2 + 2ClO_2^- + 5H_2O$$

The equation is now balanced in terms of both mass and charge. Hydrogen peroxide is the reducing agent in this reaction—it is oxidized to O_2.

PROBLEM 56.2A

Hydrogen peroxide often acts as an oxidizing agent. For example, hydrogen peroxide will oxidize chromium(III) in basic solution ($Cr(OH)_3$) to the chromate ion CrO_4^{2-}. Write a balanced equation for this reaction.

PROBLEM 56.2B

In Example 56.2, it was determined that hydrogen peroxide will reduce dichlorine heptoxide to the chlorite ion. It is probably not surprising therefore that hydrogen peroxide will also reduce chlorine dioxide ClO_2 to the chlorite ion. Write a balanced equation for this reaction in basic solution.

Transition metals at the center of the Periodic Table have variable oxidation states. In general, the higher the oxidation state, the more covalent the bonding and the more acidic the oxide. This is clearly illustrated by the three common oxides of chromium:

CrO	oxidation number +2	basic oxide	similar to MgO
Cr_2O_3	oxidation number +3	amphoteric oxide	similar to Al_2O_3
CrO_3	oxidation number +6	acidic oxide	similar to SO_3

56.3 Compounds of Sulfur

The sulfur compound analogous to water H_2O is hydrogen sulfide H_2S. However, there is no intermolecular hydrogen bonding and H_2S is a gas. It is highly toxic with a characteristic rotten egg smell. The structure of the molecule is similar to water but the H—S—H angle is only 92° (*cf.* Unit 22.6) indicating that the orbitals used in bonding are predominantly p in character. Hydrogen selenide and hydrogen telluride have very similar structures.

Hydrogen sulfide is more acidic than water; however, the pK_{a1} is 7.05 and the pK_{a2} is about 19 (K_{a2} is only about 10^{-19}). This means that the sulfide ion, like the oxide ion, is a strong base in aqueous solution—it doesn't exist as S^{2-} but as HS^- and OH^-. The sulfides of many metals are insoluble with very high values for K_{sp} (*cf.* Unit 45).

Sulfur has the ability to catenate and it will dissolve in aqueous solutions of sodium sulfide to produce polysulfide salts Na_2S_x, where x can be any number between 2 and 6. The parent acids, called polysulfanes, can be obtained by adding acid to the polysulfides. When x is 2, the polysulfane is H_2S_2. This the analog of hydrogen peroxide and it has a similar structure (with an angle in the gas state of 91°). The polysulfide ion S_2^- is the analog of the superoxide ion O_2^-. Like the superoxide ion, it is a paramagnetic species with an odd electron.

> The green or blue color of lapis lazuli is due to the presence of the polysulfide ions S_2^- and S_3^- in the aluminosilicate mineral. The actual color depends upon the relative amounts of S_2^- (green) and S_3^- (blue) present. Lapis lazuli was once ground up to provide blue pigment for artists' paints. Ultramarine is now made synthetically and used for the same purpose.

The Sulfur Oxides, Oxoacids, and Oxoanions

The two principal oxides of sulfur are sulfur dioxide SO_2 and sulfur trioxide SO_3. The corresponding oxoacids are sulfurous acid H_2SO_3 and sulfuric acid H_2SO_4. Sulfur dioxide is a colorless, toxic gas with recognizable choking smell. It occurs naturally in the atmosphere through volcanic emission and the atmospheric oxidation of hydrogen sulfide. However, the combustion of oil and coal in electricity-generating plants contributes greatly to the concentration of SO_2 in the atmosphere and to the acid rain that results. Recent efforts to scrub emissions and remove the SO_2 have reduced this pollution. The recovered sulfur is a valuable resource and helps to pay for its removal.

> There are other less stable oxides of sulfur such as S_2O, S_3O, S_4O, etc.

Sulfur dioxide (b.pt. –10°C) is a bent molecule (Figure 56.10) in which the S—O bonds are slightly stronger (548 kJ mol⁻¹) than the S–O bond in the unstable diatomic molecule S–O (524 kJ mol⁻¹). This can be contrasted with the O–O bond energies in ozone (297 kJ mol⁻¹) which are weaker than the bond in dioxygen (490 kJ mol⁻¹). Sulfur dioxide is much more stable than ozone and its stability is attributed to strong S—O multiple bonding, perhaps involving the d orbitals of the sulfur.

Sulfur trioxide (b.pt. 45°C) is a trigonal planar molecule with S—O bond lengths almost the same as those in SO_2. In the vapor and liquid states, the SO_3 molecule exists in equilibrium with the trimer S_3O_9 (Figure 56.11). In the solid state, and in the

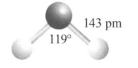

143 pm

119°

FIGURE 56.10 The structure of sulfur dioxide.

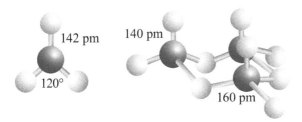

FIGURE 56.11   The SO_3 molecule and its trimer S_3O_9.

absence of any water, the trimer S_3O_9 is the only species present. As noted earlier, both sulfur dioxide and sulfur trioxide are prepared in vast amounts for the production of sulfuric acid.

Sulfurous acid is a weak diprotic acid. When sulfur dioxide dissolves in water, the SO_2 molecules react with water to some extent to form H_2SO_3 molecules. The H_2SO_3 molecules ionize to form hydrogen sulfite ions:

$$SO_2 + H_2O \rightleftharpoons H_2SO_3$$
$$H_2SO_3 + H_2O \rightleftharpoons H_3O^+ + HSO_3^- \qquad K_{a1} = 1.4 \times 10^{-2}$$
$$HSO_3^- + H_2O \rightleftharpoons H_3O^+ + SO_3^{2-} \qquad K_{a2} = 6.3 \times 10^{-8}$$

In this respect, sulfur dioxide behaves similarly to carbon dioxide. Carbonic acid, H_2CO_3, is predominantly a solution of carbon dioxide molecules in water.

Sulfuric acid is a viscous liquid which is miscible with water in all proportions. Its reaction with water is highly exothermic and addition of water to sulfuric acid is extremely dangerous due to the explosive formation of steam and the eruption of sulfuric acid at the surface. To dilute sulfuric acid, the acid should always be added slowly to water. Like sulfurous acid, sulfuric acid is dibasic. However, the loss of the first hydrogen ion is easy and the acid is strong:

$$H_2SO_3 + H_2O \rightleftharpoons H_3O^+ + HSO_3^- \qquad K_{a1} = {\sim}1 \times 10^{2}$$
$$HSO_3^- + H_2O \rightleftharpoons H_3O^+ + SO_3^{2-} \qquad K_{a2} = 1.2 \times 10^{-2}$$

Not only is sulfuric acid a strong acid, it is also a powerful dehydrating agent due to its affinity for water and a powerful oxidizing agent.

The salts of both acids are well known. Sodium sulfite Na_2SO_3, for example, is used in preserving meat.

Condensation of two molecules of sulfuric acid produces *pyro*sulfuric (disulfuric) acid $H_2S_2O_7$ (Figure 56.12). A considerable amount of this acid and its conjugate base is present in pure sulfuric acid. Further condensation to produce a cyclic *meta*sulfuric acid is impossible because such a condensation would produce the acid anhydride SO_3 instead (Figure 56.10). Peroxo derivatives of sulfuric acid can be prepared. The structures of peroxo-monosulfuric acid (Caro's acid) and peroxodisulfuric acid are illustrated in Figure 56.12.

N. Caro first made this acid in 1898.

Substitution of a sulfur atom for an oxygen atom in sulfuric acid yields thiosulfuric acid $H_2S_2O_3$. The corresponding anion is the thiosulfate ion $S_2O_3^{2-}$. A series of polythionic acids $H_2S_{n+2}O_6$ can be prepared, making use of the ability of sulfur to catenate. When n = 0, the acid is dithionic acid for which only the corresponding anion, dithionate $O_3SSO_3^{2-}$, is known. When n = 1, the acid is called trithionic acid—this is the sulfur analog of *pyro*sulfuric acid. Tetrathionic acid is the sulfur analog of peroxodisulfuric acid (Figure 56.13).

The prefix *thio*– in a name indicates the substitution of an oxygen atom by a sulfur atom.

Sodium thiosulfate was once known as sodium hyposulfite and was used to fix photographic images. It is the 'hypo' referred to in photography.

(a) Pyrosulfuric (disulfuric) acid $H_2S_2O_7$

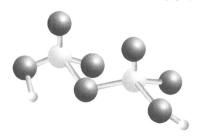

(b) Peroxomonosulfuric acid (Caro's acid)

(c) Peroxodisulfuric acid.

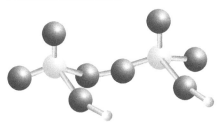

(a) Dithionic acid $H_2S_2O_6$

(b) Trithionic acid $H_2S_3O_6$

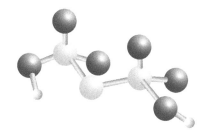

(c) Tetrathionic acid $H_2S_4O_6$

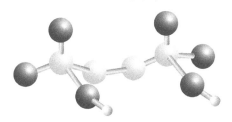

FIGURE 56.12 (a) Pyrosulfuric (disulfuric) acid $H_2S_2O_7$; (b) Peroxomonosulfuric acid (Caro's acid); (c) Peroxodisulfuric acid.

FIGURE 56.13 (a) Dithionic acid $H_2S_2O_6$; (b) Trithionic acid $H_2S_3O_6$; (c) Tetrathionic acid $H_2S_4O_6$.

G. A. Olah was awarded the 1994 Nobel Prize in Chemistry for his work on the production of carbonium ions (carbocations) using superacids.

Fluorosulfuric acid HSO_3F, made from the interaction of SO_3 and HF, is an interesting acid because when mixed with SbF_5, it is one of the strongest acids known. Often referred to as **magic acid**, or generally as a **superacid**, it is an extremely strong hydrogen ion donor. Hydrocarbons—compounds that are not normally considered bases—act as bases in magic acid to produce carbonium ions:

$$HSO_3F + SbF_5 \rightarrow H_2SO_3F^+ + FSO_3SbF_5^-$$
$$(CH_3)_3CH + H_2SO_3F^+ \rightarrow (CH_3)_3C^+ + H_2 + HSO_3F$$

EXAMPLE 56.3 OXIDATION NUMBERS

Assigning oxidation numbers to the individual sulfur atoms in the oxoacids and oxoanions of sulfur can sometimes be difficult. Usually, however, average oxidation numbers can be used quite successfully. For example,

a. What is the average oxidation number of the sulfur atom in trithionic acid $H_2S_3O_6$?

b. A hypothetical route to trithionic acid can be visualized as the addition of two moles of SO_3 to a mole of H_2S:

$$H_2S + 2\,SO_3 \rightarrow H_2S_3O_6$$

What element is oxidized, and what element is reduced in this reaction? What are the changes in the oxidation numbers?

UNDERSTAND THE QUESTION

Assigning oxidation numbers is most easily done by using the few rules that were described in Unit 9. Once oxidation numbers are assigned, the change that occurs in the reaction can be calculated.

PLAN THE SOLUTION

Oxygen very often has an oxidation state of –2 but be on the lookout for peroxides and superoxides. Hydrogen with non-metals has an oxidation state of +1. The oxidation number of the remaining element S can be determined by difference.

SOLVE THE PROBLEM

a. Trithionic acid $H_2S_3O_6$

O: $6 \times -2 = -12$

H: $2 \times +1 = +2$

S: +10 distributed over 3 S

+3 1/3 each

An alternative assignment might be +4 for each S at the ends and +2 for the S at the center (*cf.* Figure 56.13b). Or perhaps, +5 for each S at the ends and 0 for the S at the center. Multiple possibilities help to explain why averages are often used.

b. $H_2S + 2 SO_3 \rightarrow H_2S_3O_6$

In H_2S, the oxidation number of the S is –2

In SO_3, the oxidation number of the S is +6

The S in H_2S is oxidized from –2 to +3 1/3

The S in SO_3 is reduced from +6 to +3 1/3

PROBLEM 56.3A

One way to prepare trithionic acid is via is sodium salt. This salt can be prepared by the reaction of cold hydrogen peroxide and sodium thiosulfate. The solution can then be acidified to obtain a solution of the acid.

$$2 Na_2S_2O_3 + 4 H_2O_2 \rightarrow Na_2S_3O_6 + Na_2SO_4 + 4 H_2O$$

What is the oxidation state of sulfur in each sulfur compound involved in this reaction?

PROBLEM 56.3B

Peroxodisulfuric acid has the structure illustrated in Figure 56.12(c). How would you assign the oxidation numbers to the elements in this acid?

Sulfur–Halogen Compounds

There are several sulfur fluorine compounds, the simplest of which are the series SF_2, SF_4, and SF_6 (Figure 56.14). The structures of these compounds are those predicted by VSEPR theory. The use of the d orbitals of the sulfur atom for bonding in SF_4 and SF_6 is in some doubt—it seems likely that the d orbitals are not involved to the extent suggested by the hybrid schemes sp^3d and sp^3d^2 (*cf.* Units 22 and 23). Sulfur hexafluoride is thermally and chemically quite stable. It is a colorless, tasteless, nonflammable,

SF_2 SF_4 SF_6

FIGURE 56.14 The structures of SF_2, SF_4, and SF_6.

nontoxic gas. The general inertness of the gas is attributed to the sulfur atom being surrounded and protected by the six fluorine atoms so that kinetic pathways for reactions are not available.

Disulfur difluoride S_2F_2 has a structure very similar to hydrogen peroxide and O_2F_2. The dihedral angle is 88°.

Two important sulfur–chlorine compounds are the nasty–smelling yellow S_2Cl_2 (b.pt. 138°C) and red SCl_2 (b.pt. 59°C). As you might expect, the disulfur dichloride has the same structure as S_2F_2 with a dihedral angle of 85°. It is manufactured on a large scale and is used for example in the vulcanization of rubber.

Sulfur–Oxygen–Halogen Compounds

The two principal oxohalides of sulfur are the sulfuryl halides SO_2X_2 and the thionyl halides SOX_2. For example, thionyl chloride is $SOCl_2$, prepared by the chlorination of sulfur dioxide using PCl_5. It is a colorless liquid (b.pt. 76°C) that reacts vigorously with water. Sulfuryl chloride SO_2Cl_2 is also a colorless liquid (b.pt. 69°C) made by the reaction of SO_2 and Cl_2 in the presence of a catalyst. Fluorine and bromine analogs are also known.

Sulfur–Nitrogen Compounds

Sulfur–nitrogen compounds are interesting not only because of their unusual structures and properties but because the description of the bonding in some of the compounds presents a challenge. The first sulfur–nitrogen compound, the yellow-orange tetrasulfur tetranitride S_4N_4, was prepared in 1835 by W. Gregory. Ammonia is passed through a warm (50°C) solution of S_2Cl_2 in an organic solvent such as benzene:

$$16\ NH_3 + 4\ S_2Cl_2 \rightarrow S_4N_4 + S_8 + 12\ NH_4Cl$$

The structure of the S_4N_4 is a puckered eight-membered ring in which the S–N bond lengths are all the same (162 pm) and are intermediate in length between single bond and double bond lengths. The sulfur atoms on opposite sides of the ring approach quite closely (258 pm) resulting in some interaction (Figure 56.15). It is impossible to write a single valence bond picture for the bonding in S_4N_4 and several resonance hybrids must be considered.

When S_4N_4 is passed over silver wool under very low pressure at 250°C, disulfur dinitride S_2N_2 is obtained. The S_2N_2 has a square planar structure (Figure 56.16) and, as for S_4N_4, a description of the bonding in the molecule using valence bond theory is difficult. The compound explodes above 30°C. When left at room temperature, the compound slowly polymerizes to polythiazyl $(SN)_x$ which consists of long chains of

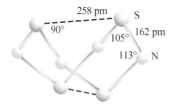

258 pm

90°

S

105°

162 pm

113°

N

FIGURE 56.15 The structure of tetrasulfur tetranitride S_4N_4.

Example 56.4 involves writing some of the resonance structures for S_4N_4. There are 44 valence electrons.

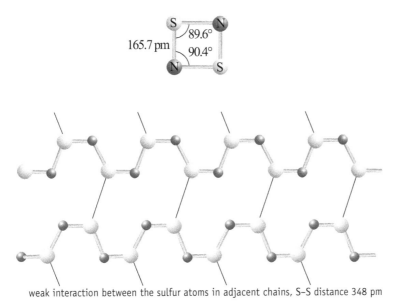

weak interaction between the sulfur atoms in adjacent chains, S–S distance 348 pm

FIGURE 56.16   The structures of the square disulfur dinitride S_2N_2 and the fibrous polymer polythiazyl $(SN)_n$.

alternating sulfur and nitrogen atoms with weak bonding between the sulfur atoms of adjacent chains. The interesting property of polythiazyl is that it conducts an electrical current along the chains—the polymer has a typical bronze colored metallic lustre. The conductivity of the polymer along the chains is almost as high as that of mercury. Polythiazyl is sometimes described as a one-dimensional metal.

Sulfur–Phosphorus Compounds

The structures of the sulfur–phosphorus compounds are similar to those of the phosphorus oxygen compounds. The basic arrangement is a tetrahedron of phosphorus atoms with a varying number of sulfur atoms along the edges of the tetrahedron or as terminal atoms on the phosphorus atoms. Two relatively important compounds are P_4S_3 which is used in match heads and P_4S_{10} which is a precursor in the synthesis of many organic compounds of sulfur and phosphorus. These two sulfur–phosphorus compounds are illustrated in Figure 56.17.

The two reactants in common match heads are P_4S_3 and potassium chlorate $KClO_3$. 70% of the material is ground glass, iron(III) and zinc oxides, glue, and water.

Safety matches separate the two reactants. The $KClO_3$ is on the match head and the side of the matchbox is covered with a mixture of red P_4, Sb_2S_3 and glue.

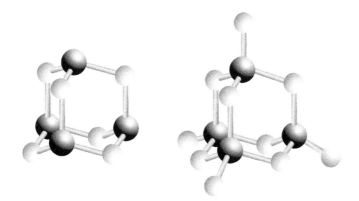

FIGURE 56.17   The structures of P_4S_3 and P_4O_{10}.

EXAMPLE 56.4 LEWIS STRUCTURES FOR S₄N₄ AND S₂N₂

Tetrasulfur tetranitride S_4N_4 is a diamagnetic orange solid (m.pt. 178°C) which tends to explode when heated or struck. The structure is an eight-membered ring (Figure 56.15) in which all the bond lengths are equal (162 pm). The bond length implies that some multiple bonding. Suggest a possible Lewis structure.

UNDERSTAND THE QUESTION

A typical S–N single bond length is approximately 178 pm. The shorter bond in S_4N_4 suggests some π bonding. The fact that the molecule is diamagnetic means that there are no unpaired electrons. The distance between the sulfur atoms on opposite corners of the eight-membered ring is 258 pm, somewhat longer than an S—S bond (208 pm), but certainly shorter than a nonbonding distance.

PLAN THE SOLUTION

Draw the ring of eight atoms and count the number of valence electrons available. Place one pair of electrons in each bond. Place a lone pair on each sulfur atom and each nitrogen atom. Add bonding electrons appropriately to accomplish an octet around each N atom. Then count how many electrons have been used and determine where to place any remaining.

SOLVE THE PROBLEM

There are 44 valence electrons (4 × 5 from N) and (4 × 6 from S)

The arrangement of atoms is:

```
   N   S   N

   S       S

   N   S   N
```

Add one bonding pair for each bond:

```
N—S—N
|     |
S     S
|     |
N—S—N
```

Add the lone pairs:

```
••  ••  ••
N—S—N
 |     |
:S     S:
 |     |
N—S—N
••  ••  ••
```

Add double bonds:

```
••  ••  ••
N—S=N
 ‖     |
:S     S:
 |     ‖
N=S—N
••  ••  ••
```

This has used 40 electrons, so there are 4 remaining. There are no further orbitals on the nitrogen (they each now have an octet), so place one on each S. There is a weak across-ring interaction which must be sufficient to cause the odd electrons to paired up:

```
••  ••  ••
N—S=N
 ‖       |
:S•——————•S:
 |       ‖
N=S—N
••  ••  ••
```

This is just one of many Lewis structures that can be drawn. The double bonds can be distributed in various ways. All structures contribute to a greater or lesser extent to the resonance hybrid.

PROBLEM 56.4A

Suggest why the polymer polythiazyl $(SN)_n$ is sometimes described as a one-dimensional metal.

PROBLEM 56.4B

The structure of disulfur dinitride S_2N_2 is an almost perfect square with an edge length of 165 pm (Figure 56.16). Draw a possible Lewis structure for the molecule. The fact that the molecule is diamagnetic illustrates the inadequacy of Lewis structures.

51.4   Oxoacids of Selenium and Tellurium

Both selenous acid H_2SeO_3 and selenic acid H_2SeO_4 exist and both can be crystallized from solution (unlike H_2SO_3). Selenous acid is a weak acid (pK_{a1} = 2.5 and pK_{a2} = 7.3). Selenic acid, like sulfuric acid, is a strong acid. Its second ionization constant pK_{a2} is 1.92. Tellurous acid H_2TeO_3 (pK_{a1} = 2.5 and pK_{a2} = 7.7) and telluric acid H_6TeO_6 (pK_{a1} = 7.7 and pK_{a2} = 11.3) also exist. Tellurous acid is similar to selenous acid but telluric acid is significantly different from selenic acid and sulfuric acid. It exists as the octahedral $Te(OH)_6$ molecule in the solid state and in aqueous solution (Figure 56.18). It is by comparison a very weak acid.

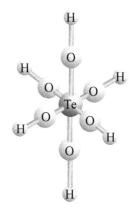

FIGURE 56.18   The octahedral structure of telluric acid H_6TeO_6.

Review Questions

1. Describe differences in the properties of oxygen and sulfur.

2. Compare the properties of H_2O and H_2S. Why are they so different?

3. Hydrogen peroxide is normally considered to be an oxidizing agent. How can it act as a reducing agent?

4. Describe the structural relationship between peroxodisulfuric acid and tetrathionic acid.

5. Look up and compare the acid strengths of sulfuric acid, selenic acid, and telluric acid.

Solutions to Problems

PROBLEM 56.1A

$$SO_3(g) + H_2O(l) \rightarrow H_2SO_4(l)$$

$$\Delta H°(\text{reaction}) = \Delta H_f°(H_2SO_4) - [\Delta H_f°(SO_3) + \Delta H_f°(H_2O)]$$

$$= -814.0 \text{ kJ mol}^{-1} - (-395.7 \text{ kJ mol}^{-1} -285.8 \text{ kJ mol}^{-1})$$

$$= -132.5 \text{ kJ}$$

PROBLEM 56.2A

The equation for the reaction is:

$$Cr^{3+}(aq) + H_2O_2(aq) \rightarrow CrO_4^{2-}(aq)$$

Divide the equation into two half-reactions:

oxidation: $Cr^{3+} \rightarrow CrO_4^{2-}$

reduction: $H_2O_2 \rightarrow$

Elements other than O and H are balanced. Balance the O by adding H_2O:

oxidation: $Cr^{3+} + 4H_2O \rightarrow CrO_4^{2-}$

reduction: $H_2O_2 \rightarrow 2H_2O$

Balance the H by adding H^+ to the appropriate side:

oxidation: $Cr^{3+} + 4H_2O \rightarrow CrO_4^{2-} + 8H^+$

reduction: $H_2O_2 + 2H^+ \rightarrow 2H_2O$

The charges now need to be balanced:

oxidation: $Cr^{3+} + 4H_2O \rightarrow CrO_4^{2-} + 8H^+ + 3e^-$

reduction: $H_2O_2 + 2H^+ + 2e^- \rightarrow 2H_2O$

The number of electrons lost (3) in the oxidation process is the same as the change in the oxidation number of the element that is oxidized ($1\times +3$) and the number of electrons gained (2) in the reduction process is the same as the change in the oxidation number of the element that is reduced (2×-1).

The two half-reactions must now be matched. Multiply the first reaction by 2 and the second by 3:

oxidation: $2Cr^{3+} + 8H_2O \rightarrow 2CrO_4^{2-} + 16H^+ + 6e^-$

reduction: $3H_2O_2 + 6H^+ + 6e^- \rightarrow 6H_2O$

The equations for the two half-reactions are now added together. The electrons cancel from both sides:

$2Cr^{3+} + 2H_2O + 3H_2O_2 \rightarrow 2CrO_4^{2-} + 10H^+$

The solution must be made basic. This is done by adding 10 OH^- ions to both sides of the equation. The H^+ and OH^- combine to form water:

$2Cr^{3+} + 10OH^- + 3H_2O_2 \rightarrow 2CrO_4^{2-} + 8H_2O$

The equation is now balanced in terms of both mass and charge. The Cr^{3+} should be written as the hydroxide:

$2Cr(OH)_3 + 4OH^- + 3H_2O_2 \rightarrow 2CrO_4^{2-} + 8H_2O$

PROBLEM 56.3A

$Na_2S_2O_3$	Na: +1	O: -2	S: +2 each
$Na_2S_3O_6$	Na: +1	O: -2	S: +3 1/3 each
Na_2SO_4	Na: +1	O: -2	S: +6 each

PROBLEM 56.4A

The polymer polythiazyl $(SN)_n$ has a bronze color and metallic luster that is typical of metals. These properties arise from the band structure of molecular orbitals characteristic of metals. The conductivity of polythiazyl is much greater along the chain than in the two other dimensions across adjacent chains. The π bonding along the long alternating S—N chain creates the partially full band of molecular orbitals necessary for conduction in that direction.

Answers to Review Questions

1. The difference between oxygen and sulfur parallels the difference between nitrogen and phosphorus, and carbon and silicon, discussed in previous chapters. The difference results from the smaller size of the Period 2 element, the nonexistence of d orbitals in the second principal quantum level, and the ability of Period 2 elements to form multiple bonds. Of all the elements in the Periodic Table, multiple bonding using p_π orbitals is particularly important for carbon, nitrogen, and oxygen.

2. The fundamental difference between H_2O and H_2S, and what makes water unique among all compounds, is its ability to form hydrogen bonds so effectively. Each water molecule has two lone pairs and two hydrogen atoms and therefore can form four hydrogen bonds. This dramatically affects the physical properties of water. The boiling point of water, for example, is 200°C higher than the trend in Group 6A would predict.

3. The oxygen in hydrogen peroxide has an oxidation state of –1. Hydrogen peroxide can therefore act as an oxidizing agent and be reduced to H_2O and it can act as a reducing agent and be oxidized to O_2.

4. Peroxodisulfuric acid and tetrathionic acid have very similar structures. A peroxo group consists of two oxygen atoms together (as in hydrogen peroxide). In tetrathionic acid the two oxygen atoms are replaced by sulfur atoms (*cf*. Figures 56.12c and 56.13c).

5. The acid ionization constants of sulfuric acid and selenic acid are very similar. Both are strong acids in aqueous solution—the first hydrogen is almost completely ionized in both cases. The second ionization constants for both are 1.2×10^{-2}. Selenic acid is a more powerful oxidizing agent than sulfuric acid. For example, unlike sulfuric acid, selenic acid will oxidize gold and palladium.

Telluric acid is quite different. It exists as octahedral $Te(OH)_6$ molecules both in the solid state and in solution. It behaves more like the iodine species $IO(OH)_5$ (*cf*. Unit 57) than sulfuric acid and selenic acid. Telluric acid is very weak, K_{a1} is about 2×10^{-8} and K_{a2} is about 5×10^{-12}.

End-of-Unit Problems

1. Identify the element in Group 6A that
   a. has the highest electronegativity
   b. is most metallic in character
   c. exists as an allotrope of eight-membered rings

2. Identify the element in Group 6A that
   a. is paramagnetic
   b. exists as an allotrope E_3 (where E is the element)
   c. has the lowest ionization energy

3. Determine the oxidation number of the underlined element in the following compounds:
   a. $\underline{O}F_2$
   b. $H_2\underline{S}O_4$
   c. $\underline{Te}(OH)_6$
   d. $\underline{O}_3$

4. Determine the oxidation number of the underlined element in the following compounds:
   a. $\underline{S}_8$
   b. $H_2\underline{S}_2O_7$
   c. $\underline{Se}O_3$
   d. $\underline{O}_2F_2$

5. Identify the Group 6A element or elements, or their compounds:
   a. An allotrope essential in absorbing high energy UV radiation from the sun.
   b. A toxic gas with a characteristic smell of rotten eggs.
   c. An element mined by the Frasch process.
   d. An unreactive gas 5.2 times more dense than nitrogen.

6. Identify the Group 6A element or elements, or their compounds:
   a. An acid that is a powerful dehydrating agent.
   b. An element once used as a photoreceptor in xerography.
   c. A compound structurally similar to hydrazine that acts as either an oxidizing agent or a reducing agent.
   d. The element found in both rhombic and monoclinic allotropes.

7. a. Why does SF_6 exist but not OF_6?
   b. Why is sulfuric acid H_2SO_4 a stronger acid than sulfurous acid H_2SO_3?

8. a. Why does oxygen have a positive oxidation state only when it is combined with fluorine—as in OF_2?
   b. Why does oxygen exist naturally as dioxygen O_2 whereas sulfur exists predominantly as the molecule S_8?

9. Hydrogen peroxide can act as an oxidizing agent or as a reducing agent. Write and balance an equation representing the reaction of hydrogen peroxide with potassium iodide to produce iodine. Is the hydrogen peroxide acting as a reducing agent or as an oxidizing agent in this case?

10. Hydrogen peroxide can act as an oxidizing agent or as a reducing agent. Write and balance an equation representing the reaction of hydrogen peroxide with potassium permanganate to produce manganese(II) in acidic solution. Is the hydrogen peroxide acting as a reducing agent or as an oxidizing agent in this case?

11. Classify the following oxides as acidic, amphoteric, or basic:
    a. Al_2O_3
    b. SO_3
    c. SnO

12. Classify the following oxides as acidic, amphoteric, or basic:
    a. Li_2O
    b. Sb_2O_3
    c. Cl_2O_7

13. What are the oxoacids that correspond to the following acidic oxides?
    a. CO_2
    b. N_2O_3
    c. P_4O_{10}

14. What are the conjugate oxoacids of the following oxoanions?
    a. $HSeO_4^-$
    b. NO_2^-
    c. $H_2PO_4^-$

15. Predict the structures of the following sulfur molecules or ions:
    a. SF_4
    b. S_2F_2
    c. SF_5^-

16. Predict the structures of the following sulfur molecules or ions:

    a. SF_6

    b. H_3S^+

    c. $S_2O_3^{2-}$

17. The sulfur trioxide trimer and the cyclic metaphosphoric acid $H_3P_3O_9$ are similar in structure. Draw both molecules and compare the two structures.

18. Draw the P_4 molecule of white phosphorus and the structures of the phosphorus oxides P_4O_6 and P_4O_{10}. Compare the structures.

19. Predict the products of the reaction between pyrosulfuric acid $H_2S_2O_7$ and water.

20. Write an equation for the reaction between concentrated sulfuric acid and sulfur at high temperatures to produce sulfur dioxide and water.

21. The reaction of sodium carbonate and sulfur dioxide in water produces sodium hydrogen sulfite and carbon dioxide:

$$Na_2CO_3 + 2\ SO_2 + H_2O \rightarrow 2\ NaHSO_3 + CO_2$$

If excess sulfur dioxide is used, what mass of sodium hydrogen sulfite can be obtained from 200 g of sodium carbonate?

22. Sodium thiosulfate is produced from the reaction of sodium sulfite and sulfur:

$$8\ Na_2SO_3 + S_8 \rightarrow 8\ Na_2S_2O_3$$

If excess sodium sulfite is used, what mass of sodium thiosulfate can be produced from 80 kg of sulfur?

UNIT 57

Halogens and Noble Gases

57.1   The Halogens

Compounds of the halogens, particularly the salt sodium chloride, have been known since antiquity. The name **halogen** is derived from the Greek meaning 'salt former'—it was a name originally applied to chlorine but now refers to all members of the group. The halogens are highly reactive elements that always occur naturally in combination with other elements. Huge mineral deposits of sodium chloride exist and the chloride ion is the most abundant anion in seawater. Fluorine occurs in the mineral fluorite (calcium fluorite CaF_2) and in fluorapatite $Ca_5(PO_4)_3F$—it is the thirteenth most abundant element in the earth's crust. Bromine is much less abundant and its main natural sources are the oceans and underground salt deposits. Iodine is even less abundant and was once recovered from seaweed that extract and accumulate the element from seawater.

Hydrochloric acid (aqua salis) was one of the acids prepared by the early alchemists and has been known for a thousand years. Chlorine gas was first prepared by C. W. Scheele in 1774 by the oxidation of HCl using MnO_2. Scheele was not aware that the gas was an element—being a proponent of the phlogiston theory he called it dephlogisticated marine acid (marine acid was one of the names for HCl).

$$4\,NaCl + 2\,H_2SO_4 + MnO_2 \rightarrow 2\,Na_2SO_4 + MnCl_2 + 2\,H_2O + Cl_2$$

Humphry Davy identified the gas as an element in 1811 and suggested the name chlorine on the basis of its color (yellow-green). Iodine was the next to be discovered; it was isolated by B. Courtois in 1811 by treating seaweed ash with sulfuric acid. The name was suggested by Gay Lussac from the Greek meaning 'violet-colored'. A. J. Balard obtained bromine by the reaction of $MgBr_2$ with chlorine water in 1826. It's interesting that Liebig had earlier misidentified a sample of bromine as iodine monochloride and so missed the discovery of the element.

Although hydrofluoric acid had been known since the late 1600s (it was made *in situ* from CaF_2 and used to etch glass), fluorine resisted the attempts of many talented chemists to separate the element from its compounds. In 1886, H. Moissan electrolyzed a mixture of anhydrous HF and KF to produce the highly reactive gas. The HF and KF combine to form the salt KHF_2. Note that F^- in aqueous solution cannot be oxidized to F_2 because the F_2 would oxidize the water.

$$2\,KHF_2(l) \rightarrow H_2(g) + F_2(g) + 2\,KF(l)$$

The properties of the halogens are summarized in Table 57.1. All halogens are diatomic molecules but the strength of the F—F bond is very weak. The trend in bond energy from iodine to fluorine ($151\ kJ\ mol^{-1} < 193\ kJ\ mol^{-1} < 242\ kJ\ mol^{-1} < 155\ kJ\ mol^{-1}$) takes a sharp drop at fluorine. A value in the region of $290\ kJ\ mol^{-1}$ might have been expected. This lower than anticipated value is attributed to the severe repulsion between the nonbonding pairs of electrons on the two fluorine atoms. The F—F bond length is longer than expected for the same reason. As a result, the F—F bond breaks easily and fluorine is an exceptionally strong oxidizing agent. It requires very careful handling. Fluorine will oxidize almost every other element. The only reason that the gas can be contained in vessels made from nickel or copper, for example, is that the metal forms a thin impervious layer of metal fluoride that protects the remaining metal.

Many chemists suffered from exposure to HF in their attempts to isolate fluorine, sometimes fatally. HF is particularly toxic, penetrating deep under the skin, causing necrosis, and attacking the calcium in bones. Small amounts on the skin can be fatal. Moissan received the 1906 Nobel Prize in Chemistry for his achievement. It's interesting that George Gore was apparently able to produce a small amount of fluorine by electrolysis in 1869. When allowed to come into contact with hydrogen, it exploded.

This is analogous to an inability to reduce Na^+ ions to Na in aqueous solution because the Na would reduce water.

The bond energies and bond lengths of O—O (peroxide) and N—N (hydrazine) deviate from the values expected on the basis of the group trends for the same reason.

This passivation of the metal is similar to the protection of aluminum from oxidation by the formation of a thin oxide layer.

TABLE 57.1 The halogens.

Name	Symbol	Melting Point °C	Boiling Point °C	ΔH°_{vap} @ b.pt. kJ mol^{-1}	Electron Affinity kJ mol^{-1}	Ionization Energy kJ mol^{-1}	Bond Energy kJ mol^{-1}	Covalent Radius pm	Ionic X$^-$ Radius pm
Fluorine	F	−219	−188	6.6	330	1681	159	71	133
Chlorine	Cl	−101	−34	20.4	349	1251	243	99	183
Bromine	Br	−7	59	29.9	325	1140	193	114	196
Iodine	I	114	185	41.6	295	1008	151	133	220

The oxidizing ability of the halogens decreases down the group. This means that F_2 will oxidize any halide, Cl$^-$, Br$^-$, or I$^-$. Likewise Cl_2 will oxidize Br$^-$ and I$^-$ and Br_2 will oxidize I$^-$:

$$F_2(g) + 2\ Cl^-(aq) \rightarrow 2\ F^-(aq) + Cl_2(g) \qquad E^\circ = 1.51\ V$$
$$Cl_2(g) + 2\ Br^-(aq) \rightarrow 2\ Cl^-(aq) + Br_2(g) \qquad E^\circ = 0.27\ V$$
$$Br_2(g) + 2\ I^-(aq) \rightarrow 2\ Br^-(aq) + I_2(g) \qquad E^\circ = 0.55\ V$$

Fluorine and chlorine are gases, bromine is a liquid, and iodine is a solid (Figure 57.1). The induced dipole attraction between the molecules (*cf.* Unit 28) increases as the size increases.

(a) Chlorine   (b) Bromine   (c) Iodine

FIGURE 57.1   Chlorine, bromine, and iodine.
(It is difficult to find a transparent container in which to photograph the colorless fluorine gas.) (a) chlorine; (b) bromine; (c) iodine.

EXAMPLE 57.1   ELECTRODE REDUCTION POTENTIALS FOR THE HALOGENS

a. Based upon the cell potentials for the reactions above, which half-cell reduction potential would you expect to be the most positive, $E^\circ_{red}(F_2|F^-)$, $E^\circ_{red}(Cl_2|Cl^-)$, $E^\circ_{red}(Br_2|Br^-)$ or $E^\circ_{red}(I_2|I^-)$?

b. If $E^\circ_{red}(Cl_2|Cl^-) = +1.36$ V, calculate the standard half-cell reduction potentials for fluorine $E^\circ_{red}(F_2|F^-)$, bromine $E^\circ_{red}(Br_2|Br^-)$ and iodine $E^\circ_{red}(I_2|I^-)$ from the data above .

UNDERSTAND THE QUESTION

The more positive a half-cell reduction potential, the better the oxidizing agent. Cell potentials are calculated by adding the two half-cell potentials, E°_{oxid} for the reaction at the anode and E°_{red} for the reaction at the cathode. If the cell potential is known, and one of the half-cell potentials is known, then the other half-cell potential can be calculated.

PLAN THE SOLUTION

Determine the order of oxidizing ability, and therefore which halogen will oxidize which. Then calculate the half-cell reduction potentials. It helps to sketch the cells using the cell notation.

SOLVE THE PROBLEM

a. The oxidizing ability decreases down the group. Fluorine is the strongest oxidizing agent and will oxidize Cl^-, Br^-, and I^-. Fluorine is therefore expected to have the most positive half-cell reduction potential; then chlorine, bromine, and finally iodine.

b. The first reaction listed can be abbreviated:

$$Cl^- \,|\, Cl_2 \,\|\, F_2 \,|\, F^- \quad E° = +1.51 \text{ V}$$

Cl^- is oxidized and F_2 is reduced. The cell potential is 1.51 V.

$$E° = E°_{oxid} + E°_{red} = -1.36 + E°_{red} = 1.51 \text{ V}$$

Note the change in the sign for the oxidation at the anode.

$$E°_{red}(F_2 \,|\, F^-) = 1.51 + 1.36 \text{ V} = +2.87 \text{ V}$$

The second reaction listed can be represented:

$$Br^- \,|\, Br_2 \,\|\, Cl_2 \,|\, Cl^- \quad E° = +0.27 \text{ V}$$

Br^- is oxidized and Cl_2 is reduced. The cell potential is 0.27 V.

$$E° = E°_{oxid} + E°_{red} = E°_{oxid} + 1.36 = 0.27 \text{ V}$$
$$E°_{oxid} = 0.27 - 1.36 \text{ V} = -1.09 \text{ V}$$
$$E°_{red}(Br_2 \,|\, Br^-) = +1.09 \text{ V} \text{ (change the sign for } E°_{red})$$

The third reaction listed can be represented:

$$I^- \,|\, I_2 \,\|\, Br_2 \,|\, Br^- \quad E° = +0.55 \text{ V}$$

I^- is oxidized and Br_2 is reduced. The cell potential is 0.55 V.

$$E° = E°_{oxid} + E°_{red} = E°_{oxid} + 1.09 = 0.55 \text{ V}$$
$$E°_{oxid} = 0.55 - 1.09 \text{ V} = -0.54 \text{ V}$$
$$E°_{red}(I_2 \,|\, I^-) = +0.54 \text{ V}$$

The order is therefore as predicted:

$$E°_{red}(F_2 \,|\, F^-) \qquad = +2.87 \text{ V}$$
$$E°_{red}(Cl_2 \,|\, Cl^-) \qquad = +1.36 \text{ V}$$
$$E°_{red}(Br_2 \,|\, Br^-) \qquad = +1.09 \text{ V}$$
$$E°_{red}(I_2 \,|\, I^-) \qquad = +0.54 \text{ V}$$

PROBLEM 57.1A

Compare the $E°_{red}(O_2 \,|\, H_2O)$ and $E°_{red}(F_2 \,|\, F^-)$. Will O_2 oxidize F^-, or will F_2 oxidize water?

$$E°_{red}(F_2 \,|\, F^-) = +2.87 \text{ V}$$
$$E°_{red}(O_2 \,|\, H_2O) = +1.23 \text{ V}$$

Write the equation for the reaction that happens.

Is it possible to calculate the cell potential for the reaction:

$$F_2(g) + 2\ I^-(aq) \rightarrow 2\ F^-(aq) + I_2(g) \qquad E° = ?\ V$$

from the data given in the three equations above? If so, do so.

Industrial Production and Uses

Fluorine is produced industrially using the method devised by Moissan. Hydrogen fluoride is fed continuously into a warm electrolyte mixture of KF and HF (the salt $K^+\ HF_2^-$). The anode is carbon and the steel vessel serves as the cathode (Figure 57.2). Care must be taken because both the fluorine gas produced and the electrolyte are highly corrosive.

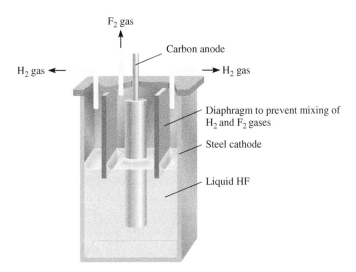

FIGURE 57.2 A modern electrolytic cell for the production of fluorine gas by the method of Moissan.

Fluorine is used to make the gas uranium hexafluoride UF_6. Uranium oxide is first converted to the tetrafluoride using HF gas. This is then treated with F_2 gas to oxidize the tetrafluoride to the hexafluoride. The tetrafluoride is an ionic solid but the hexafluoride is a covalent molecule with a relatively low sublimation temperature (~60°C). The isotopes of uranium can then be separated by gaseous diffusion.

The change in character from ionic to covalent bonding as the oxidation state increases is typical.

$$UO_2(s) + 4\ HF(g) \rightarrow UF_4(s) + 2\ H_2O(g)$$
$$UF_4(s) + F_2(g) \rightarrow UF_6(g)$$

Fluorine gas is often converted to ClF_3 which is an excellent fluorinating agent and more easily handled and transported than fluorine gas. A common fluorinated hydrocarbon is **Teflon**™ which is a polymer (**PTFE**) of tetrafluoroethylene (Figure 57.3). Other uses of F_2 and HF are in the production of chlorofluorocarbons, sodium fluoride for the fluoridation of water, and tin fluoride SnF_2 for toothpastes.

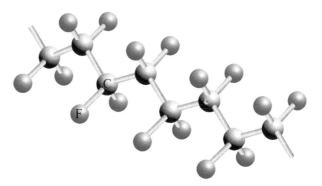

FIGURE 57.3 The structure of Teflon™.
The structure is polyethylene in which all the hydrogen atoms have been replaced by fluorine atoms.

Chlorine gas is one of the products of the **chlor-alkali industry** described earlier (*cf.* Unit 51). The electrolysis of aqueous solutions of NaCl, or fused NaCl, is carried out on a huge scale. Major uses of chlorine are in the production of chlorinated organic compounds, particularly vinyl chloride and its polymer PVC, in the production of bleaches for the paper and textile industries and water sanitation, and in the production of other inorganic chlorides. A method commonly used to prepare chlorine in the laboratory is the addition of concentrated hydrochloric acid to potassium permanganate:

$$16 \text{ HCl}(aq) + 2 \text{ MnO}_4^-(s) \rightarrow 5 \text{ Cl}_2(g) + 2 \text{ Mn}^{2+} + 6 \text{ Cl}^- + 8 \text{ H}_2\text{O}(l)$$

Bromine is produced on a much smaller scale than chlorine. Bromine is present in seawater at a concentration 650 times less than chlorine. It is more abundant in salt lakes and underground brine wells that are the usual source of the element. An historical use of bromine has been as silver bromide in photography but this use is diminishing due to the advent of digital photography. Bromine is used in the production of pesticides and fire retardants. Potassium bromide is used as a sedative and in the treatment of epilepsy.

Iodine is also obtained from natural brine. Some small amount of iodine is essential in the diet because it is a constituent of the hormone **thyroxin** (Figure 57.4) that regulates growth. For this reason, table salt usually contains 0.01% NaI. A solution of iodine in alcohol, called tincture of iodine, is used as an antiseptic. Other uses are in photography and organic chemistry (for example, Grignard reagents, *cf.* Unit 53).

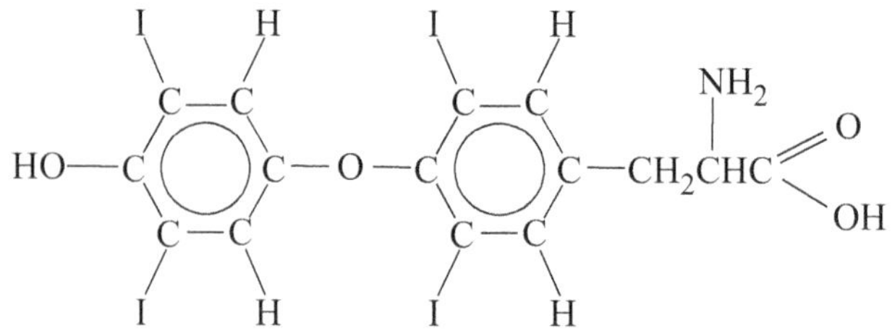

FIGURE 57.4 The hormone thyroxin produced by the thyroid gland.
A lack of iodine in the diet causes the thyroid gland to swell—a condition known as goiter.

57.2   Compounds of the Halogens

The Hydrogen Halides

All the halogens form binary diatomic compounds with hydrogen. The compounds can be prepared directly from the elements or by treating the halide salt with an acid—this is how the alchemists prepared HCl and how HF is prepared industrially:

$$H_2SO_4(l) + CaF_2(s) \rightarrow 2\ HF(g) + CaSO_4(s)$$

$$H_2SO_4(l) + NaCl(s) \rightarrow HCl(g) + NaHSO_4(s)$$

Sulfuric acid is a too powerful oxidizing agent for the production of HBr and HI and H_3PO_4 is used instead:

$$H_3PO_4(l) + KBr(s) \rightarrow HBr(g) + KH_2PO_4(s)$$

The physical properties of the hydrogen halides are summarized in Table 57.2.

TABLE 57.2   The hydrogen halides.

Name	Formula	Melting Point °C	Boiling Point °C	Bond Energy kJ mol⁻¹	pK$_a$ in Aqueous Solution
Hydrogen fluoride	HF	−83.5	19.5	574	+3.2
Hydrogen chloride	HCl	−114	−85.1	432	−7
Hydrogen bromide	HBr	−89	−67.1	362	−9
Hydrogen iodide	HI	−51	−35.1	295	−10

When dissolved in water, the hydrogen halides are acids—and all are strong acids except HF (pK$_a$ = 3.2) which is weak because of the high H—F bond strength. Hydrogen fluoride is extensively hydrogen bonded in the condensed states and association between HF molecules occurs even in the vapor state. The HF molecules form a zigzag chain of molecules (Figure 57.5). As a result, like the boiling points of NH_3 and H_2O, the boiling point of HF is anomalously high when compared to the general trend in the group. Hydrogen bonding is responsible for the formation of the HF_2^- ion in concentrated hydrofluoric acid solutions. This is the ion present in the HF/KF electrolyte used in the manufacture of fluorine. In this anion, a hydrogen atom bridges two fluorine atoms, symmetrically placed between the two (Figure 57.6).

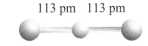

113 pm   113 pm

FIGURE 57.6   The structure of the HF_2^- ion (in its potassium salt).

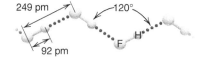

249 pm —— ——120°

92 pm

FIGURE 57.5   Hydrogen bonding between HF molecules in a liquid or solid.

Hydrogen fluoride will attack silica SiO_2 to form hexafluorosilicic acid H_2SiF_6 and for this reason HF cannot be stored in glass bottles. Hydrogen fluoride has long been used to etch glass.

Hydrogen chloride dissolves in water to produce a solution of hydrochloric acid that reaches about 38% HCl—a concentration of 12 M. Because both nitric acid and sulfuric acid are oxidizing agents, hydrochloric acid is usually the strong acid chosen if oxidation is undesirable. Hydrochloric acid will react with many metals to produce hydrogen gas and a traditional method used to generate hydrogen in the laboratory is to treat zinc metal with hydrochloric acid:

$$Zn(s) + 2\ HCl(aq) \rightarrow Zn^{2+}(aq) + 2\ Cl^-(aq) + H_2(g)$$

Halides

There are two types of halides: ionic and covalent. Metals combine with a halogen to form **ionic halides**. Because fluorine is such a strong oxidizing agent, the element with which the fluorine combines usually ends up in the highest possible oxidation state. For example, iron burns in fluorine to produce iron(III) fluoride, not iron(II) fluoride, and uranium produces uranium(VI) fluoride, not uranium(IV) fluoride. Chlorine, although not as strong an oxidizing agent as fluorine, also produces compounds of elements in the highest of their common oxidation states.

Nonmetals react with the halogens to form **covalent halides**. Three examples are:

$$S(s) + 3\ F_2(g) \rightarrow SF_6(g)$$
$$2\ P(s) + 5\ Cl_2(g) \rightarrow 2\ PCl_5(s)$$
$$C(s) + 2\ F_2(g) \rightarrow CF_4(g)$$

These reactions illustrate why fluorine reacts so vigorously. Breaking the weak F—F bonds requires only 155 kJ mol⁻¹. Making the bonds between fluorine and other elements liberates much more energy—the bonds are strong. For example, the bond energy of C—F bonds is 485 kJ mol⁻¹. The sublimation energy of carbon is 717 kJ mol⁻¹. The overall process liberates energy and is enthalpy-driven.

Interhalogen Compounds

The halogens form many binary compounds containing two different halogens called **interhalogens** (Table 57.3). They are prepared by the direct reaction of the halogens involved, mixed with an appropriate stoichiometry. The neutral molecules contain an even number of halogen atoms and the range of possible stoichiometries depend upon the relative sizes of the atoms involved. The least electronegative halogen is always at the center. The widest range of stoichiometries occurs when iodine (the largest halogen) is at the center surrounded by fluorine atoms (the smallest and most electronegative halogen). The structure of ICl_3 is unusual in that the molecule exists as a planar dimer (Figure 57.7).

TABLE 57.3 The interhalogens.

Oxidation State of the Central Atom

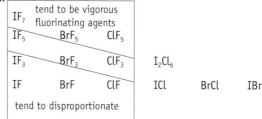

+7	pentagonal bipyramid	IF₇	tend to be vigorous fluorinating agents				
+5	square pyramid	IF₅	BrF₅	ClF₅			
+3	T–shape	IF₃	BrF₃	ClF₃	I₂Cl₆		
+1	linear	IF	BrF	ClF	ICl	BrCl	IBr
		tend to disproportionate					

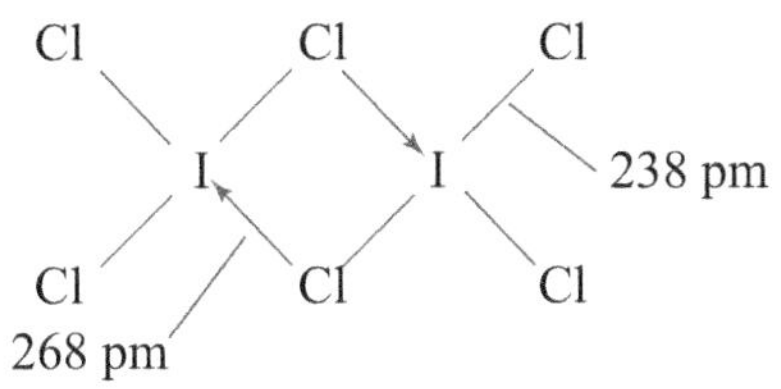

$$
\begin{array}{c}
\text{Cl} \qquad \text{Cl} \qquad \text{Cl} \\
\diagdown \qquad \diagdown \qquad \diagup \\
\text{I} \qquad \quad \text{I} \qquad \text{238 pm} \\
\diagup \qquad \diagup \diagdown \\
\text{Cl} \qquad \text{Cl} \qquad \text{Cl} \\
\text{268 pm}
\end{array}
$$

FIGURE 57.7   The dimeric structure of ICl_3.

The interhalogens range in melting and boiling points that depend upon the molecular mass and the polarity of the molecule. Some are pale or colorless gases (ClF, BrF, ClF_3); some are yellow or colorless liquids (BrF_3, BrF_5, IF_5); and some are colored solids (ICl, IBr, I_2Cl_6, IF_3).

The monofluorides IF and BrF are unstable with respect to disproportionation:

$$5\ IF \rightarrow 2\ I_2 + IF_5$$

The interhalogens with large numbers of terminal F atoms tend to be very good fluorinating agents.

$$IF_7 \rightarrow IF_5 + F_2$$

They react violently with water and organic compounds and ClF_3, for example, reacts vigorously even with asbestos. As fluorinating agents, the reactivity increases in the order $IF_n < BrF_n < ClF_n$ and increases in the order $XF < XF_3 < XF_5 < XF_7$. A diagonal zone of stability (with respect to loss of fluorine and disproportionation) lies through Table 57.3.

There are many examples of ionic salts containing polyhalide ions—both positive and negative. For example, reaction of ClF with the Lewis acid AsF_5 and the Lewis base CsF produces the Cl_2F^+ and ClF_2^- salts respectively:

$$2\ ClF + AsF_5 \rightarrow Cl_2F^+AsF_6^-$$
$$2\ ClF + CsF \rightarrow Cs^+ClF_2^-$$

The structures of the interhalogen ions are predictable using VSEPR theory unless there are a large number of terminal atoms and a single lone pair on the central atom. In this case the lone pair is often stereochemically inactive (*cf.* Unit 21.7).

The structure of the IF_5^{2-} ion is particularly elegant (Figure 57.8):

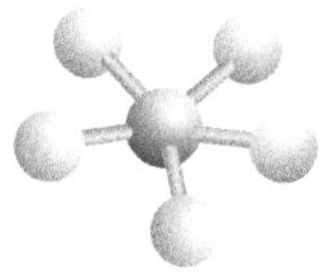

FIGURE 57.8   The pentagonal planar structure of the IF_5^{2-} ion.

EXAMPLE 57.2   SHAPES OF THE INTERHALOGEN MOLECULES AND IONS

Use valence shell electron pair repulsion theory (VSEPR) to determine the shapes of the following interhalogen species.

a. BrF_3

b. $[IBr_2]^-$

c. $[ClF_6]^+$

UNDERSTAND THE QUESTION

Valence shell electron pair repulsion theory (VSEPR) can be used to determine the shapes of most small molecules and polyatomic ions. The procedure was described in Unit 21.

PLAN THE SOLUTION

The VSEPR procedure was described in Unit 21 and used in Unit 55 for the shapes of some nitrogen and phosphorus compounds.

SOLVE THE PROBLEM

a. BrF_3: Bromine is the central atom.

The number of valence electrons is 7 (for Br) + 21 (for three F) = 28.

This is 3 × 8 with a remainder of 4 electrons (2 pairs). There are eight electrons (4 pairs) around each F, with two lone nonbonding pairs on the Br atom.

Therefore there are 5 pairs in total around the bromine.

The arrangement is trigonal bipyramidal and the shape of the molecule is seesaw.

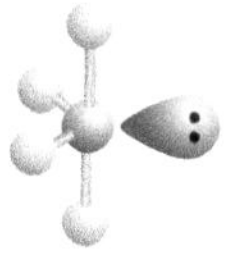

b. $[IBr_2]^-$: Iodine is the central atom.

The number of valence electrons is 7 (for I) + 14 (for two Br) + 1 (for the – charge) = 22.

This is 2 × 8 with a remainder of 6 electrons (3 pairs). There are eight electrons (4 pairs) around each Br, with three lone nonbonding pairs on the I atom.

Therefore there are 5 pairs in total around the iodine.

The arrangement is trigonal bipyramidal and the shape of the ion is linear.

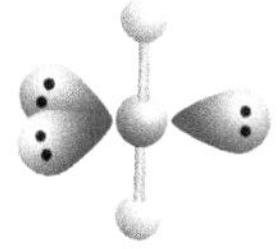

c. $[ClF_6]^+$: Chlorine is the central atom.

The number of valence electrons is 7 (for Cl) + 42 (for six F) – 1 (for the + charge) = 48.

This is exactly 6 × 8 with no electrons remaining to be placed on the central atom as lone pairs. There are eight electrons (4 pairs) around each F.

There are 6 pairs in total around the chlorine.

The arrangement is octahedral and the shape of the ion is octahedral.

PROBLEM 57.2A

Suppose that you used valence shell electron pair repulsion theory (VSEPR) to determine the shape of the ion $[IF_8]^-$. You would quickly determine that there are more than six pairs of electrons around the central atom. What do you suppose is the structure of this polyatomic ion?

PROBLEM 57.2B

Use valence shell electron pair repulsion theory (VSEPR) to determine the shapes of the following interhalogen species.

a. IF_5

b. $[BrF_2]^+$

c. $[ClF_4]^-$

The Oxoacids of the Halogens

The oxidation number of the halogen in the oxoacids ranges from +1 to +7 (Table 57.4).

Hypofluorous acid is an exception because the fluorine is in a −1 oxidation state (as usual) and therefore the oxygen is in a formal oxidation state of zero. HOF does not ionize in water but reacts to form hydrogen peroxide and HF:

$$HOF + H_2O \rightarrow H_2O_2 + HF$$

The oxidation states for oxygen of zero (in HOF) and −2 (in H_2O) result in an oxidation state of −1 (in H_2O_2). In other words, HOF is not really an oxoacid.

The other hypohalous acids are weak acids in aqueous solution. Although they cannot be isolated from solution, their salts such as NaOCl can be. They are powerful oxidizing agents and alkaline NaOCl is often used as a bleach. The salts are unstable with respect to disproportionation to halate and halide. For example, the hypoiodite ion decomposes quite quickly to iodate and iodide:

$$3 \, OI^- \rightarrow IO_3^- + 2 \, I^-$$

Chlorous acid is the least stable of the chlorine oxoacids, and the corresponding bromous and iodous acids are not known to exist. Sodium chlorite is manufactured for use as a bleaching agent.

Chloric acid $HClO_3$ is relatively stable as a 30 % solution in cold water. Upon warming, chlorine and chlorine dioxide ClO_2 are evolved. Bromic acid also decomposes when heated. Both are strong acids in aqueous solution but iodic acid is slightly weaker ($pK_a = 0.80$).

Sodium chlorate is made on a huge scale primarily to produce ClO_2 for use as a bleach in the paper industry. It is manufactured by the electrolysis of brine in a cell in which the chlorine produced at the anode is mixed with the hydroxide produced at the cathode to make hypochlorite. The hypochlorite disproportionates to produce the chlorate. Potassium chlorate is used as the oxidant in fireworks and matches.

The most stable of the chlorine oxoacids is perchloric acid. The acid is usually available as a 60% or 70% aqueous solution which is not a particularly effective oxidizing agent at room temperature. This is attributed to kinetic barriers to reaction rather than any thermodynamic reason. When heated the acid can become explosively reactive. The anhydrous acid reacts violently with most organic materials. Ammonium

TABLE 57.4 The halogen oxoacids.

Hypofluorous Acid	HOF	Hypochlorous Acid	HOCl	Hypobromous Acid	HOBr	Hypoiodous Acid	HOI
		Chlorous acid	$HClO_2$			Iodic acid	HIO_3
		Chloric acid	$HClO_3$	Bromic acid	$HBrO_3$	Periodic acid	HIO_4
		Perchloric acid	$HClO_4$	Perbromic acid	$HBrO_4$	Orthoperiodic acid	H_5IO_6

FIGURE 57.9 The launch of the space shuttle uses 700 tons of ammonium perchlorate.

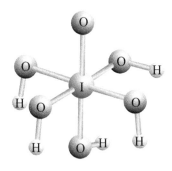

FIGURE 57.10   The structure of H_5IO_6, called either *ortho*periodic acid or *para*periodic acid.
Compare this structure to that of telluric acid (Figure 51.24).

This is due to the addition of the 10+ charge to the nucleus while filling the poorly shielding d orbitals described in Unit 18.3.

The production of the perbromate ion requires a very strong oxidizing agent. Salts of the ion are now made using F_2.

The electrode reduction potential is high:

$$E^\circ_{red}(BrO_4^-|BrO_3^-) = +1.74 \text{ V}$$

For comparison the analogous potentials for chlorine and iodine are +1.23 V and +1.64 V respectively.

perchlorate NH_4ClO_4 spontaneously decomposes at 200°C and is used as the propellant in the solid fuel rocket boosters for the space shuttle. Each launch requires about 700 tons of NH_4ClO_4 (Figure 57.9).

$$2 \text{ NH}_4ClO_4 \rightarrow N_2 + Cl_2 + 2 \text{ O}_2 + 4 \text{ H}_2O$$

Bromine has a reluctance to exhibit the +7 oxidation state and it wasn't until 1968 that the first perbromate salt $RbBrO_4$ was prepared:

$$BrO_3^- + XeF_2 + H_2O \rightarrow BrO_4^- + Xe + 2 \text{ HF}$$

Perbromic acid $HBrO_4$ was prepared shortly thereafter and is stable in aqueous solution for long periods. Although relatively inert kinetically, the perbromate ion is an exceptionally strong oxidizing agent—hence the difficulty of its preparation.

There are several periodic acids. The parent acid is HIO_4, sometimes called *meta*periodic acid. If the coordination of the I is increased from 4 to 6 (addition of two H_2O), then the result is H_5IO_6, called *ortho*periodic acid or *para*periodic acid (Figure 57.10). Both HIO_4 and H_5IO_6 are weak acids.

57.3   The Noble Gases

In 1785, Henry Cavendish reported the results of an experiment in which he repeatedly sparked a sample of air with excess oxygen (to form nitrogen oxides) in the presence of base and was left with a small residue ("not more than 1/120th of the whole") that he was unable to remove. More than one hundred years later, Lord Rayleigh (1842–1919) determined through accurate measurements that the density of 'nitrogen' obtained from air by the removal of O_2, CO_2, and water was greater than nitrogen obtained from the decomposition of ammonia. William Ramsay (1852–1916) heated magnesium in the 'nitrogen' from air to form magnesium nitride and was left, as Cavendish had been, with a small residue. The density of this residue was approximately 3/2 times that of nitrogen. Ramsay and Rayleigh discovered that the emission spectrum of the residue did not match that of any known element and suggested that it was a new element. They called it argon (derived from the Greek meaning 'lazy'). They reported their results in 1898.

In 1898, Ramsay and M. W. Travers isolated three more gases by the distillation of liquid air: krypton (hidden) in May, neon (new) in June, and xenon (strange) in July. Each gas was characterized by its unique atomic emission spectrum. The first of the noble gases, helium, had already been discovered in the sun, again by its emission spectrum, during a solar eclipse in 1868. In 1895, Ramsay identified helium as the gas often found in uranium minerals and in 1900 was able to isolate helium from the atmosphere.

Helium is the second most abundant element in the universe (after hydrogen) but is uncommon on earth. The gas drifts upward in the atmosphere and is eventually lost. Argon is the most abundant noble gas in the atmosphere. These and other properties are listed in Table 57.5.

> For this discovery of argon, and an entire new group of elements in the Periodic Table, Rayleigh was awarded the 1904 Nobel Prize in Physics and Ramsay was awarded the 1904 Nobel Prize in Chemistry.

> Pierre Janssen made the spectroscopic study of the solar radiation in India in 1868. Norman Lockyer assigned one of the lines in Janssen's spectrum to a hypothetical new element he called helium.

TABLE 57.5   The noble gases.

Name	Symbol	Abundance in Dry Air ppm	Melting Point °C	Boiling Point °C	ΔH°_{vap} @ b.pt. kJ mol^{-1}	Ionization Energy kJ mol^{-1}
Helium	He	5.24	–	−268.9	0.08	2372
Neon	Ne	18.2	−248.6	−246.1	1.74	2080
Argon	Ar	9340	−189.4	−185.9	6.52	1520
Krypton	Kr	1.14	−157.2	−153.4	9.05	1351
Xenon	Xe	0.087	−111.8	−108.1	12.65	1170

The noble gases have stable electron configurations—filled s and p orbitals of the valence shell. They are monatomic colorless gases with low melting points and boiling points. The interatomic attraction is a very weak van der Waals force. The attraction between helium atoms is so weak that it cannot be solidified at atmospheric pressure.

Industrial Production and Uses

All the noble gases can be derived from the liquefaction and subsequent fractional distillation of air although helium is obtained more economically from natural gas wells. Argon is used as an inert atmosphere in the processing of metals where nitrogen and oxygen must be avoided. It is also used to fill incandescent light bulbs. Argon, neon, krypton, and xenon, and mixtures of them, are used in discharge tubes to create colored 'neon lights'. Helium is used primarily in its liquid state as a **cryogenic liquid**, particularly to cool the superconducting electromagnets used in nuclear magnetic resonance and MRI. Some helium is used to make the gas mixtures used by deep sea divers.

57.4 Compounds of the Noble Gases

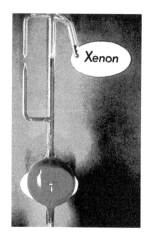

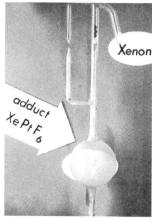

FIGURE 57.11 Bartlett's experiment.
The oxidation of xenon by platinum hexafluoride. When the red platinum hexafluoride (top) is allowed to mix with excess xenon, the yellow product (bottom) is formed.

When Ramsay had isolated sufficient argon, he sent a sample to Moissan to determine whether it would react with fluorine. It didn't. Some years later, in 1933, Linus Pauling suggested that in fact xenon should react with fluorine to form XeF_6. So D. M. Yost and A. L. Kaye passed an electric discharge through a mixture of xenon and fluorine in an attempt to make it. There was no reaction. Thus the inertness of the noble gases became accepted by chemists. Indeed, they were called the **inert gases**. Their lack of reaction with fluorine, the most reactive of all the elements, was attributed to the stability of the complete valence shell.

On March 23, 1962, Neil Bartlett, working alone in his laboratory, allowed xenon gas and red platinum(VI) fluoride gas to mix. There was an immediate reaction. The red color disappeared and a yellow solid was formed (Figure 57.11). His preliminary identification of the compound was $Xe^+PtF_6^-$. Why did Bartlett attempt this reaction? He and D. H. Lohmann had already established that PtF_6 was an exceptionally good oxidizing agent, able to oxidize dioxygen to O_2^+, and he recognized that the ionization energy for xenon (1169 kJ mol^{-1}) was slightly less than that of dioxygen (1175 kJ mol^{-1}).

The yellow product was not, in fact, $XePtF_6$ but a mixture of several compounds. The $XePtF_6$ reacts with PtF_6 to form $XeFPtF_6$ which, upon warming, reacts further to form $XeFPt_2F_{11}$.

Almost immediately, chemists in several laboratories reinvestigated the reaction between xenon and fluorine and quickly prepared XeF_4 (Figure 57.12) and then XeF_2 and XeF_6. The different fluorides are prepared by varying the stoichiometric ratio of the xenon and fluorine and by changing the conditions of the reaction. The fluorides react with water to make compounds such as $XeOF_4$, and XeO_3. Major compounds of xenon, oxygen, and fluorine are listed in Table 57.6. Some properties of the fluorides are listed in Table 57.7. Few compounds of krypton and fluorine exist; the major one being KrF_2 which decomposes at $-10°C$.

FIGURE 57.12 Crystals of xenon tetrafluoride XeF_4.

Many of the xenon compounds have structures that are predictable using VSEPR theory (*cf.* Problem 57.3). However, as was the case with the interhalogen compounds, if there is a large number of terminal fluorine atoms and just one nonbonding pair of electrons, the lone pair is stereochemically inactive. Thus XeF_6 has an approximate

TABLE 57.6 Compounds of xenon, oxygen, and fluorine.

Oxidation State of Xenon				
+2	XeF_2			
+4	XeF_4	$XeOF_2$		
+6	XeF_6	$XeOF_4$	XeO_2F_2	XeO_3
+8		XeO_2F_4	XeO_3F_2	XeO_4

TABLE 57.7 Properties of the xenon fluorides.

	m.pt. °C	Xe—F Bond Length pm	ΔH_f° kJ mol^{-1}
XeF_2	129	200	−109
XeF_4	117	195	−216
XeF_6	49.5	189	−294

octahedral structure and the salt cesium octafluoroxenate Cs_2XeF_8 has a square antiprismatic structure (Figure 57.13). Cesium octafluoroxenate is particularly stable; it doesn't decompose until heated above 400°C.

The xenon fluorides are powerful fluorinating agents. They are, however, thermodynamically stable at room temperature. Their reaction with water varies. Xenon difluoride hydrolyses very slowly and solutions are quite stable (in the absence of base) at low temperatures. Xenon tetrafluoride reacts vigorously with water to produce xenon trioxide and xenon gas—this is a disproportionation reaction. Xenon hexafluoride also reacts vigorously to produce xenon trioxide:

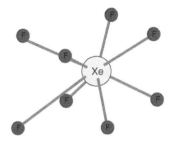

FIGURE 57.13 The square antiprismatic structure of the octafluoroxenate ion $[XeF_8]^{2-}$.

$$3\ XeF_4(s) + 6\ H_2O(l) \rightarrow XeO_3(aq) + 2\ Xe(g) + 12\ HF(aq) + 3/2\ O_2(g)$$
$$XeF_6(s) + 3\ H_2O(l) \rightarrow XeO_3(aq) + 6\ HF(aq)$$

Xenon trioxide, XeO_3, is soluble in water but is dangerously explosive. For this reason the exclusion of water in reactions of xenon, fluorine, and their compounds is highly desirable. In basic solution, xenon trioxide accepts a hydroxide ion to produce the hydrogen xenate ion which then disproportionates to yield the octahedral perxenate ion XeO_6^{4-}:

$$XeO_3 + OH^- \rightarrow HXeO_4^-$$
$$2\ HXeO_4^- + OH^- \rightarrow XeO_6^{4-} + Xe + O_2 + 2\ H_2O$$

Intermediate oxofluorides can be prepared by careful hydrolysis and the following reactions:

$$XeF_6 + H_2O \rightarrow XeOF_4 + 2\ HF$$
$$XeO_3 + XeOF_4 \rightarrow 2\ XeO_2F_2$$

If the barium salt of the perxenate ion Ba_2XeO_6 is added to cold concentrated sulfuric acid, the gas XeO_4 is produced. This tetroxide is unstable and tends to explode. It provides a route to more oxofluorides:

$$XeO_4 + XeF_6 \rightarrow XeOF_4 + XeO_3F_2$$
$$XeO_3F_2 + XeF_6 \rightarrow XeOF_4 + XeO_2F_4$$

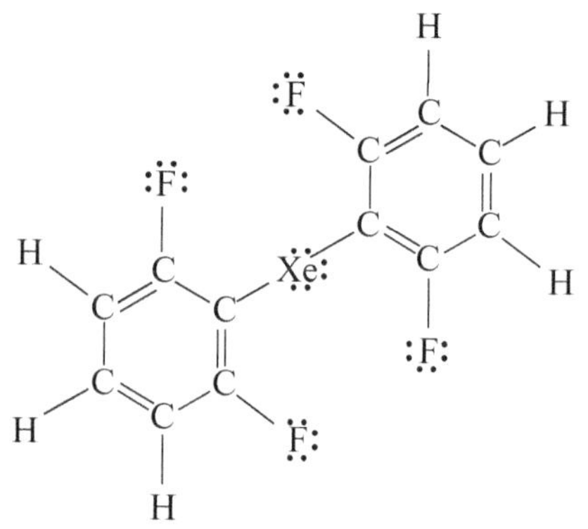

FIGURE 57.14   A compound with Xe—C bonds: bis(2,6–difluorophenyl)xenon.

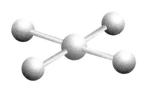

FIGURE 57.15   The square planar structure of the $[AuXe_4]^{2+}$ cation.

Compounds containing xenon–nitrogen and xenon–carbon bonds have been synthesized. For example, the bis(2,6–difluorophenyl)xenon shown in Figure 57.14 was prepared in 1995. In 2000, an entirely new type of xenon compound was prepared which contains a square planar arrangement of four xenon atoms around a gold atom, $[AuXe_4]^{2+}[Sb_2F_{11}]_2^-$ (Figure 57.15).

EXAMPLE 57.3   SHAPES AND OXIDATION STATES OF XENON COMPOUNDS

Determine the shape of the following xenon compounds and the oxidation state of the xenon in them.

  a. XeO_2F_2

  b. XeF_4

  c. XeO_3

UNDERSTAND THE QUESTION

This is another problem involving the use of valence shell electron pair repulsion theory (VSEPR).

PLAN THE SOLUTION

Use the VSEPR method described earlier. The oxidation number of the xenon can be calculated because the oxidation number of O is –2 and that of fluorine is –1.

SOLVE THE PROBLEM

  a. XeO_2F_2: Xenon is the central atom.

    The number of valence electrons is 8 (for Xe) + 14 (for two F) + 12 (for two O) = 34.

    This is 4 × 8 with a remainder of 2 electrons (1 pair). There are eight electrons (4 pairs) around each F and O, with one lone nonbonding pair on the Xe atom.

    Therefore there are 5 pairs in total around the xenon.

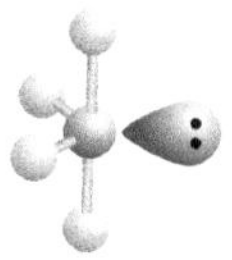

    The arrangement is trigonal bipyramidal and the shape of the molecule is seesaw.

    Two O at –2 and two F at –1 = –6

    The oxidation number of the xenon = +6

b. XeF_4: Xenon is the central atom.

The number of valence electrons is 8 (for Xe) + 28 (for four F) = 36.

This is 4 × 8 with a remainder of 4 electrons (2 pairs). There are eight electrons (4 pairs) around each F, with two lone nonbonding pairs on the Xe atom.

Therefore there are 6 pairs in total around the xenon.

The arrangement is octahedral and the shape of the molecule is square planar.

Four F at −1 = −4

The oxidation number of the xenon = +4

c. XeO_3: Xenon is the central atom.

The number of valence electrons is 8 (for Xe) + 18 (for three O) = 26.

This is 3 × 8 with a remainder of 2 electrons (1 pair). There are eight electrons (4 pairs) around each O, with one lone nonbonding pair on the Xe atom.

Therefore there are 4 pairs in total around the xenon.

The arrangement is tetrahedral and the shape of the molecule is trigonal pyramidal.

Three O at −2 = −6

The oxidation number of the xenon = +6

PROBLEM 57.3A

The molecule FXeOXeF has been prepared. Determine the shape of this molecule. What is the oxidation state of the two xenon atoms?

PROBLEM 57.3B

Determine the shape of the following xenon compounds and the oxidation state of the xenon in them.

a. $XeOF_4$ b. XeF_2 c. XeO_2F_4

Review Questions

1. Review the trends in the physical and chemical properties of the halogens.

2. Explain the reasons why noble gases acquired the reputation of being inert elements.

3. Almost all the compounds of the noble gases are compounds of xenon with oxygen and fluorine. Why xenon, and why oxygen and fluorine?

Solutions to Problems

PROBLEM 57.1A

The half-cell reduction potential for $F_2 | F^-$ is more positive. This means that F_2 is the better oxidizing agent; it is more easily reduced than O_2. The cell potential for the reaction is:

$$2 F_2 + 2 H_2O \rightarrow O_2 + 4 F^- + 4 H^+$$
$$E° = +2.87 \text{ V} − 1.23 \text{ V} = 1.54 \text{ V}$$

PROBLEM 57.2A

$[IF_8]^-$: Iodine is the central atom.

The number of valence electrons is 7 (for I) + 56 (for eight F) +1 (for the − charge) = 64.

This is exactly 8 × 8 with no remaining electrons. There are eight electrons (4 pairs) around each F, with no nonbonding pairs on the I atom.

There are 8 pairs of electrons around the bromine.

We have not yet encountered more than six pairs of electrons around the central atom in a molecule. However, if the principles of VSEPR theory hold true, these eight bonding electron pairs should be arranged around the iodine to minimize the repulsion between them. One possible arrangement is cubic—eight pairs of electrons at the corners of a cube around the iodine. Another possible arrangement is a shape called square antiprismatic. This is like a cube for which an opposite pair of faces have been twisted 45° with respect to each other. The actual shape is square antiprismatic.

PROBLEM 57.3A

The number of valence electrons is 16 (for two Xe) + 14 (for two F) + 6 (for one O) = 36.

Two electrons (one pair) in each bond = 8

Three lone pairs around the each F atom = 12

Two lone pairs on the oxygen = 4

Remaining electrons = 36 – 24 = 12 = 6 pairs.

So there must be 3 lone pairs around each xenon atom.

A total of 5 pairs around each Xe (trigonal bipyramid) and therefore a linear shape around each Xe atom.

The geometry around the central oxygen atom is V–shaped or bent (as in H_2O):

One O at –2 and two F at –1 = –4

The oxidation number of the xenon = +4

Answers to Review Questions

1. The physical properties of the halogens are listed in Table 57.1. The halogens are electronegative elements and in many of their reactions acquire electrons to form negative halide ions. They therefore tend to be good oxidizing agents, particularly fluorine at the top of the group. Fluorine will react with almost every element in the Periodic Table—reactions in which fluorine is reduced and the other element is oxidized. With metals the halogens form ionic halides. With nonmetals the halogens form covalent halides.

2. Some early attempts to make compounds of the noble gases failed. In particular, Moissan failed to observe any reaction between argon and fluorine and experiments suggested by Linus Pauling failed to produce any compound of xenon and fluorine. This lack of reaction was easily rationalized on the basis of the complete valence shell of the noble gases. This electron configuration was considered particularly stable. Indeed, other elements undergo reactions and form compounds in order to attain a 'noble gas configuration'. It was reasonable to assume that the noble gases would not react. In fact, the xenon fluorides all have negative enthalpies of formation (Table 57.7) and it was simple misfortune that Pauling's suggested experiments failed. Xenon fluoride can be made easily by leaving a mixture of xenon and fluorine in sunlight for a few hours.

3. Xenon has the lowest ionization energy of the (nonradioactive) noble gases and is therefore the most likely to form compounds. Fluorine and oxygen have the highest electronegativities of all elements. Fluorine in particular is an exceptionally strong oxidizing agent and is the element most likely to oxidize xenon.

End-of-Unit Problems

1. Explain why fluorine gas is such a powerful oxidizing agent.

2. Order the following bonds in increasing strength and explain why the order is what it is: Cl—Cl, Br—Br, F—F, I—I.

3. Explain why it is easiest to prepare compounds of xenon with fluorine, as opposed to other noble gases.

4. Why are the fluorine compounds of radon studied so little?

5. Hydrogen fluoride forms stronger hydrogen bonds than water, and yet water has a higher boiling point and a higher heat of vaporization. Explain why.

6. Of all the hydrohalic acids, hydrogen fluoride is the only one that is weak. Explain why.

7. The electrolysis of brine (sodium chloride solution) is one of the principal methods used for the manufacture of chlorine. Why can this method not be used for the manufacture of fluorine?

8. A. J. Balard obtained bromine by treating a solution of $MgBr_2$ with chlorine water in 1826. Explain what happened in this reaction. What would happen if you added bromine water to a solution of sodium chloride?

9. Identify the element in Group 7A that

    a. has the highest electronegativity

    b. has the smallest range of oxidation states

    c. has the widest range of interhalogen fluorides

    d. has the weakest bond in its diatomic molecule

10. Identify the element in Group 8A (He through Xe) that

    a. has the lowest boiling point

    b. is the most difficult to oxidize

    c. has the widest range of known oxidation states

    d. is named after the Greek for 'stranger'

11. Why is bromine reluctant to exist in its highest oxidation state? What is its highest oxidation state?

12. What oxidizing agents are capable of oxidizing BrO_3^- to BrO_4^-?

13. Determine the oxidation number of xenon in the following compounds:

    a. XeF_2

    b. Cs_2XeF_8

    c. XeF_6

    d. XeF_3^+

14. Determine the oxidation number of the underlined element in the following compounds:

    a. $\underline{I}F_7$

    b. $\underline{Cl}_2O_7$

    c. $\underline{Br}F_3$

    d. $O_2\underline{F}_2$

15. Identify the Group 7A element or elements, or their compounds:

    a. An element once obtained from seaweed.

    b. An element mistaken for ICl before the discovery of the element.

    c. An acid used to etch glass.

    d. The most common anion in the sea.

16. Identify the Group 7A element or elements, or their compounds:

    a. The element isolated for the first time by Moissan.

    b. The compound used to manufacture the polymer PVC.

    c. The most powerful oxidizer among the elements.

    d. The HX acid of the group that is weak.

17. List and name the oxoacids of chlorine and determine the oxidation number of chlorine in each. Determine which of the acids is the strongest and explain why it is the strongest.

18. The hypohalous acids have the general formula HOX, where X is the halogen. Discuss whether the compound HOF should be considered an acid. What happens when HOF is added to water?

19. Determine the structures of:

    a. XeF_2

    b. XeO_3F_2

    c. KrF_2

20. Determine the structures of:

    a. XeO_4

    b. $XeOF_4$

    c. $[XeO_6]^{4-}$

21. Bromine monofluoride BrF tends to disproportionate. Deduce the probable products of the disproportionation and write an equation representing the reaction.

22. Cesium fluoride is a Lewis base (fluoride donor). Write equations illustrating the probable products of the reaction of cesium fluoride with

    a. iodine heptafluoride IF_7

    b. xenon tetrafluoride XeF_4

    c. xenon hexafluoride XeF_6

23. Antimony pentafluoride SbF_5 is a strong Lewis acid. Predict the results of the following reactions and complete the equations. (Note that SbF_5 accepts a fluoride ion F^- to form either $[SbF_6]^-$ or $[Sb_2F_{11}]^-$)

    a. $2\ SbF_5 + IF_5 \rightarrow$

    b. $SbF_5 + BrF_3 \rightarrow$

    c. $XeF_4 + 2\ SbF_5 \rightarrow$

    d. $XeF_2 + SbF_5 \rightarrow$

24. Predict the results of the reactions between

    a. arsenic pentafluoride and chlorine trifluoride

    b. arsenic pentafluoride and xenon difluoride.

General Properties of the Transition Elements

58.1   The d-Block

The block of elements at the center of the Periodic Table is commonly called the **d-block**. This is a series of elements in which a set of five d orbitals is filled with ten electrons—so the block is ten columns wide. There are four series although we will not be concerned at all with the fourth—these are all unstable radioactive elements that have been artificially synthesized by nuclear reactions and in most cases have only a transient existence. Usually only one or two atoms are observed. We will concentrate on the first series (the 3d series) and refer to the second (4d) and third series (5d) where appropriate.

The d-block elements are often called the **transition elements or transition metals** although technically zinc (Zn), cadmium (Cd), and mercury (Hg) are *not* transition metals. These metals have a complete d orbital set and behave in many respects more like the representative (main group) metals.

Some of the d-block metals have been known for a long time and are responsible for the names given to the ages of civilization. The **bronze age** was a period during which the use of copper allowed the fabrication of tools and weapons more advanced than those of the stone age. The bronze age was succeeded by the **iron age** when higher temperatures made the reduction of iron ores possible. The industrial revolution of the 19th century was made possible by the manufacture of steel. Machines of the 20th century required other metals such as titanium, tungsten, chromium, and manganese.

Some d-block elements play an essential part in biological processes. Iron, for example, is the central element in hemoglobin, the protein in red blood cells responsible for the transport of oxygen. Cobalt is the central element in cobalamin (vitamin B12). Zinc is a component of several biologically important molecules.

We will begin this chapter with a review of the metals of the d-block with a description of their industrial production where appropriate and a survey of some of their uses. We will then examine the trends in chemical and physical properties throughout the d-block.

> Bronze is an alloy of copper and tin first made about 6000 years ago. Bronze weapons were developed about 4000 years ago.

> We will examine some of these in Units 59 and 66.

58.2   The Metals, Production and Uses

Scandium

Scandium was one of the elements predicted by Mendeleev when he constructed his first Periodic Table. Its oxide, scandia, was discovered a few years later by Nilsen in 1879. The metal itself was not isolated until 1937. The only significant mineral of scandium is thortveitite, $Sc_2Si_2O_7$, a pyrosilicate, which is relatively rare. Most scandium is obtained as a by-product of uranium production.

The second element of the group, yttrium, was discovered, along with many other elements, at Ytterby in Sweden. Yttrium and lanthanum are both extracted from lanthanide minerals. Yttrium is used to produce the red color on television screens.

> All three of Mendeleev's predicted elements were named after European regions or countries:
>
> | | |
> |---|---|
> | Scandium | Scandinavia |
> | Gallium | France |
> | Germanium | Germany |

Titanium

Titanium was discovered in the iron mineral ilmenite in 1791 by William Gregor in Cornwall, England. It was named titanium by the German chemist M. H. Klaproth. Klaproth had previously extracted zirconia (zirconium oxide) from the mineral zircon (cubic zirconia, an orthosilicate). The third member of the group, hafnium, was isolated from zircon in 1923 and named after the Latin name for Copenhagen where the work was done in Niels Bohr's laboratory.

The most significant ores of titanium are ilmenite ($FeTiO_3$) and rutile (TiO_2). Another ore is perovskite ($CaTiO_3$). Titanium, often alloyed with aluminum or tin, for example, is strong and light. The construction of gas turbine engines, particularly aircraft engines, makes use of these characteristics. It is also used in ship building and in some specialized applications such as the manufacture of bicycle frames and golf clubs. The industrial production of titanium by the **Kroll process** involves treating ilmenite with chlorine and carbon (coke) at 900°C to produce titanium tetrachloride:

$$2\ FeTiO_3 + 7\ Cl_2 + 6\ C \rightarrow 2\ TiCl_4 + 2\ FeCl_3 + 6CO$$

Reduction by carbon in the absence of chlorine produces interstitial titanium carbides that are very hard and have high melting points (above 3000°C). The titanium tetrachloride is reduced by molten magnesium in an inert atmosphere:

$$TiCl_4 + 2\ Mg \rightarrow Ti + 2\ MgCl_2$$

Titanium dioxide (titanium(IV) oxide TiO_2) is used on a large scale (approximately 2 million tons per year) as a white pigment for paints, paper, plastics, toothpaste, and cosmetics. It has replaced the toxic white lead (a mixed lead hydroxide and carbonate) that was once the white pigment used in paints.

Vanadium

Vanadium was discovered in 1801 by A. M. del Rio and named vanadium in 1830 by N. G. Sefström on account of the many attractive colors of its compounds. Both tantalum and niobium were found in the mineral columbite (niobium was originally called columbium). Columbite is a mixed iron and manganese salt of the anion $M_2O_6^{2-}$ in which M represents Nb^{5+} and Ta^{5+} in varying proportions. Tantalum and niobium have very similar properties and are difficult to separate.

Vanadium is present in minerals such as carnotite $K(UO_2)(VO_4) \cdot 1.5H_2O$ and vanadinite $Pb_5(VO_4)_3Cl$ but much is also obtained as a by-product in the production of other metals, particularly tin. The vanadium ore or by-product is heated with sodium carbonate to form sodium vanadate $NaVO_3$. This is precipitated as NH_4VO_3 which is heated to produce vanadium pentoxide V_2O_5. Reduction of the V_2O_5 produces the metal. Alternatively, a mixture of Fe_2O_3 and V_2O_5 can be reduced to make ferrovanadium to be used in steel production—the major use (about 85%) of vanadium is in steel production. Addition of vanadium to steel produces an alloy that remains strong at high temperatures and is useful for machine tools. Vanadium pentoxide V_2O_5 is the catalyst used in the oxidation of SO_2 to SO_3 for the production of sulfuric acid.

Tantalum was named after Tantalus, the son of Zeus, who was doomed to stand in water which receded every time he wanted to drink and below a branch of fruit which moved away every time he wanted to eat. Niobe was the daughter of Tantalus.

Niobium is also used in steel alloys. Tantalum has some use in the manufacture of tantalum capacitors. Tantalum is resistant to oxidation due to the formation of a thin oxide film on its surface. It is used in surgery for bond and joint replacement because of its lack of reactivity within the body.

Chromium

Molybdenum was the first element of the chromium group to be discovered. In 1778, C. W. Scheele oxidized MoS_2 and produced molybdenum oxide. The metal itself was produced soon after. Molybdenum sulfide MoS_2 is slippery and is often used as a lubricant. It is a black compound and was originally thought to be graphite which has a similar slippery nature. The name molybdenum is derived from the Greek for lead, just as graphite is called lead when used in pencils. Three years later, in 1781, Scheele isolated another oxide, this time from the mineral scheelite ($CaWO_4$) which had been known as tungsten (Swedish for 'heavy stone'). The element tungsten is also present in the mineral wolframite (a mixed iron and manganese salt of the anion WO_4^{2-}). It was this ore that gave tungsten its official name (wolfram) and symbol (W).

Chromium was discovered in 1797 by L. N. Vanquelin in the mineral $PbCrO_4$. Reduction using charcoal produced the metal. The name was based upon the variety of colors (chroma) of its compounds.

Chromium metal is produced by the aluminum or silicon reduction of chromium(III) oxide Cr_2O_3 which in turn is obtained from the mineral chromite $FeCr_2O_4$. Alternatively, the chromite can be reduced by carbon to give ferrochrome which is added to iron to produce chromium steels:

$$FeCr_2O_4 + 4\,C \rightarrow [Fe + 2\,Cr] + 4\,CO$$
$$\text{ferrochrome}$$

The major uses of chromium are in the manufacture of stainless steels and in chromium plating. Chromium has a negative standard reduction potential and is easily oxidized. However, like aluminum, it forms a thin impervious layer of oxide (chromium(III) oxide Cr_2O_3) on its surface and is quite inert. Chromium plating is an attractive and useful way to protect other metals from atmospheric oxidation. Molybdenum is also used in the production of stainless steels. Almost half of all tungsten produced is converted to the extremely hard tungsten carbide WC used to manufacture cutting tools. The other principal use of tungsten metal is to make the filaments of electric light bulbs.

Manganese

Manganese metal was isolated by Scheele and Gahn in 1774 from manganese dioxide (the mineral pyrolusite) using carbon as the reducing agent. Rhenium, named after the river Rhine, was the last nonradioactive element to be discovered (in 1925). It is very scarce and is usually obtained as a by-product in the processing of molybdenum ores. The middle element of the series, technetium, was the first element to be produced artificially in a cyclotron. It occurs naturally only in very minute quantities as a result of the natural decay of uranium.

The most important source of manganese is the mineral pyrolusite (MnO_2) of which about 80% occurs in South Africa. The manganese is usually produced in combination with iron as ferromanganese by reducing an appropriate mixture of MnO_2 and Fe_2O_3. The ferromanganese is then used directly in steel manufacture—most steels contain at least some manganese. Manganese serves two purposes when added to iron in steel manufacture. It combines with sulfur as manganese sulfide MnS which then is removed in the slag. It also increases the toughness, hardness, and wear-resistance of the steel. A typical hard steel contains about 13% manganese.

Manganese is also a component of other alloys; for example, manganese bronze is an alloy of copper, zinc, manganese and small amounts of iron and aluminum that is very corrosion resistant and is used, for example, in ships' propellers. An interesting and abundant source of manganese lies in nodules of manganese and iron oxides, with smaller amounts of copper, nickel and cobalt oxides, that occur on the ocean floor (Figure 58.1). The nodules contain up to 25% manganese but it is not yet possible to mine this resource economically. Manganese metal can be produced from pyrolusite by a thermite reaction:

FIGURE 58.1 Manganese nodules on the sea bed.

$$3\ MnO_2 + 4\ Al \rightarrow 3Mn + 2\ Al_2O_3$$

Technicium is a radioactive element used in nuclear imaging. Rhenium is used in some catalysts and in specialized alloys.

Iron

Of the three elements iron, ruthenium, and osmium, iron is by far the most important. This element was responsible for the advent of the iron age 3000 years ago and the industrial revolution 200 years ago. Iron has been known for 6000 years, initially because of its presence in meteorites. The reduction of iron ores using charcoal produced a poor quality iron that required considerable working to produce useful tools and weapons. The introduction of air bellows produced higher temperatures and improved quality. The use of coke instead of charcoal produced the iron necessary for the machines of the industrial revolution.

Ruthenium, named after Russia, was discovered in 1844 in platinum ores from the Urals in Russia. Osmium was discovered in 1803, also in platinum ores, and named for the smell of the toxic volatile oxide OsO_4.

The principal ores of iron are hematite Fe_2O_3, limonite $2Fe_2O_3 \cdot 3H_2O$, magnetite Fe_3O_4, and siderite $FeCO_3$. Pyrite FeS_2 is common but is not used in steelmaking because of the difficulty in removing the sulfur. The first step in steelmaking is the reduction of the iron ore in a **blast furnace** (Figure 58.2). In the furnace, air is blasted through a mixture of the iron ore (hematite), coke, and limestone. The coke burns and produces sufficient heat to melt the mixture. The iron ore is reduced by carbon monoxide and the limestone combines with any clay or sand present to produce calcium silicate (slag). The molten iron is run off into molds and is called **cast iron** or **pig iron** (due to the arrangement and shape of the molds used). The overall processes are:

Water is added to the air blast to control the temperature. The water reacts endothermically with the coke to form carbon monoxide and hydrogen. Both gases reduce the iron ore. If the temperature needs to be reduced, more water is added to the air blast.

$$C + O_2 \rightarrow CO_2$$
$$C + CO_2 \rightarrow 2\ CO$$
$$Fe_2O_3 + 3\ CO \rightarrow 2\ Fe + 3\ CO_2$$
$$CaCO_3 \rightarrow CaO + CO_2$$
$$SiO_2 + CaO \rightarrow CaSiO_3$$

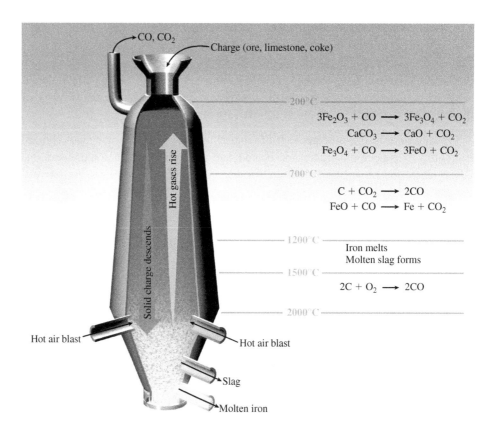

FIGURE 58.2 **A diagram of a blast furnace used in the continuous production of iron.**
The combustion of the coke generates the high temperatures within the furnace where the reduction of the iron ores (hematite and magnetite) takes place. At the same time silicate impurities are removes as slag (calcium silicate).

The pig iron contains about 4% carbon along with other undesirable impurities such as silicon, phosphorus, and sulfur. If these impurities are removed by oxidation in a process called puddling, the product is **wrought iron**, which is much less brittle and more easily worked. However, most pig iron is converted to steel while still in the molten state. This was originally done in a Bessemer converter in which compressed air is driven through the molten iron to oxidize the impurities and reduce the carbon content. The modern method is called the **basic oxygen process** because pure oxygen is used instead (Figure 58.3). The disadvantage of using air is the formation of iron nitride which makes the steel brittle. The result of the conversion is **mild steel**.

Steel is alloyed with other metals for different purposes. These metals are added to the molten iron from the blast furnace before the conversion process. Stainless steel, for example, contains approximately 15% chromium. Vanadium increases the hardness of the steel; manganese increases resistance to wear and increases the strength of the steel; nickel also increases the strength of the steel and its corrosion resistance.

In the second and third series, the six elements Ru and Os, Rh and Ir, and Pd and Pt, are known collectively as the **platinum metals**. They are all isolated from the anode sludge produced during the electrolytic refining of nickel and copper (*cf.* Unit 51). Like all the platinum metals, ruthenium and osmium are referred to

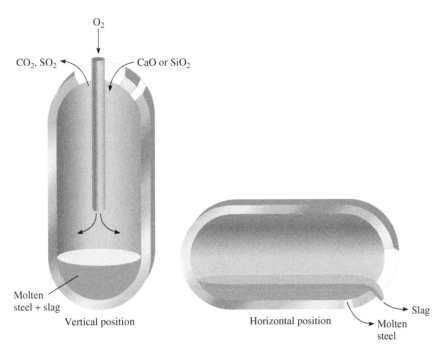

FIGURE 58.3   A basic oxygen converter.
Oxygen is blown through the molten iron. Impurities such as phosphorus, sulfur, and excess carbon are oxidized which keeps the mixture hot. More limestone is added to remove silicon. Other metals are added to produce the correct composition of the intended alloy. When all is ready, the converter is tilted to pour out the molten metal.

as precious (i.e. expensive) metals. Ruthenium has some limited use as a catalyst. Osmium has the distinction of being the densest of all elements at 22.59 g cm^{-3}, slightly more dense than iridium at 22.56 g cm^{-3}.

Cobalt

Cobalt blue is a particularly attractive shade of blue and cobalt ores have been used for at least four thousand years to color glass and pottery. The element itself was isolated in 1735 by G. Brandt. The name is derived from the German name for 'goblin' because of its undesirable presence in metal ores. Rhodium and iridium were both discovered in 1803 in the process of extracting platinum from its ores. Rhodium owes its name to the rose-colored solutions of its salts and iridium similarly owes its name to the variety of colors exhibited by its compounds.

The word iridescent, meaning a rainbow of colors, has the same origin. The Greek goddess Iris was represented by the rainbow.

Like the other platinum metals, rhodium and iridium are very rare and are classified as precious metals. Cobalt is 300,000 times more abundant than rhodium but even it is less abundant than most other 3d transition metals (scandium has an approximately equal abundance).

Cobalt occurs principally as the arsenide $CoAs_2$ or sulfide Co_3S_4 or a combination CoAsS (cobaltite). This is one reason for its bad reputation as a metal ore— **smelting** the ore releases the toxic arsenic and sulfur oxides. Most cobalt is produced in conjunction with nickel or copper because the cobalt ores are usually found alongside those of copper and nickel. Skutterudite, for example, is a mixed arsenide of cobalt and nickel $(Co,Ni)As_3$.

Smelting is a melting process in which the products of the reaction separate into two layers—usually the desired metal in a molten state and a molten slag.

A principal use of cobalt is in coloring—both in paints and ceramics. It is used as a catalyst for some reactions in organic chemistry and has some use in the production of magnetic alloys such as alnico (steel containing aluminum, nickel, and cobalt). The principal use of rhodium is in the catalytic converters of automobile exhaust systems.

Nickel

Nickel derives its name from the ore kupfernickel, $NiAs$. The ore was mistaken for the red copper(I) oxide Cu_2O and obviously resisted any attempt to extract copper from it. Kupfernickel means 'devil's copper'. The element was isolated in 1751 by A. F. Cronstedt. Native platinum has been known for thousands of years but was confused with silver—its name is derived from the Spanish meaning 'little silver'. W. H. Wollaston discovered palladium when working with platinum in 1803.

Much of the world's nickel is extracted from the Sudbury basin in Canada. The nickel occurs as the sulfide in conjunction with those of copper, cobalt, silver, gold, and the platinum metals. The sulfides are concentrated by **flotation** and then **roasted** with silica. Iron sulfide is converted to the oxide and then to the silicate which is removed as slag. The remaining reduced 'matte' consists of nickel sulfide Ni_3S_2, copper sulfide Cu_2S, and a metallic phase of copper, nickel, and precious metals. The nickel and copper metals are **refined** by electrolysis. The anode sludge contains silver, gold, and the platinum metals.

Nickel is used in several nonferrous and ferrous alloys. For example, stainless steel can contain up to 8% nickel. Nickel is alloyed with copper for use as 'silver' coins. Nickel silver, which contains no silver, is an alloy of nickel, copper, and zinc. Nichrome is an alloy of nickel and chromium.

About 40% of all platinum (about 50,000 kg) and 20% of all palladium (about 40,000 kg) extracted each year is used in the catalytic convertors of automobiles. Another 40% of platinum is used in making jewelry. About 45% of all palladium is used in the manufacture of electronic components.

Copper

The metals copper, silver, and gold are known as the **coinage metals**. All three metals exist in the native state and have been known for thousands of years. Nuggets of native gold weighing many kilograms have been found. Native copper nuggets far too large to handle were relatively common in the copper mines of the Upper Peninsula of Michigan. A nugget of native copper from Northern Michigan is shown in Figure 58.4. Although relatively small in comparison to others, it is still too heavy for one person to lift. All three metals have symbols based upon ancient names: Cu (copper) is based upon the Latin name for Cyprus where the Romans first mined the metal; Ag (silver) is based upon the Latin argentum which is itself based upon the Greek word for shiny; and Au (gold) is based upon the Latin aurum.

Copper is the most abundant of the three metals, occurring as copper pyrite $CuFeS_2$, chalcocite Cu_2S, cuprite Cu_2O, and malachite $Cu_2CO_3(OH)_2$. Silver occurs predominantly as the sulfide argentite Ag_2S. Gold occurs as the native metal in veins (in quartz) and in alluvial deposits.

Flotation is a method used to separate a metal ore from the surrounding sand, clay, and other silicate material. The ore is crushed and mixed with water, oil, and a surfactant. Air is blown through the mixture and the metal ore is carried in the froth to the surface. Silicates (rock, sand, and clay) fall to the bottom.

Roasting involves heating a sulfide ore with oxygen to convert the sulfide to the metal oxide or even to the metal itself.

The word alluvial refers to deposits caused by the flow of water, for example, deposits laid down in river beds.

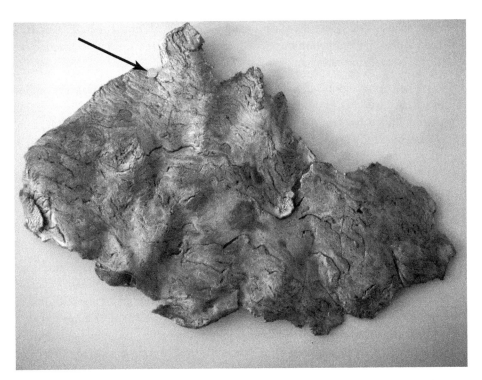

FIGURE 58.4 A nugget of native copper from Northern Michigan. The copper penny is included to indicate the size.

Mining and treatment of copper sulfide minerals involves concentration of the copper by crushing the ore and flotation. The concentrate is heated with silica at 1400°C to remove the iron as iron silicate.:

$$2\ CuFeS_2 + 3\ O_2 \rightarrow 2\ CuS + 2\ FeO + 2\ SO_2$$
$$FeO + SiO_2 \rightarrow FeSiO_3$$

A mixture of Cu_2S and remaining FeS forms a layer called copper 'matte'. The matte is mixed with more silica in a blast furnace to convert the remaining FeS to $FeSiO_3$. The copper sulfide is converted to a mixture of the oxide Cu_2O and copper metal called 'blister' copper. The blister copper is then refined electrolytically (*cf.* Unit 51).

The principal use of copper is as an electrical conductor and in plumbing (for water pipes). It is also used in coins and in alloys such as bronze (with tin), brass (with zinc), and monel (with nickel). Silver is used in photography, silverware, and jewelry. Gold is used in the electronics industry for corrosion-free electrical contacts, in jewelry, and as a monetary security.

Zinc

Zinc, alloyed with copper in brass, has been known for 2000 years. The alloy was produced from a mixture of copper and zinc ores. The isolation of the element itself was not achieved until the 13th century. Mercury, named for the messenger of the gods in Roman mythology, has also been known for a long time. The symbol Hg is derived from the Latin hydrargyrum meaning 'liquid silver'. The brilliant red cinnabar HgS was used as the pigment vermilion. Cadmium was discovered in 1817 in the zinc ore cadmia (calamine, zinc carbonate).

The major ores of zinc are zinc blende (ZnS) and calamine ($ZnCO_3$). The sulfide is concentrated, roasted to produce the oxide, then smelted with coke. The smelting process is difficult because the reduction of the ZnO occurs above the boiling point of zinc metal and the re-oxidation of the zinc by reaction with carbon dioxide as it is cooled must be prevented. Cadmium is obtained as a by-product in the production of zinc. Mercury is obtained relatively easily by heating cinnabar. The same method has been used for thousands of years.

$$HgS + O_2 \rightarrow Hg + SO_2$$

The mercury is purified by distillation under reduced pressure.

Most zinc is used for **galvanizing** to prevent corrosion. It is also used in brasses and other alloys. Another familiar use is as the anode in dry cells and alkaline cells. Zinc oxide is used as a sunscreen and as a white pigment. The major use of cadmium is in batteries, especially the rechargeable Nicad batteries. Cadmium, like mercury, is a highly toxic metal and the disposal of used batteries containing cadmium and mercury poses a serious environmental problem. Mercury is used to form **amalgams** with other metals. It is used, for example, in the extraction of gold and in dental amalgams. It has been used in the Castner-Kellner process for the production of sodium hydroxide and chlorine (*cf.* Unit 51) although this use is diminishing because of environmental concerns.

58.3 Physical Properties

The physical properties of the elements are summarized in Table 58.1.

The d-block elements differ in the number of electrons occupying the set of five d orbitals. The d orbitals are slightly higher in energy than the valence s orbitals and they are filled after the s orbital. However, once the d orbitals are occupied they

TABLE 58.1 Physical properties of the first row of the d-block elements.

Name	Symbol	Melting Point °C	Boiling Point °C	ΔH°_{fus} @ m.pt. kJ mol^{-1}	ΔH°_{vap} @ b.pt. kJ mol^{-1}	Ionization Energies kJ mol^{-1}			E°_{red} (M^{2+} | M) V	Density g cm^{-1}	Metallic Radius pm
						1st	2nd	3rd			
Scandium	Sc	1539	2748	15.8	333	631	1235	2389	–	3.0	161
Titanium	Ti	1660	3285	18.8	420	658	1310	2652	−1.63	4.51	145
Vanadium	V	1915	3350	17.5	460	650	1414	2828	−1.19	6.11	132
Chromium	Cr	1900	2690	21	342	653	1592	2987	−0.91	7.14	125
Manganese	Mn	1250	2060	13.4	220	717	1509	3248	−1.18	7.43	137
Iron	Fe	1535	2750	13.8	340	759	1561	2957	−0.44	7.87	124
Cobalt	Co	1495	3100	16.3	382	758	1646	3232	−0.28	8.90	125
Nickel	Ni	1455	2920	17.2	375	737	1753	3393	−0.23	8.91	125
Copper	Cu	1083	2570	13.0	307	745	1958	3554	+0.34	8.95	128
Zinc	Zn	419	907	7.28	114	900	1733	3833	−0.76	7.14	133

decrease in energy and become lower in energy than the s orbital. This means that the first electrons lost from a d-block element are the s electrons.

The occupancy of the d orbitals affects the physical properties of the d-block elements to some extent but all the elements have similar properties. This can be contrasted with the much more pronounced change in the physical properties of the main group elements from the left side of the Periodic Table (metallic) to the right side (nonmetallic).

The incomplete filling of the d orbitals is responsible for characteristic properties of the transition elements. Most of their compounds are highly colored; many are paramagnetic due to the presence of unpaired electrons in the d orbitals; and all form a wide variety of coordination compounds.

The d-block elements are typical metals. They are, in most cases, silver in color and highly reflective when polished (Figure 58.5). They are good conductors of electrical current and heat. Of all the metals, the coinage metals are the best conductors. Of these, silver is the best but copper is much less expensive and is used in preference. The d-block elements are malleable and ductile—properties typical of metallic bonding.

We will examine the reasons behind the colors exhibited by transition metal compounds in Unit 60 and will begin a study of the coordination compounds of the transition elements in Unit 59.

Malleable means able to be bent or deformed.

Ductile means able to be drawn into a wire.

Scandium (Sc)   Titanium (Ti)   Vanadium (V)

Chromium (Cr)   Manganese (Mn)   Iron (Fe)

Cobalt (Co)   Nickel (Ni)   Copper (Cu)

FIGURE 58.5   Samples of the transition metals in the first series.

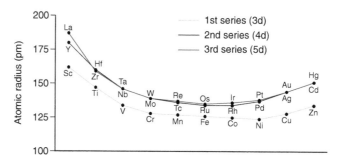

FIGURE 58.6 **The trend in metallic radii across the d-block elements.**
The preceding alkaline earth metals are included for reference.

Atomic Radii

As noted below, the increase in the number of electrons beyond halfway across the series weakens the bonding between the atoms and leads to a looser, less dense, metallic structure. The distance between adjacent atoms increases; i.e. the metallic radius increases.

Compare:
aluminum	2.70 g cm⁻³
titanium	4.55 g cm⁻³
iron	7.87 g cm⁻³
lead	11.34 g cm⁻³
gold	19.28 g cm⁻³
tungsten	19.30 g cm⁻³
uranium	18.95 g cm⁻³
plutonium	19.81 g cm⁻³
platinum	21.45 g cm⁻³
iridium	22.56 g cm⁻³
osmium	22.59 g cm⁻³

The trends in the atomic (metallic) radii of the d-block elements are illustrated in Figure 58.6. The initial decrease in the atomic radii is due to the increasing attraction of the nuclear charge as the atomic number increases. The slight increase at the end is due to the interelectronic repulsion in the almost full d orbital sets. The variation in the atomic radii within a series is, however, relatively small and one metal is often easily replaced by another within a crystal lattice. There is a wide range of such substitutional alloys.

It is interesting that the atomic radii of the second and third series are almost identical. This is due to the lanthanide contraction (*cf.* Unit 18.3). The contraction in size occurs when the first series of the f-block (the lanthanides) are filled. The 14 electrons are placed in the very poorly shielding 4f orbitals, while an additional 14+ charge is added to the nucleus. This increases the attraction of the valence ns and np electrons by the nucleus and results in a contraction in the size of the atom. The relatively small size of the third series, and their high atomic masses, is the reason why the third series elements are the densest elements in the Periodic Table. The trends in the densities of the d-block elements are illustrated in Figure 58.7.

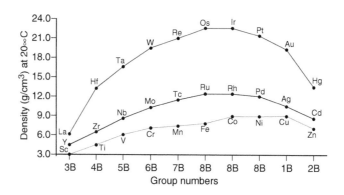

FIGURE 58.7 **The trend in densities across the d-block elements.**
Note the high densities of the elements in the third series.

Melting Points

The elements vary considerably in their melting points and boiling points—for example, mercury is a liquid at room temperature whereas tungsten melts at 3422°C. The melting points increase as the bonding between the atoms becomes stronger. This increase in the bond strength is due to the increase in the number of valence electrons in the bonding orbitals of the valence band of the metal (*cf.* Unit 23.7). At the halfway point, additional electrons enter antibonding orbitals of the band structure and the bonds between the atoms weaken and the melting points decrease.

The melting points refect the strength of the metallic bonding—which in turn is a measure of the number of valence electrons available. The enthalpies of vaporization follow almost exactly the same variation.

EXAMPLE 58.1   PHYSICAL PROPERTIES OF THE D-BLOCK ELEMENTS

Predict which element of the following pairs will have the higher melting point:

a. Fe and Ni

b. Cr and W

Predict which element of the following pairs will have the greater density:

a. Pd and Pt

b. Cu and Zn

UNDERSTAND THE QUESTION

The general trends of physical properties within the d-block are predictable. They are illustrated in Figure 58.6 and Figure 58.7. Along the first series there is a decrease in size from left to right with an increase toward the end. The densities follow an inverse trend. The increase toward the center and decrease toward the end are more pronounced for the second and third series. The lanthanide contraction is responsible for the similarity in size between the second and third series and the much higher density of the third series elements.

PLAN THE SOLUTION

Determine the relative positions of elements in the d-block and therefore the probable magnitude of the property in question.

SOLVE THE PROBLEM

Melting point:

a. Fe is further to the left in the first series and will have the higher melting point.

b. W and Cr are in the same group but W is in the third series and will have the higher melting point.

Density:

a. Pd and Pt are the same size, but Pt has the greater mass and the higher density.

b. Zn is larger than Cu (and almost the same mass), so Cu will have the higher density.

PROBLEM 58.1A

Predict which element of the following pairs will probably have the higher melting point and the higher density:

a. Fe and Os

b. Sc and V

PROBLEM 58.1B

Predict which element of the following pairs will be the larger of the two:

a. Ni and Pd

b. Ti and Cr

c. Pd and Au

Oxidation States

One of the features of the chemistry of the d-block elements that distinguishes them from the main group elements is the variability of their oxidation states. Both iron and cobalt, for example, exist in two common oxidation states, +2 and +3. The redox chemistry of the d-block elements, in which the elements change their oxidation states, is especially rich. The possible oxidation states of the elements in the first series are illustrated in Figure 58.8. Calcium, the preceding alkaline earth element, is included for reference. The most stable oxidation states are colored blue.

The preceding alkaline earth metal, calcium, has only one observed oxidation state, +2. Notice how the maximum oxidation state of the elements increases to +7 (for manganese) at the center of the series and then decreases back to +2 (for zinc). The

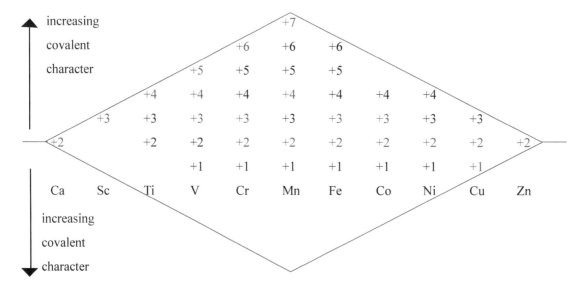

FIGURE 58.8 The oxidation states of the elements in the first series of the d-block. Calcium is included for reference. The most common oxidation states are colored blue. Negative oxidation numbers for some d-block elements occur in organometallic compounds—these are not included in this diagram. For example, $Mn(CO)_4^{3-}$ has the manganese in its lowest possible oxidation state of −3, at the bottom of the diamond outline of the figure.

central line at +2 corresponds to the loss of the two s electrons. Remember that, except for monatomic ions in an ionic compound, the oxidation number does not reflect the charge on the atom—very high oxidation numbers do not occur on monatomic ions. As the oxidation number increases, the covalent character of the bonds and sharing of electrons between the element and other atoms in the compound increases to stabilize the high oxidation state. For example, manganese has an oxidation state of +7 only in covalent compounds such as the permanganate ion MnO_4^-. The manganese in the permanganate ion does *not* have a charge of +7! This increase in covalent character to either side of the central +2 line is illustrated in Figure 58.8.

The increase in the maximum oxidation number from scandium to manganese corresponds to the increase in the number of electrons that can be 'lost'. For example, scandium has the configuration $d^1 s^2$ and can lose three electrons (and almost always does). Manganese, on the other hand, has the configuration $d^5 s^2$ and can 'lose' up to seven electrons. The decrease in the maximum oxidation number from manganese back to zinc corresponds to the filling of the available orbitals. Remember that high oxidation states require covalent bonding and orbitals must be available in which to share electrons. The situation is analogous to the trend in the stoichiometry of the hydrides or fluorides of the main group elements in Period 2 in which the x in the formulas EH_x or EF_x increases to a maximum at the center (Group 4A) and then decreases to the end as the valence orbitals become filled (Figure 58.9).

1	2	3	4	3	2	1
LiH	BeH_2	BH_3	CH_4	NH_3	OH_2	FH

FIGURE 58.9 The trend in the stoichiometries of the hydrides or fluorides of the main group elements in Period 2.
Notice how the value of x in the formula EH_x increases from 1 to 4 and then decreases as the valence orbitals are filled and become unavailable for bonding.

The oxidation state of a d-block element influences its chemical behavior. An element in a high oxidation state is easily reduced and is typically a good oxidizing agent. Therefore, the permanganate ion MnO_4^- and the dichromate ion $Cr_2O_7^{2-}$ are very good oxidizing agents. The electrode reduction potentials are:

$$E° (MnO_4^- \,|\, Mn^{2+}) = +1.51 \text{ V}$$
$$E° (Cr_2O_7^{2-} \,|\, Cr^{3+}) = +1.33 \text{ V}$$

The oxidizing ability of the dichromate ion is used in the determination of blood–alcohol content in a breathalyzer. The dichromate ion oxidizes the alcohol and is reduced to a green chromium(III) sulfate complex. By measuring the intensity of the green color produced compared to the orange color of the dichromate, the concentration of alcohol in breath can be determined. The alcohol content of the breath is directly related to the alcohol content of the blood.

Elements in a low oxidation state are expected to be easily oxidized and should be good reducing agents. For example, Cr^{2+} is easily oxidized to Cr^{3+} and is a good reducing agent. Chromium metal dissolves in sulfuric acid to produce a solution of the blue chromium(II) ion. As soon as air is introduced, the chromium(II) ion is immediately oxidized to the violet chromium(III). Similarly, Ti^{2+} is readily oxidized to Ti^{3+} and V^{2+} is readily oxidized to V^{3+}. The electrode reduction potentials are:

$$E° (Cr^{3+} \mid Cr^{2+}) = -0.41 \text{ V}$$
$$E° (Ti^{3+} \mid Ti^{2+}) = -0.37 \text{ V}$$
$$E° (V^{3+} \mid V^{2+}) = -0.26 \text{ V}$$

The colors of the various oxidation states of vanadium are shown in Figure 58.10. Starting with the yellow vanadium(V) as the VO_2^+ cation, the vanadium is reduced by zinc amalgam to produce in turn the blue vanadium(IV) as VO^{2+}, the green vanadium(III) as V^{3+}, and the violet vanadium(II) as V^{2+}. The standard reduction potentials indicate that the reduction becomes progressively more difficult:

$$E° (VO_2^+ \mid VO^{2+}) = +1.00 \text{ V}$$
$$E° (VO^{2+} \mid V^{3+}) = +0.33 \text{ V} \qquad \text{reduction gets}$$
$$E° (V^{3+} \mid V^{2+}) = -0.26 \text{ V} \qquad \text{more difficult}$$
$$E° (V^{2+} \mid V) = -1.19 \text{ V}$$

FIGURE 58.10 Two oxidation states of vanadium, +2 is violet (on the left) and +5 is yellow (on the right).

Iron is a metal with two common oxidation states, +2 and +3 and can exist in aqueous solution in both states. The oxidation of Fe to Fe^{2+} occurs relatively easily. The half-cell electrode reduction potential is negative:

$$E° (Fe^{2+} \mid Fe) = -0.44 \text{ V}$$

The half-cell reduction potential for $Fe^{3+} \mid Fe^{2+}$ is positive and oxidation to the +3 oxidation state does not occur:

$$E° (Fe^{3+} \mid Fe^{2+}) = +0.77 \text{ V}$$

However, in the presence of oxygen (air), the reaction is spontaneous:

$$4 \text{ Fe}^{2+}(aq) + O_2(g) + 4 \text{ H}^+(aq) \rightarrow 4 \text{ Fe}^{3+}(aq) + 2 \text{ H}_2O(l) \qquad E° = +0.46 \text{ V}$$

The Fe^{3+} is soluble under acidic conditions but when the solution is made basic, the insoluble red-brown oxide $Fe_2O_3 \cdot nH_2O$ precipitates. It is the formation of this insoluble iron(III) oxide that causes the red-brown stains that occur around faucets and water pipes (Figure 58.11).

FIGURE 58.11 The red-brown stain around a ship is caused by the oxidation of Fe^{2+} to Fe^{3+} and the formation of the insoluble Fe_2O_3.

The energy required for the oxidation of the elements shows a general increase from the beginning of the series to the end (Table 58.1). This corresponds to the increase in the nuclear charge. The ores of the elements at the end of the first series are therefore more easily reduced than those of the elements at the beginning of the series. It was no accident that the first metals used by humans for the fabrication of tools and weapons are those at the end of the series—copper and its alloys. Further to the left in the series, iron was extracted from its ores when higher temperatures became available. The metals at the beginning of the series, such as titanium, are isolated with more difficulty.

EXAMPLE 58.2 REDOX CHEMISTRY OF THE D-BLOCK ELEMENTS

Predict which of the following species would be the better oxidizing agent. Look up the standard half cell reduction potentials and confirm your prediction.

a. MnO_4^- and MnO_2

b. Fe^{3+} reduced to Fe^{2+} and Fe^{2+} reduced to Fe

UNDERSTAND THE QUESTION

The oxidizing ability of a d-block element is related to the oxidation state of the metal. The higher the oxidation state of an element, the better its oxidizing power. The more positive a half-cell reduction potential, the better the oxidizing agent.

PLAN THE SOLUTION

Determine the oxidization state of the transition metal in each species and therefore predict its ability to oxidize other species.

SOLVE THE PROBLEM

a. The oxidation state of Mn in MnO_4^- is +7, its oxidation state in MnO_2 is +4. The permanganate should be the better oxidizing agent. The standard half cell reduction potentials (acidic solution) are:

$E°(MnO_4^- | Mn^{2+}) = +1.51V$

$E°(MnO_2 | Mn^{2+}) = +1.23V$

b. The Fe^{3+} has the higher oxidation state and should be the better oxidizing agent.

$E°(Fe^{3+} | Fe^{2+}) = +0.77V$

$E°(Fe^{2+} | Fe) = -0.44V$

PROBLEM 58.2A

Look up the appropriate half cell reduction potentials and predict whether

a. Co^{3+} will oxidize Fe^{2+} to Fe^{3+}

b. Cr^{3+} will oxidize Co to Co^{3+}

c. Cu^{2+} will oxidize Zn to Zn^{2+}

PROBLEM 58.2B

Determine the oxidation numbers of the d-block element in the following compounds:

a. $Cu_3(OH)_4SO_4$

b. $Na_2Cr_2O_7$

c. $FeSiO_3$

d. CrO_2Cl_2

Review Questions

1. Review the methods by which metals in the first series of the d-block are produced from their ores and list some of the uses of these metals.

2. Some methods used in the production of d-block metals include roasting, smelting, flotation, and refining. Explain what each of these terms means.

3. Review the trends in the physical properties of the d-block elements.

Solutions to Problems

PROBLEM 58.1A

a. Iron and osmium are in the same group, but osmium is in the third series and iron is in the first series. Osmium will have the higher melting point and the higher density.

b. Both scandium and vanadium are in the first series. Scandium is the first element in the series and vanadium is the third. Vanadium is expected to have a somewhat stronger metallic bonding because of the greater number of valence electrons. It will have a higher melting point and a greater density.

PROBLEM 58.2A

a. Co^{3+} is a relatively good oxidizing agent:
$E^{\circ}_{red}(Co^{3+} | Co^{2+}) = +1.81$ V

The potential required for the oxidation of Fe^{2+} to $Fe^{3+} = -E^{\circ}_{red}(Fe^{3+} | Fe^{2+}) = -0.77$ V

The sum is positive (spontaneous) and therefore Co^{3+} will oxidize Fe^{2+} to Fe^{3+}.

b. The half-cell reduction potential for $Cr^{3+} \rightarrow Cr^{2+}$ is
$E^{\circ}_{red}(Cr^{3+} | Cr^{2+}) = -0.41$ V

The oxidation of $Co \rightarrow Co^{3+}$ requires $-E^{\circ}_{red}(Co^{3+} | Co^{2+})$
$= -1.81$ V

The sum is negative (-2.21 V) and the reaction not spontaneous.

c. Cu^{2+} is a moderately strong oxidizing agent:
$E^{\circ}_{red}(Cu^{2+} | Cu) = +0.34$ V

The potential required for the oxidation of Zn to $Zn^{2+} = -E^{\circ}_{red}(Zn^{2+} | Zn) = +0.76$ V

The sum is positive (*cf.* Daniell cell) and the reaction will occur.

Answers to Review Questions

1. d-Block elements often occur naturally as oxides and sulfides. Some examples are Fe_2O_3 (hematite), Fe_3O_4 (magnetite), Cu_2O (cuprite), MnO_2 (pyrolusite), $FeTiO_3$ (ilmenite), TiO_2 (rutile), ZnO (zincite), $FeCr_2O_4$ (chromite), $Cu_2CO_3(OH)_2$ (malachite), Ag_2S (argentite), ZnS (sphalerite), HgS (cinnabar), and Cu_2S (chalcocite). The first step is often the concentration of the ore by the removal of unwanted sand, clays, and other silicates. Sulfides are roasted to produce the oxides, and then the oxides are reduced, usually by carbon, or coke. Refining is the final step, often achieved electrolytically. Some of the uses of the transition metals are mentioned throughout the chapter.

2. Roasting involves heating a sulfide ore with oxygen to convert the sulfide to the metal oxide and sometimes (for example, in the case of lead) to the metal itself. The metal oxide is then reduced, often by carbon or carbon monoxide. Smelting is a melting process in which the products of the reaction separate into two layers—usually the desired metal in a molten state and a molten slag. Flotation is a method used to separate a metal ore from the surrounding sand, clay, and other unwanted silicate material. The ore is crushed and mixed with water, oil, and a surfactant. Air is blown through the mixture and the metal ore is carried in the froth to the surface where it is removed. The unwanted gangue—silicates of various kinds—fall to the bottom. Refining refers to the final step in the purification of a metal and usually involves the removal of other metals.

3. The trends in the physical properties of the d-block elements tend to be predictable but in some cases the changes across a series are relatively small. For example, the size of the atoms, or ions, decreases to a minimum and then increases toward the end—but the changes are small. Chromium, iron, cobalt, nickel, and copper have almost identical sizes. The densities depend upon the strength of the metallic bonding and the atomic masses of the elements and vary in a systematic way. The maximum oxidation states of the elements depend upon their electron configurations and increase systematically toward the center (Mn) and then decrease to Zn.

End-of-Unit Problems

1. The reduction of iron ore in a blast furnace is a continuous process fed by several reactants. These are primarily the iron ore itself, limestone, coke, air, and water. What role does each of these reactants play?

2. Much of the world's nickel is extracted from nickel sulfide ore. Processes involved include flotation, roasting, smelting, and finally refining. Describe each of these processes.

3. Copper pyrite (chalcopyrite), $CuFeS_2$, is a useful source of copper. Describe the processes by which copper is extracted from this ore. In particular, how is the iron removed?

4. Many precious metals are recovered from the anode sludge that forms at the anode during the electrorefining of copper. Why does this anode sludge form and why don't the precious metals plate out on the cathode just as copper does?

5. Which element of the following pairs has the larger metallic radius?

   a. scandium and vanadium

   b. chromium and molybdenum

6. Which element of the following pairs has the larger metallic radius?

   a. tantalum and osmium

   b. titanium and hafnium

7. Which element of the following pairs of elements has the greater density?

   a. platinum and palladium

   b. titanium and iron

8. Which element of the following pairs of elements has the lower density?

   a. gold and mercury

   b. iron and osmium

9. The heats of sublimation of the first three elements in the first series of the d-block metals are: scandium 378 kJ mol^{-1}, titanium 471 kJ mol^{-1}, and vanadium 515 kJ mol^{-1}. Explain the increase from Sc to V.

10. At the end of the first series of d-block metals, the heats of sublimation decrease from nickel, to copper, to zinc. What does this decrease suggest about the metallic bonding in these three elements? Would you expect the melting points to similarly decrease (*cf.* Table 58.1)?

11. The density of silver (10.50 g cm^{-3}) is slightly higher than that of copper (8.93 g cm^{-3}). The density of gold, however, is much greater (19.28 g cm^{-3}). Explain why.

12. In the third series of the d-block elements, the densities of the elements increase toward the center and then decrease toward the end of the series. Explain why.

13. Hafnium was first isolated from zircon (zirconium silicate). The hafnium can easily substitute for zirconium in the crystal lattice. Describe what property hafnium and zirconium have in common and why this substitution is easy.

14. Tantalum and niobium occur together in nature and are quite difficult to separate. For example, they occur together in the mineral columbite. Explain why the two metals occur together and why they are difficult to separate.

15. Determine the oxidation number of the d-block element in the following compounds:

    a. K_2CrO_4

    b. $K_2[Ni(CN)_4]$

    c. Fe_3O_4

16. Determine the oxidation number of the d-block element in the following compounds:

    a. K_3NbF_7

    b. $K_3[Mn(CN)_6]$

    c. $K_2[FeO_4]$

17. The +2 oxidation state is relatively common for all the d-block elements. Explain why.

18. The +3 oxidation state is more common for the elements at the beginning of the first series of d-block elements whereas the +2 oxidation state is preferred for the elements at the end of the series. Suggest a reason why this should be so (*cf.* Table 58.1).

19. Chromium occurs in three common oxidation states, +2, +3, and +7. Which of the following species in solution would be expected to be the best oxidizing agent and which would be the best reducing agent? Cr^{2+}, Cr^{3+}, and $Cr_2O_7^{2-}$.

20. Iron and cobalt occur in two common oxidation states, +2 and +3. Aluminum, however, has only one common oxidation state, +3. Why doesn't aluminum exist in a +2 oxidation state?

21. Of the metals in the first series of the d-block, which is most likely to form . . .

    a. an oxide with the formula MO_3?

    b. an oxofluoride with the formula MO_3F?

22. The highest known oxidation state of iron is +6 in $[FeO_4]^{2-}$.

    a. Would you expect this species to be a good reducing agent or a good oxidizing agent? Explain.

    b. You might have expected the maximum oxidation state of iron to be +8—corresponding to the loss of all eight s^2d^6 electrons. Why does this not occur?

23. Which is the stronger oxidizing agent, Cr^{2+} or Cu^{2+}? Explain.

24. The relative stability of Fe^{2+} and Fe^{3+} is affected by the presence of air. Explain.

Coordination Compounds

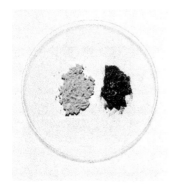

FIGURE 59.1 The colors of cobalt(III) ammine complexes.

The compound $CoCl_3 \cdot 6NH_3$ was first prepared by B. M. Tassaert in 1798.

Alfred Werner was awarded the 1913 Nobel Prize in Chemistry for his work in elucidating the structures of coordination compounds.

59.1   Alfred Werner

In the late 1890s, a Swiss chemist, Alfred Werner (1866–1919) began investigating a series of complex compounds of cobalt chloride and ammonia. Several compounds had been prepared containing varying amounts of ammonia:

$CoCl_3 \cdot 6NH_3$	yellow
$CoCl_3 \cdot 5NH_3$	purple
$CoCl_3 \cdot 4NH_3$	green
$CoCl_3 \cdot 4NH_3$	violet
$CoCl_3 \cdot 3NH_3$	green

The colors of the compounds were beautiful (Figure 59.1)—a property that stimulated their investigation. When Alfred Werner started his work, the bonding and structure of the compounds was unknown and difficult to imagine. In fact, not much was known about the bonding in chemical compounds in general—the work of G. N. Lewis and others was yet to come. S. M. Jørgensen, a Danish chemist, visualized a structure involving chains of ammonia molecules. This was in part suggested by the ability of carbon to catenate—there seemed to be no reason why nitrogen shouldn't behave in the same way.

Werner embarked upon a series of experiments in the preparation and properties of these complex compounds. One experiment in particular that helped to unravel the mystery was the reaction of solutions of the compounds with a solution of silver nitrate. The Ag^+ ions combined with Cl^- ions to precipitate AgCl—but the amount of silver chloride that precipitated differed for the various compounds even though each compound contained three chloride ions for every cobalt ion. Another experiment revealed that the conductivities of solutions of the compounds also varied—conductivity is a measure of the relative number of ions produced per mole of compound in solution:

	Cl^- ions precipitated as AgCl	*relative number of ions in solution*
$CoCl_3 \cdot 6NH_3$	$3\ Cl^-$	4
$CoCl_3 \cdot 5NH_3$	$2\ Cl^-$	3
$CoCl_3 \cdot 4NH_3$	$1\ Cl^-$	2
$CoCl_3 \cdot 4NH_3$	$1\ Cl^-$	2
$CoCl_3 \cdot 3NH_3$	no AgCl precipitated	none

The results implied that some chloride ions in the compounds were chemically different from other chloride ions. Werner realized that each cobalt ion was associated with *six* species, either NH_3 or Cl^-, and that only the excess Cl^- necessary for balancing the charge on the Co^{3+} was free in solution to contribute to the conductivity or to be precipitated by the Ag^+ as AgCl. The Co^{3+} ion and the six NH_3 or Cl^- behaved as a single unit not easily broken apart. He rewrote the formulas of the compounds to illustrate this:

$CoCl_3 \cdot 6NH_3$	rewritten as	$[Co(NH_3)_6]\ Cl_3$	three available Cl^-
$CoCl_3 \cdot 5NH_3$		$[Co(NH_3)_5Cl]\ Cl_2$	only two available Cl^-
$CoCl_3 \cdot 4NH_3$		$[Co(NH_3)_4Cl_2]\ Cl$	only one available Cl^-
$CoCl_3 \cdot 3NH_3$		$[Co(NH_3)_3Cl_3]$	no available Cl^-

The NH_3 or Cl^- within the square brackets remain attached to the cobalt ion when the compound is dissolved in water. This explained why varying amounts of chloride ion were precipitated upon addition of $AgNO_3$. The species enclosed within the square brackets is referred to as a **complex ion**, or often just as a **complex**. Werner assigned two valencies to the metal in the complex ion. The **primary valence** was the charge on the metal ion equal in this case to the number of chloride ions necessary to balance that charge. This is now referred to as the oxidation number of the metal. The **secondary valence** was the number of species, in this case NH_3 or Cl^-, surrounding the cobalt ion in the complex ion and written within the square brackets. This is now referred to as the **coordination number**. In all the compounds listed here, the coordination number is six.

It was the existence of the two compounds $CoCl_3 \cdot 4NH_3$—green and violet—that led to Werner's realization of the structure of the six NH_3 or Cl^- around the cobalt. Try as he might, Alfred Werner could not prepare a third compound with the same formula. He deduced that the arrangement of the NH_3 or Cl^- around the cobalt had to be octahedral rather than hexagonal or trigonal prismatic—both of which would have produced three different compounds with the formula $CoCl_3 \cdot 4NH_3$. The octahedral arrangement leads to two possible structures: one in which the two Cl^- ions are together (*cis–*) and one in which they are opposite (*trans–*) (Figure 59.2).

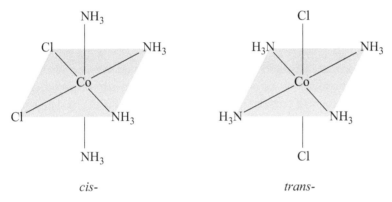

cis-   *trans-*

FIGURE 59.2   The *cis–* and *trans–* isomers of $[Co(NH_3)_4Cl_2]^+$.
In the *cis–* isomer the two Cl^- ions are next to one another. In the *trans–* isomer the two Cl^- ions are opposite one another.

EXAMPLE 59.1   COORDINATION COMPOUNDS

In the late 1890s, Alfred Werner investigated some ammonia complexes of platinum(IV). The empirical formulas of the complexes were:

$PtCl_4 \cdot 2NH_3$ no Cl^- precipitated by $AgNO_3$

$PtCl_4 \cdot 3NH_3$ 1 Cl^- precipitated by $AgNO_3$

$PtCl_4 \cdot 4NH_3$ 2 Cl^- precipitated by $AgNO_3$

$PtCl_4 \cdot 6NH_3$ 4 Cl^- precipitated by $AgNO_3$

Rewrite the formulas of these coordination compounds indicating the composition of the complex ions within square brackets. What is the coordination number in each case?

UNDERSTAND THE QUESTION

Only the Cl^- ions not coordinated to the platinum are free in solution to be precipitated by the $AgNO_3$. The Cl^- ions coordinated to the platinum are not precipitated.

PLAN THE SOLUTION

Each platinum complex contains four Cl^- ions. Subtracting the number precipitated from four determines the number of Cl^- ions that must be coordinated to the Pt.

SOLVE THE PROBLEM

$PtCl_4 \cdot 2NH_3$	rewritten as	$[Pt(NH_3)_2Cl_4]$
$PtCl_4 \cdot 3NH_3$	rewritten as	$[Pt(NH_3)_3Cl_3]Cl$
$PtCl_4 \cdot 4NH_3$	rewritten as	$[Pt(NH_3)_4Cl_2]Cl_2$
$PtCl_4 \cdot 6NH_3$	rewritten as	$[Pt(NH_3)_6]Cl_4$

The coordination number for all the complexes is six.

PROBLEM 59.1A

Show that, if a six coordinate complex compound with the stoichiometry $[MX_4Y_2]$ had a hexagonal or trigonal prismatic geometry, three different geometrical structures would be expected, as opposed to just two for an octahedral geometry.

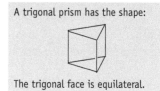

A trigonal prism has the shape:

The trigonal face is equilateral.

PROBLEM 59.1B

A compound with the stoichiometry K_2PtCl_6 dissolves in water to produce three ions per mole. Addition of $AgNO_3$ produces no precipitate of AgCl. What is the formula of the complex ion in this salt. What is the oxidation state of the platinum metal?

59.2 Coordination Compounds

We discussed what happens when a simple salt such as NaCl dissolves in water in Unit 8. The solution process can be broken down into two steps: the breaking up of the crystal lattice which requires energy and the attraction between the solute particles and the solvent molecules which releases energy. The solution process would be highly endothermic and virtually impossible without this solvation by the solvent molecules. The solvation of the ions is represented by the symbol (*aq*):

$$NaCl(s) \rightarrow Na^+(aq) + Cl^-(aq)$$

In the case of a simple salt such as NaCl, the interaction between the solvent molecule and the Na^+ cation is most easily regarded as an ion–dipole attraction although there will be some sharing of electrons and some delocalization of the positive charge.

The process is similar for the salt of a transition metal—the transition metal cation and the anion are surrounded by water molecules in solution. The process is represented for nickel(II) sulfate by the equation:

$$NiSO_4(s) \rightarrow Ni^{2+}(aq) + SO_4^{2-}(aq)$$

In this case, however, the Ni^{2+} ion is surrounded by six water molecules in a complex ion $[Ni(H_2O)_6]^{2+}$ similar to the complex ions of cobalt we have just examined (Figure 59.3).

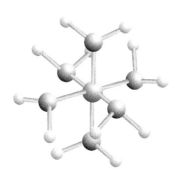

FIGURE 59.3 The octahedral structure of $[Ni(H_2O)_6]^{2+}$.

The water molecules in the complex ion are called **ligands**. Oxygen atoms of each water molecule partially donate pairs of electrons to the nickel(II) ion. A ligand, therefore, is a molecule or ion that is an electron pair donor. In other words, a ligand is a Lewis base. The metal ion or atom is a Lewis acid. The bond that is formed by the partial donation of the pair of electrons is called a **coordinate bond** and the compounds that result are called **coordination compounds**.

The metal ion, the Lewis acid, has empty orbitals into which it can accept the pairs of electrons from the ligands (Figure 59.4).

The word **ligand** is derived from the Latin 'ligare' meaning to bind. Another word with the same origin is *ligature* which is a stitch used in surgery.

The descriptions **complex** and **coordination compound** are used interchangeably. A complex *ion* is one of the ions in a coordination compound. In other words, a coordination compound is a either a neutral complex or an ionic compound in which at least one of the ions is a complex ion.

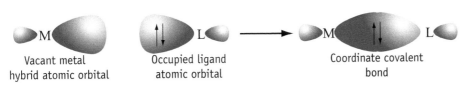

Vacant metal hybrid atomic orbital   Occupied ligand atomic orbital   Coordinate covalent bond

FIGURE 59.4 The formation of a coordinate bond by the donation of a pair of electrons from a ligand to a metal.

If a ligand that is stronger than water is added to the solution of nickel(II) in water, the ligand will replace the water molecules in the coordination compound. This type of substitution reaction is almost always accompanied by a change in the color. An example of a ligand stronger than water is ammonia and when ammonia is added to a solution of the green $[Ni(H_2O)_6]^{2+}$, the blue $[Ni(NH_3)_6]^{2+}$ is formed:

$$[Ni(H_2O)_6]^{2+}(aq) + 6\ NH_3(aq) \rightarrow [Ni(NH_3)_6]^{2+}(aq) + 6\ H_2O(l)$$

Ammonia is a stronger ligand than water because it forms a stronger bond with the metal ion; it is a stronger Lewis base. The reaction is thermodynamically driven. The structure of the nickel(II) complex with the six ammonia ligands is the same as the structure of the complex with the six water ligands (Figure 59.5). There are hundreds of transition metal complexes with the same octahedral structure.

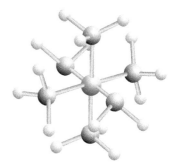

FIGURE 59.5 The octahedral structure of $[Ni(NH_3)_6]^{2+}$.

Other common geometries are the 4-coordinate tetrahedral and the 4-coordinate square-planar structures. For example, nickel(II) forms a tetrahedral structure $[NiCl_4]^{2-}$ with four Cl^- ligands and a square planar structure $[Ni(CN)_4]^{2-}$ with four cyanide CN^- ligands (Figure 59.6).

We will examine why one structure is preferred over another in Unit 60.

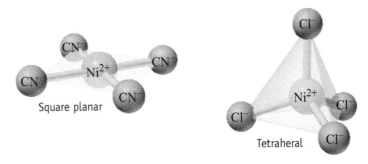

FIGURE 59.6 The tetrahedral structure of $[NiCl_4]^{2-}$ and the square-planar structure of $[Ni(CN)_4]^{2-}$.

59.3 Ligands

There are hundreds of different ligands, some very simple, some quite complicated, and some of great biological significance. Simple ligands contain atoms that are able to partially donate pairs of electrons to the metal ion or atom. These atoms are called **donor atoms** and are very often nitrogen or oxygen. Other donor atoms include carbon, phosphorus, and sulfur. Single ions that can act as ligands include the halide and hydride ions.

A ligand containing a single donor atom, or at least only one donor atom that is used, is called a **monodentate** ligand. Examples are the chloride ion, ammonia, and the cyanide ion shown in Table 59.1.

A ligand containing two donor atoms, both of which can coordinate with a metal ion, is called a **bidentate** ligand. A common example of a bidentate ligand is ethylenediamine, $H_2NCH_2CH_2NH_2$, very often abbreviated to 'en' in formulas. Ethylenediamine is a bidentate ligand in which both nitrogen donor atoms in the molecule can coordinate to the *same* metal ion. Such a ligand is called a **chelating ligand** and the resulting complex is called a **chelate**. When ethylenediamine is added to the nickel ammonia complex, three ethylenediamine molecules replace the six ammonia molecules. Notice how the color changes again, this time from blue to violet. The reaction is entropy-driven and this preference for chelating ligands is often referred to as the **chelate effect**.

$$[Ni(NH_3)_6]^{2+}(aq) + 3 \text{ en}(aq) \rightarrow [Ni(en)_3]^{2+}(aq) + 6 NH_3(l)$$

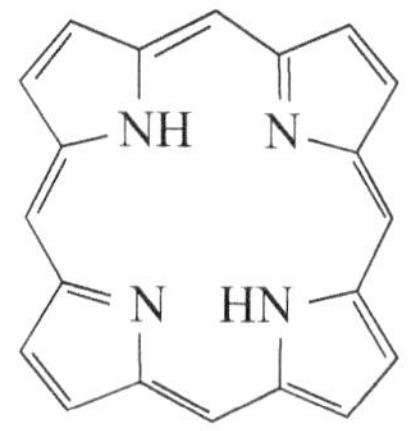

A **tridentate** ligand is one with three donor atoms and very often all three donor atoms form coordinate bonds with the same metal ion to form two chelate rings. An example is included in Table 59.1. A **tetradentate** ligand is one with four donor atoms. Among the most important tetradentate ligands are those derived from the **porphine** molecule (Figure 59.7). In this molecule, four nitrogen atoms are arranged at the corners of a square and the space available within the square is just about right for a transition metal ion in the first series. Complexes derived from the porphine molecule, with different groups substituted on the porphine ring, are called **porphyrins**. An example is the heme group of which there are four in the protein hemoglobin. The

Monodentate literally means 'one-tooth'. A ligand with more than one donor atom is called **polydentate**.

The word chelate is derived from the Greek word 'chele' meaning 'claw'.

The number of species present always increases when a chelating ligand displaces monodentate ligands.

FIGURE 59.7 **The porphine molecule.**
The loss of two H$^+$ ions leads to a tetradentate macrocyclic ligand with a 2– charge.

TABLE 59.1 Some common ligands.

Ligand Type	Examples			
Monodentate	$H_2\ddot{O}$: water	:F̈:⁻ fluoride ion	[:C≡N:]⁻ cyanide ion	[:Ö—H]⁻ hydroxide ion
	:NH₃ ammonia	:C̈l:⁻ chloride ion	[:S̈=C=N̈:]⁻ thiocyanate ion	[:Ö—N=Ö:]⁻ nitrite ion
Bidentate	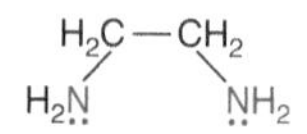 ethylenediamine (en)	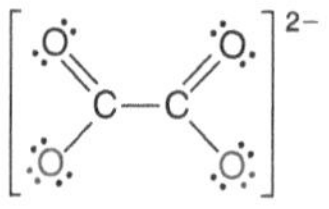 oxalate ion		
Polydentate	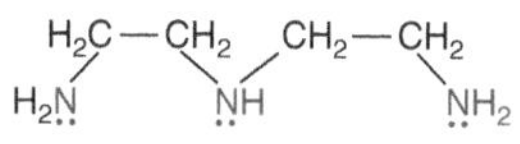 diethylenetriamine	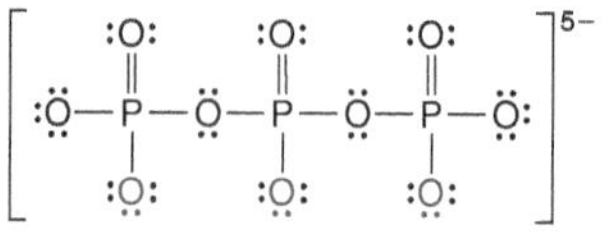 triphosphate ion	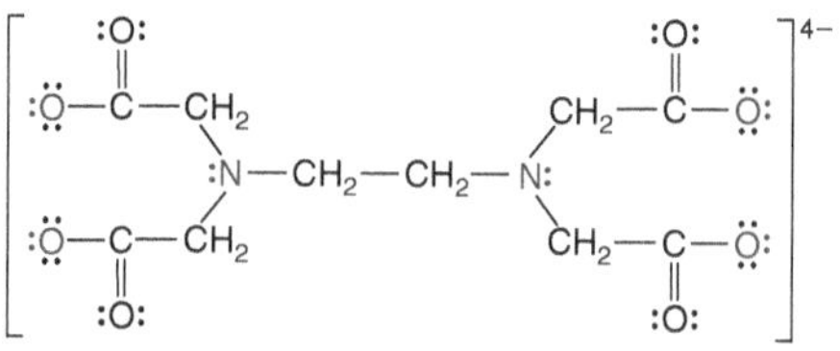 ethylenediaminetetraacetate ion (EDTA⁴⁻)	

porphine molecule is an example of what is called a **macrocyclic ligand**. This is a ligand containing a ring of several donor atoms incorporated into a cyclic structure.

The most common example of a hexadentate ligand is the ethylenediaminetetraacetate ion (EDTA) (Figure 59.8). This a is a flexible ligand that can wrap itself around a metal cation with the six donor atoms occupying all six of the octahedral sites in the complex. Such complexes are very stable. EDTA can be used to sequester metal cations and is often used in analytical procedures for the determination of the concentration of metal cations in unknown samples.

The pair of electrons donated by a ligand need not necessarily be a lone pair of electrons on a donor atom. In some organometallic complexes the donated pairs of electrons are π bonding electrons. Two typical examples are the coordination of an ethylene molecule C_2H_4 in a platinum complex called Zeise's salt and the coordination of two cyclopentadienyl ligands in the sandwich compound ferrocene shown in Figure 59.9. In Zeise's salt, the π bonding pair of electrons of the ethylene molecule is partially donated to the platinum metal ion. This weakens the π bonding in the ethylene molecule. In ferrocene, the Fe^{2+} ion is sandwiched between two cyclopentadienyl rings; each ligand shares six π electrons with the Fe^{2+} ion.

EDTA is sometimes used to treat toxic metal poisoning—the EDTA complexes the toxic metal ion and the complex is then excreted naturally.

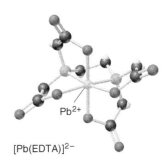

$[Pb(EDTA)]^{2-}$

FIGURE 59.8 The structure of the Pb2+ – EDTA complex showing how the ligand wraps around the metal ion with donor atoms at each position of the octahedral coordination sphere.

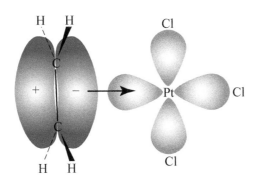

(a) Zeise's salt $[Pt(C_2H_4)Cl_3]^-$; a complex of platinum with an ethylene ligand.

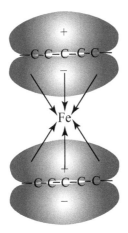

(b) Ferrocene $[Fe(C_5H_5)_2]$; a complex of iron with two cyclopentadienyl ligands. Each ligand donates 3 pairs of electrons.

FIGURE 59.9 **The structures of (a) Zeise's salt and (b) ferrocene.**
In both complexes, the electrons donated from the ligand to the metal are π bonding electrons.

59.4 Naming Transition Metal Coordination Compounds

The formula for a coordination compound of a transition metal is written in such a way that the structure of the compound can be determined quite easily. As we have seen, the ligands associated with a metal ion are written within square brackets. Cations and anions present to balance any charge on the complex ion are written outside the square brackets. Cations are written first and anions are written second.

The same is true of the names for coordination compounds. The idea is to name the compound to identify it uniquely in a logical and concise way. Complexes can indeed be quite complicated and the names are sometimes quite long. There is a set of rules and conventions intended to make the naming of coordination compounds as straightforward as possible:

1. Name the cation first and the anion second, just as the formula is written.

2. For a complex ion, name the ligands first, in alphabetical order, and the metal last.

3. A neutral ligand has the same name as the molecule, for example, ethylenediamine as a ligand is simply called ethylenediamine. There are, however, four common exceptions:

water H_2O	*as a ligand is called*	aqua
ammonia NH_3		ammine
carbon monoxide CO		carbonyl
nitric oxide NO		nitrosyl

4. Negatively charged ligands (anionic ligands) have the ending –o:

–ide	*is changed to* –o	Cl^- chloro, CN^- cyano, OH^- hydroxo
–ate	*is changed to* –ato	SO_4^{2-} sulfato, SCN^- thiocyanato
–ite	*is changed to* –ito	SO_3^- sulfito

   > There are some exceptions to this rule, for example:
   > H^- (hydride) is called hydrido
   > NO_2^- (nitrite) is called nitro

5. Greek prefixes are used to indicate the number of each ligand in the complex:

		alternative	
di–	two		bis–
tri–	three		tris–
tetra–	four		tetrakis–
penta–	five		pentakis–
hexa–	six		hexakis–

   The alternative prefix is used when some confusion might result from the use of the simpler prefix. This usually occurs when the ligand already contains a prefix (as in ethylenediamine) or if the ligand is polydentate.

6. The oxidation number of the metal ion in the complex is indicated by a roman numeral in parentheses after its name.

7. If the complex ion is an anion (negatively charged) then the suffix –ate is substituted for the normal ending –ium of the name for the metal. If the symbol for the metal is derived from a Latin name, then the Latin name is used. Some examples are:

	nickel	*changed to*	nickelate
	cobalt		cobaltate
	chromium		chromate
	manganese		manganate
but	copper		cuprate
	iron		ferrate
	gold		aurate
	silver		argentate

EXAMPLE 59.2 FORMULAS AND NAMES FOR COORDINATION COMPOUNDS

Name the compounds:

a. $[Co(NH_3)_4Cl_2]Cl$

b. $K_3[Fe(CN)_6]$

c. $[Co(H_2O)(en)_2Br]SO_4$

Write formulas for the compounds:

a. ammonium diamminedibromoplatinate(IV)

b. potassium tetraachlorocobaltate(II)

c. tetracarbonylnickel(0)

UNDERSTAND THE QUESTION

The names of coordination compounds are derived in a systematic way using the rules described above. Writing the formulas from the names is perhaps easier. The stoichiometry can be determined if the charges on the ligands are known and the oxidation state of the metal is known.

PLAN THE SOLUTION

Follow the rules given earlier. Remember the special names for H_2O, NH_3, CO, and NO when they are ligands in coordination compounds.

SOLVE THE PROBLEM

Names of complexes:

a. $[Co(NH_3)_4Cl_2]Cl$ tetraamminedichlorocobalt(III) chloride

Note the name ammine for ammonia and the prefix tetra– meaning four. The two chloride ligands are named next (c follows a) and then the metal. Note that there are no spaces in the name for the complex ion—it is one long word. Note also that the two 'a's in tetraammine are retained. The oxidation number of the cobalt can be determined by adding the negative charges on the ligands and any anions present. The ammonia molecules are neutral, the three chloride ions each have a 1– charge—so the oxidation number of the cobalt must be +3. Note also that the Cl_2 means two chloride ions, not a Cl_2 molecule!

b. $K_3[Fe(CN)_6]$ potassium hexacyanoferrate(III)

The name for the complex ion (the anion in this case) is one word. The name for the cyanide ion as a ligand is cyano– and there are six of them so the prefix is hexa–. The oxidation number for the iron must be +3 because there are three K^+ and six CN^-. Iron in an anionic complex ion is called ferrate.

c. $[Co(H_2O)(en)_2Br]SO_4$ aquabromobis(ethylenediamine)cobalt(III) sulfate

The ligands are named in alphabetical order, so aqua (for water), then bromo, then ethylenediamine. Note that any prefixes do not influence the alphabetical order. The prefix for a bidentate ligand such as ethylenediamine is bis– not di–. The oxidation state of the cobalt can be derived as before: the compound contains one bromide ion Br^- and one sulfate ion SO_4^{2-}. The oxidation state of the cobalt ion is therefore +3.

You may see the order of the ligands in a written formula different in different books. Some chemists like to arrange the ligands in alphabetical order and other chemists like to write the neutral ligands first, followed by the anionic ligands. So this compound may be written:

as $[Co(H_2O)(en)_2Br]SO_4$

or as $[Co(H_2O)Br(en)_2]SO_4$

You may often see it as

$[Co(en)_2(H_2O)Br]SO_4$

with the polydentate ligand written first.

Formulas of complexes:

a. ammonium diamminedibromoplatinate(IV) $(NH_4)_2 [Pt(NH_3)_2Br_2]$

The number of ammonium ions required can be determined from the number of bromide ions present and the oxidation state of the platinum. The platinum is +4, there are two bromide ions with a charge of −1, so there must be two ammonium ions. In the complex ion, the metal is written first, followed by the ligands, often in alphabetical order.

b. potassium tetrachlorocobaltate(II) $K_2 [CoCl_4]$

c. tetracarbonylnickel(0) $[Ni(CO)_4]$

This is a neutral complex. The oxidation state of the nickel is zero and the carbon monoxide ligands are neutral molecules.

PROBLEM 59.2A

Write the names of the following coordination compounds:

a. $K_3[V(C_2O_4)_3]$ $C_2O_4^{2-}$ is the oxalate anion
b. $Na[Ag(CN)_2]$
c. $[Zn(en)_2]Cl_2$

PROBLEM 59.2B

Write the names of the following coordination compounds:

a. $Na_3[Co(NO_2)_6]$
b. $[Pt(NH_3)_2Cl_2]$
c. $[Co(en)_2(NH_3)CN]Br_2$

59.5   Isomers

One of the consequences of arranging ligands around a metal ion in a complex is the possibility of arranging them in different ways. It was the existence of two possible arrangements of the NH_3 and Cl^- ligands in the complex ion $[Co(NH_3)_4Cl_2]^+$ that led Alfred Werner to the conclusion that the structure of the complex ion was octahedral. Complexes with different arrangements of ligands are called **isomers**.

Although they have the same chemical composition, isomers have different chemical and physical properties. Sometimes the difference in their chemical properties has great biological significance. The antitumor drug $[Pt(NH_3)_2Cl_2]$ exists as two possible isomers (Figure 59.10) but it is only the *cis–* isomer (cisplatin) that can bind with DNA and stop the growth of the tumor.

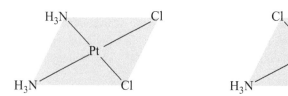

FIGURE 59.10   The *cis–* and *trans–* isomers of diamminedichloroplatinum(II).
Only the *cis–* isomer (cisplatin) is physiologically active as an antitumor agent.

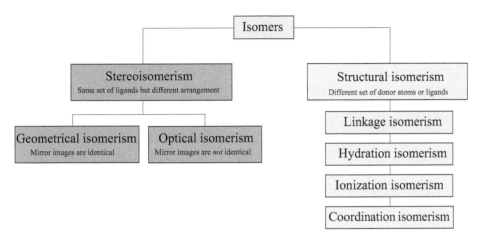

FIGURE 59.11 Classification of the various types of isomerism in coordination compounds.

The diagram in Figure 59.11 summarizes the various types of isomerism. There are two major classes: **stereoisomerism** (the more interesting of the two) and **structural isomerism**. Stereoisomerism involves structures in which the metal ion is surrounded by the *same* set of ligands but arranged in different ways. Structural isomerism involves structures in which the metal ion is surrounded by a *different* set of donor atoms and/or ligands.

Stereoisomerism

Stereoisomers have the same chemical formula. The *cis–* and *trans–* isomers of $[Pt(NH_3)_2Cl_2]$ are both written in the same way. If they need to be distinguished, the prefix *cis–* or *trans–* can be added as shown in Figure 59.10.

The prefix *cis–* means 'adjacent to' each other, the prefix *trans–* means 'across from' each other.

There are two types of stereoisomerism—**geometrical isomerism and optical isomerism**. Geometrical isomerism is the type of isomerism we have just discussed—the possibility of arranging the same set of ligands around the metal ion in a different way. This particular example is so common that geometrical isomerism is sometimes referred to as **cis–trans– isomerism**. There are, however, other forms of geometrical isomerism. The complex $[Co(NH_3)Cl_3]$ exists as two geometrical isomers (Figure 59.12). One isomer, in which all three NH_3 ligands (and all three Cl^- ligands)

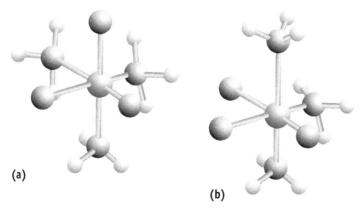

(a)

(b)

FIGURE 59.12 The *fac–* and *mer–* isomers of [Co(NH₃)₃Cl₃].
(a) In the *fac–* isomer the three Cl^- ions (and the three NH_3) are on a triangular face of the octahedron; (b) In the *mer–* isomer the three Cl^- ions (and the three NH_3) are in a single plane.

lie on a triangular face of the octahedron, is called the *facial* isomer, often abbreviated to *fac–*. In the other isomer, all three NH₃ ligands (and all three Cl⁻ ligands) lie on a meridian in the same plane. This isomer is called the *meridional* isomer, usually abbreviated to *mer–*.

Optical isomers are nonsuperimposable mirror images of each other; the individual isomers are called **enantiomers**. The word 'nonsuperimposable' means that the two mirror images are not identical—there is no way to rotate or turn one mirror image upside down to make it identical to or 'superimposable' on the other. The two mirror images of the complex ion $[Co(en)_3]^{3+}$ are nonsuperimposable (Figure 59.13). This is sometimes a little difficult to see without building a three-dimensional model and testing to determine whether or not they are nonsuperimposable.

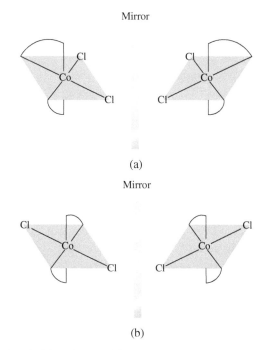

FIGURE 59.13   The *cis* (a) and *trans* (b) isomers of dichlorobis(ethylenediamine) cobalt(III) ion and their mirror images.
The two isomers are mirror images of each other and are not identical—they are nonsuperimposable.

> If a complex has a center of symmetry, or a plane of symmetry running through the center of the complex, it *cannot* be chiral.

Another word used to describe a complex that has a nonidentical mirror image is **chiral**. Or, in other words, a **chiral complex** is one which has a nonsuperimposable mirror image. An **achiral complex** is one for which the mirror image is identical.

Optical isomers are so called because they have the curious property of being able to rotate the plane of plane-polarized light. In plane-polarized light the oscillation of the electric field occurs in a single plane, as opposed to randomly throughout 360°. When plane-polarized light passes through a solution of an enantiomer, the plane of polarization is rotated either clockwise or anticlockwise. The mirror image, the other enantiomer, rotates the plane in the reverse direction. Because of this effect on plane-polarized light, enantiomers are said to be **optically-active**.

EXAMPLE 59.3   STEREOISOMERISM

Determine the possible geometrical and optical isomers of the octahedral complexes:

a. $[Co(NH_3)_3Br_2Cl]$

b. $[Co(en)_2Cl_2]^+$

UNDERSTAND THE QUESTION

Stereoisomerism involves structures in which the metal ion is surrounded by the same set of ligands but arranged in different ways. The task is to determine the different ways in which the ligands can be arranged. A model set is very useful, even if only plastic modelling clay and toothpicks.

PLAN THE SOLUTION

Systematically examine the different ways to arrange the ligands. For example, in the first case, start with the three NH_3 ligands—there are two possible arrangements: *fac–* and *mer–*. Then, for each, determine if there are different possible arrangements of the two Br^- and one Cl^- ligands. Be on the lookout for possible nonsuperimposable mirror images.

SOLVE THE PROBLEM

a. $[Co(NH_3)_3Br_2Cl]$

There are two possible ways to arrange the three NH_3 ligands: *fac–* and *mer–*.

For the *mer–* isomer, the two Br^- ligands can be either *cis–* or *trans–*.

There are therefore three geometrical isomers:

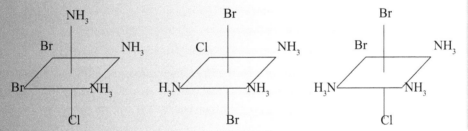

> The octahedral arrangement of ligands around a metal ion is often drawn as shown here. Bear in mind, however, that every corner of the octahedron is the same as every other—there is nothing special about the four positions shown on the corners of the square or the two positions at the top and bottom.

All three geometrical isomers have mirror planes through the center of the complex and therefore none are chiral.

b. $[Co(en)_2Cl_2]^+$

Ethylenediamine (en) is a bidentate chelating ligand. The two bonds from the chelating ligand must be adjacent to one another on the octahedron.

There are two possible ways to do this:

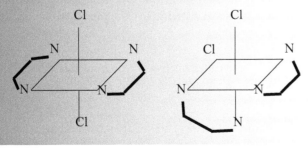

The first isomer has mirror planes passing through the complex and therefore cannot be chiral.

The second isomer, however, is chiral; it has a nonsuperimposable mirror image. Two optical isomers exist:

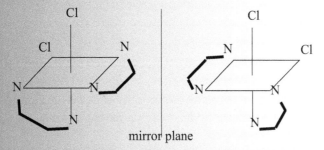

mirror plane

PROBLEM 59.3A

Determine the possible geometrical isomers of the square planar complexes:

a. $[Ni(NH_3)_2CN_2]$

b. $[Pt(en)Cl_2]$

c. Is it possible for a square planar complex to be optically active?

PROBLEM 59.3B

Determine the possible geometrical and optical isomers of the octahedral complexes:

a. $[Co(NH_3)_2(H_2O)_2Cl_2]^+$

b. $[Co(en)_3]^{3+}$

Structural Isomerism

Structural isomers are more easily recognized than stereoisomers because their formulas are written differently—the set of donor atoms around the metal ion is different. Structural isomers can be divided into four convenient categories but essentially the same principle applies to all.

Linkage isomers can occur when a ligand is **ambidentate**. An ambidentate ligand is one that can coordinate to a metal ion through two different donor atoms—the link between the ligand and the metal is different. An example of an ambidentate ligand is the nitrite ion NO_2^-. There are three donor atoms in this ion, the nitrogen atom and the two oxygen atoms, and the ligand can coordinate to a metal ion using any one of the three. In the complex $[Co(NH_3)_5NO_2]^{2+}$, the NO_2^- ion coordinates through the nitrogen atom. In the linkage isomer $[Co(NH_3)_5ONO]^{2+}$, the NO_2^- ion coordinates through one of the oxygen atoms. Notice how the formulas are written—the donor atom is written first. The name given to the nitrite ion is different for the two isomers. When coordinating through the N, it is called nitro, when coordinating through the O, it is called nitrito. Some other common ambidentate ligands and their names are listed in Table 59.2.

The properties of the two structural isomers are different because the donor atom sets around the cobalt ion in the complex are different. The two complexes, for example, have different colors (Figure 59.14). In this case the nitrito complex is slightly less stable than the nitro complex and slowly converts to the nitro complex over time.

TABLE 59.2 Ambidentate ligands and their names.

Formula	Donor Atom	Name
NO_2^-	N	nitro
NO_2^-	O	nitrito
CN^-	C	cyanide
NC^-	N	isocyanide
SCN^-	S	thiocyanate
NCS^-	N	isothiocyanate

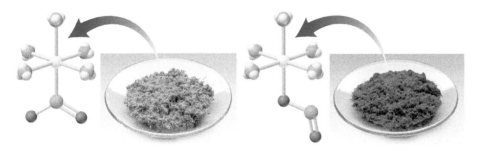

FIGURE 59.14 Two linkage isomers: the nitro complex $[Co(NH_3)_5NO_2]^{2+}$ (left) and the nitrito complex $[Co(NH_3)_5ONO]^{2+}$ (right).

Some ambidentate ligands act as bridging ligands between two metal ions. One donor atom of the ligand coordinates with one metal ion and the other donor atom coordinates to another metal ion. The KFe(III) salt of the hexacyanoferrate(II) ion $[Fe(CN)_6]^{4-}$, called Prussian blue, $KFe[Fe(CN)_6]$, is a polymeric compound in which the cyanide ligand coordinates through both the C and the N to different Fe ions in a cubic lattice (Figure 59.15).

Hydration isomers are complexes in which a water molecule is exchanged for a ligand in the complex. For example, the two complexes $[Cr(H_2O)_5Cl]Cl_2 \cdot H_2O$ and $[Cr(H_2O)_4Cl_2]Cl \cdot 2H_2O$ are hydration isomers. A similar isomerism is called **ionization isomerism**. Two ligands are again exchanged in this case. An example is the complex $[Co(NH_3)_5Cl]SO_4$ and its isomer $[Co(NH_3)_5SO_4]Cl$. When these complexes are

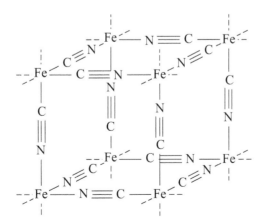

FIGURE 59.15 The structure of Prussian blue in which the ambidentate cyanide ion acts as a bidentate ligand bridging two Fe ions.

Polymerization isomerism is not a true isomerism because the set of atoms is not the same. One is some multiple of the other. For example, butene C_4H_8 is *not* considered to be an isomer of ethylene C_2H_4.

dissolved in water, different ions are produced—hence the name ionization isomerism. **Coordination isomerism** arises when ligands are exchanged between two complex ions in a coordination compound—one cationic and the other anionic. An example is the compound $[Co(NH_3)_6][CrCl_6]$ and its isomer $[Cr(NH_3)_6][CoCl_6]$. Finally, it's worth mentioning a relationship between complexes sometimes referred to as **polymerization isomerism**. This occurs when two complexes have the same empirical formulas but have different molar masses. An example is $[Pt(NH_3)_2Cl_2]$ and its isomer $[Pt(NH_3)_4][PtCl_4]$.

EXAMPLE 59.4 STRUCTURAL ISOMERISM

The following pairs of compounds are structural isomers. Identify the type of structural isomerism. Do any of these structural isomers have stereoisomers?

  a. $[Co(NH_3)_4BrCl]Cl$ and $[Co(NH_3)_4Cl_2]Br$
  b. $[Cr(en)_2(SCN)Cl]^+$ and $[Cr(en)_2(NCS)Cl]^+$

UNDERSTAND THE QUESTION

Structural isomers have different formulas. The set of donor atoms around the metal ion is different in the two isomers. Usually the ligand set is different although in the case of linkage isomerism the ligands are the same but the donor atom is different. The name for the structural isomers describes the way in which the ligand or donor atom set is different. Any complex ion may have stereoisomers—it depends upon whether different arrangements of the ligands is possible.

PLAN THE SOLUTION

Examine the two formulas for the isomers and determine in which way they are different. For each isomers, determine whether different arrangements of the ligands are possible.

SOLVE THE PROBLEM

  a. $[Co(NH_3)_4BrCl]Cl$ and $[Co(NH_3)_4Cl_2]Br$

  These are two ionization isomers. For each isomer, both *cis*– and *trans*– geometrical isomers are possible.

  b. $[Cr(en)_2(SCN)Cl]^+$ and $[Cr(en)_2(NCS)Cl]^+$

  These are two linkage isomers—the thiocyanate ligand is ambidentate. For each isomer, both *cis*– and *trans*– geometrical isomers are possible. The SCN^- and Cl^- ligands can be either adjacent to or opposite one another. For the *cis*– isomer, two optical isomers exist (*cf.* Example 54.2(b)).

PROBLEM 59.4A

Identify the structural isomerism exhibited by the following pairs of complexes:

  a. $[Co(NH_3)_6][Co(NO_2)_6]$ and $[Co(NH_3)_3(NO_2)_3]$
  b. $[Co(NH_3)_6][Cr(CN)_6]$ and $[Cr(NH_3)_6][Co(CN)_6]$
  c. $[Co(H_2O)_6]Br_2$ and $[Co(H_2O)_4Br_2] \cdot 2H_2O$

PROBLEM 59.4B

  a. Write the formula of a hydration isomer of $[Cr(H_2O)_6](NO_2)_3$ that has *cis*– and *trans*– geometrical isomers.
  b. Write the formula of an polymerization isomer of $[Co(NH_3)_6][Co(CN)_6]$ that has *fac*– and *mer*– geometrical isomers.

59.6 Biologically-Significant Coordination Compounds

About 70% of the human body is water, so most of the atoms present in the human body are hydrogen and oxygen. The organic molecules that make up most of the remainder of the human body are composed primarily of carbon, hydrogen, nitrogen, and oxygen. Together, these four elements account for 99% of all the atoms present in the human body. Another seven elements, sodium, potassium, magnesium, calcium, phosphorus, sulfur, and chlorine account for another 0.9%. The remaining 0.1% are the trace elements, present in very small amounts but essential for life. Many of these trace elements are first row d-block elements, specifically the elements chromium through zinc. It is the ability of these elements to coordinate with ligands and their ease of oxidation and reduction to different oxidation states that makes them ideal for use in biological systems. As an example, we will examine the role of iron in hemoglobin and myoglobin.

Oxygen is stored by a molecule called **myoglobin** which consists of a heme group and a protein. A protein is a large molecule constructed from α–amino acids (the molar mass of myoglobin is approximately 17,000 g mol^{-1}). The heme group is a complex of Fe^{2+} and a porphyrin ring illustrated in Figure 59.16. A fifth position around the Fe^{2+} is occupied by a nitrogen atom of a histidine ring of the protein chain leaving the sixth position available for the binding of the oxygen molecule.

Oxygen is transported within the body by **hemoglobin**. This is a protein molecule very similar to four myoglobin units containing a total of four heme groups (molar mass approximately 64,500 g mol^{-1}). In the absence of the oxygen ligand, the Fe^{2+} ion lies out of the plane of the porphyrin ring and is surrounded by five ligands in a square-pyramidal geometry. When oxygen moves into the sixth position, the Fe^{2+} ion moves into the plane of the porphyrin ring. The change in the ligands around the Fe^{2+} changes the color of the complex from blue (typical of blood in veins) to red (the color of arterial blood). When the Fe^{2+} moves into the plane of the porphyrin ring, it pulls the histidine ligand with it. This alters the conformation of the protein slightly and facilitates the binding of other oxygen molecules to the three other heme groups in the hemoglobin molecule. The binding of the four oxygen molecules and their subsequent release is referred to as a cooperative process.

The myoglobin molecule contains 153 amino acids and the hemoglobin molecule about four times as many. In people with a condition called sickle-cell anemia, an incorrect amino acid (valine) is present in place of glutamic acid in the protein in two places. This almost insignificant change has a dramatic effect on the shape adopted by the hemoglobin molecule—the red blood cells as a result are sickle-shaped rather than circular (Figure 59.17) and their ability to function properly is severely impaired.

Carbon monoxide has an affinity for hemoglobin about 200 times that of oxygen—it is a stronger ligand. The complex formed has a bright red color and the color of the blood of victims of carbon monoxide poisoning is a good indicator of the cause of death. The formation of the carbon monoxide complex prevents the normal binding of oxygen and the body is deprived of oxygen resulting in asphyxiation.

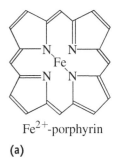

Fe^{2+}-porphyrin

(a)

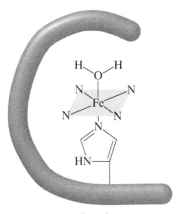

Protein

(b)

FIGURE 59.16 (a) The heme group; (b) A schematic representation of the heme group with the fifth position around the Fe^{2+} occupied by a nitrogen atom of a histidine ring of the protein chain and the sixth position occupied by an oxygen molecule.

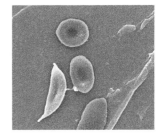

FIGURE 59.17 A normal blood cell (on the right) and a sickle cell (on the left). Magnified ×18,000.

Review Questions

1. Describe what is meant by a 'complex' ion. What is the significance of the molecules or ions enclosed within the square brackets in the formula of a complex ion?

2. Describe what a ligand is and what interaction a ligand has with a metal ion in a complex ion.

3. What is a chelating ligand? Is it possible for a ligand to be bidentate and not be a chelating ligand?

4. Review the rules for naming coordination compounds.

5. Several types of isomerism are encountered in transition metal coordination compounds. The principal division is into stereoisomerism and structural isomerism. What's the difference between the two?

6. How would you determine if a coordination compound has an optical isomer?

7. What is an ambidentate ligand? Is it possible for an ambidentate ligand to be bidentate?

Solutions to Problems

PROBLEM 59.1A

There are three ways to arrange the X and Y ligands of a complex ion $[MX_4Y_2]$ in both a hexagonal and in a trigonal prismatic geometry:

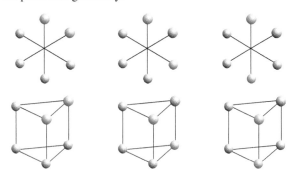

PROBLEM 59.2A

a. $K_3[V(C_2O_4)_3]$ potassium tris(oxalato)vanadate(III)

b. $Na[Ag(CN)_2]$ sodium dicyanoargentate(I)

c. $[Zn(en)_2]Cl_2$ bis(ethylenediamine)zinc(II) chloride

PROBLEM 59.3A

a. $[Ni(NH_3)_2CN_2]$ two isomers: cis– and trans–

b. $[Pt(en)Cl_2]$ only one possible arrangement; the donor atoms of the ethylenediamine ligand must be adjacent

c. A square planar complex *cannot* be optically active. There is a plane of symmetry in the plane of the molecule. The mirror images are always superimposable.

PROBLEM 59.4A

Identify the structural isomerism exhibited by the following pairs of complexes:

a. $[Co(NH_3)_6][Co(NO_2)_6]$ and $[Co(NH_3)_3(NO_2)_3]$ polymerization isomerism

b. $[Co(NH_3)_6][Cr(CN)_6]$ and $[Cr(NH_3)_6][Co(CN)_6]$ coordination isomerism

c. $[Co(H_2O)_6]Br_2$ and $[Co(H_2O)_6Br_2]\cdot2H_2O$ hydration isomerism

Answers to Review Questions

1. A complex is a compound formed by a Lewis acid and one or more Lewis bases. The Lewis bases donate electron pairs to the Lewis acid. The complex may be charged (complex ion) or neutral. The term usually refers to a transition metal ion surrounded by several ligands. The transition metal ion, and the coordinated ligands are enclosed within square brackets when the formula is written. The species within the square brackets is the complex or complex ion.

2. A ligand is a Lewis base. It has one or more electron pairs that it can donate to a metal ion that acts as the Lewis acid. The donation of an electron pair forms a coordinate bond between the ligand and the metal.

3. A bidentate chelating ligand is a ligand with two donor atoms arranged so that both can coordinate with the same metal ion. A ring of atoms is formed called a chelate ring. If the donor atoms in the ligand are not arranged so that both can coordinate to the same metal ion, chelation is impossible. The ligand in this case can bridge two metal ions—it can still be bidentate but not be able to chelate.

4. The aim is to name a compound to identify it unambiguously. The names for coordination compounds

are sometimes quite long but they are constructed in a logical and concise way. The set of rules and conventions were summarized earlier in this unit.

5. The difference between stereoisomerism and structural isomerism is that stereoisomerism involves the same set of donor atoms arranged in different ways around the metal whereas structural isomerism involves a different set of donor atoms around the metal.

6. Build or draw the structure of the complex and then build or draw the mirror image of the same complex. If the two structures are identical (superimposable) then the complex cannot be optically active—

it is not chiral. If the two structures are not identical (nonsuperimposable) then the complex is optically active—it will have an optical isomer (its mirror image) and it will be chiral. Alternatively, build or draw the structure of the complex and look for a center of symmetry or a plane of symmetry in the complex. If either is present, then the complex is achiral and will not have an optical isomer.

7. An ambidentate ligand is one that can coordinate with a metal ion through more than one donor atom. If it coordinates with both donor atoms, bridging two metal ions, then it is bidentate. An example is the cyanide ion in Prussian blue (*cf.* Figure 59.15).

End-of-Unit Problems

1. Determine the coordination number and the oxidation number of the metal in the following complexes:
   a. $Na_2[CoCl_4]$
   b. $[Co(en)_3]Br_3$
   c. $[Fe(H_2O)_4Cl_2]$
   d. $K[Ni(CN)_5]$

2. Determine the coordination number and the oxidation number of the metal in the following complexes:
   a. $[Pt(NH_3)_2Br_2]$
   b. $K[Ag(CN)_2]$
   c. $[Zn(en)_2]Cl_2$
   d. $[Co(NH_3)_3(NO_2)_3]$

3. Identify which of the descriptions monodentate, bidentate, chelating, and ambidentate, apply to the following ligands:
   a. ethylenediamine $NH_2CH_2CH_2NH_2$
   b. thiocyanate ion NCS^-
   c. bromide ion Br^-
   d. nitrite ion NO_2^-

4. Identify which of the descriptions monodentate, bidentate, chelating, and ambidentate, apply to the following ligands:
   a. fluoride ion F^-
   b. ammonia NH_3
   c. oxalate ion $O_2CCO_2^{2-}$
   d. cyanide ion CN^-

5. A coordination compound of cobalt(III) contains a sulfate ion, a chloride ion, and five ammonia molecules. When barium chloride solution is added to an aqueous solution of the complex, a precipitate of of barium sulfate is produced. When silver nitrate is added to another solution of the complex, there is no precipitate of silver chloride. What is the formula for the coordination compound?

6. A complex of chromium(III) contains six water molecules and three chloride ions. When silver nitrate is added to a solution of the complex, there is a precipitate of silver chloride corresponding to one Cl^- per complex molecule. What is the formula for the complex?

7. The *ortho*–, *meta*–, and *para*– isomers of diaminobenzene are illustrated below. Which of these isomers are bidentate ligands? Which of these isomers can chelate? Explain your answers.

8. The molecules catechol, phthalic acid, and *ortho*–phenanthroline are illustrated below. How many of these molecules can form chelates with transition metal ions? Explain your answer.

9. The following molecules are polydentate ligands. How many bonds will each ligand form with a single metal ion and how many chelate rings will be formed. Characterize each ligand as bidentate or tridentate, etc.

   a. $H_2N–CH_2–CH_2–NH–CH_2–CH_2–NH–CH_2–CH_2–NH_2$

   b.

10. The following molecules are polydentate ligands. How many bonds will each ligand form with a single metal ion and how many chelate rings will be formed. Characterize each ligand as bidentate or tridentate, etc.

    a.

    b.

11. Write the systematic names for the following complexes:

    a. $K_2[CoBr_4]$

    b. $[Co(NH_3)_4(NO_2)_2]Br$

    c. $[Cr(NH_3)_6][Co(CN)_6]$

    d. $K_3[Cr(C_2O_4)_2Cl_2]$

12. Write the systematic names for the following complexes:

    a. $Na_2[MnCl_4]$

    b. $[Cu(en)(NH_3)_2]NO_2$

    c. $trans–[Pt(NH_3)_2Cl_4]$

    d. $[Fe(H_2O)_5NCS]SO_4$

13. Write formulas for the following complexes:

    a. Bis(ethylenediamine)platinum(II) nitrate

    b. Potassium hexacyanoferrate(II)

    c. Tetraamminedichlorochromium(III) chloride

    d. Pentaamminesulfatocobalt(III) sulfate

14. Write formulas for the following complexes:

    a. Potassium tris(oxalato)ferrate(III) trihydrate

    b. Sodium tetrachlorocuprate(II)

    c. Diamminetetraaquacobalt(III) perchlorate

    d. tetraaquadibromonickel(II)

15. Draw the possible structural isomers (both ionization isomers and linkage isomers) of the coordination compound $[Co(NH_3)_5NO_2]Br_2$.

16. Draw the possible structural isomers (ionization, hydration, or linkage isomers) of the coordination compound $[Cr(H_2O)_4Cl_2]Br·2H_2O$.

17. Which of the following complexes can form $cis–$ and $trans–$ geometrical isomers? For those that do, draw the structures of the two isomers.

    a. $[Co(NH_3)_4Br_2]^+$

    b. $[Cr(NH_3)_5Cl]^{2+}$

    c. $[Pd(CN)_2I_2]$

18. Which of the following complexes can form $cis–$ and $trans–$ geometrical isomers? For those that do, draw the structures of the two isomers.

    a. $[Pt(NH_3)_3Br]^+$

    b. $[Fe(en)(H_2O)_4]^{2+}$

    c. $[Co(en)_2BrCl]^+$

19. Draw the geometrical isomers of the complex $[Pt(NH_3)_2Br_2]$.

20. Draw the geometrical isomers of the complex $[Cr(NH_3)_3I_3]$.

21. Draw the geometrical isomers of the complex $[Co(NH_3)_3Cl_2(NO_2)]$.

22. Draw the geometrical isomers of the complex $[Co(en)(CN)_2(NCS)_2]$.

23. Which of the following complexes is(are) chiral?

    a. $[Co(en)_2ClBr]^+$

    b. $[Fe(C_2O_4)_3]^{3-}$

    c. $[MnCl_4]^{2-}$

24. Which of the following complexes is(are) chiral?

    a. $[Cr(NH_3)_4ClBr]^+$

    b. $[Ni(CN)_2Cl_2]$

    c. $[Rh(en)_2(NH_3)_2]^{3+}$

25. Draw the mirror image of the complex shown and determine whether the complex and its image are superimposable or not. Is the complex chiral?

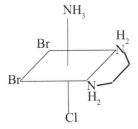

26. Are the two complexes shown mirror images? Are they nonsuperimposable? Are they chiral? Explain the difference.

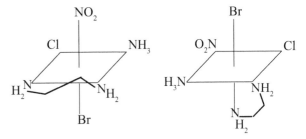

27. Is geometrical isomerism possible in a tetrahedral complex $[CoCl_2BrI]^{2-}$?

28. Is optical isomerism possible for a tetrahedral complex $[CoFClBrI]^{2-}$?

Ligand Field Theory and Molecular Orbital Theory

60.1   Valence Bond Theory

A **valence bond** is formed when two atoms approach one another so that a valence orbital on one atom overlaps a valence orbital on the other atom (*cf.* Unit 22). Two electrons share the same space between the two atoms where the orbitals overlap and the valence bond is formed. If one of the orbitals is empty and the other orbital contributes both electrons, then the bond is called a **coordinate bond**.

The atom or molecule with the empty orbital is a Lewis acid and the atom or molecule with the pair of electrons is a Lewis base. In coordination compounds, the metal atom or ion is the Lewis acid (it has empty orbitals available) and the ligand is the Lewis base (it supplies a pair of electrons) (Figure 60.1).

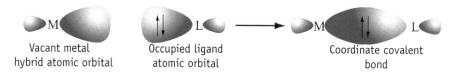

FIGURE 60.1   The formation of a coordinate bond by the donation of a pair of electrons from a ligand to a metal.

> Note that, unlike the hybridization of the orbitals for molecules of the main group elements, orbitals containing nonbonding pairs of electrons are *not* included in the hybridization.

The empty orbitals on the metal ion that accept electron pairs from the ligands are hybridized to accommodate the geometry of the coordination compound. Some of the more common hybrid orbital sets are listed in Table 60.1.

TABLE 60.1   Common geometries and the corresponding hybrid orbital sets.

Coordination Number	Geometry	Hybrid Orbital Set	Examples
2	linear	sp	$[Ag(NH_3)_2]^+$, $[CuCl_2]^-$
4	tetrahedral	sp^3	$[CoCl_4]^{2-}$, $[Ni(CO)_4]$
4	square planar	dsp^2	$[Ni(CN)_4]^{2-}$, $[Pt(NH_3)Cl_2]$
6	octahedral	d^2sp^3 or sp^3d^2	$[Co(NH_3)_6]^{3+}$, $[Cr(H_2O)_6]^{3+}$

To illustrate the application of valence bond theory to the bonding in coordination compounds, let's examine the complex ion hexaamminechromium(III), $[Cr(NH_3)_6]^{3+}$. We'll represent the valence orbitals on the chromium atom by little boxes as we did in Unit 22. The electron configuration of chromium is d^4s^2 and the loss of three electrons leads to the configuration d^3:

> Electrons are lost from the 4s orbital before the 3d orbitals.

The vacant orbitals of the chromium ion into which electron pairs from the six ammonia ligands can be accepted are the remaining two 3d orbitals, the 4s orbital, and the set of three 4p orbitals. These orbitals are hybridized to make a set of six d^2sp^3 hybrid orbitals that have the correct octahedral geometry for the complex ion:

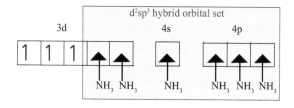

The hexaamminechromium(III) $[Cr(NH_3)_6]^{3+}$ complex ion is paramagnetic—it has three unpaired electrons (*cf.* Unit 23.4). The valence bond approach to the bonding in the $[Cr(NH_3)_6]^{3+}$ ion appears to work satisfactorily. The paramagnetism and the octahedral structure of the complex are explained.

Let's examine two other complexes, $[Co(NH_3)_6]^{3+}$ and $[CoF_6]^{3-}$. Both complexes are octahedral but the magnetic properties of the two complexes are different; the $[Co(NH_3)_6]^{3+}$ complex ion is diamagnetic (no unpaired electrons) whereas the $[CoF_6]^{3-}$ complex ion is paramagnetic (corresponding to 4 unpaired electrons). Cobalt has an electron configuration d^7s^2 and, after the loss of three electrons, the Co^{3+} ion has the configuration d^6. The difference in the magnetic properties of these two complexes is explained in valence bond theory by the use of different hybrid orbital sets. The diamagnetic $[Co(NH_3)_6]^{3+}$ complex ion has two vacant 3d orbitals available and uses the hybrid orbital set d^2sp^3. The paramagnetic $[CoF_6]^{3-}$ complex ion has no 3d orbitals available and uses a sp^3d^2 hybrid orbital set—the two d orbitals in this set are 4d orbitals:

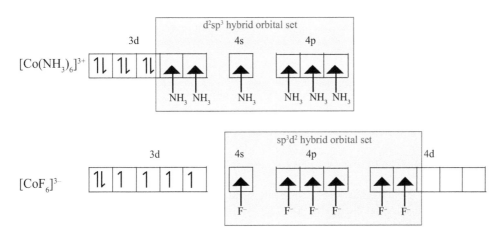

In valence bond theory, a complex that uses the d^2sp^3 hybrid orbital set is called an **inner-orbital complex** because it uses the (inner) 3d orbitals. It's also called a **low-spin complex** because it has fewer, if any, unpaired electrons. In contrast, a complex that uses the sp^3d^2 hybrid orbital set is called an **outer-orbital complex** because it uses the (outer) 4d orbitals. This complex is also called a **high-spin complex** because it has more unpaired electrons. The question that remains unanswered is why do the two complexes use different hybrid orbital sets—why is one high-spin and the other low-spin?

It requires energy to pair electrons—the interelectronic repulsion must be overcome. In valence bond theory, the energy is derived from bond formation. If sufficient energy is available, then the electrons will be paired. If not, the electrons will remain unpaired. The coordinate bonds formed by the ammonia ligands are stronger than the coordinate bonds formed by the fluoride ligands and sufficient energy is available to pair the electrons when ammonia is the ligand but not when F^- is the ligand.

Ligands can be divided into those that are **strong** (strong enough to pair in the electrons in a first-row transition metal octahedral complex) and those that are **weak** (not strong enough to pair the electrons). The division is conveniently made by the group of the donor atom (Table 60.2).

Use of the 4d orbitals is somewhat unrealistic because they are so much higher in energy than the 4s and 4p orbitals. This is the same argument mentioned previously concerning the possibility of sp^3d^2 hybridization in molecules such as SF_6.

TABLE 60.2   Strong and weak ligands for first-row transition metal octahedral complexes.

Strong		Weak	
4A	5A	6A	7A
CO	$H_2NCH_2CH_2NH_2$ (ethylenediamine)	H_2O	F^-
CN^-	NH_3	$C_2O_4^{2-}$ (oxalate)	Cl^-
	NCS^-	OH^-	Br^-
		SCN^-	I^-

The thiocyanate ion is ambidentate. When coordinated through the N it is a strong ligand but when coordinated through the S, it is weak.

EXAMPLE 60.1   VALENCE BOND THEORY

Use valence bond theory to describe the bonding and structure of the following complexes. Predict the magnetic properties of each complex:

a. $[CoCl_4]^{2-}$

b. $[Fe(ox)_3]^{3-}$ ox = bidentate oxalate $C_2O_4^{2-}$

c. $[Pt(en)_2]^{2+}$

d. $[Ag(CN)_2]^+$

UNDERSTAND THE QUESTION

In valence bond theory, the donor atoms of the ligands form coordinate bonds by donating electron pairs into vacant orbitals on the metal. The orbitals on the metal participating in the bond formation are hybridized. The hybrid set chosen should be compatible with the magnetic and structural properties of the complex. Sometimes these properties can be predicted through the use of valence bond theory. Whether the complex is high-spin or low-spin can be deduced from the strength of the ligands (*cf.* Table 60.2).

PLAN THE SOLUTION

Determine the electron configuration of the metal ion. Draw a diagram illustrating the occupancy of the metal orbitals and determine which orbitals are vacant and can accept electron pairs from the ligands. Choose an appropriate set of orbitals on the metal to accept the electron pairs from the ligands and hybridize these orbitals.

SOLVE THE PROBLEM

a. $[CoCl_4]^{2-}$ oxidation state +2   configuration d^7

Cl^- is a weak ligand

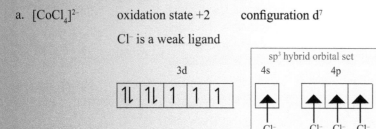

tetrahedral complex; paramagnetic (3 unpaired electrons)

b. $[Fe(ox)_3]^{3-}$ oxidation state +3   configuration d^5

oxalate^{2-} is a weak bidentate chelating ligand

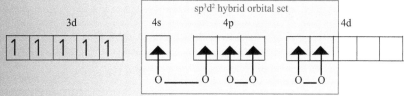

octahedral complex; paramagnetic (5 unpaired electrons)

c. $[Pt(en)_2]^{2+}$ oxidation state +2   configuration d^8

ethylenediamine is a strong bidentate chelating ligand

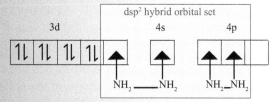

square planar complex; diamagnetic (no unpaired electrons)

d. $[Ag(CN)_2]^+$ oxidation state +1   configuration d^8

cyanide is a strong ligand

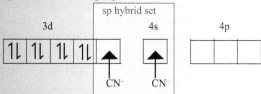

linear complex; diamagnetic (no unpaired electrons)

PROBLEM 60.1A

Use valence bond theory to explain why $[NiCN_4]^{2-}$ is square-planar, $[NiCl_4]^{2-}$ is tetrahedral, and $[Ni(CO)_4]$ is tetrahedral.

PROBLEM 60.1B

Use valence bond theory to predict whether the following complexes are diamagnetic or paramagnetic. If paramagnetic, determine the number of unpaired electrons.

   a. $[Co(H_2O)_6]^{3+}$
   b. $[Cr(en)_3]^{3+}$
   c. $[Fe(CN)_6]^{2+}$

   Valence bond theory emphasizes the covalent bonding between the ligand and the metal in a coordination compound. It can be used to explain the magnetic properties of complexes and in some cases will allow the prediction of the structure. It cannot, however, explain the colors exhibited by transition metal compounds (it describes only the ground state of the complex and provides no information about excited states) and it does not explain *why* some ligands are strong and others weak. The next approach to the bonding in transition metal complexes that we will examine emphasizes the ionic nature of the bonding between the ligand and the metal. The theory is very successful in explaining both the magnetic and spectroscopic properties (colors) of coordination compounds.

60.2   Ligand Field Theory

Crystal field theory was developed by H. Bethe and J. H. van Vleck in the early 1930s at about the same time that L. Pauling was working on valence bond theory. It was used to describe the electronic structure of metal ions within a crystal lattice. In other words, it describes what happens to the electrons and orbitals on a metal ion when the metal is surrounded by an electrostatic field caused by a symmetrical arrangement of anions.

For example, a sodium ion in sodium chloride is surrounded by an octahedral arrangement of negative chloride ions. Crystal field theory describes the effect of this octahedral electrostatic field on the electrons and orbitals of the sodium ion. Although not much use was made of this theory until the late 1950s when it was recognized that the same situation exists in transition metal coordination compounds. At this point, crystal field theory was referred to as ligand field theory. In a complex, the metal ion is surrounded by some symmetrical arrangement of ligands, often octahedral. The attraction between the ligands and the metal is attributed to the electrostatic attraction between the positive metal cation and the negative charges on the ligands and completely ignores any covalent bonding. The negative charges on the ligands are the charges on the ligands if the ligands are anions, such as Cl^-, or the negative ends of polar molecules if the ligands are neutral, such as H_2O or NH_3. In the latter case the attraction is the same as the ion-dipole attraction between ions and solvent molecules in solution (*cf.* Units 8 and 32).

What happens to the electrons (and orbitals) of a transition metal ion when it is surrounded by an octahedral arrangement of ligands? According to ligand field theory, there will be a general increase in the energies of all the electrons on the metal ion—particularly the valence electrons—as a result of the repulsion between these electrons and the negative charges on the ligands. An s orbital is spherically symmetrical and is simply raised in energy. A set of three p orbitals is also spherically symmetrical, with the individual p orbitals pointing along the three x, y, and z, axes. If the six ligands approach the metal ion along these three axes, all three p orbitals are affected equally. It's what happens to the five d orbitals that is interesting. They are all raised in energy but the orbitals that point along the x, y, and z axes are affected more than the orbitals that point between the axes (Figure 60.2).

The d orbitals lose their degeneracy—they are no longer all equal in energy. The d_{z^2} and $d_{x^2-y^2}$ orbitals point along the axes directly at the ligands and are pushed higher in energy. The d_{xy}, d_{xz}, and d_{yz} orbitals point between the axes and are not affected as much by the ligands. The d orbitals are therefore split into two groups (Figure 60.3). The higher group (the d_{z^2} and $d_{x^2-y^2}$ orbitals) is often called the e_g set and the lower group (the d_{xy}, d_{xz}, and d_{yz} orbitals) is called the t_{2g} set.

The splitting of the d orbitals into two groups is called the **crystal field splitting** and is given the symbol Δ or 10Dq. Sometimes the symbol is given a subscript 'o' or

It does not matter how the ligands approach the metal, an octahedral ligand field will affect all three p orbitals equally. It's just convenient to think of the ligands approaching along the three Cartesian axes.

The labels e_g and t_{2g} describe the symmetries of the sets of orbitals. We won't be concerned here with the symmetry representations of the orbitals but the labels are convenient to use.

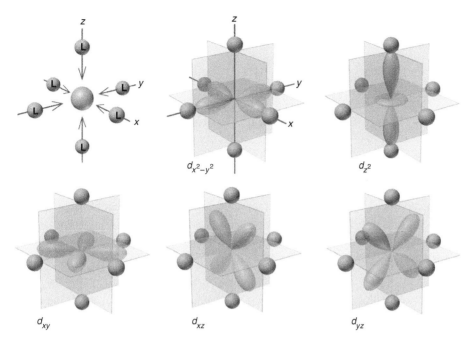

FIGURE 60.2   The set of five d orbitals in an octahedral ligand field.
The six ligands approach along the three Cartesian axes and affect the $d_{x^2-y^2}$ and d_{z^2} orbitals more than the d_{xy}, d_{xz}, and d_{yz} orbitals.

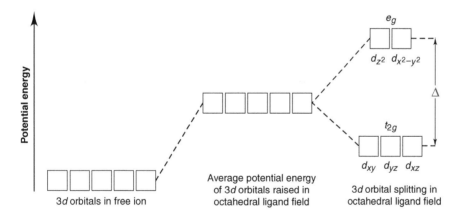

FIGURE 60.3   The splitting in energy of the set of five d orbitals in an octahedral ligand field.
The $d_{x^2-y^2}$ and d_{z^2} orbitals are raised in energy more than the d_{xy}, d_{xz}, and d_{yz} orbitals.

'oct' as in Δ_0 to indicate an octahedral complex. It is this splitting of the d orbitals into two different energy levels that provides an explanation of the color and magnetism of transition metal complexes.

The Color of Complexes

The transition of an electron from the lower t_{2g} set of orbitals to the higher e_g set of orbitals corresponds in energy to the frequency of visible radiation. Consider, for example, the Ti^{3+} ion in an octahedral $[Ti(H_2O)_6]^{3+}$ complex. A Ti^{3+} ion has a d^1 electron configuration and in its ground state this d electron is in the lower t_{2g} orbital

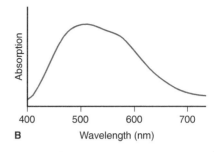

FIGURE 60.4 The (a) red-violet color and (b) absorption spectrum of $[Ti(H_2O)_6]^{3+}$.

set. Absorption of light centered at about 500 nm (blue/green/yellow) (Figure 60.4) excites the electron to the e_g level and causes the color of the complex to appear purple (red/violet). An electronic transition between d orbitals such as this is called a **d–d transition**.

The relationship between the light absorbed by a complex and the color of the complex can be illustrated on a **color wheel** (Figure 60.5). The wheel shows the colors of the visible spectrum that are complementary (on the opposite side of the wheel). For example, if a complex absorbs green light, then the complex appears red because the remainder of the visible spectrum, centered at red, passes through the solution unaffected. Radiation at the center of the visible spectrum is absorbed by the $[Ti(H_2O)_6]^{3+}$ complex, allowing the red and violet light to pass through producing the purple color.

An object exhibits a particular color because it either

• transmits or reflects that color, or

• absorbs the complementary color

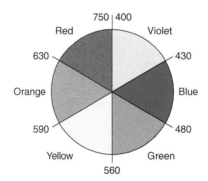

FIGURE 60.5 A color wheel illustrating complementary colors.
Complementary colors are opposite each other on the wheel. Red and green, for example, are complementary. Absorption of green light causes the transmitted or reflected light to appear red. Wavelengths shown are approximate.

Most d–block complexes are colored but in order to be colored the metal ion must have an incomplete (partially filled) d orbital set. Zinc(II) salts, for example, are colorless—the configuration of the Zn^{2+} ion is d^{10}. Titanium(IV) complexes are also colorless—the configuration of the Ti^{4+} ion is d^0. Manganese(II) in a high spin complex is almost colorless (a faint pink color) because the ground state has one electron in each d orbital (configuration d^5) and the excitation of an electron would cause a change in the number of unpaired electrons which is 'forbidden'. Some complexes that might be thought to be colorless are in fact intensely colored. The deep purple permanganate ion MnO_4^- is an example. In these cases the color is not due to a d–d transition but to a movement of an electron from the metal to a ligand or *vice versa*. These transitions are called **charge-transfer transitions**. In summary,

- d-d transitions in which the spin multiplicity changes are 'forbidden', so the absorption of light is extremely weak. The complexes have a very pale color.

- d-d transitions require a partially occupied d orbital set, but even then the absorption of light is relatively weak.

- charge–transfer transitions are 'allowed' leading to intense colors.

We will be concerned only with electronic transitions between d orbitals. The color of a complex depends upon the splitting of the d orbitals and the extent to which the d orbitals are split depends upon the identity of the metal ion, the charge on the ion, and the strength of the octahedral ligand field.

The value of Δ (10Dq) varies from about 7,500 cm^{-1} to 12,500 cm^{-1} for the M^{2+} ions of the first series of transition metals. For the M^{3+} ions of the first series, the range is approximately 14,000 cm^{-1} to 25,000 cm^{-1}. For example, [Fe(H$_2$O)$_6$]$^{2+}$ and [Co(H$_2$O)$_6$]$^{3+}$ are isoelectronic but the Fe has a 2+ charge and the Co has a 3+ charge. The values of 10Dq are 10,400 cm^{-1} and 18,600 cm^{-1} respectively. The ligands are attracted more strongly by the 3+ ion than by the 2+ ion and cause a greater splitting of the d orbitals.

The magnitude of 10Dq also increases down the series of d-block elements. For the hexaammine complexes of cobalt, rhodium, and iridium the values are [Co(NH$_3$)$_6$]$^{3+}$ 10Dq = 23,000 cm^{-1}, [Rh(NH$_3$)$_6$]$^{3+}$ 10Dq = 34,000 cm^{-1}, and [Ir(NH$_3$)$_6$]$^{3+}$ 10Dq = 41,000 cm^{-1}, In this case the larger 4d and 5d orbitals are affected more than the 3d orbitals by the approaching ligands.

The ligand has a dramatic effect on the magnitude of the crystal field splitting Δ. The crystal field splitting for a series of chromium(III) complexes is shown in Figure 60.6. The splitting increases as the ligand changes from F$^-$ (15,000 cm^{-1}) to H$_2$O (17,400 cm^{-1}), to NH$_3$ (21,600 cm^{-1}), and CN$^-$ (26,600 cm^{-1}). This change in the crystal field splitting causes a change in the frequency of the visible light absorbed by the complex. This in turn changes the color of the complex. For example, [Cr(H$_2$O)$_6$]$^{3+}$ is violet whereas [Cr(NH$_3$)$_6$]$^{3+}$ is yellow.

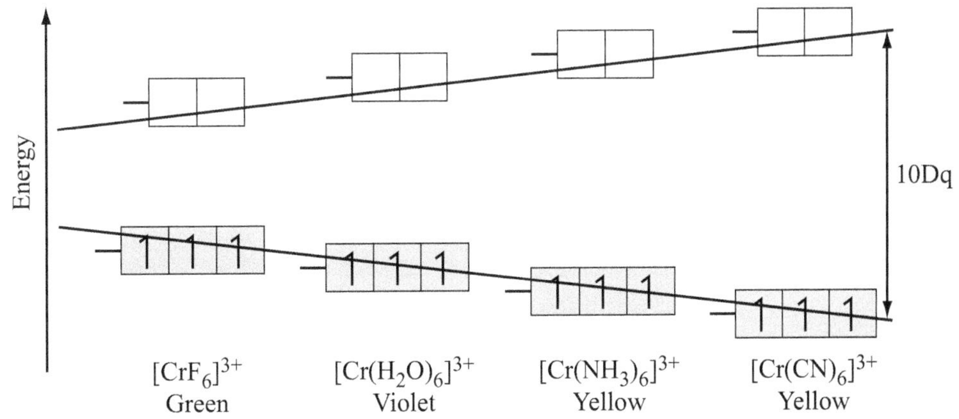

Electronic transitions between d orbitals in an octahedral complex are forbidden but comparatively slow vibrations of the complex molecule cause a temporary loss of symmetry and the transitions become partially allowed. The intensity of the absorption is relatively weak.

The unit cm^{-1} is a common unit used in describing spectra in the IR/visible/UV region. It is called the wavenumber and is equal to the reciprocal of the wavelength in cm. The visible region runs from 14,000 cm^{-1} (red) to 25,000 cm^{-1} (violet).

FIGURE 60.6   The crystal field splitting in a series of chromium(III) complexes.
The diagram illustrates the increase in the splitting 10Dq as the strength of the ligand increases.

Ligands can be arranged in order of the magnitude of the crystal field splitting that they produce. The order is known as the **spectrochemical series**. The ligands that produce a small crystal field splitting are weak ligands whereas those that cause a large crystal field splitting are strong ligands.

en = ethylenediamine

py = pyridine

PPh₃ = triphenylphosphine

———————————————————————— increasing strength ————————————————————————▶

$Br^- < SCN^- < Cl^- < F^- < OH^- < H_2O < NCS^- < py < NH_3 < en < NO_2^- < PPh_3 < CN^-$

weak-field   strong-field

The list is the same as the empirical series of ligands we encountered in the previous section when we looked at valence bond theory.

EXAMPLE 60.2   THE COLORS OF COORDINATION COMPOUNDS

The green, blue, and violet colors of the octahedral complexes $[Ni(H_2O)_6]^{2+}$, $[Ni(NH_3)_6]^{2+}$, and $[Ni(en)_3]^{2+}$ were illustrated previously. Use the color wheel shown in Figure 60.5 to estimate the relative strengths of the three ligands and confirm their placement in the spectrochemical series.

UNDERSTAND THE QUESTION

The color of a complex depends upon the frequency of the light absorbed by the complex as an electron is excited from the ground electronic state to an excited state. Other factors being equal, the energy required for the transition depends upon the strength of the ligands in the complex. A stronger ligand causes a larger splitting of the d orbitals and an increase in the frequency of light required. Note that the frequency of the absorption does not in general *equal* the crystal field splitting but it is certainly related to it.

PLAN THE SOLUTION

Determine the complementary colors of the colors exhibited by the complexes and then order the colors by increasing frequency.

SOLVE THE PROBLEM

	color	*complementary color*	*approximate wavelength*
$[Ni(H_2O)_6]^{2+}$	green	red	700 nm
$[Ni(NH_3)_6]^{2+}$	blue	orange	610 nm
$[Ni(en)_3]^{2+}$	violet	yellow	570 nm

The wavelength of the absorption decreases down this series. The frequency increases. This corresponds to an increase in the energy difference between the t_{2g} and e_g energy levels in the octahedral complex—a larger splitting of the d orbitals and therefore a stronger ligand. The order is the same as that shown in the spectrochemical series.

PROBLEM 60.2A

As chloride ions are substituted for ammonia molecules in the octahedral heaxamminechromium(III) complex $[Cr(NH_3)_6]^{3+}$, the color changes from yellow, to purple, to violet:

	color
$[Cr(NH_3)_6]^{3+}$	yellow
$[Cr(NH_3)_5Cl]^{2+}$	purple
$[Cr(NH_3)_4Cl_2]^+$	violet

Does the sequence of colors agree with your expectations regarding the relative strengths of the ammonia and chloride ligands? Predict the color of [Cr(NH₃)₃Cl₃].

PROBLEM 60.2B

Determine which of the following complexes you expect to be colored and which you expect to be colorless.

a. $[Sc(H_2O)_6]^{3+}$

b. $[Fe(en)_2Cl_2]^{2+}$

c. $[Zn(NH_3)_6]^{2+}$

Magnetism

In a weak-field transition metal complex, electrons occupy same orbitals as they do in the free (uncomplexed) ion to minimize the interelectronic repulsion. This is in accordance with Hund's rule of maximum spin multiplicity. Consider, for example, the cobalt(III) complex $[CoF_6]^{3-}$. The fluoride ion is a weak ligand and the crystal field splitting is small. The Co^{3+} ion has a d^6 configuration and the six electrons are spread out among all the orbitals, with the same spin, as much as possible (Figure 60.7).

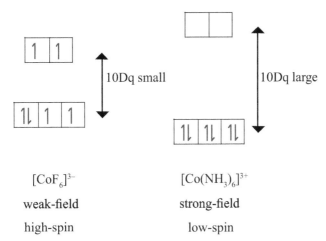

$[CoF_6]^{3-}$

weak-field

high-spin

$[Co(NH_3)_6]^{3+}$

strong-field

low-spin

FIGURE 60.7 **The different electron configurations of a cobalt(III) in a weak-field and a strong-field complex.**
In a weak-field complex, the electrons occupy the same orbitals as they do in the free ion. In a strong-field complex, the electrons are paired in the lower-energy t₂g level.

However, if the splitting is large, the electrons fill the lower level first before occupying the higher level. In this case the stabilization resulting from the crystal field is sufficient to pair the electrons in the lower level. Such is the case in the complex ion $[Co(NH_3)_6]^{3+}$.

We can calculate the octahedral **ligand field stabilization energy (LFSE)** for any d electron configuration. The splitting of the orbitals is such that the e_g set are raised in energy by 6Dq relative to the mean whereas the t_{2g} set are lowered by 4Dq relative to the mean (Figure 60.8).

The LFSE for the possible d electron configurations are listed in Table 60.3. Each electron placed in the lower t_{2g} set contributes 4Dq to the stabilization energy. We

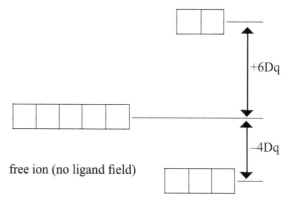

free ion (no ligand field)

octahedral ligand field

FIGURE 60.8 In an octahedral ligand field, the e_g orbitals are raised in energy by 6Dq relative to the mean. The t_{2g} orbitals are lowered by 4Dq relative to the mean.

give this a negative sign in accordance with usual convention. Each electron placed in the higher e_g set lessens the LFSE by 6Dq. This is given a positive sign. The energy required to pair two electrons is denoted by P (a positive quantity). For the configurations d^1 through d^3, there is no difference between the weak-field case and the strong-field case—no advantage can be gained by pairing the electrons. Similarly, for the configurations d^8 through d^{10}, there is no difference. For the configurations d^4 through d^7, there is competition between the additional LFSE of the low-spin configuration and the energy required to pair the electrons.

TABLE 60.3 Ligand field stabilization energies for weak and strong field octahedral complexes.

	Strong-field	**Weak-field**	
d^1	−4Dq	−4Dq	*no difference*
d^2	−8Dq	−8Dq	*no difference*
d^3	−12Dq	−12Dq	*no difference*
d^4	−16Dq + P	−6Dq	*difference* −10Dq + P
d^5	−20Dq + 2P	0Dq	*difference* −20Dq + 2P
d^6	−24Dq + 2P	−4Dq	*difference* −20Dq + 2P
d^7	−18Dq + P	−8Dq	*difference* −10Dq + P
d^8	−12Dq	−12Dq	*no difference*
d^9	−6Dq	−6Dq	*no difference*
d^{10}	0Dq	0Dq	*no difference*

If 10Dq is larger than P, the pairing energy, then the low-spin configuration will be favored. If, however, the pairing energy P exceeds 10Dq, the preferred configuration will be high-spin. For octahedral complexes of the first-row transition metals, strong ligands are those with the donor atoms N, P, and C; ligands with other donor atoms are generally weak.

EXAMPLE 60.3   MAGNETIC PROPERTIES OF TRANSITION METAL COMPLEXES

Calculate the LFSE and the number of unpaired electrons for the following octahedral complexes. Characterize the complexes as strong-field (low-spin) or weak-field (high spin).

   a. $[Co(CN)_6]^{3-}$

   b. $[Fe(ox)_3]^{3+}$

   c. $[Ni(NH_3)_6]^{2+}$

UNDERSTAND THE QUESTION

The complexes are octahedral, so the d orbitals will be split into two groups, the lower-energy t_{2g} level at −4Dq and the higher-energy e_g level at +6Dq. Once the electron configuration is known, the LFSE can be calculated. For weak-field ligands, the electrons should be placed singly in all five orbitals with parallel spins according to Hund's rule of maximum spin multiplicity before pairing any electrons. For strong-field ligands, the t_{2g} level should be filled before any electrons are placed in the e_g level.

PLAN THE SOLUTION

Determine the d electron configuration of the metal ions. Determine whether the ligands in the complex are strong or weak and fill the orbitals appropriately.

SOLVE THE PROBLEM

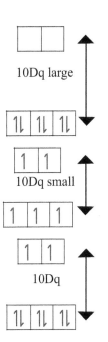

   a. $[Co(CN)_6]^{3-}$

   Co^{3+} configuration d^6 strong-field ligand

   LFSE = −24Dq diamagnetic—no unpaired electrons

   b. $[Fe(ox)_3]^{3-}$

   Fe^{3+} configuration d^5 weak-field ligand

   LFSE = 0Dq   paramagnetic—5 unpaired electrons

   c. $[Ni(NH_3)_6]^{2+}$

   Ni^{2+} configuration d^8 strong-field ligand

   LFSE = −12Dq paramagnetic—2 unpaired electrons

   The strength of the ligand has no effect upon the magnetism of a d^8 octahedral configuration.

PROBLEM 60.3A

Determine whether the following octahedral complexes are high-spin or low-spin and the number of unpaired electrons:

   a. $[Co(H_2O)_6]^{2+}$

   b. $[Cr(en)_3]^{3+}$

   c. $[Cu(NH_3)_6]^{2+}$

Draw the ligand field splitting for the following octahedral complexes and fill the orbitals appropriately with the correct number of electrons:

a. $[Mn(H_2O)_6]^{2+}$

b. $[Ni(en)_3]^{2+}$

c. $[V(H_2O)_6]^{3+}$

Thermodynamic Properties of Transition Metal Complexes

We will examine briefly just one example of the effect of the LFSE upon the thermodynamic properties of the complexes of transition metals. The lattice energies for the transition metal chlorides, represented by the reaction below, are plotted in Figure 60.9.

$$M(s) + Cl_2(g) \rightarrow MCl_2(s)$$

In the $MCl_2(s)$ lattice, each M^{2+} metal ion is surrounded by an octahedral arrangement of six Cl^- ligands. The d^0 configuration is for $CaCl_2$ and no data is available for scandium because only the $ScCl_3$ (+3 oxidation state) is known.

The chloride ion is a weak-field ligand and the d^0, d^5, and d^{10} configurations represent situations where the LFSE is zero (*cf.* Table 60.3). If a line is drawn through the lattice energies for these three configurations, it represents a base line to which other lattice energies can be compared. The interesting double hump of the graph above this base line represents the additional stabilization of the crystal lattice due to the splitting of the d orbitals. Thus the additional energies for d^1, d^2, d^3, and d^4, and d^6, d^7, d^8, and d^9, correspond approximately to 4Dq, 8Dq, 12Dq, and 6Dq in each hump. The energies obtained from these thermodynamic measurements are in quite good agreement with the values obtained from the electronic spectra of the complexes.

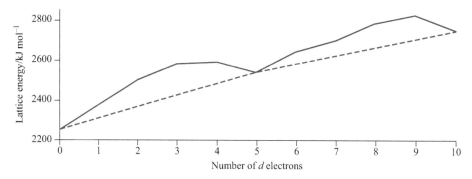

FIGURE 60.9 Lattice energies of the metal chlorides MCl$_2$ derived from Born-Haber cycle data (*cf.* Unit 19).
The base line connects metal ions with zero crystal field stabilization energy.

60.3 Other Geometries

Other common geometries for transition metal complexes are the four-coordinate tetrahedral and square-planar geometries. A different arrangement of ligands leads to a different splitting of the d orbitals.

Tetrahedral Geometry

The splitting of the d orbitals in a tetrahedral geometry is the opposite of that for an octahedral geometry. The d_{xy}, d_{xz}, and d_{yz} orbitals are higher in energy than the $d_{x^2-y^2}$ and d_{z^2} orbitals. This is because in the tetrahedral case the ligands approach the metal ion between the Cartesian axes and affect the d_{xy}, d_{xz}, and d_{yz} orbitals more than the $d_{x^2-y^2}$ and d_{z^2} orbitals. The splitting of the orbitals is 4/9 that of the octahedral splitting, partly because there are only four ligands as opposed to six and partly because the ligands do not line up exactly with orbitals as they do in the octahedral case (Figure 60.10). Because the splitting is less, all tetrahedral complexes of the first row transition metals are high spin—no ligands are strong enough to increase the LFSE sufficiently to overcome the pairing energy.

> In the tetrahedral case, the d_{xy}, d_{xz}, and d_{yz} orbitals are often given the label 't₂' and the $d_{x^2-y^2}$ and d_{z^2} orbitals are given the label 'e'. Note that the g subscripts are omitted because a tetrahedron has no center of symmetry.

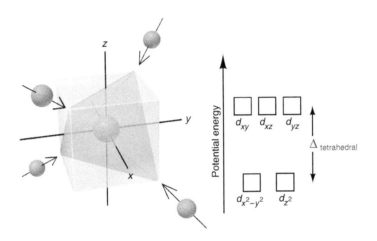

FIGURE 60.10   Crystal field splitting in a tetrahedral ligand field.
The four ligands approach between the x, y, and z axes and the splitting is the inverse of that in an octahedral field. The tetrahedral splitting, for the same ligands, is 4/9 of the octahedral splitting.

Square-Planar Geometry

Imagine an octahedral complex from which the ligands on the z axis are gradually withdrawn. Such a distortion is called a **tetragonal distortion** and is common in copper(II) complexes. If the ligands on the z axis are withdrawn, then the metal orbitals that point in the z direction will fall in energy relative to the orbitals that point in the xy direction. The d_{z^2} orbital will go down in energy and the d_{xz} and d_{yz} orbitals will go down in energy. There will be a further loss of degeneracy (Figure 60.11).

Eventually, the ligands on the z axis will be completely removed and the complex will be square-planar. The ordering of the orbitals is shown at the right in Figure 60.11. The diagram illustrates why a square-planar geometry is favored by metal ions with a d^8 electron configuration in complexes with strong ligands (such as the diamagnetic $[Ni(CN)_4]^{2+}$). All four lower energy orbitals are filled with eight electrons and the high energy d_{z^2} orbital is empty. The energy difference between the $d_{x^2-y^2}$ and d_{z^2} orbitals in a square planar complex equals 10Dq(oct).

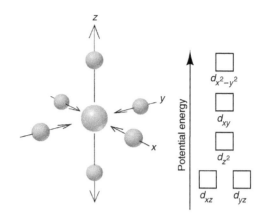

FIGURE 60.11   Crystal field splitting in a square-planar ligand field.
Orbitals that point in the z direction are stabilized as the two ligands on the z axes are withdrawn. The d_{z^2} orbital decreases in energy to a position below the d_{xy} orbital; it has more electron density in the xy plane than the d_{xz} or d_{yz} orbitals but less than the d_{xy} orbital.

EXAMPLE 60.4   TETRAHEDRAL AND SQUARE-PLANAR GEOMETRIES

Both $[PdCl_4]^{2-}$ and $[Pd(CN)_4]^{2-}$ are diamagnetic whereas $[NiCl_4]^{2-}$ is paramagnetic and $[Ni(CN)_4]^{2-}$ is diamagnetic. Explain why.

UNDERSTAND THE QUESTION

The magnetism of a complex provides information about any unpaired electrons that are, or are not, present. A diamagnetic complex has no unpaired electrons. A paramagnetic complex has unpaired electrons—the actual number of unpaired electrons present in each metal ion can be determined by measuring the strength of the paramagnetism. All the complexes $[PdCl_4]^{2-}$, $[Pd(CN)_4]^{2-}$, $[NiCl_4]^{2-}$, and $[Ni(CN)_4]^{2-}$ have a d^8 configuration. In what geometry does a d^8 configuration have unpaired electrons? In what geometry does a d^8 configuration have no unpaired electrons?

PLAN THE SOLUTION

Why should $[NiCl_4]^{2-}$, of all the complexes, have a tetrahedral rather than a square-planar geometry?

SOLVE THE PROBLEM

Palladium is a second series transition metal for which the value of 10Dq is larger. The chloride ion and the cyanide ion are both strong enough to pair the electrons. In both palladium complexes, the geometry is square-planar. There are no unpaired electrons and the complexes are diamagnetic.

Nickel is a first series transition metal and the chloride ion is a weak ligand. The nickel complex $[NiCl_4]^{2-}$ is paramagnetic and has a tetrahedral geometry. There are two unpaired electrons. In the nickel complex $[Ni(CN)_4]^{2-}$ the ligand is strong and the electrons are paired. The complex is diamagnetic and has a square-planar geometry.

PROBLEM 60.4A

As mentioned earlier, octahedral copper(II) complexes are almost always tetragonally distorted—the ligands on the z axis are slightly further away than the ligands on the x and y axes. Suggest why this happens.

PROBLEM 60.4B

Determine the number of unpaired electrons in the following tetrahedral complexes:

a. $[CoCl_4]^{2-}$ b. $[CuBr_4]^{2-}$ c. $[Co(CO)_4]^-$

60.4 Molecular Orbital Theory

Crystal field theory is very successful in explaining the spectroscopic and magnetic properties of transition metal complexes. However, it has its faults. The most serious limitation is its complete neglect of any covalent bonding between the ligand and metal. When a ligand approaches a metal, the crystal field approach to the interaction is based upon the repulsion of the electrons in the orbitals on the metal by the ligands and their *increase* in energy. In reality, bond formation is associated with a *decrease* in the energy of the valence electrons.

The molecular orbital approach incorporates the best features of both valence bond theory and crystal field theory. Valence bond theory concentrates on the formation of coordinate bonds between the ligand and the metal. Crystal field theory concentrates on the repulsion between the ligands and the electrons on the metal. Molecular orbital theory involves the construction of bonding orbitals (accommodating the ideas of valence bond theory) and the construction of corresponding antibonding orbitals (accommodating the ideas of crystal field theory). The relationship between molecular orbital theory, crystal field theory, and valence bond theory for the octahedral complex $[Co(NH_3)_6]^{3+}$ is illustrated in Figure 60.12.

The six pairs of electrons from the six ammonia molecules fill the six bonding orbitals in the lower part of the diagram. They are colored blue to distinguish them but in reality the electrons in the complex cannot be individually assigned. The six electrons of the Co^{3+} ion fill the next available orbitals. If 10Dq is sufficiently large, then

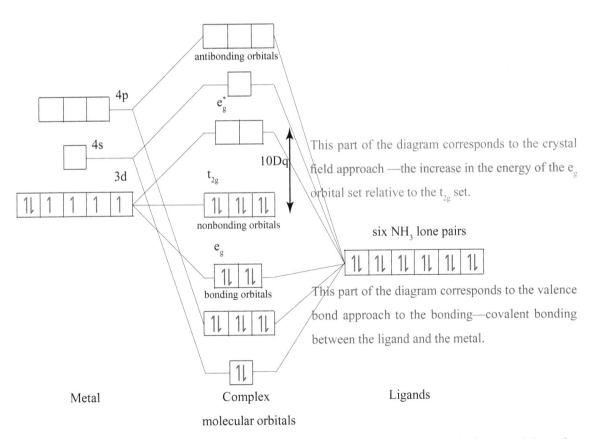

FIGURE 60.12   The relationship between molecular orbital theory, crystal field theory, and valence bond theory for the octahedral complex $[Co(NH_3)_6]^{3+}$.

all six electrons are paired in the t_{2g} set. If the ligand field is weak, then the electrons will be spread over the t_{2g} and e_g^* orbitals. This diagram illustrates only the σ bonding between the ligands and the metal and in this respect the electrons in the t_{2g} set are nonbonding.

One of the major successes of the molecular orbital approach to the bonding in transition metal complexes is an explanation of the high strength of ligands such as CO and CN^-, and the weak ligand field exerted by ligands such as Cl^-, which, with its negative charge, might have been expected to be relatively strong. The explanation lies in the possibility of π bonding between the ligands and the metal.

The orbitals on the metal that have an appropriate symmetry for π bonding are the orbitals in the t_{2g} set. The orbitals on the ligands that have the correct symmetry for π bonding are those that lie perpendicular to the metal ligand axis (Figure 60.13).

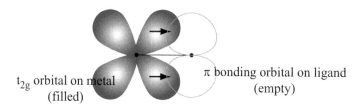

t_{2g} orbital on metal (filled) π bonding orbital on ligand (empty)

FIGURE 60.13 One of the t_{2g} orbitals on the metal and an orbital on a ligand perpendicular to the metal–ligand axis that have the appropriate symmetry for π bonding.

The t_{2g} orbitals in a transition metal ion are almost always partially or completely full. In a ligand such as CO, the π bonding orbitals on the carbon monoxide are empty—these are the π^* antibonding orbitals of the CO molecule. The π bonding involves the donation of electrons from the metal t_{2g} orbitals back to the empty ligand orbitals (Figure 60.14).

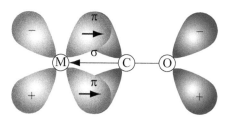

FIGURE 60.14 The back–donation of electrons from a filled metal t_{2g} orbital to a π^* antibonding orbital of the CO molecule.
The π back–donation of electrons from the metal to the ligand reinforces the donation of electrons from the ligand to the metal in the σ bonding.

This π bonding is often referred to as **back-donation**, or **synergic bonding**, because the donation of electrons from the ligand to the metal in the σ bonding is reinforced by the back-donation of electrons from the metal to the ligand in the π bonding, and *vice versa*. The effect is to stabilize the t_{2g} set of electrons and increase the value of 10Dq (Figure 60.15). Strong ligands such as CN^- and CO have empty π bonding orbitals.

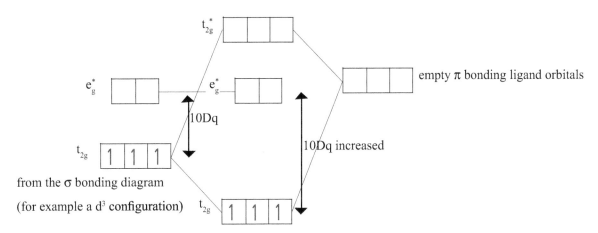

FIGURE 60.15   Empty π bonding orbitals on the ligand permit the back–donation of electrons from a filled metal t_{2g} orbital and leads to an increase of 10Dq. The t_{2g} metal set is stabilized.

The chloride ion has p orbitals perpendicular to the metal ligand axis but they are full— they cannot accept electrons from the metal t_{2g} set. In this case the interaction between the orbitals of π symmetry on the metal and the ligand increases the energy of the t_{2g} electrons and decreases the value of 10Dq (Figure 60.16). Despite the fact that the chloride has a negative charge and might therefore have been expected to exert a stronger crystal field than the neutral carbon monoxide molecule, it is the ability of the carbon monoxide molecule to synergically π bond with the metal that makes it the stronger ligand.

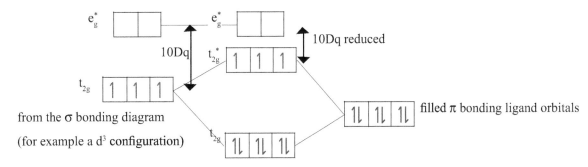

FIGURE 60.16   Filled π bonding orbitals on the ligand (lower in energy than the empty orbitals in Figure 60.15) cause the metal t_{2g} electrons to increase in energy and this reduces the magnitude of 10Dq.

Review Questions

1. Describe the way in which valence bond theory distinguishes between high-spin and low-spin complexes.

2. Describe the difference between the valence bond approach and the crystal field approach to the bonding in transition metal complexes.

3. A set of three p orbitals remains degenerate in an octahedral or tetrahedral crystal field but a set of five d orbitals is split in energy—some degeneracy is lost. Why is this?

4. Explain why, if a complex absorbs green light, then the complex appears red.

5. Describe the various factors that influence the magnitude of the crystal field splitting.

6. What relationship between 10Dq and the pairing energy P must be true if a complex of a metal ion with a d^6 electron configuration is low spin?

7. What is the spectrochemical series?

8. How does the crystal field splitting for a tetrahedral ligand field differ from that for an octahedral field?

9. What feature do the cyanide ion and the carbon monoxide molecule have in common that makes them very strong ligands?

Solutions to Problems

PROBLEM 60.1A

The cyanide ligand is a strong ligand and for d^8 configurations will lead to a square-planar geometry:

[NiCN$_4$]$^{2-}$

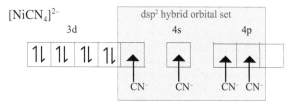

The chloride ligand is a weak ligand and for d^8 configurations will lead to a tetrahedral geometry:

[NiCN$_4$]$^{2-}$

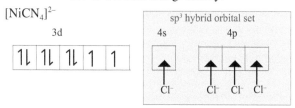

Carbon monoxide is a strong ligand but the nickel is now in a 0 oxidation state; the configuration is d^{10}.

[Ni(CO)$_4$]

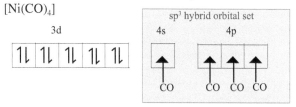

PROBLEM 60.2A

	color	complementary color	approximate wavelength
[Cr(NH$_3$)$_6$]$^{3+}$	yellow	violet	415 nm
[Cr(NH$_3$)$_5$Cl]$^{2+}$	purple	green	540 nm
[Cr(NH$_3$)$_4$Cl$_2$]$^+$	violet	greenish-yellow	570 nm

The wavelength of the absorption increases down this series (the frequency decreases). This corresponds to a decrease in the energy difference between the t_{2g} and e_g energy levels in the octahedral complex and a smaller splitting of the d orbitals as the weaker chloride ligand is substituted for the stronger ammonia ligand. The complex [Cr(NH$_3$)$_3$Cl$_3$] might be expected to absorb visible light at about 600 nm and exhibit a blue color.

PROBLEM 60.3A

Determine whether the following octahedral complexes are high-spin or low-spin and how many unpaired electrons there are:

a. [Co(H$_2$O)$_6$]$^{2+}$ weak ligand Co^{2+} d^7 $(t_{2g})^5(e_g)^2$
   3 unpaired electrons

   high-spin complex

b. [Cr(en)$_3$]$^{3+}$ strong ligand Cr^{3+} d^3 $(t_{2g})^3$
   3 unpaired electrons

   the strength of the crystal field has no effect on the number of unpaired electrons

c. [Cu(NH$_3$)$_6$]$^{2+}$ strong ligand Cu^{2+} d^9 $(t_{2g})^6(e_g)^3$
   1 unpaired electron

   the strength of the crystal field has no effect on the number of unpaired electrons

PROBLEM 60.4A

Octahedral copper(II) complexes have a d electron configuration d^9. There are three electrons in the e_g set. One of the orbitals in the set is occupied by two electrons and the other by one electron. If the orbitals could be divided in energy, one going up in energy and the other going down in energy, and the lower orbital has the two electrons, there would be a net lowering of energy—the complex would be more thermodynamically stable.

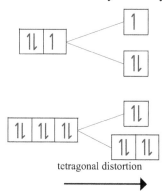

tetragonal distortion

Answers to Review Questions

1. A low-spin complex in valence bond theory is characterized as one in which the ligand–metal bond is sufficiently strong to pair the electrons. The orbitals used in the hybridization include the inner 3d orbitals and the low-spin complex is often called an inner-orbital complex. If the ligands are weak, there is insufficient energy to pair the electrons and the complex is high-spin. The d orbitals used are the outer 4d orbitals. Inclusion of the outer d orbitals in a hybridization scheme is unrealistic—they are quite high in energy.

2. The valence bond approach emphasizes the formation of coordinate covalent bonds between the ligand and the metal. The crystal field approach completely neglects any covalent character in the metal–ligand bond. It is based upon the effect of an electrostatic field produced by the ligands on the orbitals and electrons in the valence shell of the metal.

3. A set of three p orbitals remains degenerate in an octahedral or tetrahedral crystal field because all three orbitals in the set point along the x, y, and z axes. In a set of five d orbitals, two orbitals point along the axes and the other three point between the axes. The two groups are affected differently by an approaching octahedral or tetrahedral ligand field and are split in energy.

4. The relationship between the light absorbed by a complex and the color of the complex is illustrated by a color wheel. The colors of the visible spectrum that are complementary are shown on opposite sides of the wheel. If a complex absorbs green light, then the complex appears red because the remainder of the visible spectrum, centered at red, passes through the solution unaffected.

5. The magnitude of the crystal field splitting depends upon the identity of the metal ion, the charge on the ion, and the strength of the ligand field. The magnitude of 10Dq increases down the series 3d < 4d < 5d. Ligands are attracted more strongly if the charge on the ion is larger; this causes a greater splitting of the d orbitals. Ligands also have an effect on the magnitude of 10Dq—the spectrochemical series describes the relative strengths of ligands.

6. For a d^6 complex to be low-spin, the electrons must be paired. To pair the electrons, 10Dq must be larger than the pairing energy P.

7. The spectrochemical series is an arrangement of ligands in order of the magnitude of the crystal field splitting that they cause.

8. The crystal field splitting for a tetrahedral ligand field is the inverse of that for an octahedral ligand field. The d_{xy}, d_{xz}, and d_{yz} orbitals are higher in energy than the $d_{x^2-y^2}$ and d_{z^2} orbitals. The magnitude of the splitting is less—only 4/9 that of the octahedral splitting, partly because there are only four ligands as opposed to six and partly because the ligands do not line up exactly with orbitals as they do in the octahedral case.

9. The cyanide ion and the carbon monoxide molecule are strong ligands because they have empty π bonding orbitals. Electrons in the t_{2g} orbitals of the metal are donated back to the ligands through the π bonding. This back-donation reinforces the σ bonding. The effect is to stabilize the t_{2g} set of electrons and increase the value of 10Dq (*cf.* Figure 60.14).

End-of-Unit Problems

1. Determine the d electron configuration of the metal in the following complexes:

   a. $[Cr(H_2O)_6]Cl_2$

   b. $[Co(NH_3)_3(NO_2)_3]$

   c. $K[AuBr_4]$

2. Determine the d electron configuration of the metal in the following complexes:

   a. $Na_3[CoF_6]$

   b. $[Ir(NH_3)_5Br]SO_4$

   c. $K_2[Mn(CN)_6]$

3. A d^6 metal ion is described as using a d^2sp^3 hybrid orbital set in the formation of a complex ion.

   a. What geometry does the complex have?

   b. What do you expect the magnetic properties of the complex to be?

   c. Is this a strong-field or weak-field complex?

4. A d^8 metal ion is described as using a dsp^2 hybrid orbital set in the formation of a complex ion.

   a. What geometry does the complex have?

   b. What do you expect the magnetic properties of the complex to be?

   c. If another complex of the same metal ion uses an sp^3 hybrid orbital set, in what way are the ligands different?

   d. What is the geometry of the complex that uses an sp^3 hybrid orbital set?

5. Draw an energy diagram illustrating the splitting of the d orbitals for the following complexes. Fill the orbitals appropriately with the correct number of electrons.

   a. $[Fe(CN)_6]^{3-}$

   b. $[CoCl_4]^{2-}$

   c. $[Ni(CN)_4]^{2-}$

6. Draw an energy diagram illustrating the splitting of the d orbitals for the following complexes. Fill the orbitals appropriately with the correct number of electrons.

   a. $[Co(en)_3]^{3+}$

   b. $[PdCl_4]^{2-}$

   c. $[Ti(H_2O)_6]^{3+}$

7. How many unpaired electrons are there on the metal ion in the following complexes:

   a. $[Mn(CN)_6]^{3-}$

   b. $[NiCl_4]^{2-}$

   c. $[Fe(H_2O)_6]^{3+}$

8. How many unpaired electrons are there on the metal ion in the following complexes:

   a. $[Ru(NH_3)_6]^{2+}$

   b. $[CoBr_4]^{2-}$

   c. $[Co(ox)_2(H_2O)_2]^-$

9. Coordination compounds of titanium(III), vanadium(III), and chromium(III) are all colored but compounds of scandium(III) are colorless. Explain why.

10. Contamination of copper(I) chloride by copper(II) can be detected quite easily by examination for any color present. Explain why.

11. The wavelengths of maximum absorption for some chromium(III) complexes are listed:

   $[Cr(H_2O)_6]^{3+}$ 570 nm

   $[CrCl_6]^{3-}$ 750 nm

   $[Cr(NH_3)_6]^{3+}$ 455 nm

   Determine the colors corresponding to these wavelengths and therefore determine the colors of the complexes. Do the relative absorption wavelengths correspond to the positions of the ligands in the spectrochemical series?

12. Hexaaquachromium(III) chloride is violet in color and the hexchlorochromate(III) ion is a blue–green color. Predict the color of the complex $[Cr(H_2O)_3Cl_3]$.

13. The octahedral complex $[Fe(CN)_6]^{3-}$ has one unpaired electron whereas the complex $[Fe(SCN)_6]^{3-}$ has five unpaired electrons. Why?

14. Both $[Ni(H_2O)_6]^{2+}$ and $[Ni(NH_3)_6]^{2+}$ exhibit the same magnetic behavior, even though one ligand is weak and the other ligand is strong. Explain why.

15. The octahedral complex $[Co(NH_3)_6]^{3+}$ is diamagnetic. The isoelectronic complex $[Fe(H_2O)_6]^{2+}$ is paramagnetic. Why?

16. Hexaamminenickel(II) $[Ni(NH_3)_6]^{2+}$ is paramagnetic but the tetracyanonickelate(II) ion is diamagnetic. Explain why.

17. Calculate the ligand field stabilization energy for the following octahedral complexes:

   a. $[Co(NH_3)_5Br]^{2+}$

   b. $[Fe(CN)_6]^{3-}$

   c. $[Co(ox)_3]^{3-}$ (ox = oxalate, a weak ligand)

18. Calculate the ligand field stabilization energy for the following octahedral complexes:

   a. $[Ti(NH_3)_6]^{3+}$

   b. $[Mn(H_2O)_6]^{2+}$

   c. $[Cr(en)_3]^{3+}$

19. Is it true that strong ligands always produce a low-spin complex? Use chromium(III) complexes to explain your answer.

20. Is it true that all four-coordinate complexes of first-row transition metals are high-spin? Use complexes of nickel(II) to explain your answer.

21. Although the d_{z^2} and $d_{x^2-y^2}$ orbitals are degenerate (equal in energy) in an octahedral complex, they lose their degeneracy in a square-planar complex. Explain why.

22. If the axes of a linear complex are defined such that the complex lies along the z axis, derive the d orbital splitting diagram for the metal ion in this geometry.

Nuclear Stability and Radioactivity

61.1   Nuclear Reactions

Nuclear reactions are quite unlike chemical reactions. A chemical reaction is a rearrangement of atoms; the atoms themselves do not change. Bonds between atoms are broken and new bonds are formed. Electrons are redistributed at different energy levels and energy is released or absorbed as a result. A **nuclear reaction** takes place within or between the nuclei of atoms. Elements are converted into other elements or other isotopes; the atoms change. The energies involved are enormous and there is often a measurable change in the mass during the reaction.

We will examine various types of nuclear reaction in this unit and the next. They are conveniently classified as radioactivity, transmutation, fission, and fusion (Table 61.1).

TABLE 61.1   Nuclear reactions.

Natural radioactivity	the spontaneous emission of particles and/or radiation by an unstable nucleus.
Nuclear transmutation	the production of one nucleus from another by bombardment by protons, neutrons, or other nuclei.
Nuclear fission	the splitting of a large nucleus into two smaller nuclei with the release of energy.
Nuclear fusion	the combination of two small nuclei to produce a larger nucleus with the release of energy.

Symbols and Equations for Nuclear Reactions

The protium isotope of hydrogen has a single proton, and no neutrons, in the nucleus.

Except for the protium isotope of hydrogen, all nuclei contain protons and neutrons. These two particles are called **nucleons** and nuclear reactions involve the nucleons. Like chemical reactions, nuclear reactions are represented by equations and to make nuclear equations easy to balance, the symbols used in nuclear equations indicate the numbers of neutrons and protons in each species.

You may recall (*cf.* Unit 2) that an isotope of an element is characterized by two numbers—the atomic number and the mass number. The atomic number is the number of protons in the nucleus. The mass number is the number of protons *and* neutrons in the nucleus. The number of neutrons can be obtained by subtracting the two numbers. To identify a particular isotope, the mass number is often written after the name of the element. For example, there are two common isotopes of uranium: uranium–238 (the most abundant 99.3%) and uranium–235. In the symbol for the isotope, the mass number is written as a preceding superscript and the atomic number is written as a preceding subscript. The two common isotopes of uranium therefore have the symbols $^{238}_{92}U$ and $^{235}_{92}U$. The nucleus of an atom of a particular isotope is called a **nuclide**.

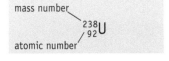

The most common elementary particles involved in nuclear reactions are shown in Table 61.2. Again, the superscript is the mass number of the species and the subscript is the atomic number of the species.

We are now in a position to write equations for nuclear reactions. Uranium–238 decays spontaneously to thorium–234 by the emission of an α–particle. The equation for this reaction is:

$$^{238}_{92}U \rightarrow {}^{234}_{90}Th + {}^{4}_{2}\alpha$$

TABLE 61.2 Elementary particles involved in nuclear reactions.

Symbol	Name
$_1^1\text{H}$ or $_1^1\text{p}$	proton
$_0^1\text{n}$	neutron
$_{-1}^0\text{e}$ or $_{-1}^0\beta$	electron
$_{+1}^0\text{e}$ or $_{+1}^0\beta$	positron
$_2^4\text{He}$ or $_2^4\alpha$	α–particle

Different symbols are used depending upon the source of the particle. For example, an electron *outside* the nucleus is normally given the symbol $_{-1}^0\text{e}$, an electron that is emitted *from* the nucleus is given the symbol $_{-1}^0\beta$.

Notice how writing the mass number and the atomic number on each symbol makes balancing the equation relatively straightforward. The sum of the mass numbers on each side of the equation must be equal (238 = 234 + 4). Similarly, the sum of the atomic numbers on each side must be equal (92 = 90 + 2). The other interesting feature of this reaction is that one element is changing into another element (the atomic number changes). This is something that *never* happens in a chemical reaction!

Before we balance more equations, we'll examine the first type of nuclear reaction—radioactivity.

> Charge is not balanced in this equation. The α–particle is a helium nucleus (a helium atom without its two electrons). To balance the equation completely, two electrons should be added to the right side of the equation, as Th^{2-} for example. Equations for nuclear reactions usually ignore the electrons outside the nucleus.

61.2   Radioactivity

Most atoms that exist naturally are stable. For these atoms, the ratio of neutrons to protons increases as the atomic number increases. Figure 61.1 illustrates a plot of the number of neutrons *vs.* the number of protons in stable nuclei. The plot curves away from the straight line representing a 1:1 ratio of protons to neutrons. Stable nuclei with atomic numbers between 1 and 20 have an approximate n/p ratio of 1:1 but the n/p ratio increases to about 3:2 for elements with atomic numbers in the region of 70–80. Stable nuclei lie within an area referred to as the **belt of stability**. Isotopes outside this belt of stability are unstable; they emit particles spontaneously to move into the belt of stability. This spontaneous decay of unstable isotopes is called **radioactivity**. Radioactive decay is a nuclear reaction—a change takes place within the nucleus. Notice that the belt of stability ends at atomic number 83 (bismuth). All known isotopes of elements with an atomic number greater than 83 are naturally radioactive.

The three common types of radioactive decay are labeled α, β, and γ (Table 61.3).

As we saw above, uranium–238 decays spontaneously by α–emission. This type of emission is typical of unstable isotopes that lie beyond atomic number 83. Very few nuclei with an atomic number less than 60 emit α–particles.

TABLE 61.3 Characteristics of α, β, and γ radiation.

	Nature	Mass	Charge
α radiation	$_2^4\text{He}$ helium nucleus	6.64×10^{-24} g	+2
β radiation	$_{-1}^0\beta$ electron	9.11×10^{-28} g	−1
γ radiation	electromagnetic radiation	zero	zero

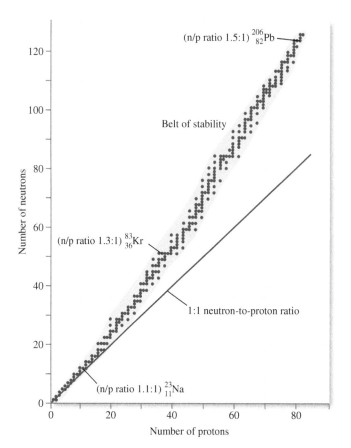

FIGURE 61.1   A plot of the number of neutrons *vs.* the number of protons for known nuclides.
Stable nuclides are represented by dots.

Iodine–131 is an isotope that decays spontaneously by β–emission:

$$^{131}_{53}\text{I} \rightarrow {}^{131}_{54}\text{Xe} + {}^{\,0}_{-1}\beta$$

The electron is produced during the conversion of a neutron to a proton within the nucleus and is emitted with high energy. The ratio of neutrons to protons in iodine–131 is 1.47—this is high. The conversion of a neutron to a proton reduces the ratio to 1.43. β–emission is typical of unstable nuclei that lie above the belt of stability and have a high n/p ratio.

A third type of radioactive emission is γ–radiation. This occurs when an isotope produced in an excited state decays to the ground state (a more stable arrangement of the protons and neutrons). There is no change in the atomic number or the mass number of the isotope.

There are two other types of nuclear reaction typical of unstable nuclei that have an n/p ratio that is too low—below the belt of stability. These are positron emission and electron capture. A positron has the same mass as an electron but an opposite charge. It is a short-lived species because it is annihilated when it collides with an

γ–radiation is high energy electromagnetic radiation.

Some radioactive nuclei emit protons. For example:

$$^{43}_{21}\text{Sc} \rightarrow {}^{42}_{20}\text{Ca} + {}^{1}_{1}\text{p}$$

This also increases the n/p ratio. Proton emission is characteristic of nuclei with an unusually low n/p ratio.

Neutron emission is a decay characteristic of nuclei with an unusually high n/p ratio.

electron—and there are many electrons in matter. Both the positron and the electron are destroyed in the collision and two photons of γ–radiation are produced. The effect of positron emission is the reverse of β–emission. A proton is converted to a neutron and the n/p ratio is increased. Carbon–11 is an isotope that decays by positron emission. The n/p ratio is low (5:6) and the positron emission increases it to 6:5:

$$^{11}_{6}\text{C} \rightarrow \,^{11}_{5}\text{B} + \,^{0}_{+1}\beta$$

Electron capture is the capture of an electron from an s orbital by the nucleus. The process has the same effect as positron emission. It converts a proton to a neutron and increases the n/p ratio. An example is:

$$^{37}_{18}\text{Ar} + \,^{0}_{-1}\text{e} \rightarrow \,^{37}_{17}\text{Cl}$$

The effect on the n/p ratio of the nuclear reactions just described is summarized in Figure 61.2.

Beta particle emission is accompanied by the emission of an antineutrino.
Positron emission is accompanied by the emission of a neutrino.
These particles have atomic numbers and mass numbers equal to zero and we'll not include them in the equations

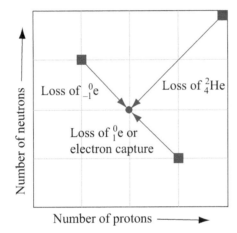

FIGURE 61.2 The effect of α–emission, β–emission, positron emission, and electron capture on the neutron/proton ratio.

Elements beyond bismuth must often undergo more than one radioactive emission to reach the belt of stability. For example, uranium–238 undergoes a series of fourteen emissions *en route* to a stable nucleus (lead–206). This series of emissions, called a **radioactive series**, is illustrated in Figure 61.3. Many of the steps are α–emission to reduce the atomic number. Other steps are β–emission to reduce the n/p ratio.

Three radioactive series currently occur in nature:

Uranium–238 to lead–206 (illustrated in Figure 61.3)

Uranium–235 to lead–207

Thorium–232 to lead–208

Others have occurred in the past but have become exhausted because the half-lives of all the isotopes involved are short compared to the age of the planet.

EXAMPLE 61.1 RADIOACTIVE DECAY AND NUCLEAR EQUATIONS

Predict the type of radioactive decay the following radioactive isotopes are likely to undergo, write the symbol for the isotope, and write an equation representing the decay.

a. uranium–234

b. rubidium–81

c. oxygen–15

UNDERSTAND THE QUESTION

The probable radioactive decay can be determined by calculating the n/p ratio of the isotope. If the ratio is high for the particular atomic number, then β–emission is likely. If the ratio is low, then positron emission or electron capture is likely. If the isotope has an atomic number above 83, then α–emission or β–emission are probable, depending upon the n/p ratio. When balancing nuclear equations, ensure that the sums of the atomic numbers on both sides are equal and the sums of mass numbers on both sides are equal.

PLAN THE SOLUTION

Calculate the n/p ratio for the species and note the position of the isotope relative to the belt of stability. Use Figure 61.1.

SOLVE THE PROBLEM

a. uranium–234

number of protons = 92

number of neutrons = 234 – 92 = 142

n/p ratio = 142/92 = 1.54

The n/p ratio is about right. The isotope lies beyond the end of the belt of stability and α–emission is most probable.

$$_{92}^{234}\text{U} \rightarrow _{90}^{230}\text{Th} + _{2}^{4}\alpha$$

b. rubidium–81

number of protons = 37

number of neutrons = 81 – 37 = 44

n/p ratio = 44/37 = 1.19

The n/p ratio is low (*cf.* Figure 61.1). Positron emission or electron capture is likely:

$$_{37}^{81}\text{Rb} + _{-1}^{0}\text{e} \rightarrow _{36}^{81}\text{Kr}$$

c. oxygen–15

number of protons = 8

number of neutrons = 15 – 8 = 7

n/p ratio = 7/8 = 0.88

The n/p ratio is low—expect a ratio near 1.0. Expect positron emission or electron capture. For example:

$$_{8}^{15}\text{O} \rightarrow _{7}^{15}\text{N} + _{+1}^{0}\text{e}$$

PROBLEM 61.1A

Write equations representing

a. the decay of potassium–40 by electron capture

b. the decay of plutonium–239 by α–emission

c. the decay of sodium–22 by positron emission

d. the decay of cadmium–109 by β–emission

PROBLEM 61.1B

Technetium is a radioactive element used in medical imaging. For example, Cardiolyte™ is a technetium complex used in imaging the heart. In fact, Cardiolyte™ is given to more than 60% of patients with serious heart problems to allow detailed images of the heart to be taken. The radioactive metal is prepared from molybdenum by neutron bombardment as shown. What particle is necessary to balance the equation?

$$^{98}_{42}\text{Mo} + ^{1}_{0}\text{n} \rightarrow ^{99}_{43}\text{Tc} + \text{?}$$

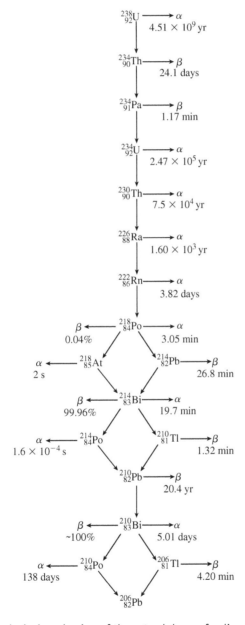

FIGURE 61.3 The principal mechanism of the natural decay of radioactive uranium–238 to the stable lead–206.

The 126 applies only to neutrons—element 126 is unknown. The next magic number is 184, but no known nuclide has 184 protons or neutrons.

Nuclear physists have recently created a stable isotope of silicon with twice as many neutrons as protons—$^{42}_{14}$Si. The isotope contains an even number of both protons (14) and neutrons (28). The number 28 is magic and 14 is 'half-magic'.

Z	N	No. of Nuclides
Even	Even	157
Even	Odd	53
Odd	Even	50
Odd	Odd	4
	TOTAL	264

FIGURE 61.4 The numbers of stable nuclides having even and odd numbers of protons and neutrons.

The rate of a nuclear decay does not depend upon the chemical environment of the atom. It is independent of the temperature, pressure, concentration, and other factors that influence the rates of chemical reactions.

Nuclear Stability

Some nuclei are more stable than others. The actual numbers of neutrons and protons within the nucleus, not just the ratio of the numbers, influence their stabilities. Experimentally, nuclei with 2, 8, 20, 28, 50, 82, or 126 protons or neutrons are more stable than others. These numbers are sometimes referred to as **magic numbers**—notice that they are all even. It is believed that these numbers represent complete shells of nucleons within the nucleus. The situation is analogous to the chemical stability of complete shells of electrons outside the nucleus. Elements with even atomic numbers almost always have more stable isotopes than elements with odd atomic numbers. In fact, more than half of all stable isotopes have even numbers of protons and neutrons (Figure 61.4). Particularly stable nuclides are "doubly-magic"; for example, $^{4}_{2}$He (2n and 2p) and $^{208}_{82}$Pb (126n and 82p).

Only four stable isotopes have an odd number of both protons and neutrons, and they are the elements with lowest possible odd atomic numbers: $^{2}_{1}$H, $^{6}_{3}$Li, $^{10}_{5}$B, and $^{14}_{7}$N.

61.3 The Kinetics of Radioactive Decay

Some radioactive isotopes decay very quickly—they have a very brief existence. Other radioactive isotopes decay very slowly and exist naturally for millions of years. Uranium–238, for example, is relatively abundant despite its instability because its decay is so slow.

Radioactive decay is a first-order process (*cf.* Unit 36) and species undergoing first order kinetic reactions have characteristic half-lives. Recall that the half-life is the time required for the concentration of the reactant to decrease to one-half of its original value and that, for first-order reactions, the half-life is independent of the original amount present. The half-lives of some radioactive isotopes, and their decay mechanisms, are listed in Table 61.4.

TABLE 61.4 The half-lives and decay of some radioactive isotopes.

Isotope	Half-life	Decay Mechanism
uranium–238	4,510,000,000 years	α–emission
potassium–40	1,280,000,000 years	β–emission
plutonium–239	24,110 years	α–emission
carbon–14	5730 years	β–emission
strontium–90	28.5 years	β–emission
tritium	12.26 years	β–emission
cobalt–60	5.27 years	β–emission
iron–59	44.6 days	β–emission
iodine–131	8.04 days	β–emission
radon–226	3.82 days	α–emission
sodium–24	14.66 hours	β–emission
carbon–11	20.4 minutes	positron emission

EXAMPLE 61.2   RATES OF RADIOACTIVE DECAY

Plutonium–239 is a toxic radioactive isotope prepared for use in nuclear reactors and nuclear weapons. It has a half-life of 24,110 years. How long will it take for a 1.00 kg sample of plutonium to decay to 1.00 g?

UNDERSTAND THE QUESTION

The relationship between the concentration or amount of a reactant and time is given by the integrated rate equation. For a first-order reaction the equation is:

$$\ln\frac{[A]_t}{[A]_0} = -kt$$

Or, taking the antilogarithm of both sides:

$$[A]_t = [A]_0\, e^{-kt}$$

The half-life of a first-order reaction, and the rate constant k, are related by the equation:

$$t_{1/2} = 0.693/k$$

PLAN THE SOLUTION

Determine the rate constant k, commonly called the **decay constant**, from the half-life. Then use the integrated rate equation to determine the time t.

SOLVE THE PROBLEM

$k = 0.693/24{,}110 = 2.87 \times 10^{-5}\ \mathrm{yr}^{-1}$

$\ln(1.00/1000) = -2.87 \times 10^{-5} \times t$

$t = 240{,}000$ years

Radioactive plutonium–239, stockpiled for nuclear weapons and nuclear fuel, will be around for a very long time. The environmentally safe storage and disposal of isotopes such as $^{239}_{94}\mathrm{Pu}$ pose serious problems.

PROBLEM 61.2A

Phosphorus–32 decays by β–emission with a half-life of 14.3 days. Write an equation representing this decay. If a sample of phosphorus–32 weighs 10 mg at the beginning of the week, how much will remain at the end of the week, seven days later?

PROBLEM 61.2B

Strontium–90 behaves biologically like calcium, the alkaline earth element above it in the Periodic Table. When ingested by dairy cows, for example, it is found in the milk of those cows and in the bones of humans drinking that milk. It has a half-life of 28.5 years. What fraction of strontium–90 remains after 100 years?

Measuring Radioactive Decay Rates

The rates of chemical reactions are usually monitored by determining the concentrations of the reactants or products of the reaction. The rates of nuclear reactions are determined by measuring or counting the decay events. The simplest radiation detector is photographic film. In 1896, Becquerel observed that a uranium salt could expose a photographic plate. The extent to which the film or plate is darkened is a measure of the amount of radiation. This technique is still used in the film badges worn by people who work in nuclear power plants or who work with radioactive materials in medicine, etc.

Two devices used to count radioactive emissions are the ionization counter and the scintillation counter. An ionization counter, such as the **Geiger counter**, is based upon the ionization of a gas produced by radioactive emission. A glass tube is coated with a metal that serves as the cathode. A wire at the center of the tube acts as the anode. The tube is filled at low pressure (about 1/10th of an atmosphere) with argon gas and a potential of 1000 V is applied across the electrodes (Figure 61.5). When a β–particle enters through the glass window at the end of the tube, it hits an argon atom and ejects electrons. These electrons accelerate toward the anode and strike other argon atoms, producing more electrons in an avalanche effect. One β–particle produces up to 10 billion electrons at the anode in a millionth of a second. This electrical current causes the potential difference across the electrodes to fall. The voltage drop is recorded and usually amplified to give an audible click.

Rutherford and his students, including Geiger, used a screen coated with zinc sulfide to detect α–particles. When an α–particle hits zinc sulfide, the zinc sulfide is excited electronically. The decay of the excited state to the ground state produces a pinpoint scintillation of visible light. Development of this technique has produced the **scintillation counter**. The light-emitting substance, called a **phosphor**, is coated on the surface of a photomultiplier tube. The photon of emitted light strikes the cathode of the photomultiplier and releases an electron (*cf.* the photoelectric effect, Unit 14.8). This electron then strikes other portions of the tube releasing more electrons. This cascading effect produces a current that can be detected and recorded.

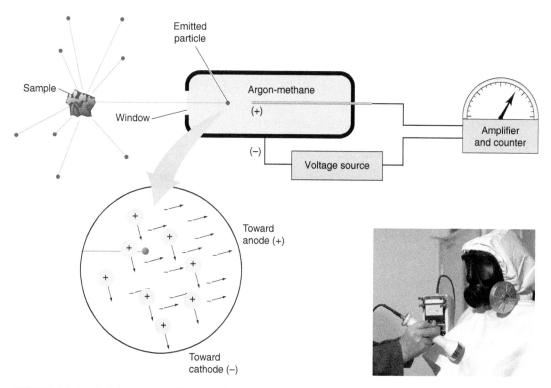

FIGURE 61.5 A Geiger counter for measuring radiation.

Units of Radioactivity

The SI unit of radioactivity is the **becquerel** (Bq). It is defined as one disintegration per second. This unit is relatively small and a more commonly used unit is the **curie** (Ci). The curie is defined as the number of disintegrations in one gram of radium per second and is equal to 3.70×10^{10} disintegrations per second. This unit is much larger than the becquerel and, in practice, the millicurie (mCi), or microcurie (μCi), are often used.

The number of disintegrations depends upon the size of the radioactive sample. The radioactivity of a particular isotope is often expressed as a **specific activity**, or the number of disintegrations per second per gram.

EXAMPLE 61.3   RADIOACTIVITY

Sodium–24 is a β–emitter and has a half-life of 14.66 hours. It is used as a tracer in cardiovascular systems to detect constrictions. Determine the initial radioactivity of a 1.0 mg sample in becquerels and curies.

UNDERSTAND THE QUESTION

The activity is the rate of disintegration of radioactive nuclides and is measured in becquerels (SI) or curies. The number of disintegrations depends upon the size of the sample.

The rate of disintegration is first-order with respect to the number of radioactive nuclei:

Activity = Rate = k N, where N is the number of radioactive nuclei.

The decay constant, k is equal to $0.693/t_{\frac{1}{2}}$ (*cf.* Unit 36).

The number of nuclei in the sample can be obtained from the mass of the sample, the molar mass of the isotope, and Avogadro's number.

$\ln(\frac{1}{2}) = -kt_{\frac{1}{2}}$
and
$\ln(\frac{1}{2}) = -0.693$

PLAN THE SOLUTION

Determine the rate constant k, from the half-life.

Determine the number of nuclei in the sample.

Then calculate the activity (i.e. the rate).

SOLVE THE PROBLEM

$k = 0.693/14.66$ hr $= 4.73 \times 10^{-2}$ hr^{-1}

mass of sample $= 1.0 \times 10^{-3}$ g

molar mass of isotope $= 24.0$ g mol^{-1}

number of moles $= 1.0 \times 10^{-3}$ g $/ 24.0$ g mol$^{-1} = 4.17 \times 10^{-5}$ mol

number of nuclei $= 4.17 \times 10^{-5}$ mol $\times 6.022 \times 10^{-23}$ mol$^{-1} = 2.51 \times 10^{19}$

rate $= k N = 4.73 \times 10^{-2}$ hr$^{-1} \times 2.51 \times 10^{19} = 1.19 \times 10^{18}$ disintegrations hr^{-1}

$= 1.19 \times 10^{18}$ disintegrations hr$^{-1} \times (1$ hr $/3600$s$) = 3.30 \times 10^{14}$ Bq

$= 3.30 \times 10^{14}$ Bq $\times (1$ Ci $/3.70 \times 10^{10}$ Bq$) = 8,910$ Ci

PROBLEM 61.3A

Calculate the activity of the 1.00 mg sample of sodium–24 referred to in Example 61.3 after 10 days have passed.

PROBLEM 61.3B

Tritium (hydrogen–3) decays by β–emission to produce helium–3 with a half-life of 12.26 years. If a sample of a compound containing tritium has an activity of 0.457 Bq, how many tritium nuclei are present in the sample?

Radioactive Dating

W. F. Libby was awarded the 1960 Nobel Prize in Chemistry for this work.

The determination of the relative abundances of isotopes in matter provides a way to establish the history of the material. One of the first successful applications of this was the carbon–14 dating method developed by Willard F. Libby.

In the upper atmosphere, high energy neutrons in cosmic radiation collide with nitrogen–14 atoms and produce carbon–14:

$$^{14}_{7}N + ^{1}_{0}n \rightarrow ^{14}_{6}C + ^{1}_{1}H$$

The carbon–14 then starts to decay by β–emission. Because the rate at which the carbon–14 is formed and the rate at which it decays balance one another, the amount of carbon–14 in the atmosphere has remained constant for a long time. The ratio of ^{14}C to ^{12}C in the environment is about $1:10^{12}$ and the specific activity due to ^{14}C in living matter is about 0.255 Bq g^{-1}.

The enormous increase in fossil fuel combustion and atmospheric nuclear testing in the last half-century have upset the $^{14}C/^{12}C$ balance.

The carbon–14 atoms combine with oxygen to produce carbon dioxide which is absorbed by plants during photosynthesis and incorporated in animals that eat those plants. Living matter then has the same ratio of ^{14}C to ^{12}C as the environment. As soon as the plant or animal dies, however, carbon–14 is no longer taken up and the $^{14}C/^{12}C$ ratio diminishes as the ^{14}C decays. This decrease in the ratio, compared with the ratio in living material, is a reflection of the amount of time that has passed since the organism died.

Carbon–14 has a half-life of 5730 years, and the radiocarbon dating method has been successfully used to date objects from 500 to 40,000 years old. More recent objects have an activity too close to the initial ratio for accurate results. Very old objects, over 40,000 years, have an activity that is too weak to be distinguished from background radiation.

The first step in the decay series for ^{238}U is the slowest step and determines the overall rate.

A similar approach is used by geologists to determine the age of rocks. As we learned earlier, uranium–238 decays through a series of intermediates to form lead–206 with a half-life of 4.51×10^9 years. By determining the ratio of uranium–238 to lead–206 in uranium containing rocks, it is possible to determine the age of the rock. How can you be sure that all the lead occurs as the result of the decay of uranium? The most abundant isotope of lead is lead–208 and if this isotope is absent, then it's reasonable to assume that the lead–206 occurs as a result of the decay of the uranium. The oldest rock on the surface of the earth is estimated to be about 3.8 billion years old. Rocks brought back from the moon by astronauts are similar in age.

Calculations based upon the decay of uranium–238 can be checked by analyzing other isotopic ratios involving long-lived isotopes. One example is the decay of potassium–40 to argon–40 by electron capture. This decay has a half-life of 1.28×10^9 years. The argon is trapped within the rock. Analyses indicate that rock retrieved from the moon solidified about 4.0 billion years ago.

EXAMPLE 61.4   RADIOACTIVE DATING

A wooden implement retrieved from a cave in Southern France has a specific carbon–14 activity of 0.172 Bq. The half-life of carbon–14 is 5730 years. Estimate the age of the implement.

UNDERSTAND THE QUESTION

The specific activity of a $^{14}C/^{12}C$ sample in living matter is 0.255 Bq g^{-1}. When the tree is cut down or the plant or animal dies, the uptake of carbon dioxide ends, and the carbon–14 decays with a half-life of 5730 years. The decay constant for carbon–14 can be calculated from the half-life.

The decay constant, k is equal to $0.693/t_{1/2}$.

The age of the artifact can be calculated by comparing the specific activities.

PLAN THE SOLUTION

Determine the decay constant k from the half-life; k is equal to $0.693/t_{1/2}$.

Use the integrated rate equation to calculate t.

SOLVE THE PROBLEM

$k = 0.693/5730 = 1.21 \times 10^{-4}$ yr^{-1}

$\ln \dfrac{[A]_t}{[A]_0} = -kt$

$\ln (0.172/0.255) = -1.21 \times 10^{-4}$ yr$^{-1} \times t$

$t = 4210$ years

The tree from which the implement was made was cut approximately 4200 years ago.

PROBLEM 61.4A

Analysis of a mineral using a mass spectrometer indicated that the ratio by mass of potassium–40 to argon–40 present in the mineral was 1.00 to 3.35. If the half-life of potassium–40 is 1.28×10^9 years, calculate the age of the mineral (the number of years since the mineral solidified).

PROBLEM 61.4B

The carbon–14 specific activity of a fragment of material from the Shroud of Turin (Figure 61.6) is 0.234 Bq. Estimate the age of this piece of material. The decay constant for carbon–14 is 1.21×10^{-4} yr^{-1}.

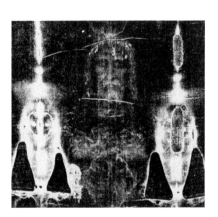

FIGURE 61.6   The Shroud of Turin shows an image of a human male, thought by many to be an image of Christ.

61.4   Transmutation

One of the principal aims of the alchemists was to change one element into another. They were unsuccessful. The **transmutation** of one element into another cannot be done by chemical means, a nuclear reaction is required.

In 1919, Ernest Rutherford bombarded nitrogen–14 with α–particles and obtained oxygen–17 and protons, the first experimental transmutation of an element.

$$\text{}^{14}_{7}\text{N} + \text{}^{4}_{2}\text{He} \rightarrow \text{}^{17}_{8}\text{O} + \text{}^{1}_{1}\text{p}$$

In 1933, Irène Curie and Frédéric Joliot performed a similar experiment. They bombarded aluminum–27 with α–particles. Neutrons and positrons were released and silicon–30 was ultimately formed. The interesting feature of this reaction was that the neutron emission ceased when the α–bombardment was stopped but the positron emission continued. They proposed a two-step process:

$$\text{}^{27}_{13}\text{Al} + \text{}^{4}_{2}\text{He} \rightarrow \text{}^{30}_{15}\text{P} + \text{}^{1}_{0}\text{n}$$

$$\text{}^{30}_{15}\text{P} \rightarrow \text{}^{30}_{14}\text{Si} + \text{}^{0}_{+1}\text{e}$$

The intermediate phosphorus–30 was the first synthetic radioactive isotope. It decays slowly with the emission of positrons to form the stable silicon–30.

Many experiments followed in which elements were bombarded with neutrons, α–particles, protons, and deuterons (deuterium nuclei ^{2}H). Positively-charged particles must move very fast to overcome the repulsion between themselves and the nuclei of the target. Devices called **particle accelerators** are used to speed up the particle and provide them with greater kinetic energy. Various designs include linear accelerators, small spiral accelerators called **cyclotrons**, and large circular accelerators.

A **linear accelerator** (Figure 61.7) consists of a series of tubes within an evacuated chamber. The voltages on the tubes alternate so that a positively charged particle is repelled by the tube it is leaving and attracted to the tube it is entering.

The cyclotron (Figure 61.8) was invented by E. O. Lawrence in 1930. It works on the same principle as a linear accelerator but saves space by accelerating the particles in a spiral path. In the schematic illustrated in Figure 61.8, the two D–shaped electrodes are made alternately positive and negative to accelerate the particles. Magnets on the top and bottom keep the particles moving in a spiral path until they reach the target.

Huge circular accelerators at CERN in Switzerland and Fermilab in Illinois are several miles in diameter. Particles are accelerated to speeds over 90% the speed of light and their kinetic energies are increased several billion times.

Accelerators are used to synthesize elements beyond uranium, to study the nature of nuclear structure, and can be used to prepare radioisotopes for medical applications. Most radioisotopes, however, are made by neutron bombardment. Neutrons cannot be accelerated (they have no charge) but they do not need to be accelerated (there is no repulsion by the target nuclei). The target material is simply lowered into a nuclear reactor where it is bombarded with neutrons. Cobalt–60 is used to treat cancer and it is prepared by neutron bombardment of iron–58:

$$\text{}^{58}_{26}\text{Fe} + \text{}^{1}_{0}\text{n} \rightarrow \text{}^{59}_{26}\text{Fe}$$

$$\text{}^{59}_{26}\text{Fe} \rightarrow \text{}^{59}_{27}\text{Co} + \text{}^{0}_{-1}\beta$$

$$\text{}^{59}_{27}\text{Co} + \text{}^{1}_{0}\text{n} \rightarrow \text{}^{60}_{27}\text{Co}$$

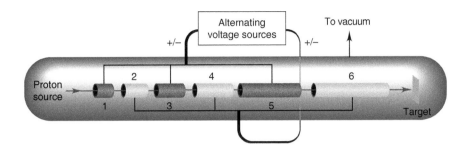

FIGURE 61.7   A schematic of a linear accelerator.
The beam of particles is accelerated in a straight line to the target. A photograph of the linear accelerator.

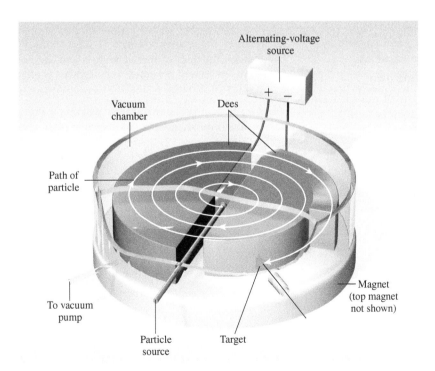

FIGURE 61.8   A schematic of a cyclotron accelerator.
The particle beam follows a spiral path toward the target.

The transuranium elements (elements with atomic numbers greater than 92) are made either by neutron bombardment or by bombardment in a particle accelerator by α–particles or the nuclei of other elements. For example, plutonium is made by the neutron bombardment of uranium:

$$^{238}_{92}U + ^{1}_{0}n \rightarrow ^{239}_{93}Np + ^{0}_{-1}\beta$$

$$^{239}_{93}Np \rightarrow ^{239}_{94}Pu + ^{0}_{-1}\beta$$

Curium is made by the α–particle bombardment of plutonium:

$$^{239}_{94}Pu + ^{4}_{2}\alpha \rightarrow ^{242}_{96}Cm + ^{1}_{0}n$$

Californium is made by the α–particle bombardment of curium:

$$^{242}_{96}Cm + ^{4}_{2}\alpha \rightarrow ^{245}_{98}Cf + ^{1}_{0}n$$

Heavier elements are made by the collision of two relatively massive nuclei. For example, meitnerium, element 109, can be made by bombarding bismuth–209 with iron–58:

$$^{209}_{83}Bi + ^{58}_{26}Fe \rightarrow ^{266}_{109}Mt + ^{1}_{0}n$$

The equations for nuclear reactions can be abbreviated by writing the target nucleus, followed by the bombarding particle and the ejected particle in parentheses, followed by the product nucleus. For example, the reaction for the production of curium above can be written using the shorthand notation:

$$^{239}_{94}Pu(\alpha,n)^{242}_{96}Cm$$

We will examine the remaining two types of nuclear reaction, fission and fusion, in the next unit.

Review Questions

1. Review the way in which isotopes and elementary particles are represented in nuclear equations.

2. Describe the common types of radioactivity.

3. Describe the way in which the type of radioactive decay may be predicted for a particular isotope.

4. Explain the principle underlying the determination of the age of an artifact using isotopic abundances.

5. Why is the transmutation of one element into another, the goal of the alchemists and the basis of many fraudulent schemes, impossible by chemical means?

6. Why is neutron bombardment inherently more easily accomplished than bombardment by charged particles?

7. Why is radioactive decay always a first order process?

Solutions to Problems

PROBLEM 61.1A

a. the decay of potassium–40 by electron capture

$$^{40}_{19}K + ^{0}_{-1}e \rightarrow ^{40}_{18}Ar$$

b. the decay of plutonium–239 by α–emission

$$^{239}_{94}Pu \rightarrow ^{235}_{92}U + ^{4}_{2}\alpha$$

c. the decay of sodium–22 by positron emission

$$^{22}_{11}Na \rightarrow ^{22}_{10}Ne + ^{0}_{+1}\beta$$

d. the decay of cadmium–109 by β–emission

$$^{109}_{48}Cd \rightarrow ^{109}_{49}In + ^{0}_{-1}\beta$$

PROBLEM 61.2A

$$_{15}^{32}\text{P} \rightarrow {}_{16}^{32}\text{S} + {}_{-1}^{0}\beta$$

$\ln = -kt$

$t_{1/2} = 0.693/k$

$k = 0.693/14.3 = 4.85 \times 10^{-2} \text{ day}^{-1}$

$\ln([R]_t/10) = -4.85 \times 10^{-2} \times 7$

$[R]_t = 7.12 \text{ mg}$

PROBLEM 61.3A

$10 \text{ days} = 10 \text{ days} \times (24 \text{ hr}/1 \text{ day}) = 240 \text{ hr}$

$k = 0.693/14.66 \text{ hr} = 4.73 \times 10^{-2} \text{ hr}^{-1}$

$\ln \dfrac{[N]_t}{[N]_0} = -kt$

$\ln([N]_t / (2.51 \times 10^{19}) = -4.73 \times 10^{-2} \text{ hr}^{-1} \times 240 \text{ hr}$

$[N]_t = 2.95 \times 10^{14}$

The number of radioactive nuclei has decreased considerably over the ten-day period.

Rate of disintegration $= k N = 4.73 \times 10^{-2} \text{ hr}^{-1} \times 2.95 \times 10^{14} = 1.39 \times 10^{13} \text{ hr}^{-1}$

$= 1.39 \times 10^{13}$ disintegrations $\text{hr}^{-1} \times (1 \text{ hr} /3600\text{s}) = 3.87 \times 10^{9} \text{ Bq}$

$= 3.87 \times 10^{9} \text{ Bq} \times (1 \text{ Ci}/3.70 \times 10^{10} \text{ Bq}) = 0.105 \text{ Ci} = 105 \text{ mCi}$

PROBLEM 61.4A

The original number of potassium–40 atoms (at the moment the mineral solidified), compared the number present at the present time, must be in the ratio (1.00 + 3.35) to 1.00.

The decay constant $k = 0.693/1.28 \times 10^{9} \text{ years} = 5.41 \times 10^{-10} \text{ yr}^{-1}$.

$\ln \dfrac{[N]_t}{[N]_0} = -kt$

$\ln (1.00/4.35) = -5.41 \times 10^{-10} \text{ yr}^{-1} \times t.$

$t = 2.72 \times 10^{9} \text{ years.}$

Answers to Review Questions

1. The symbols used in nuclear equations indicate the numbers of neutrons and protons in each species. This makes the equations for nuclear reactions relatively easy to balance. Specifically, an isotope of an element is characterized by two numbers—the atomic number and the mass number. The number of neutrons is the difference between the two. In the symbol for an isotope, the mass number is written as a preceding superscript and the atomic number is written as a preceding subscript. Elementary particles involved in nuclear reactions are represented in the same way, with a superscript equal to the mass number and the subscript equal to the atomic number.

2. The three common types of radioactive decay are labeled α, β, and γ. An α–partticle is a helium nucleus (two neutrons and two protons) and α–emission is typical of unstable isotopes that lie beyond atomic number 83. A β–particle is a high-energy electron ejected by the nucleus and β–emission is typical of unstable nuclei that lie above the belt of stability and have a high n/p ratio. The third type of radioactive emission, γ–radiation, is high energy electromagnetic radiation that occurs when an isotope produced in an excited state decays to the ground state (a more stable arrangement of the protons and neutrons). Three other types of reaction involving unstable nuclei are positron emission, electron capture, and proton emission. These are typical of nuclei that have an n/p ratio that is too low—below the belt of stability.

3. The probable mechanism of radioactive decay that occurs for an unstable nucleus can often be determined by calculating the n/p ratio of the isotope. If the ratio is high for the particular atomic number, then β–emission is likely. If the ratio is low, then positron emission or electron capture is likely. If the isotope has an atomic number above 83, then α–emission or β–emission are probable, depending upon the n/p ratio.

4. If an unstable isotope is incorporated into the artifact when it was made, and the unstable nucleus and its decay product are trapped within the artifact, then the age of the artifact can be determined by measuring the relative abundances of the unstable isotope and its decay product.

5. Transmutation, by definition, requires a change within the nucleus. The atomic number must change. This is only possible in a nuclear reaction. Chemical reactions merely rearrange the same set of atoms.

6. Neutron bombardment can be accomplished simply by lowering the target nucleus into a nuclear reactor and leaving it there for as long as necessary. Bombardment by positively-charged particles requires the acceleration of the particles to increase their kinetic energies so that the repulsion between the positively-charged particle and the target nucleus can be overcome.

7. The rate of a nuclear decay does not depend upon the chemical environment of the atom. The decay does not depend upon collisions with other atoms; it is independent of the temperature, pressure, concentration, and any of the other factors that influence the rates of chemical reactions. The radioactivity depends only upon the number of radioactive nuclides present.

End-of-Unit Problems

1. Write equations representing the following nuclear reactions:
   a. the decay of boron–8 by positron emission
   b. the decay of polonium–212 by α–emission
   c. electron capture by beryllium–7
   d. the decay of cobalt–56 by proton emission
   e. the decay of iron–59 by β–emission

2. Write equations representing the following nuclear reactions:
   a. the decay of nitrogen–12 by positron emission
   b. the decay of polonium–218 by α–emission
   c. electron capture by indium–110
   d. the decay of lithium–9 by neutron emission
   e. the decay of bismuth–214 by β–emission

3. Predict the type of radioactive decay the following radioactive isotopes are likely to undergo, write the symbol for the isotope, and write an equation representing the decay. Use Figures 61.1 and 61.2.
   a. cobalt–60
   b. tritium (hydrogen–3)
   c. radon–222
   d. carbon–14

4. Predict the type of radioactive decay the following radioactive isotopes are likely to undergo, write the symbol for the isotope, and write an equation representing the decay. Use Figures 61.1 and 61.2.
   a. copper–68
   b. americium–246
   c. cadmium–10
   d. phosphorus–29

5. Complete the following equations; what is the species represented by the "?":
   a. $^1_1H + ^1_1H \rightarrow ^2_1H + ?$
   b. $^{241}_{95}Am + ? \rightarrow 4\,^1_0n + ^{248}_{100}Fm$
   c. $^{14}_7N + ? \rightarrow ^{17}_8O + ^1_1p$

6. Complete the following equations; what is(are) the species represented by the "?":
   a. $^2_1H + ^3_2He \rightarrow ^4_2He + ?$
   b. $^{122}_{53}I \rightarrow ^{122}_{54}Xe + ?$
   c. $^{233}_{92}U + ^1_0n \rightarrow ^{133}_{51}Sb + ^{98}_{41}Nb + ?$

7. Write equations for the following nuclear reactions:
   a. the bombardment of ^{209}Bi with ^{58}Fe to produce ^{266}Mt
   b. electron capture by ^{195}Au
   c. the decay of ^{211}Po by α–emission
   d. the bombardment of ^{14}N with α–particles to produce ^{17}O

8. Write equations for the following nuclear reactions:
   a. the bombardment of ^6Li with neutrons to produce tritium and ^4He
   b. the decay of ^{122}I to ^{122}Xe
   c. the decay of ^{14}C to ^{14}N
   d. the bombardment of ^{238}Bi with ^{14}N to produce ^{246}Es

9. Americium–241 follows a radioactive decay series with the following steps: α, α, β, α, α, β, α, α, α, β, α, β emission. Identify the radioisotopes produced in this series and the final stable isotope formed.

10. Uranium–235 follows a radioactive decay series with the following steps: α, β, α, β, α, α, α, β, α, β, α emission. Identify the radioisotopes produced in this series and the final stable isotope formed.

11. The element technicium was so called because it has no stable isotopes. On the basis of Figures 61.1 and 61.4, which isotope of technicium would you expect to be the least unstable?

12. Helium–4 is a "doubly magic" nuclide. Examine the Periodic Table and Figure 61.1 to discover any other "doubly magic" nuclides.

13. Element 106 is named in honor of Glenn T. Seaborg, the principal discoverer of the transuranic elements. The element, as the isotope ^{263}Sg, was pre-

pared by bombardment of ^{249}Cf by a beam of high energy ^{18}O nuclei. Write a complete balanced equation for this reaction.

14. Lawrencium, element 103, was prepared as the isotope ^{257}Lr by bombardment of ^{249}Cf by a beam of high energy ^{10}B nuclei. Write a complete balanced equation for this reaction.

15. If the unstable isotope ^{242}Cm decays through a sequence of α–emissions and β–emissions to ^{206}Pb, how many α–particles and how many β–particles must be emitted in this series?

16. If the unstable isotope ^{232}Th decays through a sequence of a–emissions and b–emissions to ^{208}Pb, how many a–particles and how many b–particles must be emitted in this series?

17. The half-life of cobalt–60 is 5.27 years. How long does it take for a sample of cobalt–60 to decay to 5.0% of its initial radioactivity?

18. The Chernobyl disaster released a large amount of iodine–131 into the atmosphere and the neighboring countryside. If the half-life of iodine–131 is 8.04 days, how long will it take for the iodine to lose 99.9% of its initial radioactivity?

19. Tritium has a half-life of 12.26 years. What is the rate of decay (in Bq and Ci) of a 0.10 mol sample of tritium?

20. Strontium–90 has a half-life of 28.5 years. What is the rate of decay (in Bq and Ci) of a 9.00 mg sample of strontium–90?

21. The half-life of the iron–52 isotope is 8.28 hours. A sample has an activity of 1.86 μCi. What would be the activity of the sample 48 hours later?

22. The half-life of the sodium–24 isotope is 14.66 hours. A sample has an activity of 87,400 Bq. What would be the activity of the sample 5.0 days later?

23. Charcoal retrieved from the site of Stonehenge in England has a carbon–14 activity 62.0% that of carbon–14 in living plants. Assuming that the abundance of carbon–14 in the atmosphere has remained moreorless constant for past few thousand years, how old is the charcoal? The half-life of carbon–14 is 5730 years.

24. A fragment of papyrus found in a tomb in Egypt exhibited a specific activity of 0.149 Bq g^{-1}. If the specific activity of ^{14}C in living matter is 0.255 Bq g^{-1}, calculate the age of the papyrus. The half-life of carbon–14 is 5730 years.

25. Carbon–14 dating is limited to objects no older than 40,000 years. Why is this? Calculate the specific activity of ^{14}C after 40,000 years. The specific activity of living matter is 0.255 Bq g^{-1}, and the half-life of carbon–14 is 5730 years.

26. The decay of potassium–40 to argon–40 by β–emission has a half-life of 1,280,000,000 years. If a rock brought back from the moon is found to contain 17.5% ^{40}K and 82.5% ^{40}Ar, when was the rock formed?

Nuclear Fission and Fusion

62.1   Nuclear Binding Energy

The mass of a nucleus is always less than the sum of the masses of the individual protons and neutrons that make up the nucleus. For example, the mass of an α–particle (a helium nucleus) is 4.00150 g mol^{-1}. The mass of a proton is 1.007276 g mol^{-1} and the mass of a neutron is 1.008665 g mol^{-1}. The sum of the masses of two protons and two neutrons equals 4.03188 g mol^{-1}. This means that when a helium nucleus is made from its constituent nucleons, there is a loss of mass equal to 0.03038 g mol^{-1}. This mass loss is called the **mass defect**.

mass of individual nucleons		*mass of the helium nucleus*
protons:	$2 \times 1.007276 = 2.014552$ g mol^{-1}	4.00150 g mol^{-1}
neutrons:	$2 \times 1.008665 = 2.017330$ g mol^{-1}	
total:	$= 4.031882$ g mol^{-1}	
mass defect:	$= 4.031882$ g mol$^{-1} - 4.00150$ g mol^{-1}	
	$= 0.03038$ g mol^{-1}	

The mass of the two electrons of a helium atom can be included (0.0010972 g mol^{-1}). The same mass is added to both sums and has no effect upon the difference (the mass defect).

The relationship between mass and energy is given by Einstein's equation from his theory of special relativity: $E = mc^2$, where E is the energy, m is the mass, and c is the speed of light. The mass defect for a helium nucleus (0.03038 g mol^{-1}) is equivalent to 2.731×10^9 kJ mol^{-1}. This is an enormous amount of energy. It represents the energy that binds the nucleons together in the nucleus and is called the **binding energy**. For comparison, the amount of energy released in the combustion of methane is only 890 kJ mol^{-1}.

In a chemical reaction, such as the combustion of methane, there is a loss of mass that corresponds to the energy released (890 kJ mol^{-1}). However, the mass loss is immeasurably small (9.9×10^{-9} g or 9.9 ng).

To compare the binding energies of different nuclides, it is convenient to calculate the binding energy per nucleon. The binding energy per nucleon for the helium–4 nucleus is 2.731×10^9 kJ mol^{-1} /4 nucleons = 6.828×10^8 kJ mol^{-1} nucleon^{-1}. This is the energy, on average, that would be necessary to separate each nucleon in a helium nucleus. In other words, it describes the energy with which each nucleon is bound to the nucleus. A plot of the binding energies per nucleon for a series of isotopes is illustrated in Figure 62.1. It's interesting that the binding energy increases to iron–56

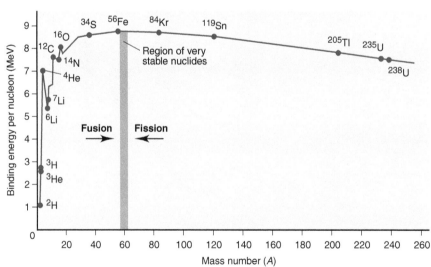

FIGURE 62.1   The variation in the binding energy per nucleon through the Periodic Table.
The nuclear stability is greatest at iron–56.

and then decreases; iron–56 is the most stable nuclide. The increase in the stability of nuclei to a maximum at iron–56 is the fundamental reason for the enormous amounts of energy released in fusion and fission reactions. The line is steeper on the fusion side—more energy is released in fusion processes than fission processes.

EXAMPLE 62.1   CALCULATION OF THE MASS DEFECTS AND BINDING ENERGIES OF NUCLIDES

The mass of a fluorine–19 atom is 18.9984 u. The masses of a proton and a neutron are 1.007276 u and 1.008665 u respectively. The mass of an electron is 0.00054858 u. Calculate for a fluorine–19 atom,

a. the mass defect
b. the binding energy
c. the binding energy per nucleon

UNDERSTAND THE QUESTION

The mass defect is the difference between the mass of a nuclide and the sum of the masses of the individual nucleons. It can be expressed in g mol^{-1}, as we saw earlier, or it can be expressed in atomic mass units (u), as in this question. Be careful to note whether the mass provided is the mass of the atom (nucleus + electrons) or just the mass of the nucleus. The binding energy is the energy equivalent to the mass defect according to Einstein's equation $E = mc^2$. This energy can be expressed in kJ mol^{-1} or in MeV (megaelectronvolts) per nucleus or per nucleon.

PLAN THE SOLUTION

Calculate the sum of the masses of the individual nucleons and compare with the mass of the nuclide. Calculate the energy equivalent using Einstein's equation.

1 eV is the energy gained by an electron when it moves through a potential of 1 volt. The charge on an electron is 1.6022×10^{-19} C, so
$1 \text{ eV} = 1.6022 \times 10^{-19}$ C × 1 V
$= 1.6022 \times 10^{-19}$ J
and
$1 \text{ u} = 1.6606 \times 10^{-27}$ kg
so the energy equivalent to 1 u is:
$E = mc^2$
$= 1.6606 \times 10^{-27}$ kg ×
$(2.9979 \times 10^8 \text{ ms}^{-1})^2$
$= 1.4924 \times 10^{-10}$ J

$= \dfrac{1.4924 \times 10^{-10}}{1.6022 \times 10^{-19}}$ eV

$= 9.3147 \times 10^5$ eV
$= 931.47$ MeV

SOLVE THE PROBLEM

a. *mass of individual nucleons*   *mass of the fluorine atom*

protons:	9×1.007276	$= 9.065484$ u	18.9984 u
neutrons:	10×1.008665	$= 10.086650$ u	
electrons:	9×0.00054858	$= 0.004937$ u	
total:		$= 19.157071$ u	

mass defect: $= 19.157071$ u $- 18.9984$ u $= 0.1587$ u

b. $E = mc^2$

$= 0.1587$ u $\times (2.9979 \times 10^8 \text{ ms}^{-1})^2 = 1.426 \times 10^{16}$ u m^{2}s^{-2}

These units are not especially useful. We can convert the units into J or MeV per nucleus or kJ per mole of nuclei:

$$= 1.426 \times 10^{16} \text{ u m}^2\text{s}^{-2} \times \left(\frac{1.6606 \times 10^{-27} \text{ kg}}{1 \text{ u}} \right) \times \left(\frac{1 \text{ J}}{1 \text{ kg m}^2\text{s}^{-2}} \right) = 2.368 \times 10^{-11} \text{ J nucleus}^{-1}$$

$$= 2.368 \times 10^{-11} \text{ J/nucleus} \times \left(\frac{1 \text{ eV}}{1.6022 \times 10^{-19} \text{ J}} \right) \times \left(\frac{1 \text{ MeV}}{10^6 \text{ eV}} \right) = 147.8 \text{ MeV nucleus}^{-1}$$

$$= 1.426 \times 10^{16} \text{ g mol}^{-1} \text{ m}^2\text{s}^{-2} \times \left(\frac{1 \text{ kg}}{10^3 \text{ g}} \right) \times \left(\frac{1 \text{ J}}{1 \text{ kg m}^2\text{s}^{-2}} \right) \times \left(\frac{1 \text{ kJ}}{10^3 \text{ J}} \right) = 1.426 \times 10^{10} \text{ kJ mol}^{-1}$$

Alternatively, multiply 0.1587 u by 931.47 MeV/u = 147.8 MeV.

Notice that 1.426×10^{16} u can be expressed equally well as 1.426×10^{16} g mol^{-1}.

c. There are 19 nucleons:

Binding energy per nucleon = 147.8 MeV/ 19 nucleons = 7.78 MeV/nucleon

PROBLEM 62.1A

Uranium–238 decays spontaneously to thorium–234 by the emission of an α–particle. The equation for this reaction is: $^{238}_{92}U \rightarrow {}^{234}_{90}Th + {}^{4}_{2}\alpha$

The mass of a uranium–238 atom is 238.05079 u; the mass of thorium–234 is 234.0436; the mass of an α–particle is 4.00150 u; and the mass of an electron is 0.00054858 u.

Determine the change in mass during this reaction and calculate the equivalent energy.

PROBLEM 62.1B

Is energy required or released in the reaction: $^{27}_{13}Al + {}^{4}_{2}\alpha \rightarrow {}^{30}_{15}P + {}^{1}_{0}n$?

The atomic mass of aluminum–27 is 26.9815 u; the mass of an α–particle is 4.00150 u; the atomic mass of phosphorus–30 is 29.9783 u; the mass of a neutron is 1.008665 u; and the mass of an electron is 0.00054858 u.

a. What is the change in mass in this reaction?

b. What is the energy equivalent to this change in mass?

62.2   Nuclear Fission

The data in Figure 62.1 indicate that iron–56 has the maximum binding energy per nucleon. From iron through the remainder of the Periodic Table, the binding energy per nucleon slowly decreases. This means that if a heavier nuclide were to break up into two smaller nuclides, both having a mass greater than iron–56, energy would be released in the process. This breakup of a heavy nuclide into two smaller nuclides is called **nuclear fission**.

In 1934 Enrico Fermi and his co-workers bombarded a mixture of uranium–238 and uranium–235 with thermal neutrons. **Thermal neutrons** are relatively slow-moving (approximately 2000 m s^{-1}) compared to the fast neutrons emitted from a typical neutron source or in in a fission reaction. They are called thermal neutrons because their average kinetic energy corresponds to a temperature of about 25°C. As a result of the bombardment, β–particles were emitted.

In 1938 Otto Hahn and Fritz Strassman identified the β–emitters as radioactive isotopes of elements such as barium—much to their surprise. They thought they were looking for new **transuranic elements**. In 1939, Lise Meitner suggested that the bombardment of the uranium with neutrons caused the uranium atoms to split into two smaller nuclei—a process for which she coined the term nuclear fission. It was the uranium–235 isotope that underwent fission and more than 370 nuclides of more than 30 different elements have been identified as the products of the fission. The distribution of the nuclides produced in uranium–235 fission is illustrated in Figure 62.2.

Most of the fission products are radioactive because they have a high n/p ratio (hence the β–emission). However, on average, the nuclides have a slightly lower n/p ratio than uranium. This results in the emission of 'extra' neutrons during the fission of

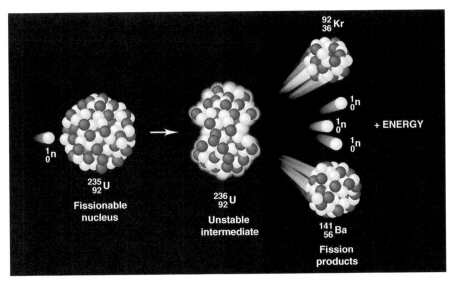

FIGURE 62.2 **The distribution of fragments produced by the fission of uranium-235.**
The splitting of the uranium nucleus is rarely symmetrical; typically the ratio of the masses of
the two fragments is about 95 u:140 u. Note that the Relative abundance scale is logarithmic.

the uranium nucleus. These neutrons are emitted with high energies and two or three
neutrons are emitted in each fission reaction. Typical reactions are:

$$^{235}_{92}U + {}^1_0n \rightarrow {}^{72}_{30}Zn + {}^{162}_{62}Sm + 2\,{}^1_0n$$

$$^{235}_{92}U + {}^1_0n \rightarrow {}^{94}_{36}Kr + {}^{139}_{56}Ba + 3\,{}^1_0n$$

$$^{235}_{92}U + {}^1_0n \rightarrow {}^{90}_{38}Sr + {}^{143}_{54}Xe + 3\,{}^1_0n$$

The implication of this production of neutrons in the fission process was the
possibility of a chain reaction. If the three neutrons produced in the fission of one
uranium–235 nucleus went on to produce the fission of three other uranium nuclei,
and the nine neutrons thus produced went on to initiate the fission of nine other uranium nuclei, and so on, the reaction would quickly get out of control, liberating an
enormous amount of energy. A possible fission chain reaction is illustrated in Figure 62.3. The energy released in the fission reaction can be calculated from the difference in the binding energies of the uranium–235 and the fission products. In the third
of the reactions shown above, the difference in the binding energies is 3.3×10^{-11} J per
uranium nucleus. This corresponds to 2.0×10^{10} kJ per mole of uranium, an enormous
amount of energy compared to chemical combustion reactions.

In December 1942 in Chicago, Enrico Fermi and his co-workers demonstrated
that a self-sustaining sequence of nuclear fission reactions was possible. They had a
sufficient amount of uranium present (40 tons of uranium metal and uranium oxide)
to ensure that enough of the emitted neutrons collided with other uranium–235 atoms
before escaping from the sample. They slowed down the emitted neutrons to increase
the likelihood of their reaction with another uranium nucleus by using a graphite
moderator. They controlled the chain reaction by inserting cadmium **control rods** to
absorb the neutrons produced. Cadmium is a good neutron absorber and removes the
neutrons from the chain reaction.

At the beginning of World War II, the development of nuclear explosives by Germany was considered by some scientists to be a dangerous possibility. Albert Einstein,

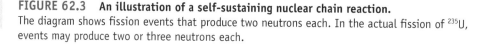

FIGURE 62.3 **An illustration of a self-sustaining nuclear chain reaction.**
The diagram shows fission events that produce two neutrons each. In the actual fission of ^{235}U, events may produce two or three neutrons each.

The critical mass is a mass of fissionable material above which a self-sustaining nuclear fission reaction occurs.

Separation of the isotopes of uranium by gaseous effusion is a tedious process. The masses of the two hexafluorides are very close. Modern separation techniques involve ultra high speed centrifuges.

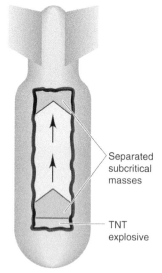

FIGURE 62.4 The design of the uranium–235 fission bomb "Little-boy" dropped on Hiroshima.

and others, wrote to President Roosevelt to inform him of the danger. As a result, soon after the United States entered the war, the President authorized the production of a nuclear fission bomb in a program called the Manhattan Project.

In 1945, the United States dropped two atomic bombs on Japan. The first bomb, dropped on Hiroshima, was based upon the fission of uranium–235. Uranium–235 is much less abundant (0.72%) than uranium–238. Ordinarily, neutrons emitted by the ^{235}U are captured by the ^{238}U. The first problem was to concentrate the ^{235}U so that a **critical mass** of ^{235}U could be constructed. This was done by converting the uranium into the gaseous uranium hexafluoride UF_6 and separating the isotopes by gaseous effusion. Weapons-grade uranium is at least 94% ^{235}U. The second problem was in the construction of the bomb itself. The uranium could not be allowed to become super-critical until a nuclear explosion was intended and then the uranium had to be held in a supercritical state long enough to allow the chain reaction to take hold. One subcritical mass of ^{235}U was fired into another using a conventional TNT explosive (Figure 62.4). The total mass of ^{235}U was 60 kg. In a fission bomb such as this, only a limited frac-tion, certainly less than 20%, of the fissionable material actually undergoes fission before the bomb blows apart.

Three days later, the second bomb was dropped on the city of Nagasaki (Figure 62.5). This bomb was based upon the fission of 8 kg of a synthetic nuclide, plutonium–239. Plutonium is made by bombarding uranium–238 with neutrons in a nuclear reactor—the first nuclear reactor built by Fermi in Chicago was designed for the production of plutonium. The plutonium is isolated from the reaction products by ordinary chemical separation techniques. A hollow plutonium core is surrounded by a conventional explosive that compresses the core and causes the plutonium to go critical. This implosion method is more efficient than the gun method because the implosion increases the density of the plutonium mass which in turn increases the rate of fission. However, the explosion must be carefully shaped to provide a perfectly spherical implosion. Otherwise the plutonium core would be squeezed out of any gaps. The spherical shock wave is produced by accurately shaped explosive charges, called explosive lenses, fitted around the core. The Nagasaki bomb had 32 lenses; modern devices have many more.

FIGURE 62.5 The explosion of the plutonium–239 fission bomb over Nagasaki in 1945.

Nuclear Reactors

The peaceful extraction of the energy available in a nuclear fission reaction is accomplished in a nuclear reactor (Figure 62.6). The nuclear reaction takes place in the reactor core. The surrounding fluid coolant, often water under high pressure, is heated to about 300°C by the nuclear reaction, which is circulated to a heat exchanger where water is boiled to create steam. The steam drives a turbine connected to an electrical generator. The steam is then condensed and returned to the heat exchanger.

Ordinarily the critical mass of plutonium is 15 kg. By imploding the subcritical mass of ^{239}Pu, the density is increased and the critical mass is less.

The reactor core is composed of three components: the fissile fuel, a moderator, and control rods. The fuel is often uranium enriched in the ^{235}U isotope—the fraction of ^{235}U is increased from 0.7% to 3%. Other fissile fuels are plutonium–239 and uranium–233.

Fissile, as opposed to **fissionable**, means that the fission of the nucleus occurs upon impact of thermal neutrons, as opposed to fast neutrons.

As noted earlier, the moderator slows down the emitted neutrons so that they have kinetic energies typical of gas molecules at room temperature and more easily react with other ^{235}U nuclei (rather than the ^{238}U nuclei). The moderator must be able to slow down the neutrons without absorbing them. If it did so, undesirable radioactive products would be formed. Water is an ideal moderator. If ordinary water is used, the reactor is called a 'light-water' reactor. If deuterium oxide, D_2O, is used, the reactor is called a 'heavy-water' reactor. The advantage of a heavy-water reactor is that is does not require enriched uranium—it works fine with the natural ^{235}U/^{238}U mixture. It does however require a sufficiently cheap source of heavy-water. Another possible moderator is graphite—this was used by Enrico Fermi in his first uranium 'pile'.

Slow neutrons do not cause the fission of fissionable isotopes such as uranium–238, they are more easily absorbed by the fissile uranium–235, and they allow the control rods to work more efficiently because the slower neutrons are absorbed more easily.

The control rods absorb neutrons. The rods are raised or lowered to increase or decrease the rate of the fission process. The control rods are often made of cadmium or boron encased in zirconium.

A typical nuclear reactor uses 2 or 3 kg of uranium–235 a day. Eventually, fission products build up in the fuel rods and the rods have to be replaced. The problem is what to do with the spent fuel rods. Currently most nuclear waste is stored on site at nuclear reactors and remains to be dealt with. The spent fuel contains highly radioactive and dangerous isotopes. One possibility is to reprocess the rods

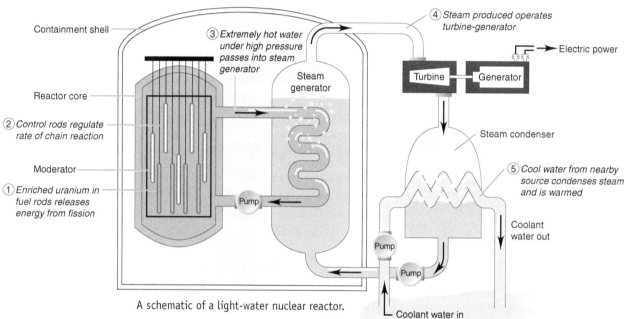

Containment shell

③ *Extremely hot water under high pressure passes into steam generator*

④ *Steam produced operates turbine-generator*

Steam generator

Electric power

Turbine

Generator

Reactor core

Steam condenser

② *Control rods regulate rate of chain reaction*

⑤ *Cool water from nearby source condenses steam and is warmed*

Moderator

① *Enriched uranium in fuel rods releases energy from fission*

Pump

Coolant water out

Pump

Pump

A schematic of a light-water nuclear reactor.

Coolant water in

FIGURE 62.6 **A nuclear power plant.**
The containment building on the right encloses the nuclear reactor. The large structure on the left is the cooling tower used to condense the steam from the steam turbine.

to extract isotopes such as plutonium–239 which itself can be used as a fuel. This is desirable because plutonium has such a long half-life (24,110 years). There are, however, other isotopes present such as strontium–90 which have relatively long half-lives (strontium–90 has a half-life of 28.5 years). This means that, even if the ^{239}Pu is removed, the spent fuel must be stored for hundreds of years before it becomes biologically nonhazardous. The waste must be kept secure from the environment. In France, where nuclear energy provides 75% of the nation's electrical requirement, the waste is stored deep in the earth in old salt mines. Other nations have been less responsible, simply dumping the waste material in the sea. Current ideas involve incorporating the spent nuclear fuel in impermeable glass or ceramic blocks and storing them underground, where they would remain for the five or six hundred years it takes for the radioactivity to diminish to safe levels.

Breeder reactors are intentionally designed to produce ^{239}Pu from ^{238}U, or ^{233}U from ^{232}Th. The ^{238}U or ^{232}Th is placed in the reactor core to absorb neutrons and produce these fissionable isotopes. A breeder reactor produces more fissile fuel than it uses.

$$^{238}_{92}U + {}^{1}_{0}n \rightarrow {}^{239}_{92}U$$
$$^{238}_{92}U \rightarrow {}^{239}_{93}Np + {}^{0}_{-1}\beta \qquad t_{1/2} = 23.4 \text{ min}$$
$$^{239}_{94}Np \rightarrow {}^{239}_{94}Pu + {}^{0}_{-1}\beta \qquad t_{1/2} = 2.35 \text{ days}$$
and
$$^{232}_{90}Th + {}^{1}_{0}n \rightarrow {}^{233}_{90}Th$$
$$^{233}_{90}Th \rightarrow {}^{233}_{91}Pa + {}^{0}_{-1}\beta \qquad t_{1/2} = 22 \text{ min}$$
$$^{233}_{91}Pa \rightarrow {}^{233}_{92}U + {}^{0}_{-1}\beta \qquad t_{1/2} = 27.4 \text{ days}$$

Nuclear Accidents

The operation of nuclear reactors for the generation of electrical energy involves some risk and accidents do happen. In 1957, a fire in the graphite-moderated reactor at the Sellafield facility in the UK released an estimated 20,000 Ci of radioactive iodine–131. Milk and other produce from surrounding farms had to be destroyed. In 1979, the Three Mile Island reactor in the US partially melted due to a failure of water coolant pumps. The release of radioactivity into the environment was small in comparison—only about 15 Ci of iodine–131 were released. The disaster at Chernobyl in the Ukraine in 1986 released an estimated 40,000,000 Ci of iodine-131. The **Chernobyl accident** occurred during a test of the reactor in which almost all the control rods were withdrawn from the core. The reactor went out of control despite attempts to reinsert all the control rods; the steam generated blew the top off the reactor and reacted with metal to produce hydrogen; air entered and the hydrogen and graphite (moderator) ignited. A plume of radioactive debris drifted over the Ukraine, Belarus, Russia, Eastern Europe and Scandinavia. The accident required the evacuation and resettlement of about 200,000 people. All the operators in the Reactor 4 building at Chernobyl at the time of the accident died within three weeks. It is estimated that the accident at Chernobyl released 400 times the radioactive contamination of the bomb at Hiroshima in 1945. However, this pales in comparison to the widespread contamination caused by atmospheric nuclear weapons testing in the mid-20th century.

> Note that nuclear reactors cannot explode as a nuclear bomb does, the fuel is not dense enough. They can, however, overheat and melt down.

The latest nuclear 'event', rated at level 7, the highest on the INES (International Nuclear Event Scale), occurred in March 2011 at the Fukushima Daiichi Plant in Japan. An earthquake and subsequent tsunami flooded the nuclear power plant and put the emergency generators out of action. Three of the six reactors experienced full melt-down; the other three were not operating at the time. Approximately 4,000,000 Ci of iodine-131 was released, approximately 1/10th that at Chernobyl. Radioactivity led to the evacuation of all people within a 12 mile radius of the disaster.

62.3 Nuclear Fusion

For light elements, up to iron–56, the nuclear stability, expressed as the binding energy per nucleon, increases as the atomic number increases (*cf.* Figure 61.1). This means that if two light nuclei were to combine to form a larger, more stable nucleus, energy would be released. This combination of two nuclei to form a larger nucleus is called **nuclear fusion**.

The sun at the center of our solar system is a giant nuclear fusion reactor. The basic reaction is the combination of hydrogen nuclei to form helium nuclei involving the following steps. There's enough hydrogen in the sun to keep the reaction going for five billion years.

$$\begin{aligned} {}^1_1\text{H} + {}^1_1\text{H} &\rightarrow {}^2_1\text{H} + {}^0_1\beta \\ {}^1_1\text{H} + {}^2_1\text{H} &\rightarrow {}^3_2\text{He} \\ {}^3_2\text{He} + {}^3_2\text{He} &\rightarrow {}^4_2\text{He} + 2\,{}^1_1\text{H} \\ {}^3_2\text{He} + {}^1_1\text{H} &\rightarrow {}^4_2\text{He} + {}^0_1\beta \\ \hline 4\,{}^1_1\text{H} &\rightarrow {}^4_2\text{He} + 2\,{}^0_1\beta \end{aligned}$$

After the ¹H is exhausted, other fusion processes take over.

The overall process is the conversion of four hydrogen nuclei into a helium nucleus with the liberation of 24.7 MeV.

A fusion bomb, often called a **thermonuclear weapon** because of the high temperatures required for the fusion reaction, uses lithium–6 deuteride as the fuel. The fusion reaction is initiated by a fission bomb, which in turn is initiated by a conventional shaped charge. A simpler use of fusion is to place deuterium and tritium inside the hollow core of plutonium in a fission device. The fission of the plutonium causes the fusion of the deuterium and tritium.

$$ {}^2_1\text{H} + {}^3_1\text{H} \rightarrow {}^4_2\text{He} + {}^1_0\text{n} $$

This fusion reaction generates huge numbers of neutrons which enter the surrounding plutonium. This increases the efficiency of the fission reaction. The amount of energy from the fusion reaction is almost negligible in comparison to that from the fission process. The effect of the fusion reaction is to double the yield of the fission process.

Considerable effort has been made to harness the energy available in nuclear fusion for the generation of electricity. The fusion of deuterium and tritium illustrated above releases 17.6 MeV. The neutrons produced in this reaction can be used to make tritium by the reaction:

$$ {}^6_3\text{Li} + {}^1_0\text{n} \rightarrow {}^3_1\text{H} + {}^4_2\text{He} $$

The energy required to initiate these reactions is enormous—temperatures of the order of millions of degrees are required to provide enough energy to overcome the repulsion between the nuclei. The energy profile for the reaction between two deuterium nuclei to form a helium nucleus is illustrated in Figure 62.7. The activation energy for the fusion process is relatively small compared to the energy released in the reaction but the kinetic energy required by the deuterium nuclei to overcome the barrier is about 5×10^7 kJ mol^{-1}—corresponding to a temperature of 5 million K. There is no material that

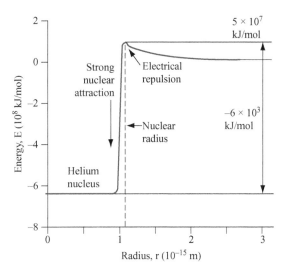

FIGURE 62.7 **The energy profile for the fusion of two deuterium nuclei to form a helium nucleus.**
Although the amount of energy released is enormous, the activation energy is prohibitive.

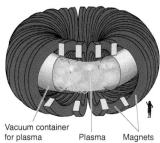

Vacuum container
for plasma Plasma Magnets

FIGURE 62.8 **The tokamak fusion test reactor.**
A massive experimental device in which a hot, ionized plasma containing deuterium, tritium, and lithium–6 nuclei and electrons is held within a donut-shaped magnetic field. The plasma is heated by intense laser beams.

can withstand such high temperatures. At these temperatures the nuclear fuel itself exists as a plasma of atomic nuclei and electrons and experiments have concentrated on holding this plasma within a powerful magnetic field (Figure 62.8). The high temperatures required are produced by high energy lasers. Even if a fusion reaction was achieved, the problem of how to harness the energy produced remains. Most of the energy released would be in the form of electromagnetic radiation.

The successful development of a fusion reactor would, however, have great benefits. The supply of the deuterium fuel is almost inexhaustible; there are no undesirable radioactive products of the process; and the demand for fossil fuels would be alleviated.

EXAMPLE 62.2 NUCLEAR FISSION AND FUSION

The overall reaction in the sun is the fusion of four hydrogen atoms to form a helium atom:

$$4\,{}^{1}_{1}H \rightarrow {}^{4}_{2}He + 2\,{}^{0}_{1}\beta$$

The mass of a proton = 1.007276 u

The mass of a helium nucleus = 4.00150 u

The mass of a positron = 0.000549 u

a. Calculate the mass defect when the four hydrogen atoms fuse to form the helium atom.

b. Calculate the energy released in MeV per helium nucleus.

UNDERSTAND THE QUESTION

Mass is lost in the fusion process in the sun. It is this mass loss that is responsible for the immense amount of energy produced by the sun. The mass defect can be calculated from the masses of the products (helium and positrons) and the mass of the reactants (hydrogen). The energy equivalent can be calculated using Einstein's equation $E = mc^2$.

PLAN THE SOLUTION

Determine the masses of the components on each side of the equation and calculate the difference. Then calculate the energy equivalent to the mass difference.

SOLVE THE PROBLEM

a. *mass of the hydrogen nuclei* *mass of the product nuclei*

$_1^1H$: 4×1.007276 = 4.029104 u	$_2^4He$	4.00150 u
	$2 \, _1^0\beta$	2×0.000549 u
totals: = 4.029104 u		4.002598 u
mass defect: = 4.029104 u	−	4.002598 u = 0.026506 u

b. Energy = 0.026506 u × 931.5 MeV u^{-1} = 24.7 MeV

PROBLEM 62.2A

Lithium deuteride LiD is used as the fuel in most thermonuclear weapons. The LiD forms two helium nuclei according to the equations:

$$_3^6Li + _0^1n \rightarrow _1^3H + _2^4He$$

$$_1^2H + _1^3H \rightarrow _2^4He + _0^1n$$

Overall: $_3^6Li + _1^2H \rightarrow 2 \, _2^4He$

Calculate the energy released in this reaction.

The mass of a lithium–6 atom = 6.015121 u

The mass of a deuterium atom = 2.014000 u

The mass of a helium atom = 4.002600 u

PROBLEM 62.2B

Nuclear warheads are commonly described in terms of the amount of TNT that would be required to create the same explosion. A megaton bomb is equivalent to 1 million tons of TNT and is defined the release of 4.184 GJ of energy. If lithium–6 deuteride is used in a five–megaton warhead, how much LiD is required in the bomb if it fuses according to the data in the previous question?

The Hiroshima 'Little-boy' was a 13 kiloton device (54TJ). The Nagasaki 'Fat-man' was a 20 kiloton device (84 TJ).

62.4   The Effects of Radiation

Radiation (α, β, and γ radiation) from radioactive materials consists of high energy particles or electromagnetic radiation. When the radiation impacts material, energy is transferred to the atoms and molecules of the material. The primary result is the ionization of the atoms and molecules—electrons are forcibly ejected, bonds between atoms are sometimes broken, and much heat and electromagnetic radiation is produced. Radiation that causes ionization is referred to as **ionizing radiation** and is dangerous. Note that, in general, α, β, and γ radiation will not make other matter radioactive.

If the material is biological, ionizing radiation will destroy cells, and illness and death may result. The human body is primarily water and ionizing radiation has the ability to ionize the water, producing free radicals. These free radicals are very reactive and disrupt the normal chemical processes that occur in biological cells, sometimes completely destroying the cells.

The Hiroshima and Nagasaki bombs killed some 155,000 people immediately but 135,000 who survived the initial blasts died within a year due to the effects of the radiation—both the initial radiation produced in the explosion and the radiation from the radioactive nuclides produced in the reaction. In the Chernobyl disaster, the reactor operators and the initial firefighters on the scene died within weeks from the effects of the radiation; some died by the end of the same day. Many others downwind of the reactor suffer from the effects of radiation from the radioisotopes produced. The incidence of thyroid cancer (due to iodine–131) and leukemia is much greater than in other areas.

Of the three types of radiation, α–particles have the greatest ionizing power. One α–particle will produce thousands of ions as it passes through matter. The ionizing power of β–radiation is much less and γ–radiation has the lowest ionizing power of all.

However, the different types of radiation have different penetrating powers: α–radiation is stopped by two or three layers of paper (or the outer layer of skin); β–radiation will penetrate a stack of 200 sheets of paper (or human tissue to a depth of about 1 cm); and γ-radiation will pass all the way through the human body (Figure 62.9). γ–radiation is therefore the most dangerous source of radiation outside the body, but ingestion of α or β emitters is particularly hazardous. Tissues that are most susceptible to damage are those that contain cells that reproduce rapidly, such as bone-marrow and white-blood cells.

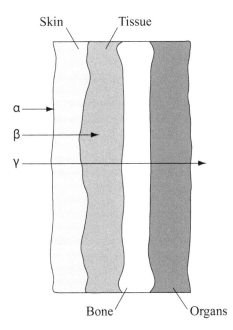

FIGURE 62.9   The relative penetrating abilities of α–radiation, β–radiation, and γ-radiation.

Radiation has long been measured by a unit called a **rad** (radiation absorbed dose). One rad corresponds to the absorption of 0.010 J of energy per kg of matter. The SI unit of radiation dose is the **gray** (Gy) which is equal to 100 rad, or the absorption of 1.00 J of energy per kg of matter. A more common unit used in measuring dosages of radiation absorbed by biological matter is the **rem** (roentgen equivalent for man). The rem equals the rad multiplied by a **relative biological effectiveness** (rbe) that takes into account the type of radiation, its energy, and its effect upon biological matter.

$$rem = rad \times rbe$$

The SI unit that corresponds to the rem is the **sievert** (Sv), so that one Sv equals 100 rem, and

$$Sv = Gy \times rbe$$

We are continually exposed to ionizing radiation from a variety of sources. Some are natural; others are a result of human activities. Examples of typical radiation doses from natural and artificial sources are listed in Table 62.1. People living near nuclear test sites, or at high altitudes, or in areas of high radon concentration, or workers in the nuclear power industry, will experience higher doses. Workers in nuclear power plants are limited to 5 rem per year.

TABLE 62.1 Typical radiation doses from natural and artificial sources.

Natural Source of Radiation	Typical Exposure per Year
Cosmic radiation	35 mrem
Radiation from the ground	25 to 150 mrem
Radiation from the air (radon)	20 to 250 mrem
Radiation from radioactive isotopes in the body	40 mrem
Artificial Source of Radiation	
medical and dental x–rays	50 to 75 mrem
air travel	4 mrem
nuclear weapons testing	4 mrem
nuclear power generation and waste	1 mrem

How much radiation is safe? A dose of 2,500 rem is almost certainly fatal. A dose of 500 rem will kill half the number of people exposed within 30 days. This is referred to as the LD_{50} (lethal dose for 50%). Smaller doses, from 100 to 500 rem, lead to sterility, bone marrow destruction, leukemia, reduced resistance to infection, growth retardation, vomiting and diarrhea. Doses from 5 to 100 rem lead to reduction in white blood cell count, possible chromosomal damage, and general tiredness and sickness.

Radioisotopes in Medicine

γ–Radiation from radioactive isotopes destroys cells. This property is used in medicine to destroy the cells in malignant tumors. Because cells in cancers reproduce rapidly and out of control, they are adversely susceptible to radiation. The radiation source can be implanted within the tumor; for example, a suitable radioactive isotope is encased within a platinum pellet and placed in the tumor where the γ–radiation is concentrated where it is needed. In some cases the radioactive isotope is ingested. An example of this is the treatment of thyroid cancer by drinking a solution of sodium iodide–131 ($t_{1/2}$ = 8.04 days). Most iodine in the diet is used to make the hormone thyroxin in the

---

Different nuclei emit α, β, and γ radiation with different energies.

The rbe for β and γ radiation is 1. The rbe for α radiation is 20 times larger.

The opposite treatment is often applied in the case of the release of iodine–131 in a nuclear accident such as Chernobyl. Children downwind of the radioactive plume were given large doses of normal sodium iodide; their thyroid glands became saturated with iodine, preventing the uptake of the radioactive iodine–131.

thyroid gland and the ingested radioactive iodine–131 ends up in the thyroid gland where it is needed. Sometimes, when surgical implantation of a radioisotope is impossible, an external radioactive source of γ–radiation is used, typically cobalt–60. The highly penetrating γ–radiation affects healthy cells as well as the cancerous cells and side effects (nausea, tiredness, a reduced resistance to infection, etc.) are unavoidable.

Radioactive isotopes are also used in medicine as tracers. For example, sodium–24 (a β–emitter with $t_{1/2}$ = 14.66 hr), is used to monitor the flow of blood and detect any constrictions. Iron–59 is incorporated in hemoglobin and can also be used to monitor blood flow. Technicium–99 is often used for imaging internal organs such as the thyroid, lungs, liver, and heart. Technicium–99 does not occur naturally and is made continuously in a technicium generator from molybdenum–99. The technicium is produced in an excited nuclear state, often designated ^{99m}Tc (or technicium–99m) that decays to the ground state with the emission of γ–radiation ($t_{1/2}$ = 6.02 hr).

A **PET (positron emission tomography)** scan is a technique used for monitoring biochemical processes within the body. The radioactive isotope used may be carbon–11 or nitrogen–13 (in a suitable organic molecules), oxygen–15 (in water), or fluorine–18 (in a glucose analog). These isotopes are short-lived which minimizes the radiation damage to the patient. When a positron is emitted, it is annihilated almost immediately by reaction with an electron and the event emits two γ–ray photons in opposite directions (180° apart). The γ–rays pass through the patient's body and are detected by surrounding scintillation counters. The position of the annihilation must lie on a straight line between the scanners and very precise three dimensional imaging is possible. The uptake of fluorine–18 tagged glucose, for example, indicates energy use within the brain. Figure 62.10 shows the different activities within a normal brain and one affected by Alzheimer's disease.

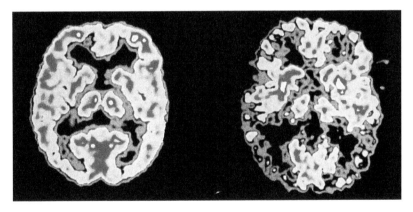

FIGURE 62.10   Brain activity shown by PET scans.
The different colors indicate high activity. The activity shown on the left is that of a normal person. The brain activity on the right is that of a patient with Alzheimer's disease.

Radioisotopes in Food Preservation

Irradiation of food by γ–radiation from sources such as ^{60}Co or ^{137}Cs kills the microorganisms that cause the food to rot and the food therefore has a much longer shelf-life and is safer to eat. For example, the radiation inhibits the growth of mold on strawberries (Figure 62.11). Mild exposure to radiation inhibits crops such as potatoes from sprouting. Of particular significance is the elimination of salmonella from raw eggs, trichinosis from undercooked pork, and illness due to *E. coli.* from undercooked meat. There is no

FIGURE 62.11   Strawberries irradiated by γ-rays are preserved longer.

danger of the food becoming radioactive although some opponents of the procedure believe that the nutritional value of the food may be adversely affected by the radiation. Some fraction of the complex molecules present, such as vitamins, are broken down by the radiation. In addition, the radiation may produce free radicals in the food, just as the radiation does in the human body. These free radicals may react with other molecules present to produce undesirable (toxic or carcinogenic) compounds.

Similar methods are used to sterilize medical supplies such as sutures and bandages.

Radioisotopes in Chemistry

Melvin Calvin received the Nobel Prize in Chemistry in 1961 for this work.

The ability to track a radioactive isotope during a chemical reaction has provided great insight into the mechanisms of reactions and the structures of the products. Of particular significance was the elucidation of the mechanism of photosynthesis by Melvin Calvin and his associates using ^{14}C as the tracer. Starting with ^{14}C-labeled CO_2, the pathway was followed through 13 steps for each of the six molecules of CO_2 incorporated in the glucose molecule.

$$6\ CO_2(g) + 6\ H_2O(l) \rightarrow C_6H_{12}O_6(aq) + 6\ O_2(g)$$

Radioisotopes in Industry

Radioactive isotopes used to follow the path of atoms of the element through a chemical reaction are called **tracers**.

Radioisotopes are used in a variety of applications in industry. The flow of a fluid through a pipe, or the flow of water through geological formations, can be followed by dissolving a compound containing an appropriate radioactive isotope.

A particularly useful application of radioactive isotopes is a technique called **neutron activation analysis (NAA)**. A sample under investigation is bombarded with neutrons. This converts some atoms to radioactive isotopes which are then identified by their characteristic decay patterns. Mechanical engineers use neutron activation to measure wear on the moving parts of engines. The surface subject to wear is irradiated with neutrons. If the surface is steel, for example, some of the iron atoms will be converted to the iron–59 radioisotope. Monitoring the radiation from the isotope over time indicates how much wear the part is experiencing.

Review Questions

1. What is the nuclear binding energy and what is its relationship to the mass defect?

2. Why is it that heavy elements undergo fission whereas lighter elements undergo fusion?

3. What are the requirements for a nuclear fission explosion? What are the requirements for a nuclear fusion explosion?

4. What are the functions of the moderator and the control rods in a nuclear fission reactor?

5. Review the various sources of background radiation.

6. What is the difference between a rad and a rem?

7. Irradiation of food will not make the food radioactive. Why not? If you *wanted* to make the food radioactive, what would you do?

Solutions to Problems

PROBLEM 62.1A

a. *mass on the reactant side*   *mass on the product side*

uranium atom: 238.05079 u   thorium atom: 234.0436 u

                                α–particle: 4.00150 u

we need to add two electrons to the product side:

electrons: $2 \times 0.00054858 = 0.001097$ u

totals: 238.05079 u   238.04620 u

mass loss: 238.05079 u $-$ 238.04620 u = 0.004593 u

$E = mc^2$

$\quad = 0.004593$ u $\times (2.9979 \times 10^8 \text{ ms}^{-1})^2 = 4.128 \times 10^{14} \text{ u m}^2\text{s}^{-2}$

Converting the units into J/nucleus:

$= 4.128 \times 10^{14} \text{ u m}^2\text{s}^{-2} \times \left(\dfrac{1 \text{ kg}}{6.022 \times 10^{26} \text{ u}}\right) \times \left(\dfrac{1 \text{ J}}{1 \text{ kg m}^2\text{s}^{-2}}\right) = 6.854 \times 10^{-13} \text{ J/nucleus}$

Converting the units into MeV/nucleus:

$= 6.854 \times 10^{-13} \text{ J/nucleus} \times \left(\dfrac{1 \text{ eV}}{1.6022 \times 10^{-19} \text{ J}}\right) \times \left(\dfrac{1 \text{ MeV}}{10^6 \text{ eV}}\right) = 4.278 \text{ MeV/nucleus}$

PROBLEM 62.2A

The overall balanced equation is:

$$^{6}_{3}\text{Li} + ^{2}_{1}\text{H} \rightarrow 2\,^{4}_{2}\text{He}$$

mass on the reactant side   *mass on the product side*

lithium–6 atom: 6.015121 u   two helium atoms: 2×4.002600 u

deuterium atom: 2.014000 u

the electrons are balanced:

totals: 8.029121 u   8.005200 u

mass loss: 8.029121 u $-$ 8.005200 u = 0.023921 u

Energy released = 0.023921 u $\times$ 931.47 MeV/u = 22.3 MeV per formula unit of LiD

Answers to Review Questions

1. The nuclear binding energy is the energy theoretically released when all the subatomic particles making up a nucleus come together to form that nucleus. It is the energy that would have to be supplied to break up the nucleus into the individual particles. It is often expressed as the binding energy per nucleon.

   The mass defect is the difference in the mass between the mass of the nucleus and the sum of the masses of the individual nucleons making up that nucleus. It equals the mass lost when the nucleus is formed from its constituent nucleons.

   The relation between the binding energy and the mass defect is given by Einstein's equation $E = mc^2$.

2. The isotope with the strongest binding energy per nucleon is iron–56. Lighter elements have progressively lower binding energies and heavier isotopes also have progressively lower binding energies. This means that the splitting of a heavy nucleus into two smaller nuclei will release energy—corresponding to the increase in the binding energy per nucleon. Similarly, when two light nuclei fuse into a larger nucleus, there is an increase in binding energy and a release of energy (*cf.* Figure 62.1).

3. An explosion requires an accelerating chain reaction. This happens in a nuclear fission reaction because the fission process releases more neutrons than it absorbs. The neutrons that are produced must be captured by other nuclei; so the concentration of the fissile material must be high enough. The size of the sample when the chain reaction becomes self-sustaining is called the critical mass.

   There is no critical mass necessary for a fusion reaction. What is necessary, however, is a sufficiently high temperature so that the kinetic energies of the fusing nuclei can overcome the repulsion between the nuclei.

4. The moderator slows down the neutrons to thermal energies so that they are more readily absorbed by the uranium–235. The control rods are made from neutron absorbers and reduce the rate of fission—they control the reaction. The moderator (for example graphite or water) improves the efficiency of the control rods because slowing down the neutrons makes it easier for the control rod material to absorb them.

5. Sources of background radiation, and the various rem values are:

Cosmic radiation (depends upon altitude)	35 mrem
Medical x–rays	50–75 mrem
The earth	47 mrem
Elements in your body	40 mrem
Inhaled (for example radon)	20–250 mrem
Fallout from nuclear testing	4 mrem
Stone, rock, or concrete house construction	3 mrem
Industrial waste, watches, TV tubes	2 mrem
Nuclear power industry	1 mrem

6. The rad is a measure of the radiation absorbed; one rad is defined as the absorption of 0.010 J per kg of matter. The rem is a unit that takes into account the type of radiation, its energy, and its effect upon biological matter.

7. The radiation used to sterilize food is not sufficiently strong to make radioactive isotopes from the atoms in the food. If the food was placed in a nuclear reactor, irradiation by high energy neutrons would convert some of the atoms within the food into radioactive isotopes. Alternatively the food could be made the target in a particle accelerator.

End-of-Unit Problems

1. Iron–56 is the isotope with the highest binding energy per nucleon. Calculate the mass defect and the binding energy per nucleon from the following data:

   mass of proton = 1.007276 u

   mass of neutron = 1.008665 u

   mass of electron = 0.0005486 u

   atomic mass of iron–56 = 55.9349 u

   Express your answer in units of J nucleon^{-1} and in MeV nucleon^{-1}.

2. Calcium–40 is a stable isotope (two magic numbers). Calculate the mass defect and the binding energy per nucleon from the following data:

   mass of proton = 1.007276 u

   mass of neutron = 1.008665 u

   mass of electron = 0.0005486 u

   atomic mass of calcium–40 = 39.96259 u

   Express your answer in units of J nucleon^{-1} and in MeV nucleon^{-1}.

3. The fission of americium–244 produces iodine–134 and molybdenum–107. Write the equation. How many neutrons are also produced in the fission of each americium–244 nuclide?

4. The fission of a californium–252 nucleus produces one barium–142 nucleus and one molybdenum–106 nucleus. Write the equation. How many neutrons are produced in this reaction?

5. Berkelium–243 was first prepared at the University of California at Berkeley by the bombardment of americium–241 with alpha particles. Write the equation. How many neutrons are emitted in each reaction?

6. Element 111, roentgenium ^{272}Rg, was prepared by the bombardment of bismuth–209 with high energy ^{64}Ni. Write the equation for this reaction. How many neutrons are emitted?

7. When a positron and an electron collide they are annihilated. Two γ–ray photons are emitted in opposite directions. If both γ–ray photons have the same energy, calculate the frequency and wavelength of the γ–radiation. The masses of a positron and electron are both 0.00054858 u.

8. When an excited technicium–99m nucleus decays to the ground state, technicium–99, a γ–ray photon is emitted with an energy equal to 0.143 MeV.

   a. What is the wavelength of this γ–ray photon?

   b. What is the difference in mass between ^{99m}Tc and ^{99}Tc?

9. When a uranium–238 spontaneously emits an α–particle to form thorium–234, energy is released. Given the atomic masses listed below, calculate the amount of energy released for each uranium nucleus undergoing the decay. If the energy, as kinetic energy, is divided equally between the thorium–234 nucleus and the α–particle, calculate the kinetic energy and the speed of the α–particle.

   mass of uranium–238 atom = 238.0508 u

   mass of thorium atom = 234.0436 u

   mass of α–particle = 4.00150 u

   mass of electron = 0.00054858 u

10. When two hydrogen nuclei fuse, a deuterium nucleus and a positron are produced:

    $$\,^1_1H + \,^1_1H \rightarrow \,^2_1H + \,^0_{+1}e$$

    The mass of a hydrogen atom = 1.00782505 u

    The mass of a deuterium atom = 2.0141079 u

    The mass of a positron, and an electron = 0.00054858 u

    Balance the equation to take account of the electrons and calculate energy released in the fusion reaction,

    a. for the formation of one deuterium atom, in MeV

    b. for the fusion of one gram of hydrogen, in kJ.

11. A 10–kiloton fission bomb releases an amount of energy equivalent to 10,000 metric tons of TNT. By convention, one ton of TNT is defined as 4.184×10^9 J (the actual explosive power of TNT is about 60% of this). If the fission of *one* uranium–235 nucleus releases, on average, 2.9×10^{-11} J, what mass of uranium–235 undergoes fission in a 10–kiloton bomb?

12. If the quantity of ^{235}U in a 10–kiloton bomb is 60 kg, what fraction of the ^{235}U undergoes fission when the bomb explodes? Use data derived from the previous question. Why doesn't all the ^{235}U undergo fission in the explosion? How can the bomb be made more efficient, so that more of the ^{235}U is used?

13. If the total release of iodine–131 from the Chernobyl disaster in 1986 was 40,000,000 Ci and the half-life of iodine–131 is 8.04 days, what mass of iodine–131 was released in the accident?

14. A resident of Belarus was exposed to iodine–131 as a result of the accident at Chernobyl. Shortly after the accident, the dose of iodine–131 was measured to be 2.8 mCi. The half-life of iodine–131 is 8.04 days. What was the activity after 6 months? What would the activity due to iodine–131 be now, twenty years after the accident?

Organic Chemistry: Aliphatic and Aromatic Hydrocarbons

63.1   Organic Compounds

It is remarkable that the vast majority of all known compounds contain carbon and that approximately 90% of all new compounds synthesized each year are also compounds of carbon. In most of these compounds carbon is combined with relatively few other elements, especially hydrogen, nitrogen, and oxygen. Compounds of carbon are called **organic compounds** and their study is referred to as **organic chemistry**. The origin of this name was the idea that some vital or living force was necessary to produce them (*cf.* Unit 4.1), in part because the compounds appeared to be more complex than simple inorganic compounds.

Organic chemistry plays an essential role in our everyday life and is a major part of modern chemical industry. Synthetic fibers, polymers, plastics, composite materials, pharmaceuticals, food and food additives, insecticides, and a host of other products are in large part made up of organic compounds. Our most useful sources of energy, heating oil, gasoline, coal, and natural gas, are organic compounds.

The molecules responsible for the existence and maintenance of life as we know it on this planet are organic compounds called **biomolecules**. These molecules are often large and highly complex and the study of their structures, properties, and reactions is called **biochemistry**. We'll review some of these compounds in Unit 66.

Carbon is at the center of the second period in the Periodic Table. It is intermediate in electronegativity and has no strong tendency either to lose or to gain electrons—it forms covalent bonds. It is the ability of carbon to form strong single and multiple bonds with itself—a property called **catenation**—that is the fundamental reason for the huge number of carbon–based compounds. Organic compounds usually incorporate chains or rings of carbon atoms—these chains or rings form the backbone or framework of all organic compounds. Carbon is often referred to as **electron-perfect**—four electrons in four valence orbitals able to form four valence bonds. There are no empty valence orbitals on the carbon atom; nor are there any lone pairs of electrons. As a result, the carbon chains are kinetically unreactive. Carbon also forms a strong covalent bond with hydrogen—their electronegativities are very similar—and it is able to form strong single and double bonds with elements to the right of it in the second period—nitrogen and oxygen.

The geometry of the bonds around a carbon atom depends upon the numbers of σ and π bonds. When carbon forms four σ bonds, the bonds are oriented toward the corners of a tetrahedron. In valence bond theory the hybridization of the carbon valence orbitals is described as sp^3 (*cf.* Unit 22). When carbon forms three σ bonds and one π bond, the bonds are oriented toward the corners of a triangle—the hybridization is sp^2. And when carbon forms two σ bonds and two π bonds, the bonds are oriented linearly and the hybridization is sp.

These bonding characteristics are responsible for the millions of different possible combinations of relatively few elements in organic compounds.

In this unit, we will introduce **hydrocarbons**—a class of compounds containing just hydrogen and carbon. These compounds can be divided into two distinct groups, those that contain one or more benzene rings, called **aromatic** hydrocarbons, and those that don't, called **aliphatic** hydrocarbons. Some hydrocarbons contain both an aromatic part and an aliphatic part.

In 1828 Friedrich Wöhler prepared urea, an organic compound, from ammonium cyanate, an inorganic compound. His experiment put an end to the idea of a 'vital force'.

$NH_4CNO \rightarrow NH_2CONH_2$

Sometimes the framework incorporates other atoms such as oxygen and nitrogen.

The range of organic compounds, and their reactions, is so vast that several separate chemistry courses are devoted entirely to their study.

The word aromatic *has its origin in the usually pleasant smells of various substances from trees and shrubs. It now indicates a class of organic compounds that contain planar rings of atoms with delocalized π bonding.*

The word aliphatic *is derived from the Greek for fat.*

In Unit 64 we will examine and classify some derivatives of the hydrocarbons that have **functional groups**. These are groups of atoms such as carbon, hydrogen, oxygen, nitrogen, and the halogens that give the organic compound characteristic properties. You will quickly come to the conclusion that the number of possibilities is almost endless.

63.2 Aliphatic Hydrocarbons

The simplest organic molecule is methane, CH_4, a carbon atom surrounded by a tetrahedral arrangement of hydrogen atoms (Figure 63.1). Methane, however, is just the first in an almost infinite series of hydrocarbons called **alkanes** that have the general formula C_nH_{2n+2}, where n is an integer. The first ten members of the series are listed in Table 63.1. Ethane, C_2H_6, contains two carbon atoms. The third member, propane, C_3H_8, has a chain of three carbon atoms, and so on.

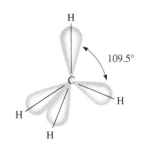

FIGURE 63.1 The structure of the molecule methane. The orbitals on the carbon atom are sp³ hybridized and the molecule is tetrahedral in shape.

Methane is a major constituent of natural gas.

An older name for the alkanes is the *paraffins*.

TABLE 63.1 The first ten members of the alkane hydrocarbons.

Name	Condensed Structural Formula	Molar Mass	Melting Point(°C)	Boiling Point(°C)	Number of Structural Isomers
Methane	CH_4	16	−182	−161	1
Ethane	CH_3CH_3	30	−183	−89	1
Propane	$CH_3CH_2CH_3$	44	−187	−42	1
Butane	$CH_3CH_2CH_2CH_3$	58	−135	−0.5	2
Pentane	$CH_3CH_2CH_2CH_2CH_3$	72	−130	36	3
Hexane	$CH_3CH_2CH_2CH_2CH_2CH_3$	86	−95	68	5
Heptane	$CH_3CH_2CH_2CH_2CH_2CH_2CH_3$	100	−91	98	9
Octane	$CH_3CH_2CH_2CH_2CH_2CH_2CH_2CH_3$	114	−57	125	18
Nonane	$CH_3CH_2CH_2CH_2CH_2CH_2CH_2CH_2CH_3$	128	−54	151	35
Decane	$CH_3CH_2CH_2CH_2CH_2CH_2CH_2CH_2CH_2CH_3$	142	−30	174	75

Alkanes are nonpolar molecules and the attraction between the molecules is due to London forces (*cf.* Unit 28). This intermolecular attraction increases with the size of the molecule and the number of valence electrons. Therefore, as the number of carbon atoms in the molecule increases, the molar mass increases, the size of the molecule increases, and the melting points and boiling points increase. The first four alkanes are gases at room temperature, those with chains of between five and 18 carbon atoms are liquids, and alkanes with more than 18 carbon atoms are viscous liquids and solids (paraffin waxes).

The alkanes listed in Table 63.1 are referred to as straight-chain, or **normal hydrocarbons**—the carbon atoms are linked in a continuous chain. The hybridization on each carbon atom is sp³ and the chain follows a zigzag pattern. Two representations of butane, C_4H_{10}, are shown in Figure 63.2. The ball-and-stick model illustrates the zigzag pattern; the space-filling model provides a more accurate overall picture of the electronic distribution.

Alkanes with 1 to 4 carbon atoms are used as gaseous fuels. An example is the butane canister used for camping stoves. Alkanes with 5 to 7 carbon atoms are used as solvents. Those with 6 to 12 carbons atoms are used in gasoline. Larger alkanes, with 11 to 16 carbon atoms, are used in kerosene for diesel fuel and jet fuel. Alkanes with 14 to 18 carbon atoms are used as domestic heating oil. Those with 15 to 24 carbon atoms are used as lubricating oils and greases. Those with 23 to 35 carbon atoms are paraffin waxes and those with more than 35 carbon atoms are components of asphalt.

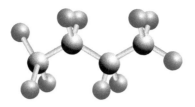 

FIGURE 63.2 **Two representations of the butane molecule C$_4$H$_{10}$.**
The ball-and-stick model illustrates the sp^3 hybridization at each carbon atom, the 109.5°
angle between the bonds, and the overall zigzag pattern of the carbon chain. The space-filling
model illustrates the overall shape of the molecule.

If the carbon atoms are not connected in a straight chain, then the alkane is
referred to as a **branched-chain alkane**. Butane exists as a straight-chain molecule
and as a branched chain molecule (Figure 63.3). The two molecules are called structural isomers (*cf.* Unit 59). Structural isomerism occurs when the atoms in molecules
having the same formula are connected to each other in different ways. Because the
two isomers of butane have different structures, their physical properties are slightly
different. For example, the boiling point of butane (–0.5°C) is higher than the boiling point of isobutane (–12°C), indicating a slightly stronger intermolecular attraction between the straight-chain molecules. The number of possible structural isomers
increases dramatically as the number of carbon atoms in the alkane increases. Decane,
C$_{10}$H$_{22}$, with only ten carbon atoms, has 75 different structural isomers. The alkane
eicosane, C$_{20}$H$_{42}$, has 366,319 structural isomers!

> The straight chain molecules can
> line up and get closer together
> than the branched molecules.

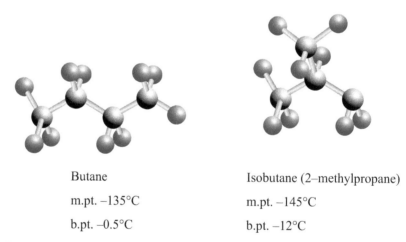

Butane

m.pt. –135°C

b.pt. –0.5°C

Isobutane (2–methylpropane)

m.pt. –145°C

b.pt. –12°C

FIGURE 63.3 The two structural isomers of butane.

EXAMPLE 63.1 STRUCTURAL ISOMERS OF THE ALKANES

Determine the number of possible structural isomers of pentane, C$_5$H$_{12}$, and draw their structures.

UNDERSTAND THE QUESTION

The simplest structure for an alkane involves a linear chain of carbon atoms—in this case a chain of five carbon
atoms. Structural isomers can be derived by reducing the length of the longest chain and linking remaining carbon
atoms to other carbon atoms within the chain. The number of bonds around each carbon atom is always four but these
may be bonds to either H atoms or C atoms.

PLAN THE SOLUTION

Start with the carbon skeleton of the straight-chain isomer. Then reduce the length of the chain by one and attach the fifth carbon atom to one of the carbon atoms in the middle of the chain. Add hydrogen atoms to complete the bonding around each carbon atom. Then reduce the length of the chain by one again and attach the two remaining carbon atoms to carbon atoms in the middle of the chain. Again complete the bonding around each carbon atom by adding H atoms. Continue this process as long as necessary.

SOLVE THE PROBLEM

The straight-chain isomer has the carbon skeleton C—C—C—C—C. Completing the bonding around each carbon by adding H atoms produces the structure:

$$\begin{array}{ccccc} H & H & H & H & H \\ | & | & | & | & | \\ H-C-C-C-C-C-H \\ | & | & | & | & | \\ H & H & H & H & H \end{array}$$

The length of the chain is now reduced to four, and the fifth carbon atom is attached to one of the carbon atoms in the middle of the chain:

$$\begin{array}{c} C \\ | \\ C-C-C-C \end{array}$$

Note that the structures below are all equivalent to this one:

$$\begin{array}{ccc} C & & \\ | & & \\ C-C-C-C & C-C-C-C & C-C-C-C \\ & | & | \\ & C & C \end{array}$$

The length of the chain is now reduced to three and the two remaining carbon atoms are attached to the carbon atom in the middle of the chain:

$$\begin{array}{c} C \\ | \\ C-C-C \\ | \\ C \end{array}$$

These are the only possible arrangements of the five carbon atoms of pentane. The space-filling models of the three structural isomers (showing the attached hydrogen atoms) are illustrated below:

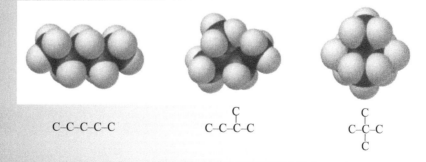

$$C-C-C-C-C \qquad\qquad \begin{array}{c} C \\ | \\ C-C-C-C \end{array} \qquad\qquad \begin{array}{c} C \\ | \\ C-C-C \\ | \\ C \end{array}$$

PROBLEM 63.1A

Decane, $C_{10}H_{22}$, has 75 structural isomers. Of these, some contain a chain of nine carbon atoms with a carbon atom attached to one of the carbon atoms between the ends of the chain of nine. How many of the 75 isomers have a chain of nine carbon atoms?

PROBLEM 63.1B

Determine the number of possible structural isomers of hexane, C_6H_{14}, and draw their structures.

63.3 Naming Alkanes

There are so many isomers of so many alkanes that a systematic method of naming these hydrocarbons is essential. The rules are summarized below:

- The alkanes have names ending in –ane.
- The length of the longest carbon chain is denoted by a prefix derived from Latin numbers: penta–, hexa–, hepta–, octa–, nona–, deca–, and so on. The first four alkanes have the long-established common names: methane, ethane, propane, and butane.
- The substituents on the longest chain are identified by name and the position on the chain. The name of the substituent, called an **alkyl group**, is derived from the name of the alkane. Note how the ending –ane is replaced by the ending –yl. For example, a CH_3– substituent is called a methyl group because the parent hydrocarbon is methane. Similarly, a CH_3CH_2– substituent is called an ethyl group because the parent alkane is ethane, and so on. Some common hydrocarbon substituents are listed in Table 63.2.
- The position of the substituent is indicated by numbering the carbon atoms in the longest chain, starting at the end nearest to a substituent. A hyphen is used to separate the number from the name of the substituent. Commas are used to separate numbers.
- When more than one substituent is present, they are listed in alphabetical order.
- Prefixes such as *di*–(two), *tri*–(three), *tetra*–(four), *penta*–(five), etc. are used to indicate the number of a particular substituent.

TABLE 63.2 Common hydrocarbon substituents (alkyl groups).

Name	Condensed Structural Formula		
Methyl	CH_3–		
Ethyl	CH_3CH_2–		
Propyl	$CH_3CH_2CH_2$–		
Isopropyl	$CH_3\overset{|}{C}HCH_3$	or	$(CH_3)_2CH$–
Butyl	$CH_3CH_2CH_2CH_2$–		
sec-Butyl	$CH_3\overset{|}{C}HCH_2CH_3$		
tert-Butyl	$CH_3\overset{|}{\underset{\underset{CH_3}{|}}{C}}HCH_3$	or	$(CH_3)_3C$

EXAMPLE 63.2 NAMING ALKANES

What are the systematic names for the following alkanes?

a.
$$CH_3-\overset{\overset{\displaystyle CH_3}{|}}{\underset{\underset{\displaystyle CH_3}{|}}{C}}-CH_2-CH_3$$

b.
$$CH_3-\overset{\overset{\displaystyle CH_3}{|}}{C}H-\overset{\overset{\displaystyle |}{|}}{C}H-CH_3$$
$$\qquad\qquad CH_2-CH_3$$

UNDERSTAND THE QUESTION

Alkanes have systematic names based upon the set of logical rules just described. The name of the parent alkane is based upon the longest chain in the structure. Substituents on this longest chain are identified by name and position.

PLAN THE SOLUTION

Find the longest chain of carbon atoms. Note that the longest chain need not be written in a straight line in the structural formula. Identify the substituents and their positions on the chain. Name the compound according to the set of rules.

SOLVE THE PROBLEM

a.

$$CH_3-\underset{\underset{CH_3}{|}}{\overset{\overset{CH_3}{|}}{C}}-CH_2-CH_3$$

The longest chain is indicated in gray. It consists of four carbon atoms and the parent alkane is a butane. The two substituents are both methyl groups and therefore the compound is one of the isomers of hexane, a dimethylbutane. The longest chain is numbered from the end that gives the substituents the lowest number. The compound is 2,2–dimethylbutane.

b.

$$CH_3-\underset{2}{\overset{\overset{CH_3}{|}}{CH}}-\underset{\underset{CH_2-CH_3}{|}}{\overset{3}{CH}}-CH_3$$

The longest chain is indicated in gray. It consists of five carbon atoms and is therefore a pentane—not a butane as you might initially think. The two substituents are again both methyl groups and therefore the compound is a dimethylpentane. The longest chain is numbered from the end that gives the substituents the lowest number. The compound is 2,3–dimethylpentane, one of the structural isomers of heptane.

PROBLEM 63.2A

a. What is the systematic name for the alkane:

$$CH_3-\underset{\underset{CH_3}{|}}{\overset{\overset{CH_2}{|}}{C}}-CH_2-\underset{\underset{CH_2-CH_3}{|}}{CH}-CH_3$$

b. Draw the structure of 3–isopropyl–2,3–dimethylhexane.

PROBLEM 63.2B

a. An alkane was incorrectly named as 2–ethyl–2–methylpropane. What is its correct name?

b. What is the systematic name for the isomer of decane with the structure:

$$CH_3-\underset{\underset{CH_2}{|}}{\overset{\overset{CH_2-CH_3}{|}}{CH}}-CH-CH_2-CH_3$$
$$\underset{CH_2-CH_3}{}$$

The prefix iso– is a little unusual in that the *i* counts in the alphabetical ordering of the substituents. No attention is paid to other prefixes such as *sec*– and *tert*–, or the prefixes di–, tri–, etc. when the substituents are ordered.

63.4 Cycloalkanes

In **cycloalkanes**, the carbon atoms form a ring. The smallest possible ring is cyclopropane, C_3H_6, although in this ring the bond angles between the C—C bonds are much less (60°) than the desired angle (109.5°) and as a result the molecule is very strained—the bonds are weaker than normal and the ring is readily broken. The bonds in the next member of the series, cyclobutane C_4H_8, are also strained (90°) but cyclopentane, C_5H_{10}, in comparison, is quite stable. The three-membered and four-membered rings are approximately planar, and the five-membered ring is slightly bent (Figure 63.4).

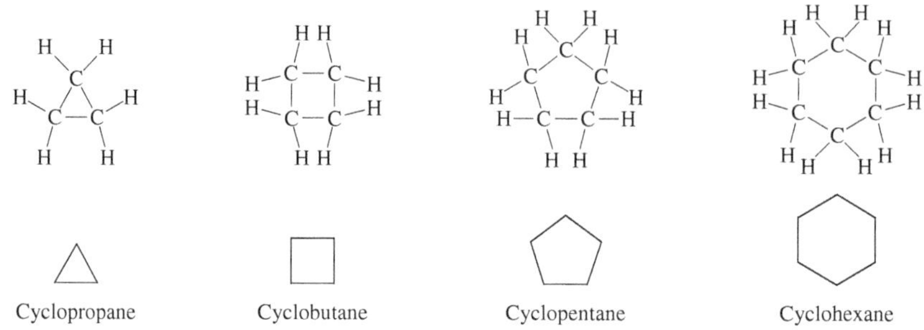

FIGURE 63.4 The structures of the cycloalkanes.

In cyclohexane, C_6H_{12}, the bond angles are very close to the ideal tetrahedral angle. To achieve this, the cyclohexane ring is puckered (nonplanar) and can exist in two forms (Figure 63.5). The chair form is the more stable form and at room temperature more than 99% of cyclohexane exists in this form. The alternative form is the boat form. Like all alkanes, the cyclohexane molecule is very flexible due to ready rotation about the single C—C bonds and the molecule converts easily between one chair form and another through a boat form.

> The chair and boat forms are *not* isomers—they are different conformations of the same molecule.

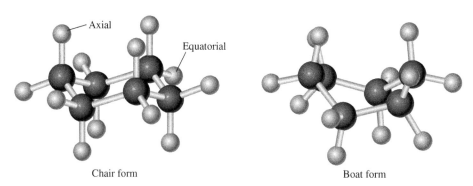

FIGURE 63.5 The flexibility of cyclohexane.
One chair form can change into another chair form quite easily through the boat form.

The naming of cycloalkanes with alkyl substituents follows the same rules as the ordinary alkanes. The name of the cycloalkane is used as the basis of the name. The substituents are identified by name and their positions on the ring. The substituents are named in alphabetical order and the numbering is chosen to give the second substituent the lower number. For example, the cycloalkane

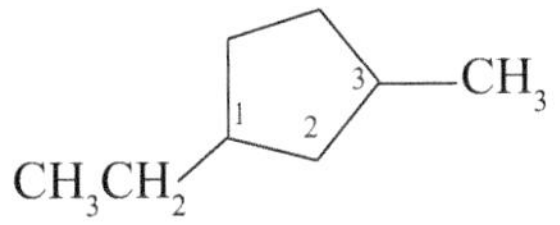

CH_3CH_2 ⟨ring⟩ —CH_3 is called 1–ethyl–3–methycyclopentane.

Organic chemists often extend this way of representing structures to all organic compounds, especially large complicated molecules. For small molecules it isn't necessary. Methane, for example would be represented by a single dot and ethane with a single line.

The cyclic hydrocarbons are often represented by line structures such as those shown in Figure 63.4. The carbon and hydrogen atoms are not shown explicitly. A carbon atom is present at every junction of the lines and the appropriate number of hydrogen atoms required to give each carbon atom four bonds are understood to be present.

EXAMPLE 63.3   NAMING CYCLOALKANES

Identify the ring present in the following cycloalkanes and name the compounds systematically.

a.
⟨hexagon ring⟩ —CH_3
CH_3CH_2

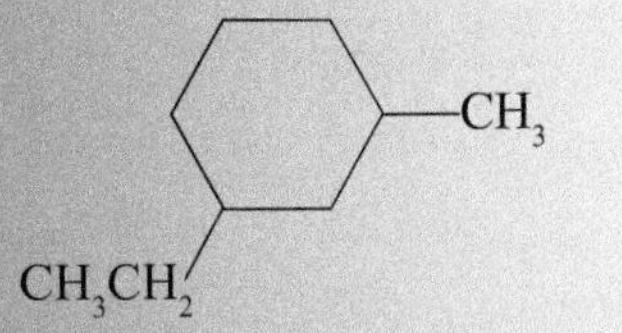

b.
⟨square ring⟩ —CH_3
CH_3

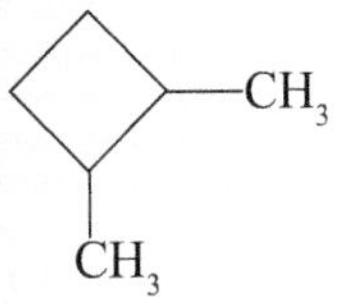

UNDERSTAND THE QUESTION

The cycloalkane ring is the basis of the name. The substituents are named alphabetically and the position on the ring is indicated by the appropriate number.

PLAN THE SOLUTION

Identify the ring. Name the substituents and sort alphabetically. Number them so that the second substituent has the lower possible number.

SOLVE THE PROBLEM

a.
⟨hexagon ring, positions 1, 2, 3⟩ —CH_3
CH_3CH_2

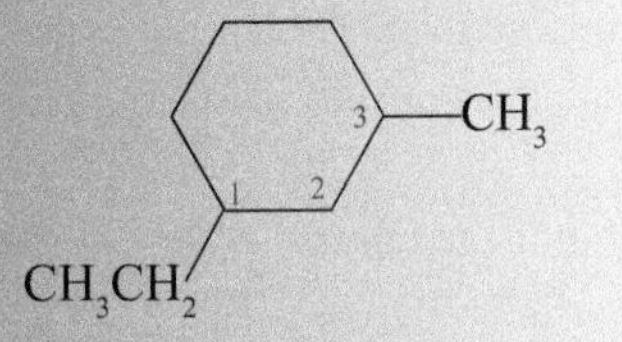

1–ethyl–3–methylcyclohexane

b.
⟨square ring, positions 1, 2⟩ —CH_3
CH_3

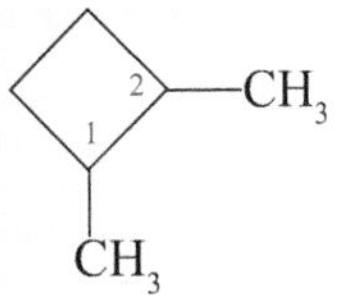

1,2–dimethylcyclobutane

PROBLEM 63.3A

What is the systematic name for the cycloalkane:

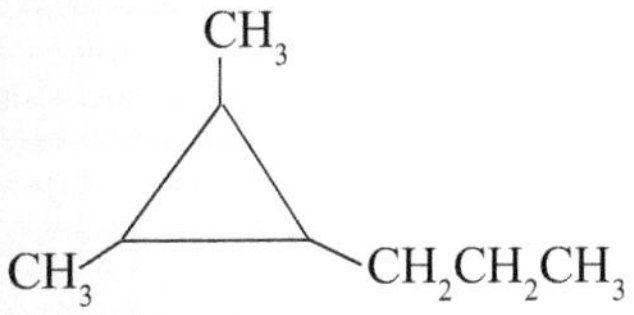

CH_3
⟨triangle ring⟩
CH_3 $CH_2CH_2CH_3$

PROBLEM 63.3B

Draw the structure of 1–isopropyl–2–methylcyclopentane.

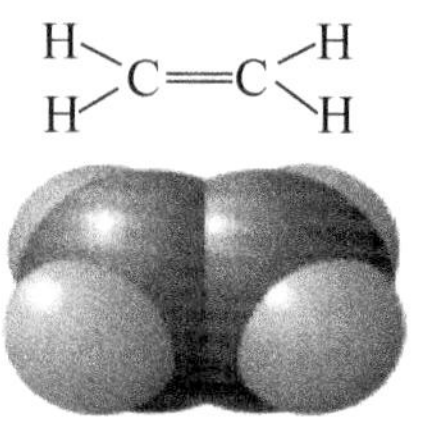

FIGURE 63.6 The structure of the ethylene molecule showing the double bond between the two carbon atoms.

An older name for an alkene is *olefin*.

Vegetable oils are fatty acid derivatives of glycerol (*cf.* Unit 64).

63.5 Alkenes

Alkenes, unlike the alkanes, are hydrocarbons that have one or more C=C double bonds. The first member of the alkene series is ethene, commonly called ethylene, with the molecular formula C_2H_4 (Figure 63.6). The next members of the series are propene (often called propylene), butene, pentene, etc. The general formula of the alkenes is C_nH_{2n} where n is an integer. The alkenes are named in a similar manner to the alkanes, but with the ending –ene instead of –ane (Table 63.3). Alkenes are prepared industrially by the high temperature catalytic dehydrogenation of alkanes derived from petroleum.

TABLE 63.3 The first seven members of the alkenes.

Name	Condensed Structural Formula	Molar Mass	Melting Point (°C)	Boiling Point (°C)
Ethene	$CH_2=CH_2$	28	−169	−104
Propene	$CH_3CH=CH_2$	42	−185	−48
1–Butene	$CH_3CH_2CH=CH_2$	56	−185	−6
1–Pentene	$CH_3CH_2CH_2CH=CH_2$	70	−165	30
1–Hexene	$CH_3CH_2CH_2CH_2CH=CH_2$	84	−139	64
1–Heptene	$CH_3CH_2CH_2CH_2CH_2CH=CH_2$	98	−119	93
1–Octene	$CH_3CH_2CH_2CH_2CH_2CH_2CH=CH_2$	112	−102	121

Alkenes are **unsaturated**. This means that they have fewer hydrogen atoms than the alkane with the same number of carbon atoms. For example, unsaturated vegetable oils contain one or more C=C double bonds. When such oils are hydrogenated, two hydrogen atoms are added across a double bond and the double bond becomes a single bond. The molecule is then at least partially, and perhaps completely, saturated. Hydrogenation of the double bonds converts the oil to a saturated fat.

When there are four or more carbon atoms in the carbon chain, it is possible to draw structures with the double bond in different positions. For example, the double bond in butene can be at the end of the chain or in the middle of the chain (Figure 63.7).

The double bond can be at the end of the chain:

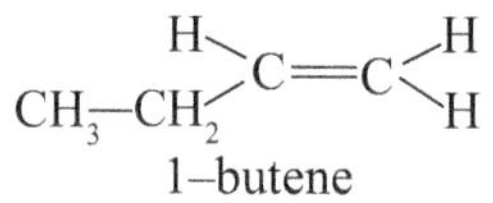

1–butene

or in the middle of the chain:

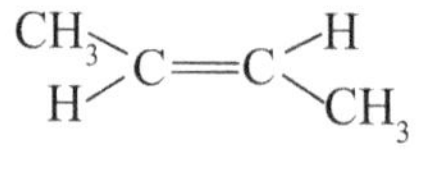

2–butene

FIGURE 63.7 Structural isomers of butene.

The position of the double bond is indicated by a number preceding the root name for the alkene and the number should be the lowest possible. If the double bond is at the center of the chain, the numbering starts from the end nearer to any substituent. The numbering and naming of alkyl substituents follow the same rules as for the alkanes.

The hybridization of the valence orbitals on the carbon atoms participating in the double bond is sp^2 and the arrangement of bonds around the carbon atoms is trigonal planar. The p orbital not used in the sp^2 hybridization is perpendicular to the trigonal plane and is used to make the π component of the double bond.

Rotation around double bonds is inhibited by the presence of this π bond (Figure 63.8) because rotation around the bond would require that the π bond be broken.

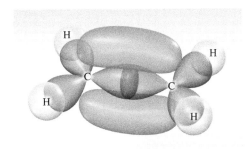

FIGURE 63.8   The π bond in ethylene.
Rotation around double bonds is inhibited by this π bond because rotation around the bond requires that the π bond be broken.

This barrier to rotation—about 240 kJ mol^{-1}—gives rise to the possibility of geometrical isomerism. For example, 2–butene can exist in both *cis–* and *trans–* forms (Figure 63.9). Again, the slightly different structures result in slightly different physical properties. For example, the *cis–*2–butene boils at 4°C whereas the *trans–*2–butene boils at 0.9°C.

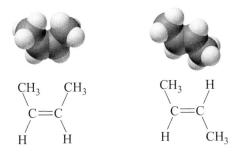

FIGURE 63.9   The *cis–* and *trans–* geometrical isomers of 2-butene.
In the *cis–* isomer, the two identical groups, two hydrogen atoms or two methyl groups, lie on the same side of the double bond. In the *trans–* isomer, the identical groups lie on opposite sides.

EXAMPLE 63.4 STRUCTURAL AND GEOMETRICAL ISOMERS OF ALKENES AND THEIR SYSTEMATIC NAMES

Draw the structural and geometrical isomers of pentene and name them.

UNDERSTAND THE QUESTION

Pentene is an alkene—it has a C=C double bond. The double bond can be situated at any point along the carbon chain. Structural isomerism similar that previously described for the alkanes is also possible. Finally, geometrical cis–trans isomerism about the double bond is sometimes possible.

PLAN THE SOLUTION

Start with the straight-chain isomers and determine the number of positions possible for the double bond. Then determine if geometrical isomerism is possible. Reduce the length of the chain by one and again determine the number of positions possible for the double bond. Attach the fifth carbon atom, as a methyl group, to one of the carbon atoms in the middle of the chain. Continue this process as long as necessary.

SOLVE THE PROBLEM

Straight-chain isomers: 1–pentene:

CH_2=CH—CH_2—CH_2—CH_3 no geometrical isomers

2–pentene:

CH_3—CH=CH—CH_2—CH_3 one *cis*– and one *trans*–

Branched-chain isomers: 2-methyl–1–butene:

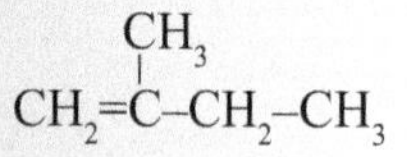

$$CH_2=\overset{\overset{\displaystyle CH_3}{|}}{C}-CH_2-CH_3$$

no geometrical isomers

> If one of the carbon atoms participating in the double bond has two identical groups attached, then *cis-trans* isomerism is impossible.

3–methyl–1–butene:

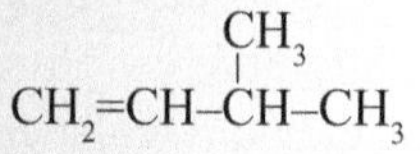

$$CH_2=CH-\overset{\overset{\displaystyle CH_3}{|}}{C}H-CH_3$$

no geometrical isomers

2–methyl–2–butene:

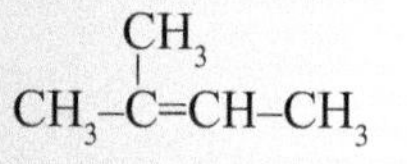

$$CH_3-\overset{\overset{\displaystyle CH_3}{|}}{C}=CH-CH_3$$

no geometrical isomers

The length of the longest chain cannot be reduced further and still incorporate a double bond (the central C atom would have four substituents).

PROBLEM 63.4A

Which of the following alkenes exhibit cis–trans isomerism?

a. 2,3–dimethyl–2–butene

b. 2–hexene

c. 1–heptene

d. propene

PROBLEM 63.4B

Draw the structures of the geometrical isomers of 3,4–dimethyl–3–hexene.

allene   butadiene

FIGURE 63.10 Allene and butadiene.
Both molecules have two double bonds. In allene the double bonds are in planes at right angles to each other. In butadiene the two double bonds point in the same direction—the molecule is planar.

It is possible to have more than one double bond in the carbon chain of an alkene. Two examples are allene and 1,3–butadiene (Figure 63.10).

The remaining type of isomerism discussed in Unit 59 was stereoisomerism. Stereoisomerism is possible in hydrocarbons when one of the carbon atoms in the molecule has four different alkyl groups attached to it. In general, stereoisomerism will occur in organic compounds when any four different groups are attached to a single carbon atom. Such a carbon atom is called an **asymmetric carbon atom** and its presence confers optical activity upon the molecule.

63.6 Alkynes

Alkynes are hydrocarbons that have a C≡C triple bond. The most familiar member of the series is ethyne, commonly called acetylene, with the molecular formula C_2H_2 (Figure 63.11). The following members of the series are propyne, butyne, pentyne, etc. and the general formula is C_nH_{2n-2} where n is an integer. The alkynes are named in a similar manner to the alkanes and alkenes, but with the ending –yne instead of –ane or –ene. Again, when there are four or more carbon atoms in the chain, it is possible to draw structures with the triple bond in different positions. However, unlike in the alkenes, *cis–trans* isomers do not exist because of the linear geometry (sp hybridization) about the carbon atoms involved in the triple bond.

$$H—C≡C—H$$

FIGURE 63.11 The structure of acetylene.

63.7 Reactions of the Alkanes, Alkenes, and Alkynes

The alkanes are generally inert compounds and do not readily react with acids, bases, most oxidizing and reducing agents, and other common reagents. The C—C and C—H bonds are relatively strong (348 and 412 kJ mol^{-1} respectively) and there is usually no thermodynamic advantage in breaking them and forming other bonds. The exception is the combustion of alkanes to form carbon dioxide and water. In this case, stronger C=O and O—H bonds (743 and 360 kJ mol^{-1} respectively) are formed and the reaction is exothermic. Alkanes are commonly used as fuels—two familiar examples are natural gas and gasoline. Alkanes also react with halogens in free-radical **substitution reactions**. For example, a mixture of chlorine and methane will react under the influence of UV radiation or heat to produce chloromethane, CH_3Cl, dichloromethane, CH_2Cl_2, chloroform $CHCl_3$, and carbon tetrachloride CCl_4. The UV radiation splits the chlorine molecule to form highly reactive chlorine atoms (free radicals) that react with the alkane molecules to eventually replace all the hydrogen atoms.

Free-radical chain reactions such as this are described in Unit 37.

The chemistry of the alkenes and alkynes is predominated by **addition reactions**. In these reactions, reagents are added across the double and triple bonds. The reactant forms two σ bonds to the two carbon atoms involved in the double bond and the double bond is converted to a single bond. Examples include the addition of hydrogen in the process called **hydrogenation** already mentioned, the acid-catalyzed addition of water to produce alcohols, the addition of chlorine to produce dichloro–derivatives, and the addition of hydrogen chloride to produce chloro–derivatives:

The acid-catalyzed addition of water to ethylene to produce ethanol is performed on a huge scale. Much of the ethanol produced is added to gasoline to be used as fuel for automobiles.

$$H_2C{=}CH_2 + H_2 \rightarrow CH_3{-}CH_3 \qquad \text{(platinum or palladium catalyst)}$$

$$H_2C{=}CH_2 + H_2O \rightarrow CH_3{-}CH_2OH \qquad \text{(H}_2\text{SO}_4 \text{ catalyst)}$$

$$H_2C{=}CH_2 + Cl_2 \rightarrow CH_2Cl{-}CH_2Cl$$

$$H_2C{=}CH_2 + HCl \rightarrow CH_3{-}CH_2Cl$$

If the alkene is unsymmetrical (for example, propene), the addition of a hydrogen halide or other unsymmetrical reactant leads to the product in which the positive end of the molecule, usually hydrogen, adds to the carbon atom of the alkene which already has the most hydrogens attached:

$$CH_3CH{=}CH_2 + HCl \rightarrow CH_3{-}CHCl{-}CH_3$$

This rule is known as Markovnikov's rule.

The same rule applies to the addition of similar molecules to the alkynes:

$$CH_3C{\equiv}CH + 2\,HBr \rightarrow CH_3{-}CBr{=}CH_2 + HBr \rightarrow CH_3{-}CBr_2{-}CH_3$$

63.8 Aromatic Hydrocarbons

Aromatic compounds, in general called **arenes**, contain planar rings of atoms with delocalized π bonding. The prototypical aromatic compound is benzene and we will restrict our attention to those compounds that contain one or more benzene rings.

Although the benzene ring is often represented by one of the two Lewis structures illustrated in Figure 63.12, all the bonds in the ring are identical in length and strength. To emphasize the equivalence of all C—C bonds in the ring, the benzene molecule is often drawn as a hexagonal ring with a circle inside.

These structures for benzene are often called Kekulé structures, after August Kekulé who first proposed this cyclic structure for benzene in 1865.

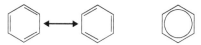

FIGURE 63.12   Representations of the benzene ring.

The molecular bonding in benzene is described in Unit 23.

The six p_π orbitals of the carbon atoms perpendicular to the plane of the ring overlap to form six π molecular orbitals—three bonding and three antibonding. The six electrons occupy the three bonding orbitals. The electrons in these three molecular orbitals are delocalized. They are shared by all six carbon atoms in the ring. The lowest energy π molecular orbital is illustrated in Figure 63.13.

In a Lewis approach to the bonding in benzene, the true structure is considered to be a resonance hybrid of the two Kekulé structures—hence the **resonance energy**. In molecular orbital theory, the concept of resonance is unnecessary and a better name would be **delocalization energy**.

The delocalization of the π electrons confers particular stability to the benzene ring—often referred to as the **resonance energy**. The molecule, for example, does not undergo the typical addition reactions of alkenes. Reaction with bromine in the presence of an FeBr$_3$ catalyst produces bromobenzene, C_6H_5Br, in which a bromine atom replaces a hydrogen atom attached to the ring. Similarly, nitration by nitric acid in

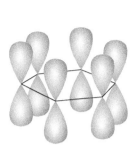 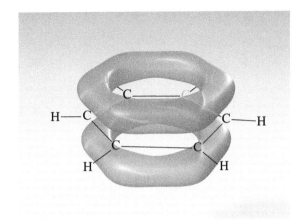

FIGURE 63.13 **The six p_π orbitals of the carbon atoms perpendicular to the plane of the ring overlap to form six π molecular orbitals.**
The six electrons occupy the three bonding orbitals. The electrons in these three molecular orbitals are delocalized. The lowest energy π molecular orbital is illustrated—there are five other orbitals higher in energy.

the presence of sulfuric acid produces nitrobenzene, $C_6H_5NO_2$ (Figure 63.14). In both reactions, the integrity of the delocalized bonding within the benzene ring is preserved.

Substituents on a benzene ring often direct the substitution to a particular position on the ring. For example, the nitration of phenol occurs much more easily than the nitration of benzene and the nitration always occurs at the *ortho–* and *para–* sites. The –OH group of the phenol partially donates electrons into the delocalized π system of the ring, in particular increasing the electron density at the *ortho–* and *para–* sites, making those sites more susceptible to attack. Other substituents on a benzene ring withdraw electron density from the delocalized π system and make the benzene less susceptible to attack. A carboxylic acid functional group is an example. Nitration of benzoic acid occurs much more slowly than the nitration of benzene and results in substitution predominantly at the *meta–* position.

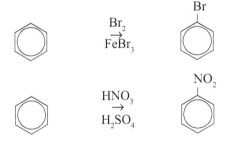

FIGURE 63.14 **Reactions of benzene.**
In both reactions the delocalization of π electrons in the benzene ring remains intact.

Other aromatic hydrocarbons include toluene, the xylenes, naphthalene, anthracene, and phenanthrene (Figure 63.15). The xylenes (dimethylbenzenes) occur as three different structural isomers. The isomers differ in the positions of the methyl substituents on the benzene ring. An older convention used to name the different isomers of disubstituted benzenes is by the use of the prefixes ortho (*o–*), meta (*m–*), and para

Coal, and coal tar, is a rich source of aromatic hydrocarbons.

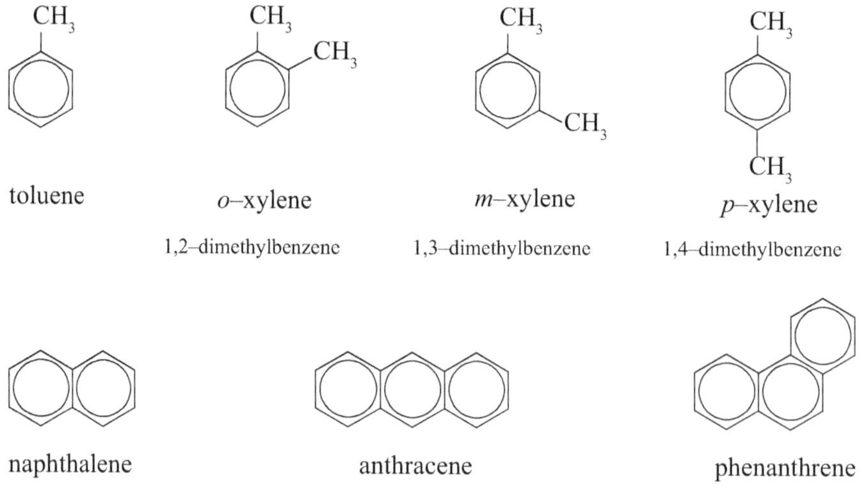

CH₃ structures:

toluene

o–xylene
1,2–dimethylbenzene

m–xylene
1,3–dimethylbenzene

p–xylene
1,4–dimethylbenzene

naphthalene   anthracene   phenanthrene

FIGURE 63.15   Other aromatic hydrocarbons.

(*p*–). They can be named more systematically by the numbers of the carbon atoms to which the substituents are attached as shown in Figure 63.15.

In most cases, simple compounds involving a benzene ring are named as derivatives of benzene. Examples are bromobenzene and nitrobenzene illustrated in Figure 63.14. However, in more complicated molecules, it is often easier to name the benzene ring as a substituent on the larger molecule. In this case benzene as a substituent is called a phenyl group. For example, the compound

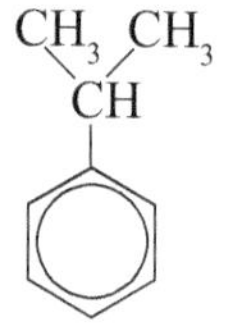

could be called 2–phenylpropane or isopropylbenzene.

Review Questions

1. Review the reasons why there are so many compounds of carbon compared to other nonmetals.

2. Describe the attractive forces between alkane molecules and explain why the melting points and boiling points increase as the molar mass of the alkane increases.

3. Three series of hydrocarbons are the alkanes, the alkenes, and the alkynes. What distinguishes one from another? Which series are classified as unsaturated?

4. Describe the difference between structural and geometrical isomerism. Of the alkanes, alkenes, and alkynes, only the alkenes exhibit *cis–trans* isomerism. Why?

5. Review the rules for naming the alkanes, alkenes, and alkynes.

6. What distinguishes a cyclic hydrocarbon such as cyclohexane from a cyclic hydrocarbon such as benzene?

Solutions to Problems

PROBLEM 63.1A

There are only four structural isomers of decane that include a straight chain of nine carbon atoms. The methyl group can be placed on the second, third, fourth, or fifth (center) carbon atom of the chain.

PROBLEM 63.2A

a. There are 7 carbon atoms in the longest chain.

3,3,5–trimethylheptane.

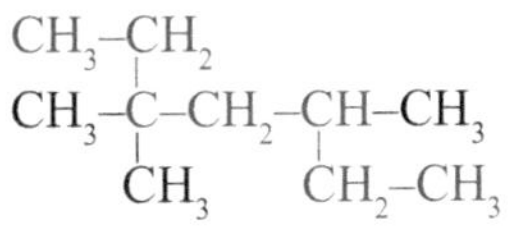

$$CH_3-C-CH_2-CH-CH_3$$

with CH_3-CH_2 above and CH_3 and CH_2-CH_3 below

b. 3–isopropyl–2,3–dimethylhexane:

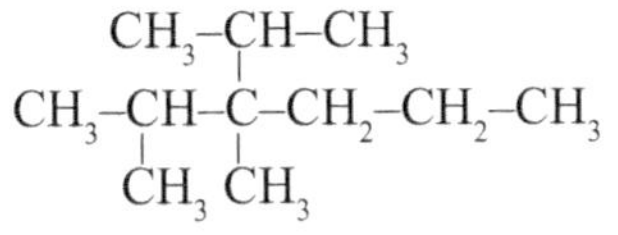

$$CH_3-CH-C-CH_2-CH_2-CH_3$$

with $CH_3-CH-CH_3$ above and CH_3 CH_3 below

PROBLEM 63.3A

1,2–dimethyl–3–propylcyclopropane.

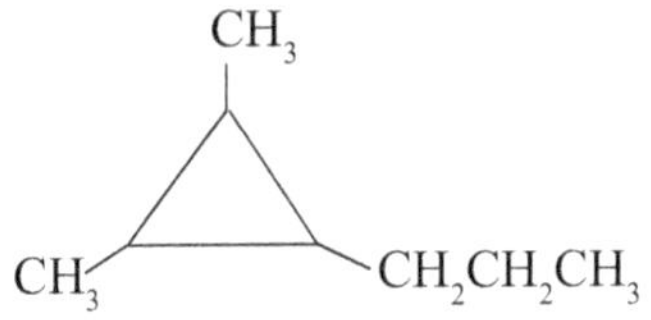

CH_3 at top, CH_3 at lower left, $CH_2CH_2CH_3$ at lower right on a cyclopropane ring.

PROBLEM 63.4A

Cis–trans isomerism can only exist when the two groups attached to both carbon atoms involved in the double bond are different from one another.

a. 2,3–dimethyl–2–butene   no geometrical isomers

same groups

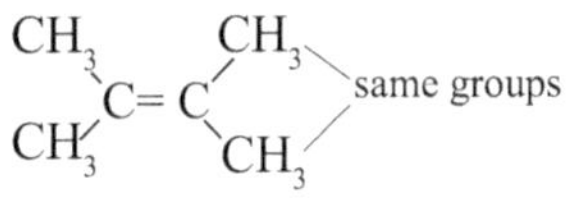

b. 2–hexene   *cis–* and *trans–* isomers

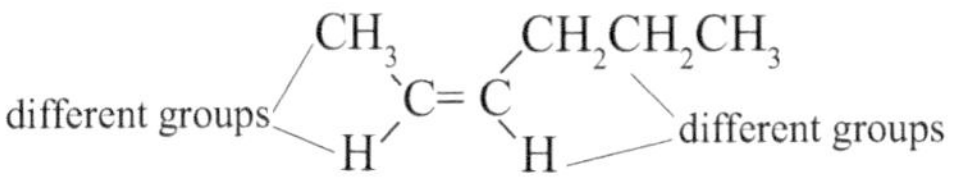

different groups

c. 1–heptene   no geometrical isomers

same groups

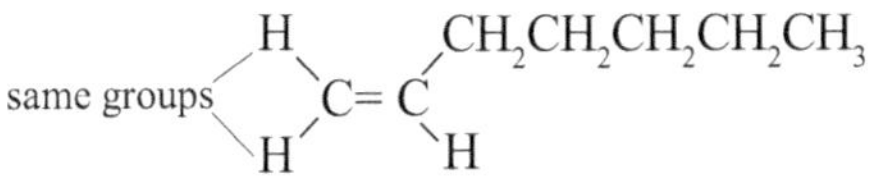

d. propene   no geometrical isomers

same groups

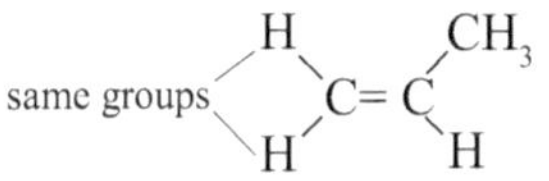

Answers to Review Questions

1. Carbon is intermediate in electronegativity and in the vast majority of its compounds it forms covalent bonds. The reason for the huge number of carbon-based compounds is the ability of carbon to form strong covalent bonds with itself—a property called **catenation**. Chains or rings of carbon atoms form the backbone or framework of all organic compounds.

2. Alkanes are nonpolar molecules and the attraction between the molecules is due to London forces. This intermolecular attraction increases with the size of the molecule and the number of valence electrons. Therefore, as the molar mass of the alkane increases, the size of the molecule increases, and the melting points and boiling points increase.

3. The three series of hydrocarbons, alkanes, alkenes, and alkynes, differ in the presence, or absence, of multiple C–C bonds. Alkanes are saturated; they contain no multiple bonds. Alkenes contain one or more double bonds; they are unsaturated. Alkynes contain triple bonds and are also unsaturated. An unsaturated hydrocarbon is a hydrocarbon with fewer hydrogen atoms than the alkane with the same number of carbon atoms.

4. Structural isomerism occurs when the atoms in molecules having the same formula are connected to each other in different ways. Geometrical isomerism occurs when the atoms of a molecule are connected in the same way but have different arrangements in space (the geometry is different). Alkanes, and alkyl substituents on alkenes and alkynes exhibit structural isomerism. Alkenes and alkynes exhibit structural isomerism in the position of the double or triple bonds in the carbon chain. Only alkenes exhibit

geometrical isomerism (about the double bond). Alkynes cannot exhibit geometrical isomerism because the arrangement about the triple bond is linear.

5. The hundreds of isomers of alkanes, alkenes, and alkynes require a systematic method of nomenclature. There is a set of rules that aims to make the naming of hydrocarbons as straightforward as possible. The root name for the hydrocarbon is based upon the longest chain. The positions of any double or triple bonds are denoted by their positions along the chain. Alkyl substituents on the longest chain are identified by name, number, and their positions on the chain.

6. Cyclic hydrocarbons such as benzene are aromatic. They have delocalized systems of π electrons and are particularly stable. In most reactions, the aromatic portion of the molecule remains intact. Cyclic hydrocarbons such as cyclohexane and cyclohexene are simply alkanes and alkenes in which the two ends of the molecule are joined. As such, they have chemical properties very similar to those of the open-chain alkanes and alkenes.

End-of-Unit Problems

1. Heptane has 9 structural isomers. Of these, some have a chain of six carbon atoms. Draw the carbon skeletons of these isomers.

2. Heptane has 9 structural isomers. Draw those that have a straight chain of five carbon atoms.

3. A structural isomer of hexane was drawn incorrectly as:

$$CH_3\text{-}\underset{\underset{CH_3}{|}}{\overset{\overset{CH_3}{|}}{CH}}\text{-}CH_2\text{-}CH_3$$

What is wrong with this structure?
Draw the correct structure.

4. A structural isomer of octane was drawn incorrectly as:

$$CH_3\text{-}\underset{\underset{CH\text{-}CH_3}{|}}{\overset{\overset{CH_3}{|}}{CH}}\text{-}CH_2\text{-}CH_2\text{-}CH_3$$

What is wrong with this structure?
Draw the correct structure.

5. Draw the structures of
   a. 2,2,4–trimethylpentane
   b. 2–ethyl–3–isopropylhexane
   c. 4–propyloctane
   d. 1,2–dimethylcyclopropane

6. Draw the structures of
   a. 2,4–dimethylheptane
   b. 3–ethyl–4–methyloctane
   c. 3,4,5–triethyldecane
   d. 1–ethyl–4–methylcyclohexane

7. Name the isomer of nonane with the structure:

$$CH_3\text{-}\underset{\underset{CH_3}{|}}{\overset{\overset{CH_3}{|}}{CH}}\text{-}\overset{\overset{CH_3}{|}}{CH}\text{-}CH\text{-}CH_2\text{-}CH_3$$

8. Name the isomer of decane with the structure:

$$\underset{CH_3\text{-}CH_2}{\overset{}{CH_3\text{-}CH\text{-}CH_2\text{-}CH_2\text{-}\overset{\overset{CH_2\text{-}CH_3}{|}}{CH}\text{-}CH_3}}$$

9. The following names for alkanes are incorrect. Draw structures based upon these incorrect names and then name them correctly.
   a. 4–ethylhexane
   b. 2,3–dimethylcyclopentane
   c. 2,4–diethylpentane

10. The following names for alkanes are incorrect. Draw structures based upon these incorrect names and then name them correctly.
    a. 2–ethylpropane
    b. 4,4–dimethylpentane
    c. 1,4–diethylcyclopentane

11. Which of the following alkenes exhibit *cis–trans* geometrical isomerism? Draw the structures.
    a. 2–pentene
    b. 2,4–dimethyl–2–heptene
    c. 2–methyl–2–butene

12. Which of the following alkenes exhibit *cis–trans* geometrical isomerism? Name the compounds.

    a.
    $$CH_2=\overset{\overset{\displaystyle CH_3}{|}}{C}-CH_2-CH_2-CH_3$$

    b.
    $$CH_3-CH_2-\overset{\overset{\displaystyle CH_3}{|}}{C}=CH-CH_3$$

    c. 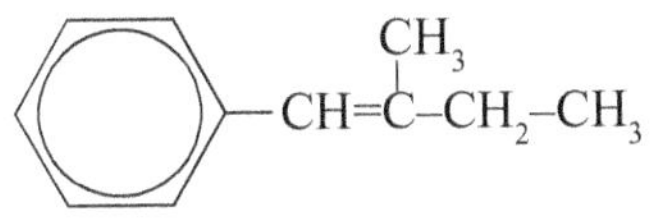
    $$-CH=\overset{\overset{\displaystyle CH_3}{|}}{C}-CH_2-CH_3$$

13. The molecular formula C_5H_8 could represent an alkyne, a diene, or a cycloalkene. In each case there is more than one isomer. Draw possible structures for these hydrocarbons.

14. There are five alkenes with the molecular formula C_5H_{10}. Draw the possible structures. For which of the alkenes is *cis-trans* isomerism possible?

15. Draw the structure of the molecule propadiene. Pay particular attention to the orientation of the π bonds in the molecule and explain why they are oriented as they are.

16. Draw the structure of the molecule 1,3–butadiene. Explain why the molecule is planar.

17. How many isomers of octene are there with the double bond in different positions? Draw the structures of *cis*–4–octene and *trans*–4–octene.

18. How many isomers of nonene are there with the double bond in different positions? Draw the structures of *cis*–2–nonene and *trans*–2–nonene.

19. Write equations representing the following reactions:

    a. The addition of hydrogen bromide to methylpropene.

    b. The nitration of benzene in the presence of sulfuric acid.

    c. The hydrogenation of 2–butene.

    d. The addition of chlorine to cyclohexene.

20. Write equations representing the following reactions:

    a. The addition of hydrogen chloride to 1–butyne.

    b. The reaction of benzene with chlorine in the presence of $FeCl_3$.

    c. The addition of water to propene in the presence of sulfuric acid.

    d. The substitution reaction between Cl_2 and ethane in the presence of UV radiation.

21. Explain why the melting points of the following alkanes increase in the order in which they are written: ethane, propane, butane, pentane, hexane.

22. Explain why methylpropane boils at a lower temperature than butane, even though the two molecules have the same molar mass.

Organic Chemistry: Functional Groups

Organic compounds are classified by family according to their structural characteristics. We have already seen that hydrocarbons can be identified as alkanes, alkenes, alkynes, or arenes.

The presence of the double bond in an alkene gives the molecule a set of characteristic properties and is an example of a **functional group**. The chemical properties of a functional group are largely independent of the identity of the remainder of the molecule. For example, the double bond in propylene behaves in the same way as the double bond in cyclohexene and the molecules therefore exhibit similar properties. Both molecules react with bromine to produce compounds in which the bromine molecule is added across the double bond. The double bond provides a particular function or property. The chemical properties of an organic compound are determined by the functional groups possessed by the molecule.

In this unit we will examine the behavior of several functional groups. The more common functional groups, with examples, are listed in Table 64.1.

64.1 Haloalkanes

The **haloalkanes**, more commonly called the alkyl halides, are alkanes in which one or more hydrogen atoms have been replaced by halogen atoms. Common examples are carbon tetrachloride (tetrachloromethane) CCl_4 and chloroform (trichloromethane) $CHCl_3$.

Many halogen-organic compounds are toxic. For example, carbon tetrachloride was once heavily used in the dry-cleaning industry and in fire-extinguishers but such use has been discontinued because of its tendency to cause liver cancer. The environment is still threatened by the presence of halogen-containing organic compounds due to the use of chlorine in industrial processes. These compounds tend to be water-insoluble (hydrophobic) and quite stable. They accumulate in body fat and are not excreted easily. Many are carcinogenic and cause neurological damage in humans. Particularly troublesome are a class of stable derivatives called polychlorinated biphenyls (PCBs) (Figure 64.1). These were once used as insulating fluids in electrical transformers and discarded into the environment where they are eaten by microbes and invertebrates. These in turn are eaten by fish and the fish are then consumed by birds, humans, and other mammals.

Large chlorinated hydrocarbons are widely used as insecticides. One that once caused severe ecological damage before its use was curtailed in 1972 is the insecticide DDT. Another example is the insecticide Lindane™ (hexachlorocyclohexane). Currently, the presence of dioxins in the environment is cause for concern. Dioxins

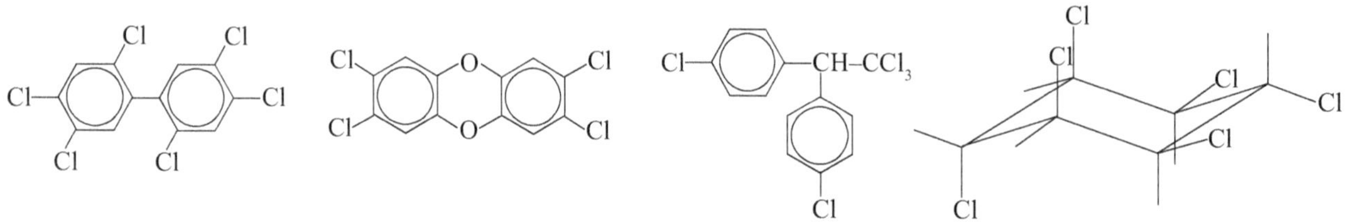

Although the use of CCl_4 in fire-extinguishers has been discontinued because of its toxicity, modern fire suppressants called **halons** are closely related. Two examples are $CBrClF_2$ and CF_3Br.

These fire suppressants work by producing free radicals that disrupt the combustion reaction by terminating the propagation of the chain reaction.

FIGURE 64.1 The structures of (a) a polychlorinated biphenyl (PCB) and (b) a dioxin and the structures of two insecticides, (c) DDT and (d) Lindane™.

TABLE 64.1 Some common functional groups.

Name	Formula of Functional Group	Suffix	Example	Name
Alkene	$-\overset{\mid}{C}=\overset{\mid}{C}-$	–ene	$CH_2=CH_2$	ethene (ethylene)
Alkyne	$-C\equiv C-$	–yne	$HC\equiv CH$	ethyne (acetylene)
Arene	(benzene ring)	usually –ene	(benzene ring)$-CH_3$	toluene
Halide	$-X$ where X = F, Cl, Br, I	prefix halo–	$CHCl_3$	trichloromethane (chloroform)
Alcohol	$-O-H$	–ol	CH_3CH_2-OH	ethanol (ethyl alcohol)
Ether	$-O-$	–ether	$CH_3CH_2-O-CH_2CH_3$	diethylether
Amine	$-NH_2$, $-\overset{\mid}{NH}$, or $-\overset{\mid}{\underset{\mid}{N}}$	–amine	CH_3-NH_2	methylamine
Aldehyde	$-\overset{\overset{H}{\mid}}{C}=O$	–al	$CH_3-\overset{\overset{H}{\mid}}{C}=O$	ethanal (acetaldehyde)
Ketone	$-\overset{\overset{O}{\parallel}}{C}-$	–one	$CH_3-\overset{\overset{O}{\parallel}}{C}-CH_3$	propanone (acetone)
Carboxylic acid	$-\overset{\overset{O}{\parallel}}{C}-OH$	–oic acid	$CH_3-\overset{\overset{O}{\parallel}}{C}-OH$	ethanoic acid (acetic acid)
Ester	$-\overset{\overset{O}{\parallel}}{C}-O-$	–oate	$CH_3-\overset{\overset{O}{\parallel}}{C}-O-CH_2CH_3$	ethyl ethanoate (ethyl acetate)
Amide	$-\overset{\overset{O}{\parallel}}{C}-N-$	–amide	$CH_3-\overset{\overset{O}{\parallel}}{C}-NH_2$	ethanamide (acetamide)
Acid chloride	$-\overset{\overset{O}{\parallel}}{C}-Cl$	–yl chloride	$CH_3-\overset{\overset{O}{\parallel}}{C}-Cl$	acetyl chloride
Nitrile	$-C\equiv N$	–nitrile or prefix cyano–	CH_3-CN	cyanomethane

are not intentionally produced but are formed in the disposal of chlorine wastes from bleaching (for example in the paper industry) and in the degradation of other chlorine-containing hydrocarbons.

The impact of another series of haloalkanes, the chlorofluorocarbons (CFCs), upon the ozone layer has already been described (*cf.* Unit 26).

The predominant reactions of the haloalkanes are substitution reactions in which the halogen is replaced by other functional groups. For example, treatment of a haloalkane with a strong base replaces the halogen with an —OH group and produces an alcohol. Other groups, such as —CN and —NH$_2$ can also be substituted.

Haloalkanes do, despite the risks, have several important uses, particularly as industrial solvents, in the synthesis of other organic compounds, and in the production of the precursors for very useful polymers.

64.2   Alcohols and Ethers

Alcohols are organic molecules in which a hydrogen atom attached to a carbon atom has been replaced by an —OH group. They can also be regarded as derivatives of water in which one of the hydrogen atoms has been replaced by an organic group (Figure 64.2). **Ethers** are derivatives of water in which both hydrogen atoms have been replaced by an organic group.

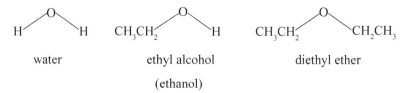

water   ethyl alcohol   diethyl ether
                        (ethanol)

FIGURE 64.2   The structures of alcohols and ethers and their relationship to water.

Just as in water, the —OH functional group of alcohols forms strong intermolecular hydrogen bonds. As a result, alcohols have higher melting and boiling points, and lower vapor pressures, than their parent alkanes. The —OH group is also responsible for the solubility of alcohols in water. Ethers, on the other hand, have no —OH group; they are much more volatile than alcohols and are immiscible with water. For example, diethylether CH$_3$CH$_2$—O—CH$_2$CH$_3$, and butanol, CH$_3$CH$_2$CH$_2$CH$_2$OH, are structural isomers but have quite different properties (Table 64.2).

> Alcohols become progressively less soluble in water as the length of the alkyl chain increases. Methanol, ethanol and propanol are completely miscible. Butanol is only moderately soluble.
>
> Similarly, salts such as NaCl are progressively less soluble:
>
> in water: 36.2 g/100 mL
> in methanol: 1.4 g/100 mL
> in ethanol: 0.06 g/100 mL

TABLE 64.2   Comparison of *n*–butanol, diethylether, and the parent alkane, butane.

Name	Structural Formula	m. pt.	b. pt.	Soluble in Water?
butane	CH$_3$—CH$_2$—CH$_2$—CH$_3$	–138°C	–0.5°C	no
diethylether	CH$_3$—CH$_2$—O—CH$_2$—CH$_3$	–116.2°C	34.5°C	no
n–butanol	CH$_3$—CH$_2$—CH$_2$—CH$_2$—OH	–89.5°C	117.3°C	yes (9 g /100 g H$_2$O)

The names of alcohols are based upon the names of the parent alkane. The ending –ane is changed to –ol and the position of the —OH on the alkane chain is indicated by the number of the carbon atom in the chain to which it is attached. Some alcohols are known by older common names. For example, ethanol is often called ethyl alcohol and 2–propanol is usually called isopropyl alcohol or isopropanol. If you purchase rubbing alcohol from a pharmacy you will see it labeled as isopropyl alcohol.

The first member of the alcohol series, methanol CH$_3$OH, was originally called wood alcohol because it was prepared by heating wood in the absence of oxygen. It is toxic, causing blindness and ultimately death when ingested in relatively small amounts (about 200 mL). Methanol is currently produced from synthesis of gas using a Cu|ZnO|Cr$_2$O$_3$ catalyst at 250°C and high pressure:

$$CO + 2\,H_2 \rightarrow CH_3OH$$

The second member of the series is ethanol CH_3CH_2OH. This is the alcohol present in beers, wines, and spirits. It is produced by the **fermentation** of carbohydrates by yeast. Most industrial ethanol is produced by the acid-catalyzed addition of water to ethylene. Similarly, isopropanol is produced by the acid-catalyzed addition of water to propene.

Alcohols are divided into three classes according to the number of organic groups attached to the carbon with the —OH group. A **primary alcohol** has the general formula RCH_2—OH, where R represents an organic group. A **secondary alcohol** has the general formula R_2CH—OH (the R groups are not necessarily the same), and a **tertiary alcohol** has the formula R_3C—OH. This same terminology is used for other organic families.

Some alcohols contain more than one —OH group. Two important and familiar examples are ethylene glycol (1,2–ethanediol) used in antifreeze and glycerol (1,2,3–propanetriol) (Figure 64.3). The viscosity of the alcohols increases as the number of —OH groups increases due to increased hydrogen bonding between the molecules.

$$CH_2OH$$
$$|$$
$$CH_2OH$$

ethylene glycol

(1,2–ethanediol)

$$CH_2OH$$
$$|$$
$$CHOH$$
$$|$$
$$CH_2OH$$

glycerol

(1,2,3–propanetriol)

FIGURE 64.3 Ethylene glycol and glycerol.

Two examples of aromatic alcohols are phenol and cresol. In these alcohols, the —OH group is attached to a benzene ring (Figure 64.4). The —OH group of a phenol is more acidic ($pK_a = 10$) than that of an aliphatic alcohol because the negative charge of the conjugate base is delocalized around the benzene ring. In other words, the phenoxide ion $C_6H_5O^-$ is less basic than the ethoxide ion $C_2H_5O^-$ because it is stabilized by the delocalization of the negative charge.

Recall (*cf.* Unit 40) that the less basic the base, the more acidic its conjugate acid:

$$K_a \times K_b = K_w$$

phenol

o–cresol (also *m*– and *p*–)

FIGURE 64.4 Phenol and cresol.

Alcohols can be oxidized using reagents such as potassium dichromate in acid. The C—OH group is converted into a C=O group:

$$CH_3CH_2CH_2OH \rightarrow CH_3CH_2CHO$$

The removal of water from an alcohol in a dehydration reaction produces an alkene—this type of reaction is often called **elimination**:

$$CH_3CH_2OH \rightarrow CH_2{=}CH_2 + H_2O$$

Potassium dichromate is orange-yellow in color and is reduced to the green Cr^{3+} in the oxidation of the alcohol. This color change is the basis of the Breathalyser test for intoxication.

Other reactions involve substituting other functional groups for the —OH. For example, reaction of an alcohol with hydrobromic acid, HBr, converts the alcohol into a bromoalkane:

$$CH_3CH_2CH_2OH + HBr \rightarrow CH_3CH_2CH_2Br + H_2O$$

The most common ether is diethylether CH_3CH_2—O—CH_2CH_3 once used extensively as an anesthetic. The molecules cannot form hydrogen bonds with one another but are miscible with alcohols. They are weak Lewis bases and are useful solvents, particularly for electron deficient compounds. An example is their use as a solvent for Grignard's reagents (*cf.* Unit 53).

A particularly interesting class of ethers is the set of cyclic polyethers, commonly called **crown ethers**, that are able to complex alkali metal ions (*cf.* Unit 52).

64.3 Amines

Just as alcohols can be regarded as derivatives of water, **amines** can be regarded as derivatives of ammonia. Replacement of one of the H atoms of ammonia by an alkyl group leads to a **primary amine**, R–NH_2. Replacement of two H atoms leads to a **secondary amine**, R_2NH (the R groups are not necessarily the same), and replacement of all three H atoms of ammonia leads to a **tertiary amine**, R_3N. Three methyl derivatives are shown in Figure 64.5.

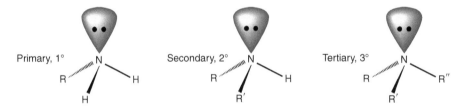

FIGURE 64.5   Primary, secondary, and tertiary amines.

Amines are named by describing the groups attached to the nitrogen atom in alphabetical order followed by the suffix amine. Appropriate prefixes are used to denote the number of groups as illustrated in Figure 64.5. Sometimes it is more convenient to regard the —NH_2 group as a substituent on another organic compound. In this case it is called an amino– group. For example, $CH_3CH(NH_2)CH_3$ can be called either isopropylamine or 2–aminopropane. Amines occur in nature through the decomposition of living matter. Two aptly named amines partly responsible for the smell of decaying flesh are putrescine, $H_2NCH_2CH_2CH_2CH_2NH_2$ (1,4–diaminobutane) and cadaverine, $H_2NCH_2CH_2CH_2CH_2CH_2NH_2$ (1,4–diaminopentane). Another similar diamine, hexamethylenediamine, $H_2NCH_2CH_2CH_2CH_2CH_2NH_2$ (1,6–diaminohexane) is used in the manufacture of nylon.

Examples of aromatic amines are aniline, pyridine (in which the nitrogen atom is incorporated in the aromatic ring), and *o*–phenylenediamine (1,2–diaminobenzene) (Figure 64.6).

Amines, like ammonia, are basic. Most are insoluble in water but react with acids to form soluble salts. For example, amphetamine is a primary amine and methamphetamine is a secondary amine (Figure 64.7). These drugs are usually used in the form of their hydrochloride salts which are soluble in water. The 'free base' forms are more volatile. Cocaine, a tertiary amine, also forms a hydrochloride salt. The base itself is often referred to as free base or crack cocaine.

Many common organic compounds have more than one name—common names given to them before a systematic nomenclature was established.

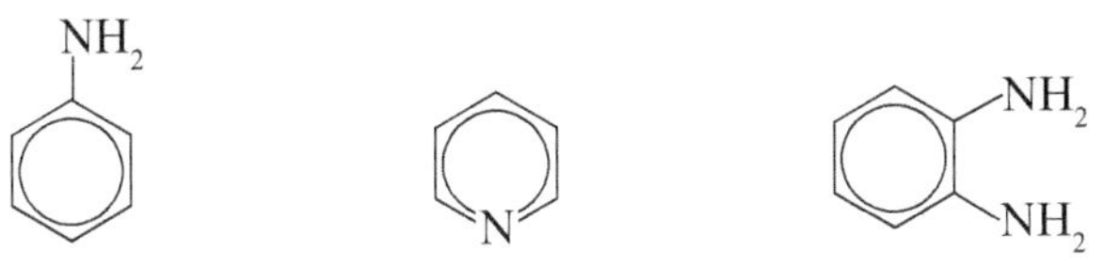

aniline pyridine *o*–phenylenediamine

FIGURE 64.6 Aromatic amines.

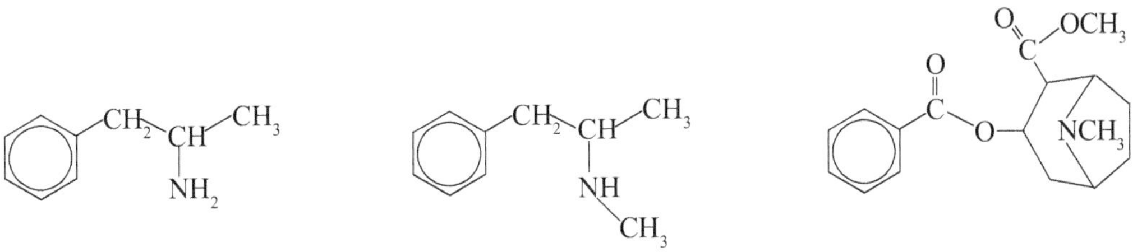

amphetamine
primary amine

methamphetamine
secondary amine

cocaine
tertiary amine

FIGURE 64.7 Examples of primary, secondary, and tertiary amines.

64.4 Aldehydes and Ketones

Hint: Ketone begins with the letter k which comes in the middle of the alphabet, just as the carbonyl group is in the middle of the carbon chain in a ketone.

The group >C=O is called the **carbonyl group** in organic compounds and it is a feature of several functional groups. Two classes of compounds in which it occurs by itself are the **aldehydes** and the **ketones** (Figure 64.8).

The general formula for a ketone is $R_2C{=}O$, where the two R groups are not necessarily the same. In other words, the C=O group occurs in the middle of a carbon chain. The general formula for an aldehyde is RCH=O in which the C=O group occurs at the end of a carbon chain. Two examples are illustrated in Figure 64.9.

aldehyde ketone

FIGURE 64.8 Aldehydes and ketones.
An aldehyde is a carbonyl group at the end of a carbon chain. A ketone is a carbonyl group in the middle of a carbon chain.

The systematic names for the aldehydes are derived from the parent alkane by removing the final *–e* and adding *–al*. For the ketones, the ending *–e* is replaced by the ending *–one*. Note that the carbon atom of the aldehyde or ketone functional group is counted when determining the name of the parent alkane.

Two aromatic aldehydes are illustrated in Figure 64.10. One is benzaldehyde and the second is a derivative called vanillin, the compound responsible for the smell of vanilla beans.

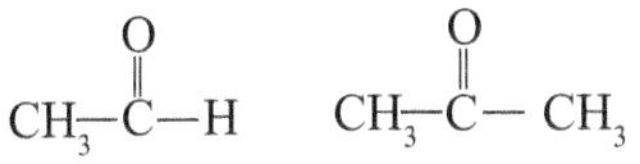

acetaldehyde acetone

FIGURE 64.9 Acetaldehyde (ethanal), an aldehyde, and acetone (propanone), a ketone.

Ketones have useful solvent properties. For example, acetone is a solvent very common in chemistry laboratories; it is also the solvent found in some nail polish and paint removers.

The preparation of aldehydes and ketones usually involves the oxidation of the corresponding alcohol. Primary alcohols yield aldehydes and secondary alcohols yield ketones:

$$\underset{\text{ethanol}}{CH_3CH_2OH} \xrightarrow{\text{oxidation}} \underset{\text{acetaldehyde (ethanal)}}{CH_3\overset{\overset{H}{|}}{C}{=}O}$$

$$\underset{\text{isopropyl alcohol}}{CH_3\overset{\overset{CH_3}{|}}{C}HOH} \xrightarrow{\text{oxidation}} \underset{\text{acetone}}{CH_3\overset{\overset{CH_3}{|}}{C}{=}O}$$

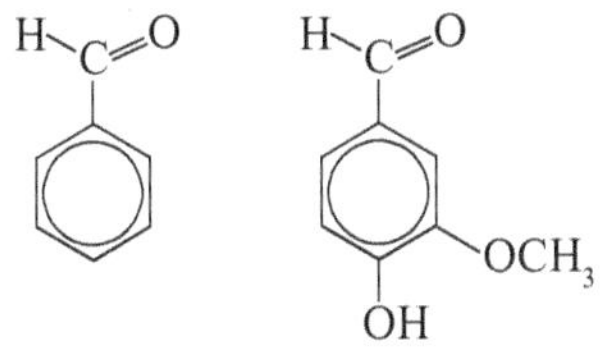

benzaldehyde vanillin

FIGURE 64.10 Two aromatic aldehydes, benzaldehyde and vanillin.

EXAMPLE 64.1 IDENTIFYING AND NAMING ALCOHOLS, AMINES, ALDEHYDES, AND KETONES

Identify the functional group(s) present in the following compounds. Determine whether alcohols and amines are primary, secondary, or tertiary. Finally, name the compounds.

a. $CH_3CH_2CH(OH)CH_3$

b. $CH_3CH(CH_3)NHCH_3$

c. $CH_3CH_2COCH_2CH_3$

d. $(CH_3)_2CHCHO$

UNDERSTAND THE QUESTION

The formulas for the compounds are written in a condensed form. The first task is to interpret these formulas. Recall that a group written in parentheses adjacent to, and usually following, a carbon atom is a group attached to that carbon atom. It also helps to realize that all carbon atoms are connected using a total of four bonds. If in doubt, draw the structural formula in greater detail.

PLAN THE SOLUTION

Draw the structural formulas of the compounds in detail and then look for, and recognize, the functional groups that are present.

SOLVE THE PROBLEM

a. $CH_3CH_2CH(OH)CH_3$

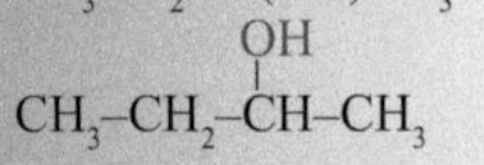

$$CH_3-CH_2-\overset{\overset{\displaystyle OH}{|}}{CH}-CH_3 \qquad \text{—OH group} \qquad 2\text{–butanol} \qquad \text{a secondary alcohol}$$

b. $CH_3CH(CH_3)NHCH_3$

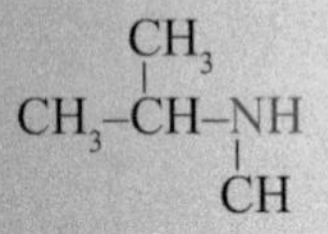

$$CH_3-\overset{\overset{\displaystyle CH_3}{|}}{\underset{\underset{\displaystyle CH}{|}}{CH}}-NH \qquad \text{—NH group} \qquad \text{isopropylmethylamine} \qquad \text{a secondary amine}$$

c. $CH_3CH_2COCH_2CH_3$

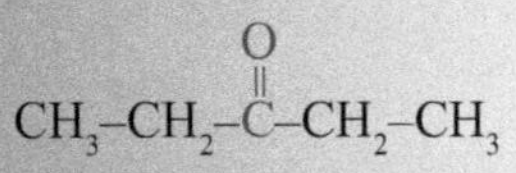

$$CH_3-CH_2-\overset{\overset{\displaystyle O}{||}}{C}-CH_2-CH_3 \qquad \text{—C}{=}\text{O group} \qquad 3\text{–pentanone} \qquad \text{a ketone}$$

d. $(CH_3)_2CHCHO$

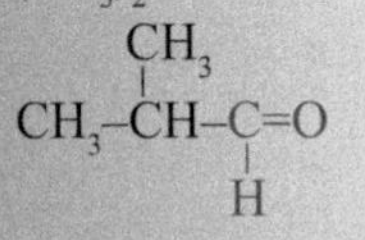

$$CH_3-\overset{\overset{\displaystyle CH_3}{|}}{\underset{\underset{\displaystyle H}{|}}{CH}}-C{=}O \qquad \text{—CHO group} \qquad 2\text{–methylpropanal} \qquad \text{an aldehyde}$$

PROBLEM 64.1A

The functional groups present in the following molecules are noted. Draw possible structures of the compounds.

a. C_3H_8O an ether

b. C_3H_7O an aldehyde

c. C_3H_9N a tertiary amine

d. C_4H_8O a ketone

e. C_3H_8O a secondary alcohol

f. C_8H_8 an alkene with an arene group

PROBLEM 64.1B

Identify the functional group(s) present in the following compounds. Determine whether alcohols and amines are primary, secondary, or tertiary. Finally, name the compounds.

a. $CH_2(OH)CH_2(OH)$

b. $CH_3OCH_2CH_3$

c. $CH_3CH(NH_2)CH_3$

d. $(CH_3CH_2)_2CO$

64.5 Carboxylic Acids, Esters, and Amides

Carboxylic acids contain the **carboxyl** functional group, $-C\!\!\begin{smallmatrix}\nearrow O \\ \searrow OH\end{smallmatrix}$ commonly written in condensed structural formulas as $-CO_2H$ or $-COOH$.

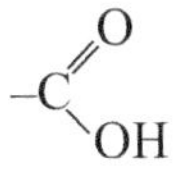

The most familiar carboxylic acid is acetic acid CH_3CO_2H, present (5%) in vinegar. Carboxylic acids are usually relatively weak in aqueous solution and are only slightly ionized. Recall that the acid ionization constant K_a for acetic acid is only 1.8×10^{-5} at 25°C.

Proper names for the carboxylic acids are derived from the name of the alkane with the same number of carbon atoms by deleting the final *–e* and adding *–oic acid*. The systematic name for acetic acid therefore is ethanoic acid. Formic acid, HCO_2H, has the proper name methanoic acid.

Many organic carboxylic acids are found naturally. Formic acid is the acid found in ant venom and its name is derived from the Latin for ant (formica). Butyric acid, or more properly butanoic acid, $CH_3CH_2CH_2CO_2H$, is the acid that gives rancid butter its characteristic foul smell. Citric acid, the acid that is responsible for the tart taste of citrus fruits, is a tricarboxylic acid and lactic acid is present in sour milk (Figure 64.11).

Carboxylic acids can be prepared by the oxidation of primary alcohols. For example, acetic acid can be made by the oxidation of ethanol:

$$CH_3CH_2OH \rightarrow CH_3CHO \rightarrow CH_3CO_2H$$

ethanol   acetaldehyde   acetic acid

                           (ethanal)   (ethanoic acid)

Formica is also the name given to a urea–formaldehyde resin containing $-CH_2-$ links.

FIGURE 64.11 Two naturally occurring carboxylic acids.

TABLE 64.3 Common fatty acids.

Name	Number of Carbon Atoms	Formula	Melting Point(°C)	
Saturated				
Lauric acid	12	$CH_3(CH_2)_{10}CO_2H$		
Myristic acid	14	$CH_3(CH_2)_{12}CO_2H$	54	
Palmitic acid	16	$CH_3(CH_2)_{14}CO_2H$	63	
Stearic acid	18	$CH_3(CH_2)_{16}CO_2H$	69	
Unsaturated				
Oleic	18	$CH_3(CH_2)_7CH{=}CH(CH_2)_7CO_2H$	13	one double bond
Linoleic	18	$CH_3(CH_2)_4CH{=}CHCH_2CH{=}CH(CH_2)_7CO_2H$	−5	two double bonds
Linolenic	18	$CH_3CH_2CH{=}CHCH_2CH{=}CHCH_2CH{=}CH(CH_2)_7CO_2H$	−11	three double bonds

Carboxylic acids are generally soluble in water due to the hydrophilic carboxyl group. As noted above, vinegar is a solution of acetic acid in water. However, as the hydrocarbon chain increases in length, the acid becomes less soluble. Acids with long hydrocarbon chains are called **fatty acids** and are components of biologically important molecules called **lipids**. The most common examples of saturated fatty acids are palmitic acid $CH_3(CH_2)_{14}CO_2H$, with a 16-carbon atom chain, and stearic acid $CH_3(CH_2)_{16}CO_2H$, with an 18-carbon atom chain. The most common unsaturated fatty acid is oleic acid, $CH_3(CH_2)_7CH{=}CH(CH_2)_7CO_2H$, with an 18-carbon atom chain (Table 64.3)

Carboxylic acids react with alcohols in the presence of a strong acid to produce **esters**—a reaction commonly referred to as **esterification**. The reaction involves the elimination of a molecule of water as the acid and alcohol combine. The general term for the combination of two compounds by the elimination of a small molecule is **condensation**. Esterification is a condensation reaction. In the reaction the acid supplies the carbonyl group of the ester functional group and the alcohol supplies the —O— part of the link. An example is the combination of acetic acid and ethanol to produce the ester ethyl acetate:

acetic acid   ethanol   ethyl acetate $+$ H_2O

(ethanoic acid)   (ethyl ethanoate)

The name of the ester is derived from the names of the acid and alcohol. The alkyl group of the alcohol is named first followed by the name of the acid with the ending changed from –*oic acid* to –*oate*.

An important ester is the one formed by the reaction of salicylic acid and acetic acid:

salicylic acid   acetylsalicylic acid

The ester is called acetylsalicylic acid, the drug commonly called aspirin used in huge quantities as a pain killer (analgesic).

Another ester of salicylic acid, in which it plays the part of the acid rather than the alcohol, is methyl salicylate, or oil of wintergreen. The pleasant smell of oil of wintergreen is typical of many esters. The smell of bananas is due to the ester pentyl acetate, the smell of pineapple is due to butyl butanoate, and the smell of oil of jasmine is due to benzyl acetate.

Salicylic acid was originally obtained from willow bark and an infusion of willow bark obtained by heating the bark in boiling water has been used as a pain reliever since Hippocrates recommended it in 400 BC. The acid, however, severely irritates the stomach, and in 1897 the acetyl derivative was found to be much less irritating. Salicylic acid is also found in a wild flower called *Spirea ulmaria* from which the name aspirin was derived.

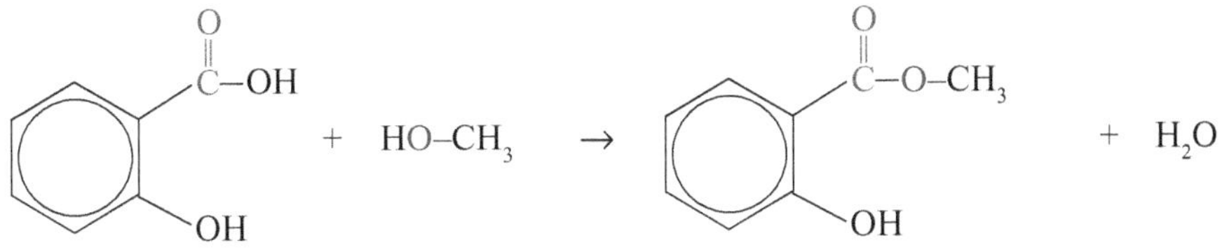

salicylic acid + HO–CH₃ → methyl salicylate + H_2O

Just as in the case of the carboxylic acids, the esters become less soluble in water as the hydrocarbon chain increases in length. Beeswax, for example is composed of the palmitic acid esters of long chain alcohols (Figure 64.12).

It's interesting that the foul smell of butanoic acid becomes the pleasant smell of pineapples when it is converted to its butyl ester, the smell of strawberries when converted to the ethyl ester, and the smell of apples when converted to its methyl ester.

$$CH_3-(CH_2)_{24}-\overset{\overset{\displaystyle O}{\|}}{C}-O-(CH_2)_{25-33}-CH_3$$

FIGURE 64.12 Beeswax is composed of the palmitic acid esters of long chain alcohols.

The fats and oils that occur in animals and vegetables are fatty acid esters of the alcohol, glycerol, and are commonly called **triglycerides**. In these compounds, three fatty acid molecules form ester links with the three –OH groups of the glycerol molecule (Figure 64.13). The main function of the triglycerides in animal life is to supply fuel—when metabolized, the molecules provide energy. The properties of the fat or oil depend upon the identity of the fatty acid. In general, animal fats tend to contain more saturated fatty acids and vegetable oils contain more unsaturated acids. For example, soybean oil contains triglycerides derived from oleic and linoleic acids—both unsaturated acids—and only 15% saturated fats. Beef fat (and human fat) contains triglycerides derived from oleic acid, palmitic acid, stearic acid, and myristic acid—the last three are saturated acids. There are exceptions—coconut oil contains 92% saturated fatty acids (principally lauric acid $CH_3(CH_2)_{10}CO_2H$ and myristic acid $CH_3(CH_2)_{12}CO_2H$)) and only 8% monounsaturated and polyunsaturated fats.

Vegetable oil (an ester) is *not* the same as petroleum oil (a hydrocarbon).

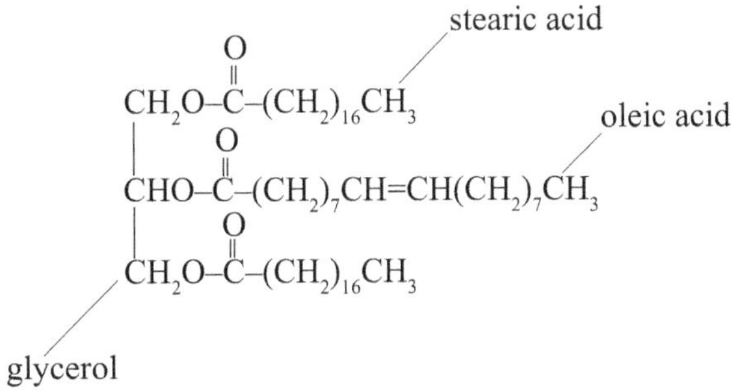

FIGURE 64.13 A typical animal fat.
Notice that the fatty acids of a fat need not necessarily be the same.

Fats containing saturated fatty acids are solids and those containing unsaturated fatty acids are oils. The difference is due to the intermolecular attraction between the long hydrocarbon chains. In the saturated acids the chains are flexible and are able to approach one another more closely. In the unsaturated acids, the double bonds make the chains less flexible and the ability of the molecules to pack together is impaired. The less effective intermolecular attraction in the unsaturated fats lowers the melting point and boiling point.

The reverse of an esterification reaction is **hydrolysis**. Animal fat, for example, is hydrolysed by strong bases to form the sodium or potassium salt of the fatty acid and glycerol (Figure 64.14). In this case the reaction is called **saponification**, from the Latin for soap. The soap is the salt of the fatty acid and this reaction has been the basis of soap manufacture since ancient times. The anion of the soap consists of a long hydrocarbon chain and the carboxylate functional group. The hydrocarbon tail is hydrophobic and dissolves in oil. The carboxylate functional group is hydrophilic and dissolves in water. The soap molecule therefore acts as a surfactant at the interface between oil and water and allows oil to be removed with water when you wash.

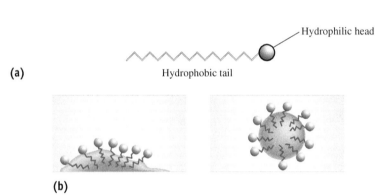

FIGURE 64.14 **(a) Sodium stearate, an example of a soap. (b) The surfactant action of soap in facilitating the removal of oil.**
The carboxylate (ionic) end of the soap molecule dissolves in the water and the long alkyl chain dissolves in the oil. The soap molecule provides an interface between the water and the oil droplet. It effectively makes the oil soluble in water allowing it to be removed.

If an amine is used instead of an alcohol in a condensation reaction, an **amide** is produced:

$$CH_3-C\underset{OH}{\overset{O}{\diagup}} \quad + \quad H-\underset{H}{\overset{\mid}{N}}-CH_3 \quad \rightarrow \quad CH_3-C\underset{NH-CH_3}{\overset{O}{\diagup}} \quad + \quad H_2O$$

acetic acid   methylamine   *N*–methylacetamide

In practice, other methods of preparation are used. For example, the reaction of the amine with an acid chloride is an easier reaction.

The name of the amide is derived by indicating the alkyl groups on the N with the prefix *N–*, and changing the ending of the acid from *–oic acid* to *–amide*.

Other examples of amides are *N,N–*dimethylformamide (DMF), a solvent often encountered in chemistry laboratories and the analgesic acetaminophen found in the pain-relievers Tylenol™ and Excedrin™ (Figure 64.15).

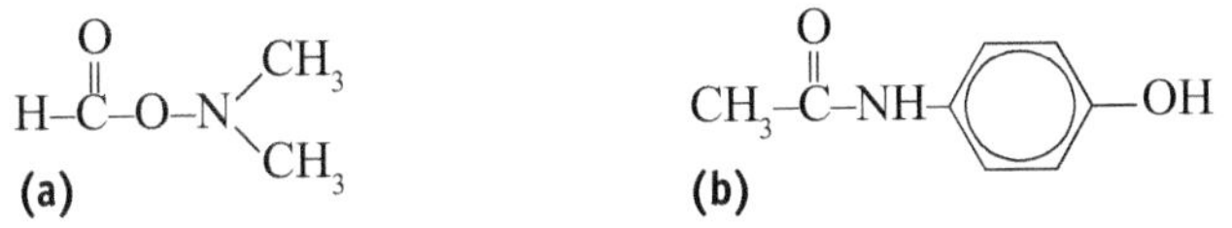

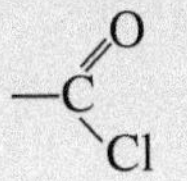

FIGURE 64.15 Examples of amides.
(a) *N,N–*dimethylformamide (DMF); (b) the analgesic acetaminophen.

An acid chloride is a molecule with the functional group:

Perhaps the most important examples of amides are biological compounds called proteins. The basic building blocks of proteins are molecules called α–amino acids. These are molecules containing a carboxyl group and an amine group attached to the same carbon atom. The amino acids link through condensation reactions between the carboxyl group on one molecule with the amine group on another molecule to form the chains of molecules called proteins. The link is an amide, more often called a **peptide** in this case. A protein therefore is a **polypeptide**. The artificial sweetener aspartame found in Nutrasweet™ and Equal™ is a **dipeptide** formed from two amino acids—the amide link is shown in Figure 64.16. We'll look further at the structures of proteins in Unit 66.

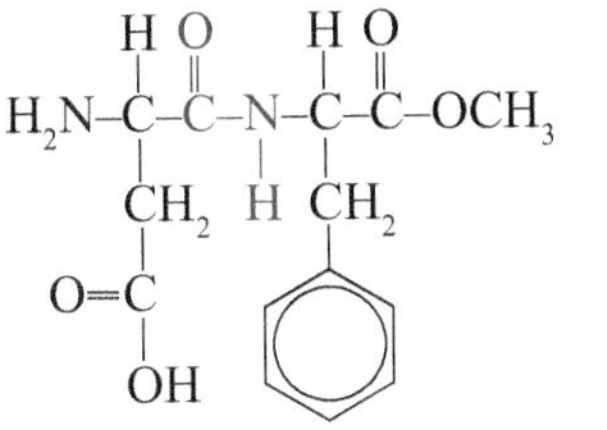

FIGURE 64.16 The artificial sweetener aspartame.
The peptide (amide) link is shown in blue.

Another significant example of molecules containing an amide link is nylon, a **polyamide** and the first example of an artificial fiber similar in structure to the natural polyamides found in silk and wool. We'll examine polymers in the next unit.

Wallace Carothers (1896–1937) first produced nylon–6,6 in 1935 at the Du Pont Chemical Company. Nylon stockings first went on sale in 1937 but soon after all production effort was devoted to the manufacture of material for the war effort.

64.6 Organic Reactions

Most reactions in organic chemistry involve the conversion of one functional group into another or the interaction between two functional groups, one on one molecule and one on another molecule. An example of the former is the reduction of a ketone to produce a secondary alcohol. An example of the latter is the condensation of an alcohol with a carboxylic acid to produce an ester. A summary of the reactions discussed in Units 63 and 64 is presented in Figure 64.17.

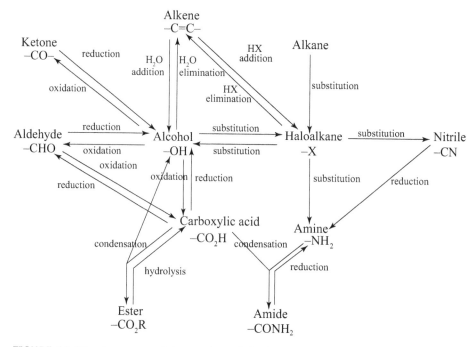

FIGURE 64.17   A summary of the reactions of the functional groups.

EXAMPLE 64.2   PREDICTING THE PRODUCTS OF REACTIONS IN ORGANIC CHEMISTRY

Predict the products of the following reactions:

a. Reduction of acetaldehyde CH_3CHO

b. Oxidation of isopropyl alcohol $CH_3CH(OH)CH_3$

c. Reaction of ethylene with HCl

d. Condensation of ammonia with propionic acid $CH_3CH_2CO_2H$

UNDERSTAND THE QUESTION

The functional groups of organic molecules each have their own set of characteristic properties. The examples described in this chapter represent just a fraction of the many reactions that are possible. However, reactions such as elimination, substitution, oxidation, reduction, condensation, and hydrolysis are typical.

PLAN THE SOLUTION

Recognize the functional group(s) that is(are) present in the molecule and determine the type of reaction that is occurring. Then the product of the reaction may be predicted.

SOLVE THE PROBLEM

a. Reduction of acetaldehyde CH_3CHO:

Aldehydes can be oxidized or reduced. In this case the aldehyde is reduced to a primary alcohol:

$$CH_3CHO \rightarrow CH_3CH_2OH$$

b. Oxidation of isopropyl alcohol $CH_3CH(OH)CH_3$:

When an alcohol is oxidized, the product depends upon whether the alcohol is primary or secondary. Isopropyl alcohol is a secondary alcohol and is oxidized to a ketone, acetone:

$$CH_3CH(OH)CH_3 \rightarrow CH_3COCH_3$$

c. Reaction of ethylene with HCl:

This is an addition reaction typical of unsaturated hydrocarbons. The HCl molecule adds across the double bond to produce a haloalkane, in this case, ethyl chloride or chloroethane:

$$CH_2{=}CH_2 \rightarrow CH_3CH_2Cl$$

d. Condensation of ammonia with propionic acid $CH_3CH_2CO_2H$:

The two condensation reactions discussed in this chapter are the reaction of a carboxylic acid with an alcohol to produce an ester and the reaction of a carboxylic acid with ammonia or an amine to produce an amide. This is an example of the latter; the amide produced is propionamide:

$$CH_3CH_2CO_2H \rightarrow CH_3CH_2CONH_2$$

PROBLEM 64.2A

Predict the products of the following reactions:

a. The hydrolysis of ethyl propionate $CH_3CH_2CO_2CH_2CH_3$

b. The elimination of HCl from 2–chloropropane $CH_3CHClCH_3$

c. The condensation of formic acid with dimethylamine

PROBLEM 64.2B

a. The reaction of 2–methylbenzoic acid $CH_3C_6H_4CO_2H$ with ethylamine

b. The reduction of butanoic acid

c. The elimination of water from isopropyl alcohol

Review Questions

1. Explain the meaning of the description 'functional group'.

2. Functional groups can be divided into various categories. For example, those that contain just oxygen and hydrogen, or just nitrogen and hydrogen, or those that do, or do not, contain a carbonyl group. Examine the functional groups described in this chapter and devise a scheme for classifying them.

3. What is the difference between an amide and an amine? And between a carbonyl group and a carboxyl group?

4. List the characteristic properties of the functional groups.

Solutions to Problems

PROBLEM 64.1A

a. C_3H_8O an ether

the functional group is —O—

structure: CH_3—O—C_2H_5 ethyl methyl ether

b. C_3H_7O an aldehyde

the functional group is —CHO

structure: CH_3CH_2—CHO propanal

c. C_3H_9N a tertiary amine

the functional group is an N with no hydrogens attached.

structure: CH_3–N–CH_3 trimethylamine
$\quad\quad\quad\quad\quad$ |
$\quad\quad\quad\quad\quad CH_3$

d. C_4H_8O a ketone

the functional group is —CO—

structure: CH_3CH_2—CO—CH_3
ethyl methyl ketone or butanone

e. C_3H_8O a secondary alcohol

the functional group is an C—OH with two alkyl groups attached to the C.

structure: CH_3–CH–OH isopropanol
$\quad\quad\quad\quad\quad$ |
$\quad\quad\quad\quad\quad CH_3$

f. C_8H_8 an alkene with an arene group

the functional groups are ⬡ and C=C.

structure: ⬡—CH=CH$_2$

PROBLEM 64.2A

a. The hydrolysis of ethyl propionate $CH_3CH_2CO_2CH_2CH_3$

→ propionic acid $CH_3CH_2CO_2H$ and ethanol CH_3CH_2OH

b. The elimination of HCl from 2–chloropropane $CH_3CHClCH_3$

→ propene $CH_3CH=CH_2$

c. The condensation of formic acid with dimethylamine

→ the formation of N,N–dimethyformamide $HCO_2N(CH_3)_2$

Answers to Review Questions

1. A functional group is a group of atoms in an organic molecule that contributes a set of characteristic properties to the compound. The chemical properties of a functional group are largely independent of the identity of the remainder of the molecule. Thus the properties of an organic compound can be considered to be the sum of the properties of the functional groups present.

2. The functional groups described in this chapter are listed in Table 64.1. Some are more closely related than others. For example, the functional groups that contain a carbonyl group can be divided into two categories. In the first group are the aldehydes and ketones; in the second group are carboxylic acids and their derivatives, the esters and amides.

3. An amide is an organic compound containing the functional group —CONH$_2$. The hydrogen atoms on the N may be substituted by alkyl or other organic groups. It is produced by the condensation of a carboxylic acid and an amine.

An amine is an organic compound containing the functional groups — NH_2(primary), —NHR(secondary), or —NR$_2$(tertiary). It can be considered to be a derivative of ammonia in which one, two, or all three hydrogen atoms are replaced by alkyl or other organic groups.

A carbonyl group is the group >C=O that occurs in aldehydes, ketones, carboxylic acids, esters, and amides. A carboxyl group is the functional group —CO$_2$H.

4. Some characteristic properties of the functional groups are summarized in Figure 64.17. The reactions are often described by terms such as oxidation, reduction, elimination, substitution, addition, condensation, hydrolysis, dehydrogenation, etc. These descriptions indicate the type of reaction involved. Entire textbooks are devoted to the structure, properties, and reactions of organic compounds and only a very brief overview is provided in this unit.

End-of-Unit Problems

1. Identify the following functional groups. R and R' represent alkyl groups.
   a. R—CHO
   b. R—CONH$_2$
   c. R—CO—R'
   d. R—NH—R'

2. Identify the following functional groups. R and R' represent alkyl groups.
   a. R—CO$_2$H
   b. R—CO$_2$—R'
   c. R—CH$_2$OH
   d. R—NH$_2$

3. Name the following compounds:
   a. CH$_3$CH$_2$OCH$_3$
   b. CH$_3$CH$_2$CHO
   c. CH$_3$CH$_2$CH$_2$CO$_2$H
   d. C$_6$H$_5$CO$_2$NH$_2$

4. Name the following compounds:
   a. CH$_3$COCH$_2$CH$_3$
   b. CH$_3$CH$_2$CO$_2$C$_2$H$_5$
   c. (CH$_3$CH$_2$)$_3$N
   d. CH$_3$CO$_2$H

5. Classify the following alcohols and amines as primary, secondary, or tertiary.
   a. ethyl methyl amine
   b. 2–pentanol
   c. isopropyl alcohol

6. Classify the following alcohols and amines as primary, secondary, or tertiary.
   a. 2–aminobutane
   b. 2–methyl–3–pentanol
   c. trimethyl amine

7. Circle and identify all the functional groups in the following compound:

$$HO-\underset{}{\bigcirc}-\overset{\displaystyle O}{\overset{\|}{C}}-O-\overset{\displaystyle CH_3}{\underset{}{\overset{|}{C}H}}-CH_3$$

8. Circle and identify all the functional groups in the following compound:

$$CH_3-\overset{\displaystyle CH_3}{\underset{\underset{O}{\|}}{\overset{|}{C}}}-CH-CH=CH-CH_2-NH-CH_3$$

9. Draw possible structures for the following compounds.
   a. C$_4$H$_{10}$O   a primary alcohol
   b. C$_3$H$_8$O$_2$ an ester
   c. C$_3$H$_9$N   a secondary amine
   d. C$_3$H$_6$O   a ketone

10. Draw possible structures for the following compounds.
    a. C$_2$H$_5$NO   an amide
    b. C$_3$H$_6$O   an aldehyde
    c. C$_2$H$_7$N   a primary amine
    d. C$_5$H$_{10}$O$_2$ a carboxylic acid

11. Draw the structures of all the alcohols with the molecular formula C$_5$H$_{12}$O. Classify the alcohols as primary, secondary, or tertiary.

12. Draw the structures of the aldehyde and the ketone with the molecular formula C$_4$H$_8$O. Name the two compounds.

13. Draw the structures of all the amines with the molecular formula C$_4$H$_{11}$N. Classify the amines as primary, secondary, or tertiary.

14. Draw the structures of the carboxylic acid and the four esters with the molecular formula C$_4$H$_8$O$_2$. Name the compounds.

15. The molecular formula C$_4$H$_{10}$O is common to both alcohols and ethers. Write the structural formulas for one example of each. Which of the two has the higher boiling point? Why?

16. Three amines, primary, secondary, and tertiary, have the molecular formula C$_3$H$_9$N. Draw their structures. Arrange the secondary and tertiary amines in order of increasing boiling point and explain your decision. Of the two possible primary amines, which has the higher boiling point? Why?

17. Draw the structures of a carboxylic acid and an ester with the molecular formula C$_2$H$_4$O$_2$. If you had samples of both compounds, what would be a relatively easy way to distinguish between them?

18. Draw the possible structures of amides having the same formula C$_5$H$_{11}$NO.

19. Write the equations for, and draw the structures of the principal products of, the following reactions:
    a. butanoic acid and ethanol
    b. propionic acid and diethyl amine
    c. acetyl chloride and methanol

20. Write the equations for the preparation of the following alcohols by the reduction of ketones or aldehydes. Draw the structures of the appropriate ketone or aldehyde and the structures of the products.

    a. 2–butanol

    b. 1–propanol

    c. 3–pentanol

21. Write equations representing

    a. The preparation of acetic acid from acetaldehyde and air using a manganese acetate catalyst.

    b. The dehydrogenation of 2–propanol using a copper(II) oxide catalyst at 500°C to produce acetone.

22. Write equations representing

    a. The hydrolysis of isopropyl acetate to produce acetic acid and 2–propanol.

    b. The dehydrohalogenation of 2–bromobutane in ethanol solution to produce 2–butene.

23. Name the aromatic compounds:

    a.

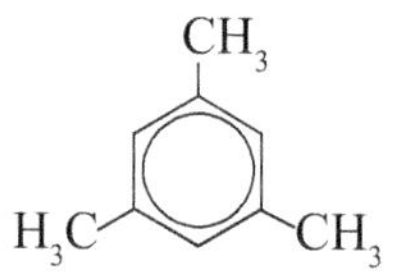

    b.

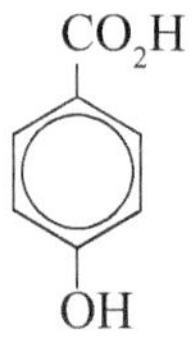

24. Draw the structures of

    a. p–dichlorobenzene

    b. 2,4,6–trinitrotoluene

    c. triphenylamine

Polymer Chemistry and Composite Materials

65.1 Synthetic Polymers

A **polymer** is a large molecule formed when many small molecules called **monomers** bond together. Many important biological molecules are polymers. The structural integrity of trees and plants is due to cellulose which is a polymer of a simple sugar molecule, glucose. Starch is also a polymer of glucose but, unlike cellulose, can be digested by humans. **Proteins** are polymers of amino acids. Sheep's wool, for example, is made up of a protein fiber called keratin and silk is constructed from another fibrous protein called fibroin. **Nucleic acids**, which are responsible for the coding of genetic information are polymers of nucleotides.

In this unit we will examine synthetic polymers. These polymers are intrinsically less complicated than the naturally-occurring polymers mentioned above. Synthetic polymers play an enormous role in everyday life. Look around and almost everywhere you will see synthetic polymers—whether it's the fabric from which your clothes are made, the ballpoint pen you are writing with, the chair you're sitting on, or the carpet you're standing on, to name just a few.

The first attempts to synthesize a polymer involved manipulating the natural cellulose polymer found in wood and cotton. When treated with nitric acid, cellulose forms cellulose nitrate (Figure 65.1). One, two, or all three —OH groups on the glucose molecule can be nitrated. In the mid-1800s it was found that cellulose nitrate mixed with camphor and some ethanol produced a clear plastic material that could be molded. Called **celluloid**, it was used initially as a substitute for ivory in making billiard balls and piano keys, but was subsequently used as an artificial fiber and for photographic film. It is still used today to make ping-pong balls.

Silk, from the cocoons of silk worms that eat the leaves of mulberry trees, has been known for thousands of years. The Chinese discovered how to boil the cocoons and unravel the silk filament. Several filaments, which are extremely fine, are required to make the silk thread from which the fabric is woven.

The nitration of cellulose was discovered in the early 1800s by Henri Braconnot (1832) in France and by Christian Schöenbein (1846) in Switzerland.

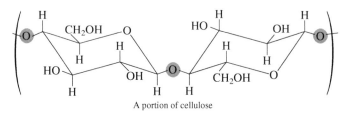

A portion of cellulose

FIGURE 65.1 The molecular structure of the cellulose polymer.
One, two, or all three of the —OH groups on each glucose ring can be nitrated to —O—NO$_2$.

Cellulose nitrate suffers from the disadvantage of high flammability and instability (the explosive gun cotton and smokeless gunpowder are cellulose trinitrate) and so the nitrate was later replaced by acetate. Cellulose acetate (and the diacetate and triacetate) is also used as a fiber and as a film for photography. **Rayon** is a general term for a cellulose derivative but now most often refers to cellulose xanthate—made by reacting cellulose with sodium hydroxide and carbon disulfide, CS$_2$, which replaces some of the —OH groups of the cellulose with xanthate groups (—OCS$_2^-$). The modified cellulose is soluble in basic solution. When extruded through a small hole into acidic solution the rayon fiber is produced. If extruded through a slit instead, a film called **cellophane** is produced.

The first truly synthetic polymer was made by Leo Baekeland in 1909 by the condensation of phenol and formaldehyde. He named his material **Bakelite**™. The

Cellulose triacetate films are still used today for some applications, but have largely been replaced with polyester films that are stronger and more stable.

condensation reaction leads to a vast three-dimensional network of phenol molecules linked by —CH_2— bridges as the water released in the condensation reaction is driven off (Figure 65.2). Once formed, the polymer cannot be melted and molded—it is an example of a thermoset polymer.

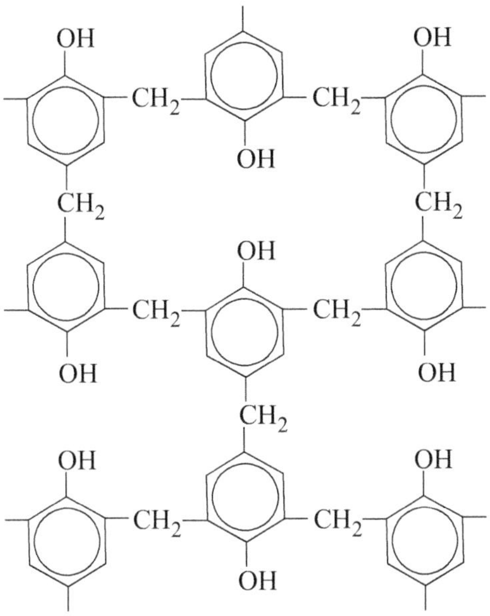

FIGURE 65.2   The structure of a phenol–formaldehyde polymer.
The —CH_2— groups from the formaldehyde bridge the phenol molecules at the *ortho*– and *para*– positions to form an extensive three-dimensional network.

Early plastics, or polymers, were often of poor quality—fragile, brittle, and easily broken. So much so that the word plastic became a pejorative term for something cheap. Modern polymers, plastics, and composite materials, however, are exceptional in their properties and structural characteristics and it is almost impossible to imagine life without them.

In this unit we will examine the synthesis and the structures of various polymers and several terms used to describe the macroscopic properties of polymers that we will encounter on the way. Some properties of polymers of interest are rigidity *vs.* flexibility, crystallinity, ability to be drawn into a fiber, elasticity, toughness, impact resistance, transparency, and tensile strength. A distinction can be made between polymers that are **plastics** and those that are **fibers**. The former are polymers molded into sheets or blocks and the latter are polymers drawn into fibers. Many polymers, for example nylon, polyvinyl chloride, and cellulose acetate, fall into both categories. An **elastomer** is a fiber that can be stretched but regains its original shape when released.

> Tensile strength is a measure of how much the fiber can be stretched without breaking.

Plastics can be divided into two types. **Thermosets**, once formed, cannot be reformed by heating. Bakelite is an example already mentioned. **Thermoplastics**, on the other hand, can be melted and remolded. Polyethylene is an example.

From a synthetic point of view, there are two principal types of polymers: **addition polymers** and **condensation polymers**. We'll examine each in turn.

65.2 Addition Polymers

Polyethylene

One of the first addition polymers was prepared in the 1930s shortly before the advent of World War II. The polymer was made by joining together ethylene molecules in the presence of an initiator under high pressure and heat. The initiator is an organic peroxide or azo compound that readily breaks to form two free radicals. These radicals initiate the chain reaction in which molecules of ethylene join together to form polyethylene (Figure 65.4).

Polyethylene (Figure 65.5) comes in many different forms depending upon the conditions under which it is made. They differ in the structure of the polymer and how the long chain polymer molecules interact with one another. In high density polyethylene (HDPE), the polymer chains are largely linear and pack closely together. The material is tough and rigid. A familiar use is in one-gallon milk jugs. In low density polyethylene (LDPE), there is more branching of the chains and they interact less efficiently. Branched chain alkanes have lower melting points and boiling points than their straight chain isomers for exactly the same reason. The attraction between the polymer chains is due to London forces and these forces are more effective if the molecules line up adjacent to one another. The low density polymer is more flexible. Common examples are plastic bags and squeeze bottles.

Control of the type of polymer produced is achieved by the use of appropriate catalysts in the polymerization process. One of the most important of these is the **Ziegler-Natta catalyst** which is a mixture of titanium tetrachloride and triethylaluminum. The use of this catalyst causes the polymer chain to grow symmetrically at the ends of the chains and inhibits branching. When the Ziegler-Natta catalyst is used, the polymer chains that result pack together well with a high degree of crystallinity and a high density polymer is produced.

Typical HDPE and LDPE polyethylenes have molecular masses in the range of 200,000 to 500,000 g mol^{-1}. Polyethylenes with molar masses between three and six million g mol^{-1} can be made using a transition metal metallocene catalyst. These ultrahigh molecular weight polyethylenes (UHMWPE) are extremely strong (15 times stronger than steel) and the fibers are used to make bulletproof vests, climbing equipment, and high performance sails. The fibers are sold under the tradenames Dyneema^{TM} and Spectra^{TM}.

Polypropylene is similar in many respects to polyethylene. It is a long alkane chain of $-CH_2-$ units in which every other unit has a methyl group. It is a tough

The $-O-O-$ bond in the peroxide molecule is relatively weak—about 150 kJ mol^{-1}.

The name of the polymer can be misleading—polyethylene is *not* a polyalkene but a long alkane chain.

Karl Ziegler and Giulo Natta were awarded the 1963 Nobel Prize in Chemistry for their discoveries in the field of the chemistry and technology of high polymers.

Crystallinity is a measure of the order in the arrangement of polymer chains. In a typical polymer there are regions of high crystallinity and regions of more random arrangements (Figure 65.3). The higher the crystallinity, the more rigid, more dense, and stronger the polymer.

Regions of high crystallinity

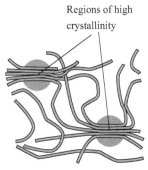

FIGURE 65.3

Initiation: $R-O-O-R \rightarrow R-O\cdot + \cdot O-R$
Propagation: $R\text{-}O\cdot + CH_2{=}CH_2 \rightarrow R-O-CH_2-CH_2\cdot$
                $R-O-CH_2-CH_2\cdot + CH_2{=}CH_2 \rightarrow R-O-CH_2-CH_2-CH_2-CH_2\cdot$
Termination: $R-O-(CH_2)_p-CH_2\cdot + \cdot CH_2-(CH_2)_q-O-R \rightarrow R-O-(CH_2)_n-O-R$

The number of $-CH_2-$ units in the final chain, n, is several thousands.

FIGURE 65.4 The initiation and propagation of a free-radical polymerization of ethylene to produce polyethylene.
R represent an organic group. For example, the peroxide might be benzoyl peroxide.

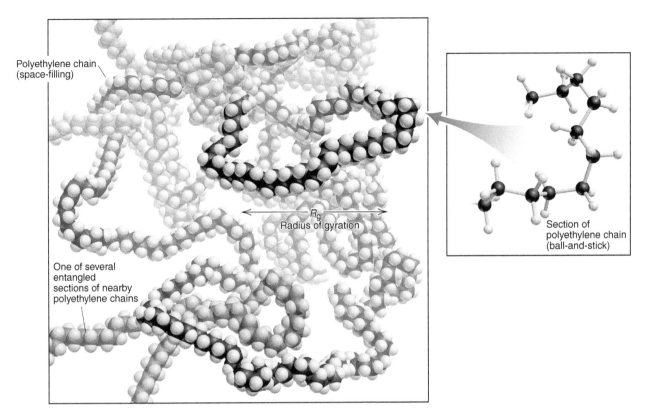

Polyethylene chain (space-filling)

R_g
Radius of gyration

One of several entangled sections of nearby polyethylene chains

Section of polyethylene chain (ball-and-stick)

FIGURE 65.5 The structure of polyethylene.

material used, for example, for automobile battery cases and luggage. The alkyl substituent on the ethylene monomer, a methyl group in the case of polypropylene, can be made longer. In a polymer called linear low density polyethylene (LLDPE), used in making plastic film, the alkyl substituent is a butyl group. The *n*–butyl substituted polymer is made by copolymerizing ethylene and 1–hexene in the presence of a Ziegler-Natta catalyst. The copolymerization results in fewer substituents than in polypropylene. Innovex™ is a LLDPE copolymer in which the substituent is an *iso*-butyl group. An LLDPE polymer has relatively short well-defined side chains (unlike the random long side chains of LDPE). The side chains decrease the crystallinity and density of the polymer making it more flexible.

The side chains in a substituted polyethylene such as polypropylene can be arranged in different conformations (Figure 65.6). In the **isotactic** form, all the methyl groups are on the same side of the chain. In the **syndiotactic** form, they alternate regularly from side to side and in the **atactic** form the methyl groups are arranged randomly. The Ziegler-Natta catalyst produces the isotactic polymer. Natta later developed a catalyst to produce the syndiotactic polymer.

Substituted Polyethylenes

Substituted ethylene molecules may be used as the monomers in polymerization reactions to produce a wide variety of polymers with different properties and uses. Polypropylene is an example. Some are listed in Table 65.1.

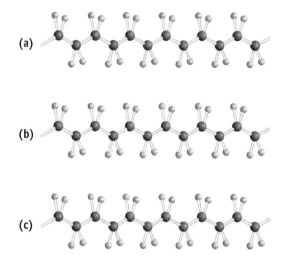

FIGURE 65.6 The structures of isotactic (a), syndiotactic (b), and atactic (c) polypropylene. The R group (blue) is CH_3.

TABLE 65.1 Some addition polymers of ethylene and its derivatives.

Monomer	Monomer Formula	Polymer Formula	Polymer Name	Some Uses
ethylene	$H_2C=CH_2$	$-[CH_2-CH_2]_n-$	polyethylene	bags, bottles, packaging
propylene	$H_2C=CH-CH_3$	$-[CH_2-CH]_n-$ CH_3	polypropylene	rope, bottles, carpets
vinyl chloride	$H_2C=CH-Cl$	$-[CH_2-CH]_n-$ Cl	polyvinyl chloride (PVC)	pipes, electrical insulation
styrene	$H_2C=CH-$⬡	$-[CH_2-CH]_n-$ ⬡	polystyrene	styrofoam cups, thermal insulation
1,1–dichloroethylene	$H_2C=CCl_2$	$-[CH_2-CCl_2]_n-$	polyvinylidene chloride	food wrap (Saran™)
acrylonitrile	$H_2C=CH-CN$	$-[CH_2-CH]_n-$ CN	polyacrylonitrile (PAN)	**carpets, fibers (Orlon™, Acrilan™)**
tetrafluoroethylene	$F_2C=CF_2$	$-[CF_2-CF_2]_n-$	**polytetrafluoroethylene (PTFE)**	Teflon™, nonstick coating

vinyl acetate	$H_2C=CH-O-\overset{\overset{O}{\|\|}}{C}CH_3$	$-[CH_2-CH]_n-$
		     $O-CCH_3$
		         $\|\|$
		         O
			polyvinyl acetate (PVA)	adhesives, paints

methyl methacrylate	$\overset{CH_3}{H_2C=C}\overset{}{C-O-CH_3}$
	       O
		$-[CH_2-\overset{CH_3}{C}\overset{}{C-O-CH_3}]_n-$
		         O
			polymethyl methacrylate	Lucite™, Perspex™, Plexiglass™

Polystyrene results from the polymerization of styrene. Styrene is ethylene in which one of the hydrogen atoms is replaced by a benzene ring. This polymer is often produced as a foam (Styrofoam™) familiar as disposable coffee cups, packing 'peanuts', and the sheets of insulation used in sheathing houses.

Polyvinyl chloride (PVC) is familiar as the white tubes used in plumbing; it is also used for shower curtains and car upholstery. To make the polymer more pliable, it is mixed with a compatible molecule of much lower molar mass. These molecules interrupt the attraction between the polymer chains and make the material more flexible. A commercial example is Naugahyde™. The additive is known as a **plasticizer** and its evaporation from the PVC is responsible for the smell of new shower curtains and the upholstery in new cars. As the plasticizer evaporates over time, the plastic becomes more brittle and starts to crack. PVC can also be drawn into fibers.

Polytetrafluoroethylene (PTFE) was discovered by accident by Roy Plunkett at DuPont in 1938. Some tetrafluoroethylene was stored in a metal canister for later use in the manufacture of new chlorofluorocarbons. When the canister was opened, however, no tetrafluoroethylene gas remained. It had all polymerized to a white slippery solid. The new polymer was chemically inert and resistant to corrosion. Its first significant use was to line the vessels used to separate the uranium–235 and uranium–238 hexafluorides by gaseous diffusion in the Manhattan Project. Now it is more familiar as Teflon™, the coating on nonstick kitchenware.

Polymethylmethacrylate, known as Plexiglass™, Perspex™, Lucite™, or just PMMA, depending upon the manufacturer, is a clear plastic used as safety glass. It is the material used in shower cubicles and the shielding around hockey rinks, where it sometimes takes quite a beating without breaking. It is also used for the thick viewing windows in large aquariums.

Polyacetylene is an interesting polymer because the polymerization process reduces the triple bonding to a series of conjugated double bonds—the polymer is a conjugated alkene (Figure 65.7). Just as in butadiene and other conjugated alkenes, the π bonding extends over the entire molecule and the electrons in the π bonds are delocalized. As a result the polymer can conduct an electrical current along the chains. The polymer has other properties characteristic of metals; it is shiny and, when made into film, looks like metal foil. When oxidized by bromine or iodine, the conductivity of the polyacetylene approaches that of copper metal!

PVC was discovered by accident in Germany in 1912 when some vinyl chloride polymerized. It was rediscovered in the US in 1926 and immediately used for shower curtains and in other waterproofing applications.

Polychlorinated biphenyls (PCBs) were once used as plasticizers but are now banned. Current plasticizers are often esters of phthalic acid.

Gore-tex™ is PTFE which has been quickly stretched at high temperature. Gore-tex is a breathable water-resistant fabric and is used for outdoor wear.

Alan J. Heeger, Alan G. Macdiarmid, and Hideki Shirakawa were awarded the 2000 Nobel Prize in Chemistry for the discovery and development of conductive polymers.

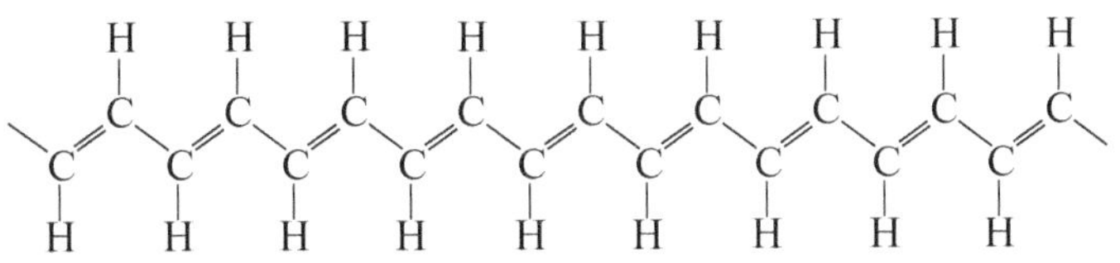

FIGURE 65.7   The structure of polyacetylene.

Rubber

Naturally-occurring rubber is a polymer of isoprene. Isoprene is a substituted butadiene: 2–methyl–1,3–butadiene (Figure 65.8). The rubber is harvested from a rubber tree by scarring the bark. The rubber drips from the scar as a milky-white suspension in water called latex (Figure 65.9). When separated from the water, the natural rubber

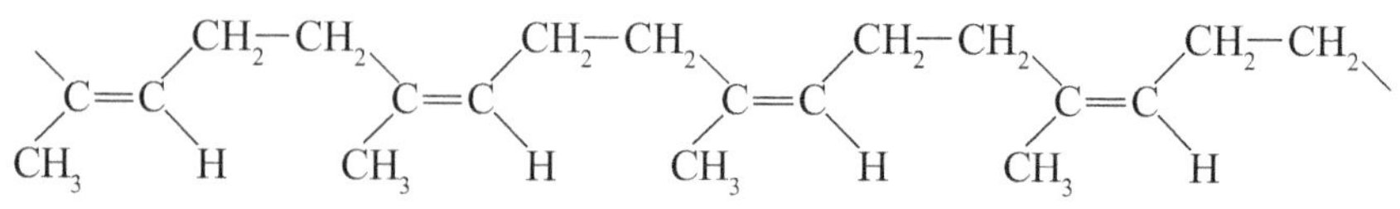

FIGURE 65.8 The structure of polyisoprene in natural rubber.

is soft and becomes gooey when heated. Natural rubber was introduced into Europe in 1740 and was used to erase, or rub out, pencil marks—hence the name. Early articles made from rubber proved problematic because the rubber would become hard and brittle in winter and then melt to a somewhat smelly, sticky liquid in the heat of summer. In 1823, Charles Macintosh used rubber to waterproof clothing made of cotton and the raincoats came to be known as mackintoshes or macs.

FIGURE 65.9 Collecting latex from a rubber tree.

Charles Goodyear spent years experimenting with rubber in attempts to improve its characteristics. He eventually succeeded in 1839 when he mixed sulfur with molten rubber. Goodyear was a poor businessman and died in 1860 greatly in debt.

Automobile tires contain other additives to enhance the properties of the rubber. Carbon black strengthens the elastomer and nylon or steel cords are used to provide reinforcement.

It was a discovery by Charles Goodyear in 1839 that revived the rubber industry. Heating sulfur with the rubber creates $-S_n-$ cross-links (where n = 2 or more) between the polyisoprene chains (Figure 65.10). This hardens the rubber and improves its tensile strength and elasticity. This is a typical result of **cross-linking** polymer chains. The flexibility of a cross-linked polymer can be varied by adjusting the number of cross-links. For an automobile tire, the number of cross-links is high and the rubber is quite hard. For rubber kitchen gloves, the number of cross-links is perhaps five times fewer and the rubber is more flexible and stretchable. Cross-linking the rubber molecules by adding sulfur became known as **vulcanization**. Vulcanized rubber is an example of an elastomer—a polymer that can be stretched and then regain its original shape when released. The polymer chains can be stretched (elongated) but then are pulled back into position by the cross-linking. This has an interesting application in the perming of hair as we'll see in the next unit.

Chemists were unable to polymerize isoprene to produce rubber—attempts resulted in a random mixture of *cis–* and *trans–* arrangements of the isoprene units

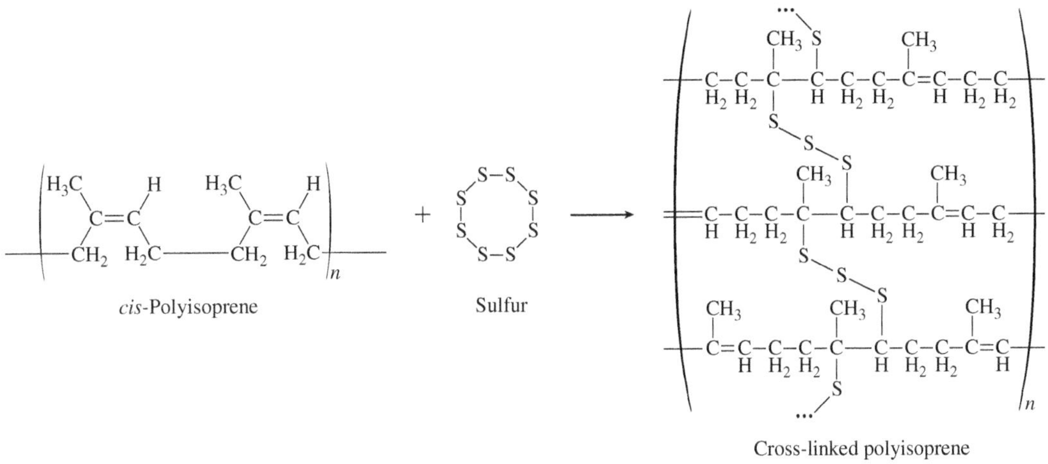

FIGURE 65.10 **The cross-linking of polyisoprene molecules by chains of sulfur atoms in the vulcanization of rubber.**
Notice the sulfur atoms that bridge the isoprene polymer chains.

and a sticky and unusable polymer. In natural rubber the arrangement is always *cis–* (Figure 65.8). However, with the use of a Ziegler-Natta catalyst, almost pure *cis–*polyisoprene can be produced. Almost a billion kilograms of synthetic *cis–*polyisoprene is manufactured each year in the US—about as much as the amount of natural rubber imported.

At the beginning of World War II, when sources of natural rubber in Malaysia and Indonesia were cut off, great effort was made to synthesize artificial substitutes. One of the most successful is a **copolymer**, a polymer made by polymerizing a mixture of two or more monomers. A copolymer of styrene and butadiene in a 1 to 3 ratio is called **styrene-butadiene rubber (SBR)** (Figure 65.11) and is produced in

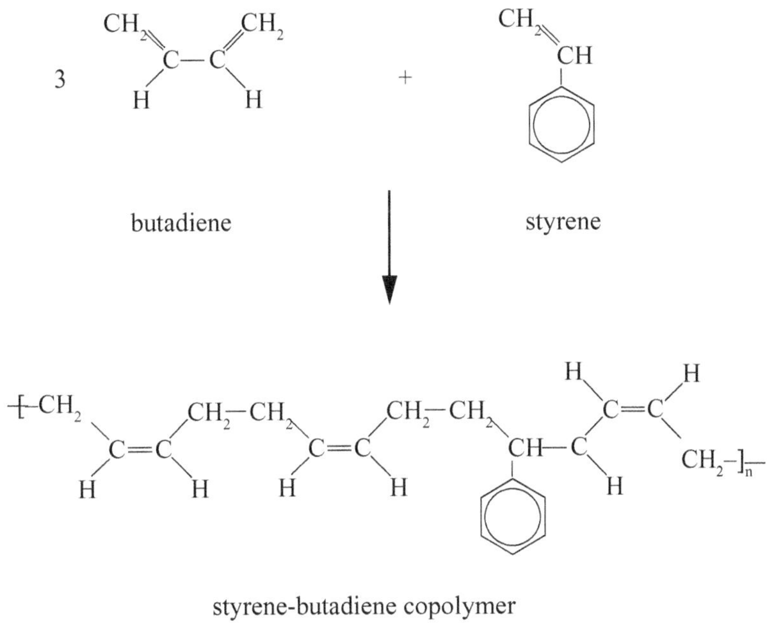

The all-*trans* isomer of polyisoprene also occurs naturally in the sap of certain rubber trees and is known as *gutta-percha*. It is used as the hard cover on golf balls.

FIGURE 65.11 The structure of styrene-butadiene rubber (SBR).

greater quantities than *cis*–polyisoprene specifically for the manufacture of automobile tires. Polybutadiene itself can be made relatively easily but the polymer is not as strong as SBR. The polymer of 2–chloro–1,3–butadiene is called **neoprene** and is used for gasoline hoses and other items where resistance to oils and gasoline is necessary.

Another copolymer, similar to SBR, is one produced by the copolymerization of three monomers in equal amounts: acrylonitrile, butadiene, and styrene (Figure 65.12). This polymer, called ABS, is a tough, shock resistant, and chemically resistant polymer often used to house electronic instruments.

Silicone rubber has an alternating silicon–oxygen backbone quite unlike the carbon based polymers described so far. This rubber has a distinct advantage of remaining elastic over a wide temperature range.

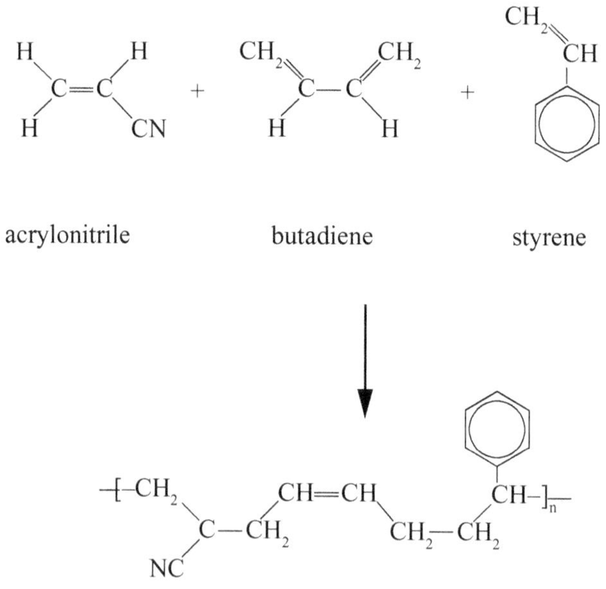

FIGURE 65.12   The structure of acrylonitrile-butadiene-styrene copolymer (ABS).

65.3   Condensation Polymers

As described in Unit 64, when two molecules combine with the elimination of a small molecule, often water, the process is called **condensation**. Two examples are the formation of an ester from a carboxylic acid and an alcohol, and the formation of an amide from a carboxylic acid and an amine.

If a molecule contains two carboxylic acid groups, it can react with a molecule containing two amine groups to form an infinite chain. The formation of each link eliminates a molecule of water. Similarly, if a molecule contains a carboxylic acid functional group at one end and an amine functional group at the other, it can condense with other similar molecules to form a long chain. The formation of polypeptides from α–amino acids is an example of this type of polymerization. The only requirement for polymerization reactions like these is that each molecule contains at least two functional groups (that can react with functional groups on another molecule).

Nylon

In 1928, Wallace Carothers at the Du Pont Chemical Company started an investigation of long chain molecules such as those found in rubber, natural fibers, and resins. The research led to the discovery of the first synthetic polyamide called **nylon**. This polymer was made by condensing adipoyl chloride, which is a molecule with an acid chloride function group at both ends, with 1,6–diaminohexane, which is a molecule with an amino group at both ends (Figure 65.13). The two compounds react to produce long chains of the polyamide, nylon–66 (Figure 65.14).

FIGURE 65.13 Nylon is formed at the interface between adipoyl chloride and 1,6–diamino-hexane.
In this condensation reaction, molecules of HCl, not water, are eliminated. The dicarboxylic acid (adipic acid) could be used but the reaction with the acid chloride occurs much more readily. Adipic acid is used in the industrial process.

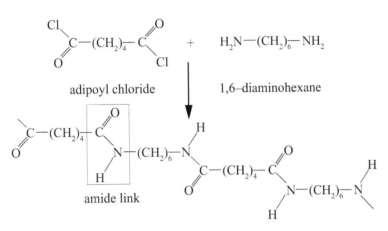

FIGURE 65.14 The formation of nylon–66 by the condensation of adipoyl chloride and 1,6–diaminehexane.

When mixed, the two compounds combine to form a slimy globular material that at first sight doesn't appear very promising. However, when the product is extruded through small holes in a device called a **spinneret**, much as a spider spins its web, the nylon fiber is formed. Squeezing the polymer through the spinneret causes the long molecules to line up sideways. Hydrogen bonding between adjacent chains holds the molecules together and produces the strong fiber (Figure 65.15). The hydrogen bonding between the chains is not as strong as the covalent bonding in a cross-linked polymer and this results in a very flexible fiber. The number of hydrogen bonds between the long nylon polymer molecules provides high tensile strength. This type of hydrogen bonding occurs in all polyamides, including naturally occurring polypeptides.

As mentioned earlier, a polymer similar to nylon–66 can be made if a chain of five —CH_2— groups has an amine group at one end and a carboxylic acid group at the other end. The polymer is called nylon–6, or Perlon™. If condensation between an amine group and a carboxylic acid group can occur, you may wonder why one end of the molecule doesn't condense with the other end to form a ring? Indeed it does. In fact, the starting material for the manufacture of nylon–6 is the ring compound

The numbers 66 in nylon–66 refer to the number of carbon atoms in the two different segments of the chain. Other nylons such as nylon–6, nylon–610 and nylon–11 are also commercially important.

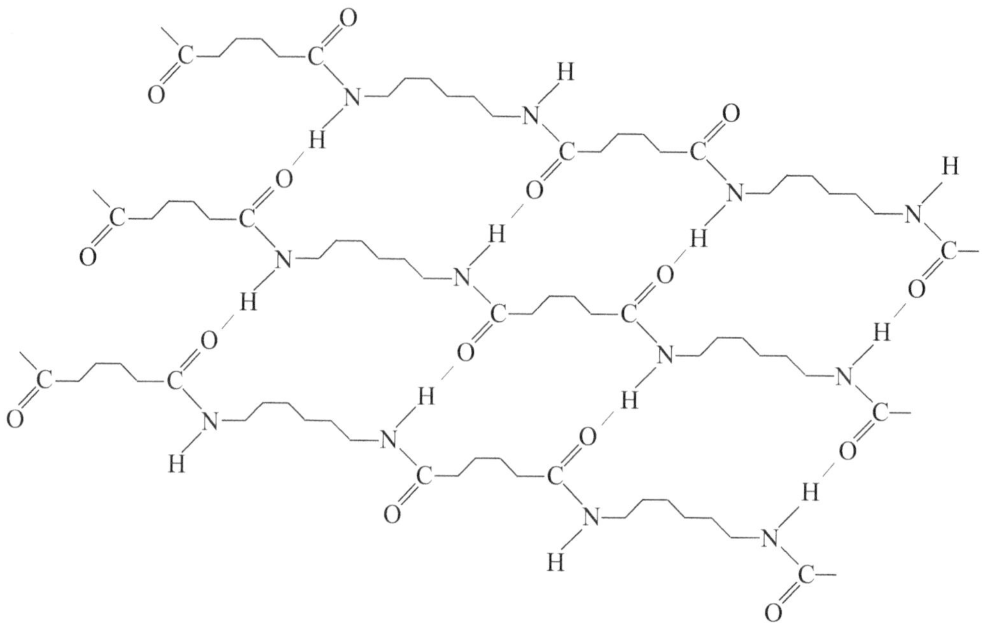

FIGURE 65.15   Hydrogen bonding between the chains of nylon–66.
The oxygen atoms of the carbonyl (C=O) groups form hydrogen bonds with the hydrogen atoms attached to the nitrogen atoms.

ε–caprolactam (Figure 65.16). In a ring–opening polymerization process, the amide link in the ring is hydrolysed to form the long chain amino acid (6–aminohexanoic acid) which then attacks another caprolactam ring to extend the chain. This continues over and over again to form the nylon–6 polymer.

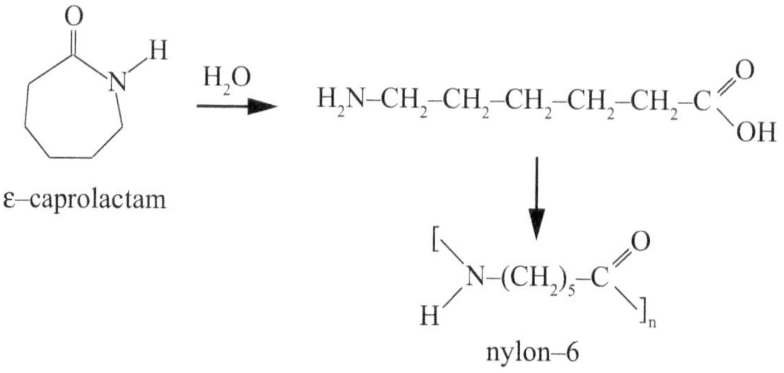

ε–caprolactam

nylon–6

FIGURE 65.16   The self-condensation of 6-aminohexanoic acid to form nylon–6.
The amino acid exists as the ring compound ε-caprolactam. In a ring-opening polymerization process, the amide link in the ring is hydrolysed to form the 6-aminohexanoic acid which then attacks another caprolactam ring to form the polymer chain.

FIGURE 65.17   Modern climbing equipment relies on synthetic polymers such as perlon for ropes and dyneema for slings.

Aramids

Another polyamide that is particularly useful is Kevlar. This polyamide is made by condensing terephthalic acid and phenylenediamine (1,4–diaminobenzene) (Figure 65.18).

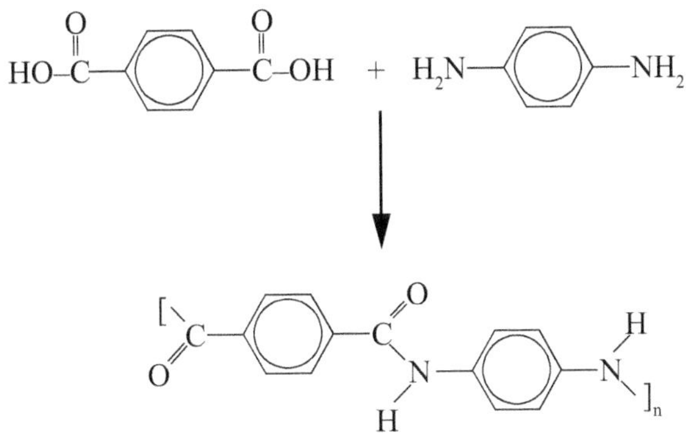

FIGURE 65.18 The condensation of terephthalic acid and phenylene diamine to produce the polyamide Kevlar.

Fabric made from Kevlar is exceptionally strong—stronger than an equal mass of steel—and it is used in the construction of bulletproof vests. The chains of the polyamide are strong and somewhat inflexible because they are held together by many hydrogen bonds between the carbonyl groups and amide groups of adjacent chains. This hydrogen bonding is more effective in Kevlar than nylon because the Kevlar chains line up in a more regular linear array due to way in which the benzene rings force the geometry about the amide link to be all *trans–* (Figure 65.19). In contrast, the conformation in nylon is a mixture of *cis–* and *trans–*. The Kevlar polymer is described as having high crystallinity.

The general term for a polymer such as Kevlar is **para–aramid**—the aromatic ring is disubstituted in the *para* positions (1,4–disubstituted). Nomex™ is a fiber very similar to Kevlar but it is a **meta–aramid** (the substitution is at the 1 and 3 positions of the benzene rings (Figure 65.20). Nomex is fire resistant and is used for the clothing of fire-fighters and helicopter pilots, often in a blend with Kevlar.

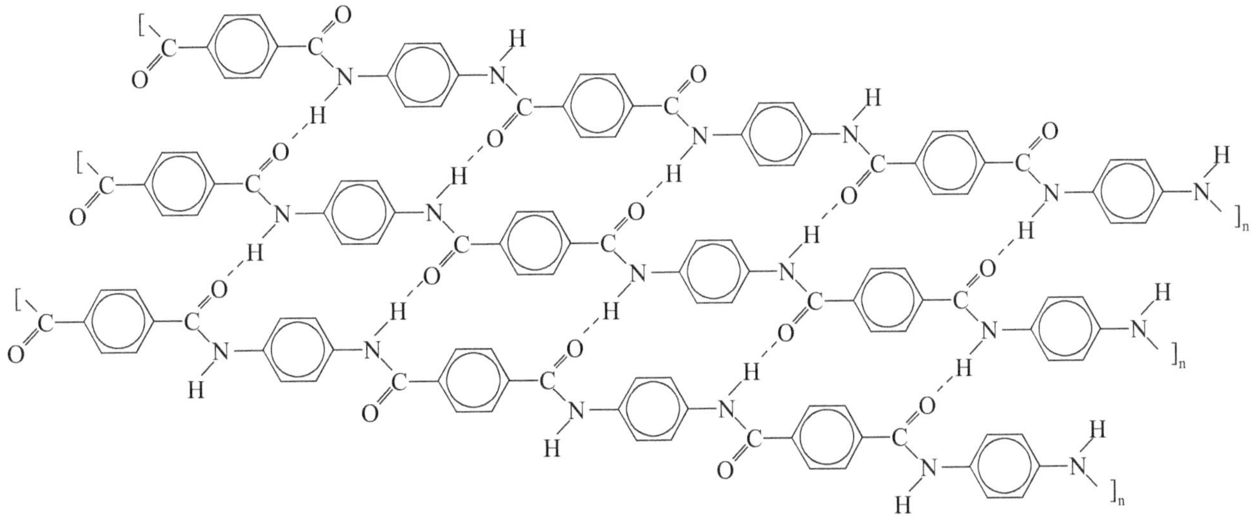

FIGURE 65.19 Hydrogen bonding in Kevlar.
The amide links are all *trans*.

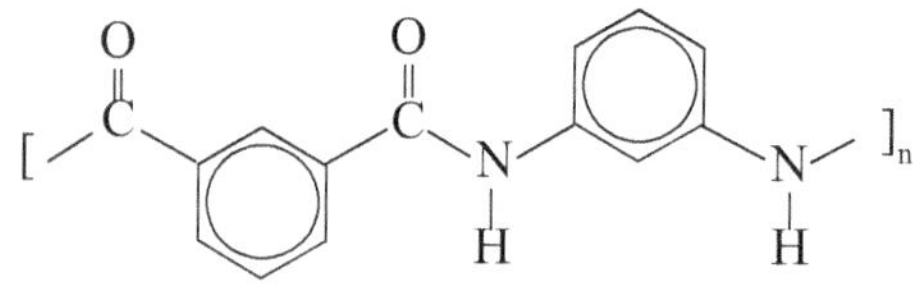

FIGURE 65.20 The structure of Nomex, a meta-aramid.

Polyesters

Another major class of condensation polymers are the **polyesters**. A common example is the polyester made from terephthalic acid and ethylene glycol, called polyethylene terephthalate and known by the trade names Dacron™ and Terylene™. When this polyester is formed into a film instead of a fiber, it is called Mylar™. Industrially, the polyester is made from the dimethyl ester of terephthalic acid and ethylene glycol. The reaction is a trans-esterification in which the glycol replaces the methanol as the alcohol part of the ester. Both the acid and the alcohol have two functional groups and the result is a long polymer chain (Figure 65.21). Dacron is used extensively in clothing, very often blended with cotton. It is also used as synthetic blood vessels in bypass operations because of its inertness and nonallergenic properties.

The structure of the polyester can be modified to improve or alter its physical characteristics. For example, if the single benzene ring of the terephthalate is replaced by naphthalene, the result is polyethylene naphthalate (PEN). This polymer is more resistant to high temperatures than polyethylene terephthalate; it doesn't soften so easily. The length of the $—(CH_2)_n—$ chain can be varied by using different alcohols.

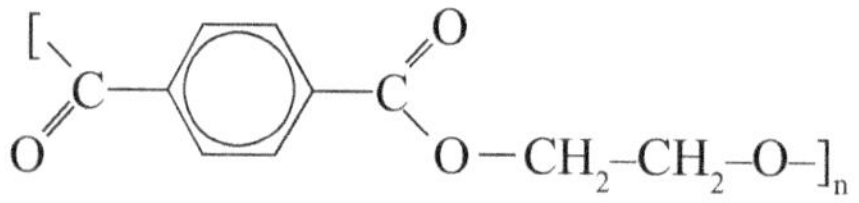

FIGURE 65.21 The structure of polyethylene terephthalate, known by the trade names Dacron™ and Terylene™.

Resins

The original synthetic polymer, mentioned at the beginning of the unit, is a condensation polymer made from phenol and formaldehyde. The condensation eliminates water molecules in the formation of a three dimensional network. Each phenol molecule has three $—CH_2—$ bridges to other phenol molecules in the *ortho–* and *para–* positions around the benzene ring. The result is a rigid thermoset resin which is intractable and cannot be reformed once made. Most of the phenol–formaldehyde resin manufactured is used to bind the sheets of wood in plywood.

A similar three-dimensional thermoset resin can be made from formaldehyde and melamine (Figure 65.22). The melamine itself is made from the condensation of urea; three urea molecules condense to form one six-membered melamine ring. The resin is a urea–formaldehyde resin and is used for example in Formica™ tabletops. Linear urea–formaldehyde polymers can also be made.

Probably the most familiar thermoset resin is epoxy resin. This is the material supplied in two tubes that, when mixed, sets into a solid polymer used to stick

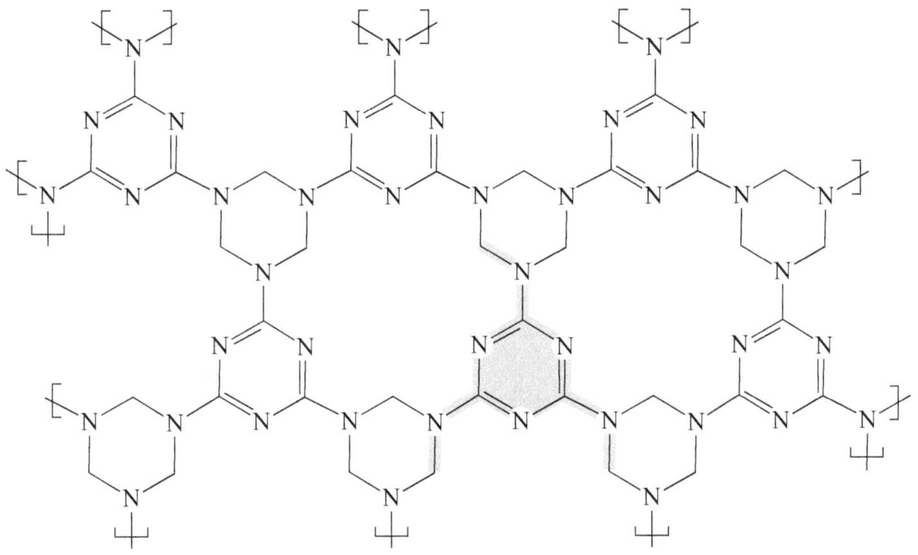

FIGURE 65.22   The urea–melamine resin used in Formica™ tabletops.

almost anything together. Like other substances used to make the condensation polymers that we have already discussed, one tube contains a relatively small molecule with a functional group, in this case an epoxy group, at each end; the molecule is a diepoxy. The second tube also contains a molecule with two functional groups, a diamine. When mixed together the two molecules condense to form a three-dimensional matrix (a thermoset resin). The ability of the epoxy resin to stick to many different materials is due to the —OH groups on the polymer chains.

> The diepoxy compound is usually a **prepolymer**—a copolymer of bisphenol and epichlorohydrin about 10 units long. The diamine, often referred to as the **curing agent**, cross-links the prepolymers as shown in Figure 65.23.

Polycarbonates

If the bisphenol used in the manufacture of the diepoxy for epoxy resin is condensed with phosgene (carbonyl chloride) instead, a polycarbonate polymer is produced (Figure 65.24). The bisphenol groups are joined by CO_3 units—hence the name. Approximately 1.5 million tons of this polymer is made each year. It is a transparent, thermally stable, tough material and is used, for example, for riot shields, the face plates of astronauts' suits, bulletproof glass, headlamp lenses, traffic lights, and safety helmets. It is generally known by the trade name Lexan™.

Polyurethanes

The urethane functional group is an ester of carbamic acid and has the general formula R—NH—CO—O—R, where the R symbols represent alkyl or other groups and are not necessarily the same. The —NH—CO— part of the group is the same as that found in amides. Polyurethanes are polymers with urethane links and an example is the polymer derived from ethylene glycol illustrated in Figure 65.25. The polyurethane is made by the condensation of a diisocyanate with the ethylene glycol. A similar reaction can be performed with a diamine in place of the glycol to form a polyurea, often also referred to as a polyurethane (Figure 65.25). Polyurethanes are used in paints, varnishes, adhesives, and foams for cushions.

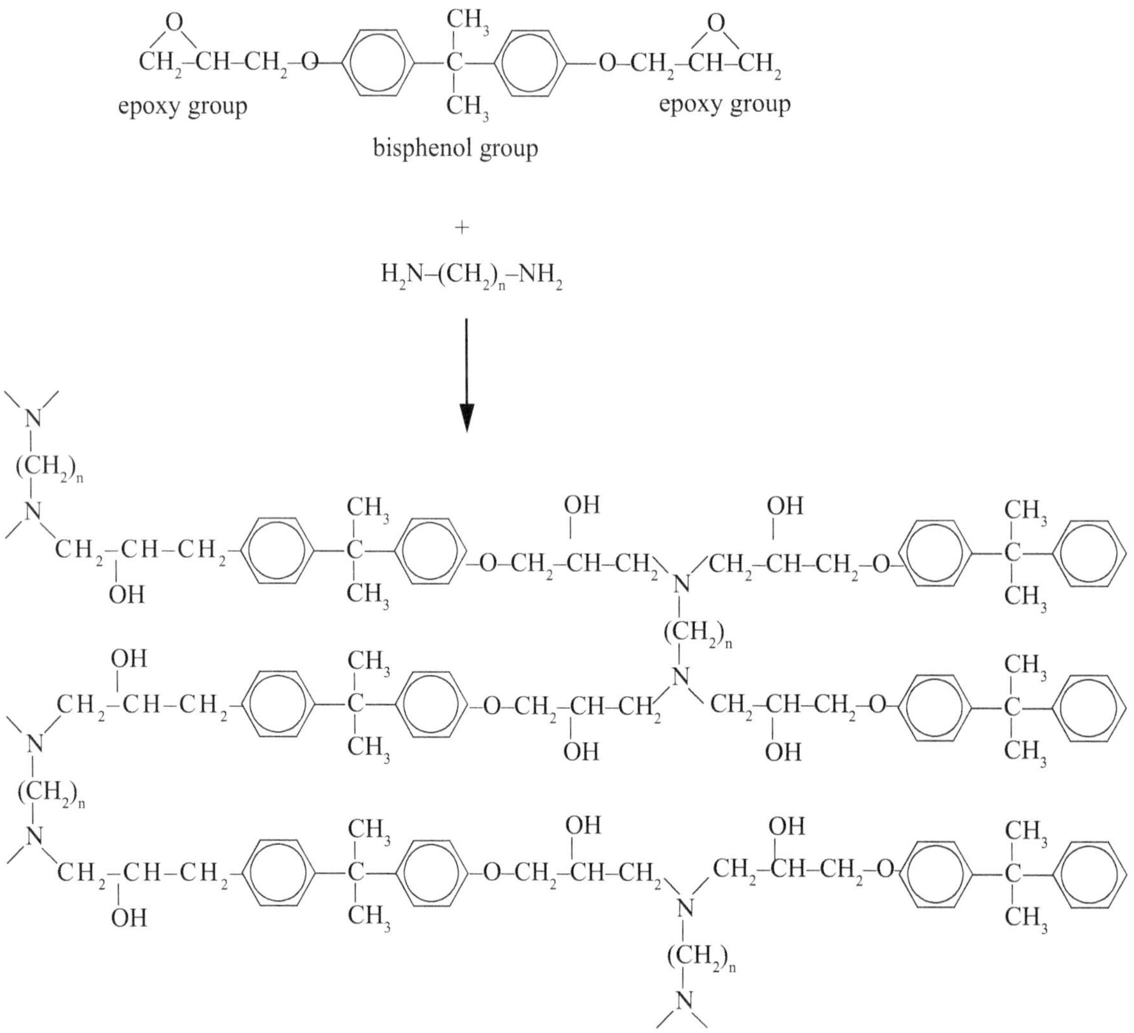

FIGURE 65.23 The formation of epoxy resin from its two components.

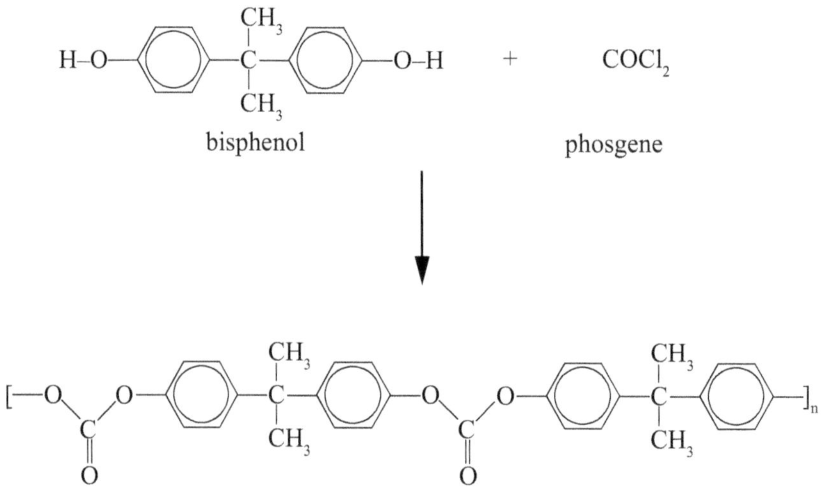

FIGURE 65.24 The structure of polycarbonate.

Polyurethanes are made by reacting diisocyanates with dialcohols. For example,

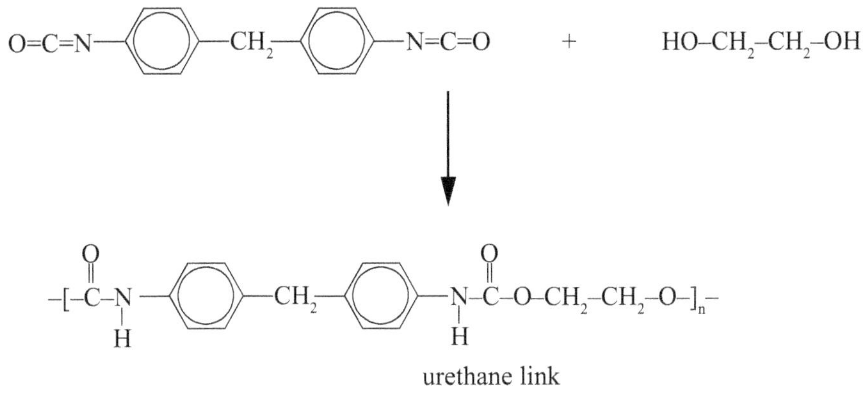

urethane link

Polyurea: Polyureas are made by reacting diisocyanates with diamines. For example,

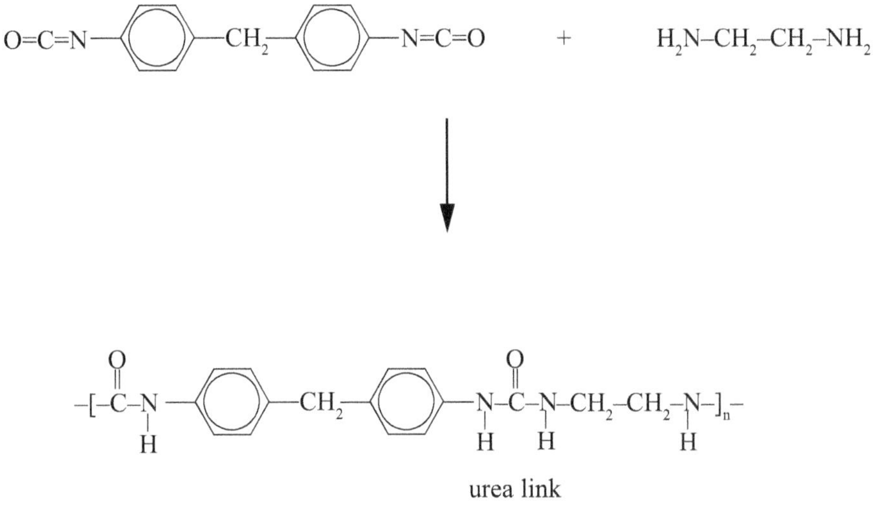

urea link

FIGURE 65.25 Polyurethane.

A remarkable polyurethane is a copolymer made with a long segments of polyglycol and short segments of polyurethane. The polyurethane segments are rigid and attract similar segments of other chains to provide regions of high crystallinity. The long polyglycol chains are flexible and stretchable. The result is an elastomeric fiber called spandex or Lycra™ (Figure 65.26). Usually blended with nylon or other polymers, or natural fibers such as wool, silk, and cotton, spandex is used for athletic clothing, swimwear and dancewear.

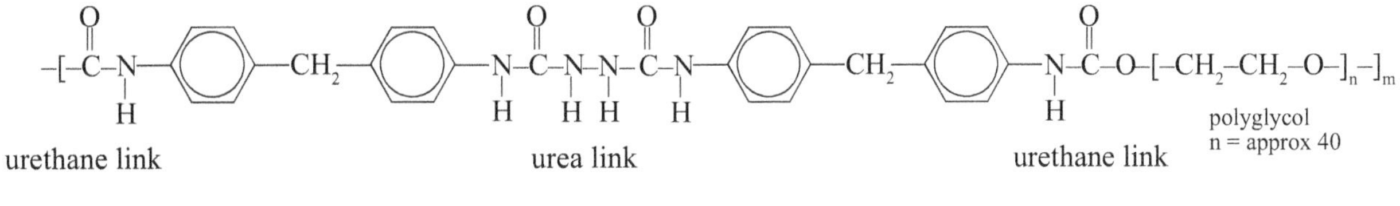

urethane link   urea link   urethane link

polyglycol
n = approx 40

FIGURE 65.26 The structure of spandex.
The polymer is composed of rigid crystalline segments and flexible and stretchable polyglycol segments.

EXAMPLE 65.1 IDENTIFYING POLYMERS

Identify the polymer produced by the condensation of malonic acid HO$_2$C—CH$_2$—CO$_2$H and ethylene glycol HOCH$_2$—CH$_2$OH. Draw a portion of the polymer chain produced in the reaction and classify the type of polymer.

UNDERSTAND THE QUESTION

The two principal types of polymerization reactions are addition and condensation reactions. Addition reactions involve derivatives of ethylene or acetylene. Condensation reactions involve molecules with two functional groups, one at each end, that react with other molecules, also with two functional groups, one at each end. Typical examples are the production of polyamides and polyesters.

PLAN THE SOLUTION

Examine the two starting materials and determine the functional groups that are present. Look for a double bond for an addition polymerization reaction, or two functional groups that react with one another for a condensation reaction.

SOLVE THE PROBLEM

Malonic acid, HO$_2$C—CH$_2$—CO$_2$H, has a carboxylic acid group at each end. Ethylene glycol, HOCH$_2$—CH$_2$OH, has an alcohol group at each end. Condensation leads to a polyester. A portion of the polymer is:

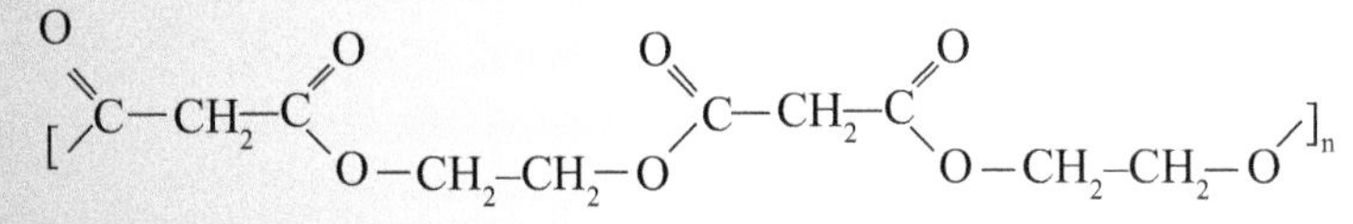

PROBLEM 65.1A

Suppose that you wished to make a polyamide with a chain of four carbon atoms between the amide links. One approach would be to use the condensation of 4–aminobutanoic acid with itself. Another would be to condense 1,4–aminobutane with succinic acid HO$_2$C—(CH$_2$)$_2$—CO$_2$H. Would the products from these two reactions be the same, or different? If different, in what way would they differ?

PROBLEM 65.1B

Identify the polymer produced by the condensation of 4–aminobenzoic acid. Draw a portion of the polymer chain produced in the reaction and classify the type of polymer.

65.4 Composite Materials

Composite materials are heterogeneous combinations of two or more components. The idea is to create a combination that exploits the best characteristics of each of the components. In a typical composite structure, one of the components provides the bulk of the material, called the matrix, and the other component serves to reinforce the matrix. The matrix surrounds the reinforcement, adheres to it, and protects it.

Composites have been known for thousands of years. For example, wattle and daub (mud) was used for hundreds of years as the primary material for building the walls of houses. Animal hair was added to plaster or clay to increase its strength. The waterproof rainwear developed by Charles Macintosh was made of rubber reinforced with layers of woven cotton. A more modern example is reinforced concrete that incorporates steel rods to increase the tensile strength of the concrete. Concrete itself is a composite of a cement matrix with gravel reinforcement.

The matrix of a composite material may be metallic, ceramic, or polymeric. The reinforcing fibers for a metallic matrix are limited to those able to survive the high temperatures of the molten metals. Examples are carbon or boron fibers, silicon carbide fibers, and other ceramic fibers. The same is true of the ceramic matrix composites. However, the manufacture of such composites produces materials able to withstand very high temperatures, which polymer matrix composites cannot do. The tiles on the space shuttle are ceramic composites.

The composites that are most familiar are those in which the matrix is a thermoset resin. The development of polymers, particularly the thermoset plastics, has led to composite materials that are stronger and much lighter than steel.

Most polymer-matrix composites are reinforced by fibers. The fibers can be used as filaments oriented in a particular direction, randomly oriented in all directions, or as woven mats, depending upon the particular use for the composite. In general, the tensile strength of the composite is very high in the direction in which the fibers are aligned, but relatively low perpendicular to that direction. In Fiberglas™, as you may have noticed if you have seen a sample, the glass fibers are arranged randomly. The matrix is a cross-linked resin made from styrene and an unsaturated polyester. The body of the Chevrolet Corvette has been made of this composite since 1953.

The most common fibers used in reinforcing polymeric matrices are glass fibers, aramid fibers (Kevlar and Nomex), carbon or boron fibers, and UHMWPE (polyethylene) fibers. Glass fibers have the overwhelming advantage of being cheap. A carbon-fiber reinforced polymer is strong but more brittle than a comparable Kevlar composite—the Kevlar reinforced composite tolerates shock better—it absorbs energy without breaking. The UHMWPE composite outperforms both carbon-fiber and Kevlar reinforced resin in terms of both strength and ability to tolerate shock. The fiber is, however, slippery and difficult to incorporate in the resin matrix.

The resin used in polymer-matrix composites is commonly an epoxy or cross-linked polyester resin. For high temperature applications, a phenol-formaldehyde resin (the original Bakelite) is sometimes used. Fiber-reinforced composites have found numerous uses in the automotive and aerospace industries. Many vehicles have dent-resistant doors made from composites that stand up to corrosion better than equivalent steel components. Stealth F-117A fighters and other modern military aircraft use fiber-reinforced epoxy composites in place of metal to reduce weight without compromising integrity. Modern sports equipment from bicycle frames, tennis rackets, skis, snowboards to fishing rods are now made of composite materials. In terms of weight and strength, modern equipment made from composite materials far outperforms the original equipment.

There is no doubt that polymers and composites will play an increasing important role in the future. Particularly exciting are the biomedical applications of these

The tiles on the space shuttle vary depending upon their location. The most obvious difference is the white ceramic tiles on the top to protect against solar radiation and the black tiles on the bottom to radiate heat generated during reentry. The hottest location is on the nose cone, where the tiles protect against temperatures up to 1,260°C. The actual body of the craft is aluminum which has to be kept below 180°C. Because the aluminum body expands and contracts with change in temperature, the tiles cannot be fixed directly on the aluminum—the ceramic would crack. Instead the tiles are mounted on a Nomex felt pad.

materials. Some examples of current applications are the replacement of heart valves and diseased arteries, joint replacements, and artificial skin grafts. One of the major problems in the development of replacement body parts is overcoming the natural tendency of the body to reject foreign objects. However, as polymer technology and the understanding of the biochemistry of different materials increases, more effective biocompatible devices will become available.

65.5   Resources and Disposal

The precursors and monomers from which polymers and composites are made are derived in most part from oil and natural gas. But both oil and natural gas are nonrenewable resources. Some years in the future, it may well be that people will look back on this period and be astonished that a resource that took millions of years to form was simply pumped out of the ground and burned.

Coal, the other major fossil fuel, remains available in vast quantities although it is not yet used as a significant source of petrochemicals. It is much more difficult to manipulate coal and extract useful components than it is to distill petroleum. Coal contains more carbon and less hydrogen than crude oil and is rich in aromatic hydrocarbons. It often contains considerable quantities of sulfur and particulate matter and these result in more environmental pollution than oil particularly when the coal is used as fuel. Much research is done to develop methods for converting coal into more useful and cleaner fuels.

The fermentation of agricultural products is a resource for ethanol from which ethylene, and hence polyethylene, can be made.

The very properties that make modern polymers so desirable—their toughness, durability, and resistance to chemical and biological attack—make their disposal a problem. It is significant that about 50% of all plastic waste is derived from packaging. It is discarded almost as soon as it is used! Efforts have been made to make such plastics biodegradable by basing the synthetic polymer on starch. Another way to hasten the decomposition of packaging materials is to make them sensitive to light and hence encourage their photochemical decomposition. Most plastic material, however, ends up in a landfill, or irresponsibly discarded into the environment. Some thermoplastic polymers are recycled, particularly LDPE, HDPE (milk jugs), and PET (Figure 65.27). In an effort to stimulate more effective recycling, containers and other packaging are now stamped with a code indicating their composition (Table 65.2).

Incineration is possible for some polymers. In fact, burning them is a useful source of heat for the generation of electrical energy. However, some polymers such as acrylonitrile and others that contain nitrogen produce toxic fumes when burned. Polyvinyl chloride produces hydrogen chloride when burned and has been linked to the production of chlorinated hydrocarbons harmful to the environment. Those polymers, such as polyethylene, that are the most useful fuels are also those polymers that are best recycled.

FIGURE 65.27   Plastic (PET) bottles collected for recycling. Making bottles for bottled water requires more than 1.5 million barrels of oil per annum in the US. Ironically, the bottled water, often no better than tap water, costs the consumer more than gasoline (as much as $10 per gallon).

TABLE 65.2   Recycling codes for plastics.

Symbol	Structure of Polymer	Polymer Name
1 PET	$-[O-CH_2-CH_2-O-\overset{\overset{O}{\|\|}}{C}-\langle\bigcirc\rangle-\overset{\overset{O}{\|\|}}{C}]_n-$	polyethylene terephthalate
2 HDPE	$-[CH_2-CH_2]_n-$	high density polyethylene
3 PVC	$-[CH_2-\underset{\underset{Cl}{\|}}{CH}]_n-$	polyvinyl chloride
4 LDPE	$-[CH_2-CH_2]_n-$	low density polyethylene
5 PP	$-[CH_2-\underset{\underset{CH_3}{\|}}{CH}]_n-$	polypropylene
6 PS	$-[CH_2-\underset{\underset{\bigcirc}{\|}}{CH}]_n-$	polystyrene
7		other polymers

Review Questions

1. Define the terms monomer, polymer, and copolymer.

2. Describe the difference between an addition polymer and a condensation polymer. Give two examples of each.

3. Describe the importance of catalysts in polymerization reactions.

4. Describe the importance of intermolecular forces and how they influence the properties of polymers.

5. In what way does a resin such as a urea-formaldehyde resin differ from a polymer such as nylon or polyethylene?

Solutions to Problems

PROBLEM 65.1A

The products from the two condensation reactions would be different in the orientation of the amide links. The difference parallels the difference between nylon–66 and nylon–6 (perlon). In this case the polymers could be called nylon–44 and nylon–4. The figures illustrate regularity in the geometry about the amide groups. In reality, the chains are flexible and the amide links are randomly oriented:

Production of nylon–44:

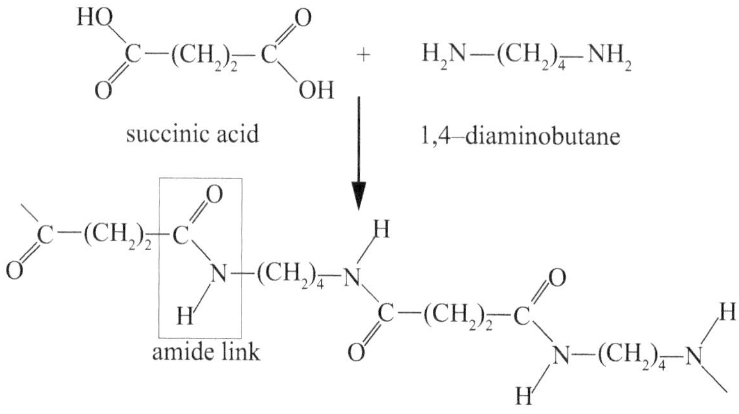
HO
O
C—(CH2)2—C
O
OH
+
H2N—(CH2)4—NH2
succinic acid
1,4–diaminobutane
amide link

Production of nylon–4:

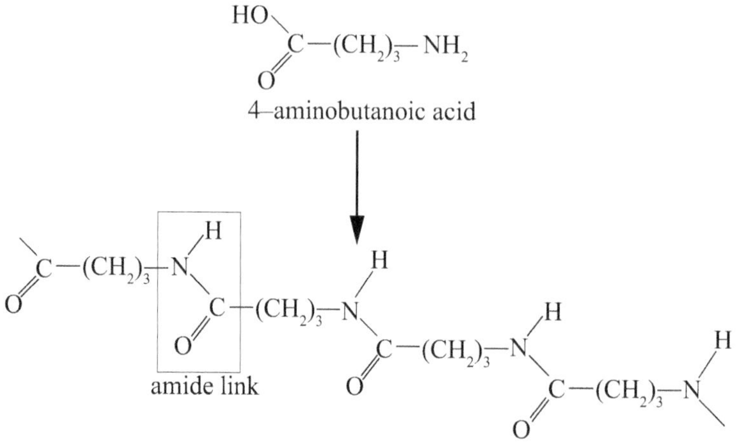
HO
C—(CH2)3—NH2
O
4–aminobutanoic acid
amide link

Answers to Review Questions

1. A monomer is a small molecule which reacts chemically with other molecules to produce a long chain molecule. The long chain molecule is called a polymer. A copolymer is a polymer derived from a mixture of different monomers; styrene butadiene rubber (SBR) is an example.
2. An addition polymer is a polymer formed by the free radical reaction of alkenes or alkynes in which the number of double bonds is reduced to form links between the molecules. Two examples are polyethylene and polyvinyl chloride. A condensation polymer is a polymer formed by the condensation reactions of molecules with two functional groups, one at each end. A small molecule, often water, is eliminated in each condensation reaction. Two examples are nylon–66 (a polyamide) and polyethylene terephthalate (a polyester).
3. Catalysts in polymerization reactions (particularly addition reactions) influence the conformation of the polymer as the molecule is built step by step. By

using appropriate catalysts, the polymer chain can be made isotactic or syndiotactic, as opposed to randomly atactic. The arrangement of substituents on the polymer chain influences the attraction between the chains and the strength and crystallinity of the material. For example, atactic polypropylene is soft and rubbery and has little commercial use. Isotactic polypropylene is more rigid and mechanically much stronger. Catalysts also direct the formation of straight chain, rather than branched chain, polymers and allow the formation of much longer molecules.

4. The tensile strength of thermoplastic polymers depends upon the strength of the intermolecular attraction between adjacent chains. The degree of attraction varies enormously. In a cross-linked resin, the polymer chains are covalently interbonded and an intractable and rigid thermoset is produced. The extent of the sulfide bridging in vulcanized rubber influences the hardness of the rubber—from hard rubber tires to soft rubber gloves. Hydrogen bonding in nylon and the aramids holds the chains together to produce strong fibers. The hydrogen bonding is more effective in the para-aramids than nylon, and Kevlar is stronger than nylon–66. The attractive forces in the polyethylenes are dispersion forces. These increase as the length of the polymer chain increases. For example UHMWPE is much stronger than HDPE.

5. Resins such as urea-formaldehyde or epoxy resin are heavily cross-linked polymers. The cross-links are covalent bonds and a rigid three-dimensional matrix is formed. The polymer is a thermoset. Polymers such as nylon or polyethylene are thermoplastics. The long chain molecules are able to flow past one another. These polymers can be melted and molded.

End-of-Unit Problems

1. Draw segments of the addition polymers produced from
   a. vinyl chloride $H_2C{=}CHCl$
   b. tetrafluoroethylene $F_2C{=}CF_2$
   c. methylmethacrylate $H_2C{=}C(CH_3)CO_2CH_3$

2. Draw segments of the addition polymers produced from
   a. acrylonitrile $H_2C{=}CHCN$
   b. styrene $H_2C{=}CHC_6H_5$
   c. vinyl acetate $H_2C{=}CHO_2CCH_3$

3. What monomer would you use to produce the addition polymer:

$$-CH_2\underset{\underset{CN}{|}}{\overset{\overset{CH_3}{|}}{C}}-CH_2\underset{\underset{CN}{|}}{\overset{\overset{CH_3}{|}}{C}}-CH_2\underset{\underset{CN}{|}}{\overset{\overset{CH_3}{|}}{C}}-CH_2\underset{\underset{CN}{|}}{\overset{\overset{CH_3}{|}}{C}}-$$

4. What monomer would you use to produce the addition polymer:

$$-CH_2\underset{\underset{Cl}{|}}{\overset{\overset{Cl}{|}}{C}}-CH_2\underset{\underset{Cl}{|}}{\overset{\overset{Cl}{|}}{C}}-CH_2\underset{\underset{Cl}{|}}{\overset{\overset{Cl}{|}}{C}}-CH_2\underset{\underset{Cl}{|}}{\overset{\overset{Cl}{|}}{C}}-$$

5. Classify the following polymers as either addition or condensation polymers:
   a. UHMWPE (polyethylene)
   b. Dacron (polyester)
   c. Kevlar (para–aramid)

6. Classify the following polymers as either addition or condensation polymers:
   a. PVC (polyvinyl chloride)
   b. Lucite (polymethylmethacrylate)
   c. Lexan (polycarbonate)

7. Dacron is a condensation polymer of terephthalic acid (1,4–benzenedicarboxylic acid) and ethylene glycol (1,2–ethanediol). Draw a schematic diagram illustrating the condensation of the two molecules and include in the diagram a segment of the polymer formed. Characterize the link between the monomer units.

8. Kevlar is a condensation polymer of terephthalic acid (1,4–benzenedicarboxylic acid) and 1,4–diaminobenzene. Draw a schematic diagram illustrating the condensation of the two molecules and include in the diagram a segment of the polymer formed. Characterize the link between the monomer units.

9. Draw the structure of the condensation polymer produced from glutaric acid and 1,3–diaminopropane:

$$HO_2C{-}(CH_2)_3{-}CO_2H + H_2N{-}(CH_2)_3{-}NH_2 \rightarrow$$

10. Draw the structure of the condensation polymer produced from malonic acid and ethylenediamine:

$$HO_2C{-}CH_2{-}CO_2H + H_2N{-}CH_2{-}CH_2{-}NH_2 \rightarrow$$

11. Explain why

    a. UHMWPE (polyethylene) has a much greater tensile strength than LDPE or HDPE.

    b. LDPE (polyethylene) tears when stretched but the lightly cross-linked rubber used in rubber gloves returns to its original shape when stretched and released.

12. Explain why

    a. Branching in a polyethylene decreases the crystallinity of the polymer.

    b. Resins, such as Bakelite, break when deformed but elastomers, such as vulcanized rubber, do not.

13. Explain why the isotactic form of polypropylene is much harder and more rigid than the atactic form.

14. Explain why the polyamide Kevlar can be used as the material for a bulletproof vest whereas the polyamide nylon cannot.

15. What is the difference between nylon–6 and nylon–66?

16. Spandex is composed of rigid crystalline segments and flexible and stretchable polyglycol segments. Describe what characteristics each segment contributes to the properties of the polymer. How does the length of the polyglycol segment influence the properties of the material?

Biochemistry

Emil Fischer (1852–1919) was awarded the 1902 Nobel Prize in Chemistry for working out the structures of the saccharides. His analysis of the structures was based upon the theory of van't Hoff that the arrangement of bonds around carbon was tetrahedral. Van't Hoff received the first Nobel Prize in Chemistry in 1901.

A living organism is a collection of chemical compounds and each compound plays its part in supporting the life of the organism. Within the cells of the organism, there are molecules, some very large and complicated, ions, and a lot of water. In this unit we will examine some of the molecules involved in the countless reactions that are taking place all the time within the cells of a living organism such as the human body. There are carbohydrates and fats to supply energy; there are proteins that act as catalysts for reactions and that provide the structural materials for cells; and there are nucleic acids that store genetic information to enable replication.

66.1 Carbohydrates

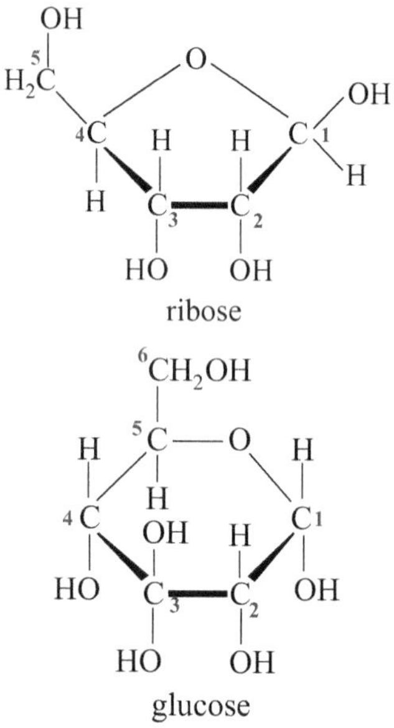

The empirical formulas of carbohydrates have the form $C_x(H_2O)_y$—hence the name carbohydrate. However, the structures of the carbohydrates are more complicated than this simple empirical formula might suggest. The simplest carbohydrates are the **monosaccharides** and, of these, the most important are those containing five carbon atoms (a pentose) or six carbon atoms (a hexose). An example of a pentose is ribose, $C_5H_{10}O_5$, and an example of a hexose is glucose, $C_6H_{12}O_6$ (Figure 66.1).

The glucose molecule exists predominantly as a six-membered ring in which one of the atoms in the ring is an oxygen atom—it is a cyclic ether. The five carbon atoms of the ring each have a hydrogen atom attached and either a —OH group or a —CH₂OH group. Less than a tenth of one percent of the glucose exists in a linear (open) form in aqueous solution (Figure 66.2). When the linear form closes to form the ring form, it can do so in two different ways to produce two isomers, α–glucose, in which the –OH group at carbon atom 1 points downward in an axial position, and 1β–glucose, in which the —OH group points upward in an equatorial position. The α– and β– forms of glucose interconvert via the open form and cannot be separated in solution. The β–isomer is favored 2:1 over the α–isomer.

As we shall see, the difference in the orientation of the –OH group at carbon atom 1 significantly alters the shapes and properties of the corresponding polymers,

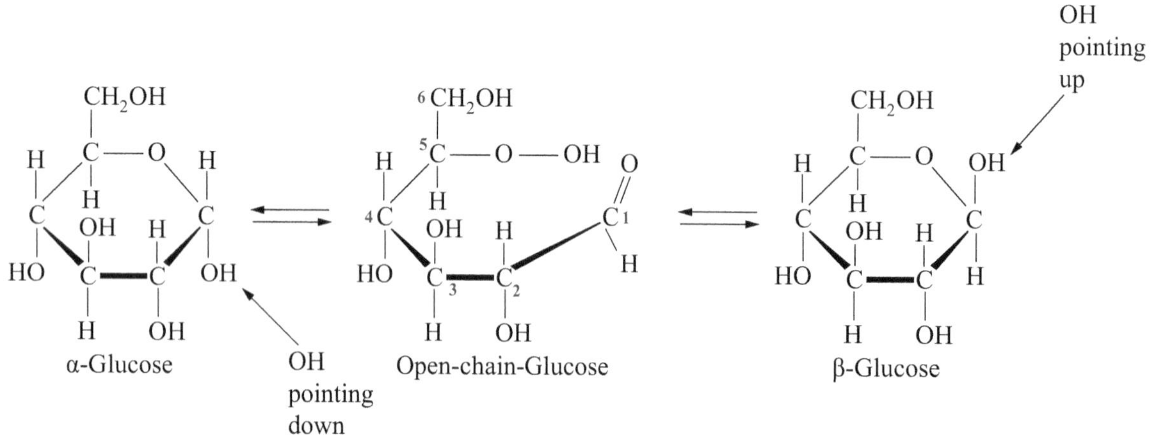

FIGURE 66.1 The monosaccharides ribose (a pentose) and glucose (a hexose).

FIGURE 66.2 **The α– and β– forms of glucose interconvert via the open form in aqueous solution.** In α–glucose, the —OH group points downward in an axial position, and β–glucose, the —OH group points upward in an equatorial position. The six membered rings are often represented as planar rings as shown in this figure. In reality, the rings have a chair-like conformation similar to that of cyclohexane (*cf.* Figure 63.5). The representation shown here is referred to as a Haworth representation. W. N. Haworth was awarded the 1937 Nobel Prize in Chemistry for his work on carbohydrates.

the **polysaccharides**. The glucose molecule, and most other monosaccharides, contain asymmetric carbon atoms and are therefore chiral. In the open form, carbon atoms 2, 3, 4, and 5 are chiral. As a result there are 16 different configurations possible. In the cyclic form, carbon atom 1 is also chiral—giving rise to the two α– and β– forms of glucose.

You may see glucose labelled D-(+)-glucose. The D describes the configuration of groups around the carbon atom 5 and the (+) describes the direction in which plane-polarized light is rotated. The (+) designation means **dextrorotatory** (a clockwise rotation) and (–) indicates **levorotatory** (an anticlockwise rotation). There is no correlation between the two labels D or L and (+) or (–); the first is a description of the structure and the second is determined by experiment. In nature the D configuration is preferred. Three examples of hexoses are shown as Fischer projections in Figure 66.3.

The condensation of two monosaccharides produces a **disaccharide**, with the elimination of a water molecule. Two examples are:

glucose + glucose → maltose + H$_2$O

glucose + fructose → sucrose + H$_2$O

The structures of the disaccharides depend upon whether the –OH group involved in the condensation is in the α–position (pointing down) or in the β–position (pointing up). In maltose, for example, both glucose molecules used are the α–isomers (Figure 66.4).

Disaccharides can be hydrolyzed to two monosaccharides by acid catalysis or by using the appropriate enzyme. For example, sucrose can be hydrolyzed to glucose and fructose. Both sucrose and glucose are dextrorotatory but fructose is levorotatory—to a greater extent than glucose is dextrorotatory. This results in a change in the direction

> Almost all organic compounds that exhibit optical activity contain asymmetric carbon atoms—carbon atoms with four different groups attached.

> The 8 isomers of glucose, corresponding to different configurations about carbon atoms 2, 3, and 4 are:
>
> allose   gulose
>
> altrose   idose
>
> glucose   galactose
>
> mannose   talose

> A Fischer projection is a way to represent the configuration of the —H and —OH groups in the sugar molecule.

> Fructose is a hexose that forms a five-membered ring. It has two —CH$_2$OH groups on the ring. It is a ketose, rather than an aldose such as glucose:

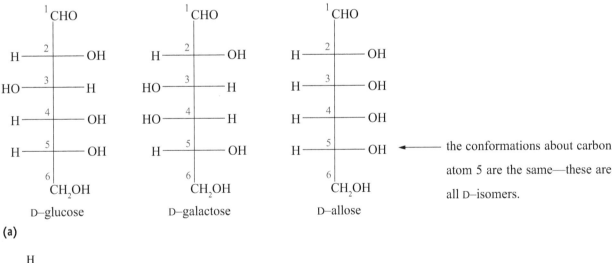

FIGURE 66.3   (a) Fischer projections of some hexoses; (b) the cyclic structure of α–D–glucose.

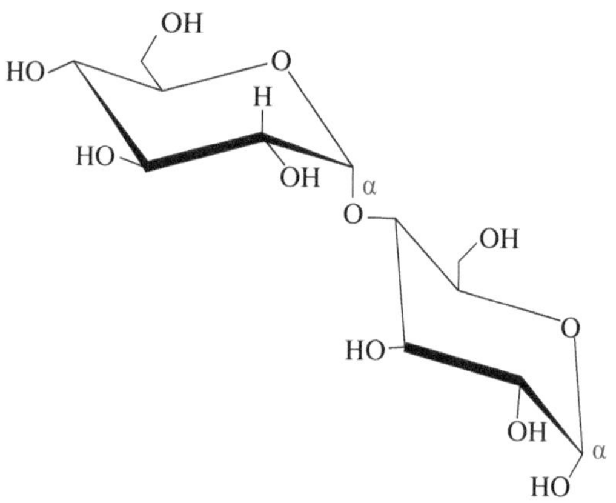

FIGURE 66.4 The structure of the disaccharide maltose. Both glucose molecules are the α–isomers.

Sucrose is common table sugar. It is produced on a massive scale, about 8 million tons per annum in the US alone. Worldwide, about a third is produced from sugar beet and two thirds from sugar cane. In the US, more than half is produced from sugar beet.

in which plane-polarized light is rotated when sucrose is hydrolyzed. The hydrolysis of sucrose is therefore referred to as inversion and the mixture of glucose and fructose that results is called **invert sugar**. Honey bees possess an enzyme called invertase that catalyzes this hydrolysis and are able to process sugar into a mixture of glucose and fructose that is honey.

Extending the linking of glucose molecules beyond the disaccharides produces the polysaccharides. In starch, the glucose molecules are all linked in the α–position. In other words, starch is a polymer of α–glucose. Abundant sources of starch are rice and other grains, corn, and potatoes. The two forms of starch in plants are amylose and amylopectin. Amylose consists of long chains of glucose molecules and amylopectin is similar but is a branched polymer (Figure 66.5). When eaten, the starch is broken

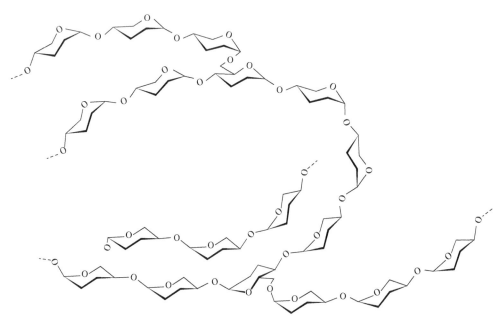

FIGURE 66.5 The segment of the glucose polymer amylopectin in starch. Branching occurs at position 6 on some glucose molecules.

down by enzymes into glucose molecules which are then metabolized to provide energy. Animals have the ability to store glucose in tissue in the form of glycogen—so that it is readily available when energy is required. Glycogen has a structure very similar to amylopectin. If excess starch is eaten, then the body converts the excess starch into fat.

Cellulose is a very regular polymer of β–glucose (Figure 66.6). The number of glucose molecules in the polymer may be as high as 3000. Animals lack the enzymes necessary to break down the β–links between the glucose molecules in cellulose and the glucose is therefore inaccessible. There are, however, bacteria in the stomachs of cows, sheep, and goats that are able to break the link so that humans and other animals can obtain the energy secondhand. Cellulose is the most abundant polysaccharide in the environment. Cellulose fibers consist of bundles of the polymeric glucose chains and the fibers have remarkable strength. Hydrogen bonding between the polymer chains holds them together and provides the structural integrity necessary in trees and plants.

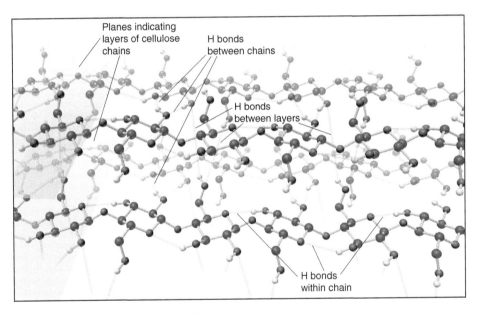

FIGURE 66.6   **The structure of cellulose.**

EXAMPLE 66.1   STRUCTURES OF DISACCHARIDES

The disaccharide lactose, found in milk, is made from β–galactose and α– or β–glucose. Using Figure 66.3 as a guide, draw the cyclic structure of β–galactose. Then, using Figure 66.4 as a guide, draw the structure of the disaccharide lactose.

UNDERSTAND THE QUESTION

Disaccharides are made from two monosaccharides. The link between the two may be α– or β–. These labels indicate the orientation of the —OH group on the carbon atom 1 adjacent to the —O— in the hexose ring. The —OH is directed down in the α–orientation and up in the β–orientation.

PLAN THE SOLUTION

Examine Figure 66.3 and determine how the galactose molecule differs from the glucose molecule. Then draw the cyclic structure. There are two possible isomers, α– or β–. The β–isomer is the one in which we are interested. Then draw the glucose molecule and connect it via carbon atom 4 to the β–galactose.

SOLVE THE PROBLEM

Galactose differs from glucose at the carbon 4 position. The —H and —OH groups are reversed. The β–isomers of the two molecules are:

β–galactose   β–glucose

The structure of the disaccharide β–lactose is therefore:

The glucose is the α–isomer in α–lactose.

PROBLEM 66.1A

Gulose is an isomer of glucose:
Draw the cyclic structure of the β–isomer and then draw the structure of the disaccharide derived from two molecules of β–gulose.

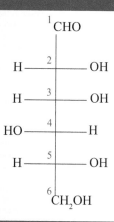

PROBLEM 66.1B

Mannose is an isomer of glucose:
Draw the cyclic structures of both α–mannose and β–mannose.

66.2 Proteins

Proteins are made from α–amino acids and are major components of all living cells. They play a variety of critical roles in the biochemical reactions taking place all the time in humans and other animals. Some, called enzymes, function as catalysts for the reactions that manufacture the complex molecules that are necessary to maintain life. Others act as the structural components of muscles, tendons, and other tissue. Some proteins transport molecules, such as oxygen, to places where they are needed, and others act as biochemical messengers to regulate reactions.

Proteins are polymers of α–amino acids; they are polyamides. The links between the amino acids are amide links the same as those in nylon and Kevlar. In proteins the links are usually referred to **peptide links** and the polymers are called **polypeptides**. Hydrolysis of proteins yields the individual α–amino acids from which they are made. There are 20 common naturally-occurring amino acids (Table 66.1) and all have the basic structure R–CH(NH$_2$)–CO$_2$H in common; they differ only in the identity of the R group. Amino acids can be represented by a three letter abbreviation. For example, glycine is denoted by Gly and alanine is denoted by Ala. At neutral pH, the amino acids exist predominantly as zwitterions, in which the –NH$_2$ group is protonated

Proteins are polypeptides of biological significance.

A polypeptide may or may not be a protein.

TABLE 66.1 The 20 naturally occurring amino acids.

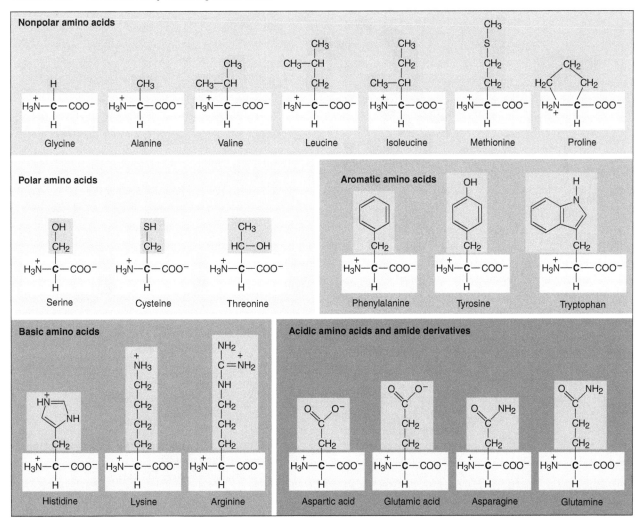

($—NH_3^+$) and the carboxylic acid group loses its hydrogen ion ($—CO_2^-$). However, for convenience, the amino acids are often written in the nonionic form.

The essential amino acids, which must be included in a healthy diet, are:

valine	leucine
isoleucine	phenylalanine
threonine	methionine
cysteine	tryptophan
lysine	histidine

Although some of the amino acids can be synthesized within the human body, some cannot. Those that cannot be made must be ingested and are therefore essential ingredients of our diet.

Except in the simplest amino acid, glycine, the α–carbon atom of the amino acid is chiral. All the amino acids that occur in proteins are the L enantiomers. This consistency in the chirality of the amino acids permits the chain of amino acids to form a helical structure, called an α–helix (Figure 66.7). The chain is held in the coiled configuration by hydrogen bonds between the N—H and C═O groups on adjacent amino acids.

The helical structure of some proteins was demonstrated using x-ray crystallography by Linus Pauling and Robert Corey.

Whenever possible, the chains of amino acids making up a polypeptide are drawn so that the amino group is on the left and the carboxylic acid group is on the right. The individual amino acids are named successively from left to right, changing the ending of the names for all the amino acids except the last from –ine, or other ending, to –yl. For example, the artificial sweetener aspartame is the methyl ester of a dipeptide (Figure 66.8). The two amino acids are aspartic acid and phenylalanine and so the name of the dipeptide is L–aspartyl–L–phenylalanine methyl ester. The L designation is often omitted because all amino acids in proteins are L. A shorthand representation of the aspartame molecule is $H_2N—Asp—Phe—CO_2CH_3$.

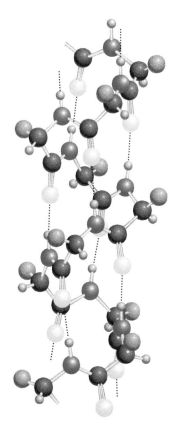

FIGURE 66.7 The α-helix structure of proteins.
Hydrogen bonding occurs between amino acids in the coiled chain.

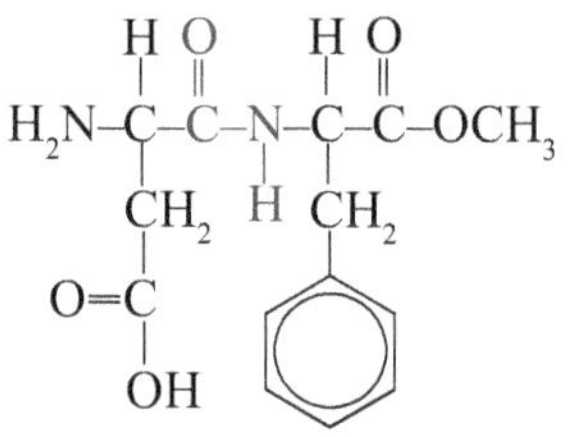

FIGURE 66.8 Aspartame, the artificial sweetener known as Nutrasweet™.
The peptide link is shown in blue.

EXAMPLE 66.2   STRUCTURES OF POLYPEPTIDES

Draw the structure of the tripeptide lysylalanylglycine and derive its shorthand notation.

UNDERSTAND THE QUESTION

A polypeptide is formed when the amino group of one amino acid condenses with the carboxylic acid group of another. The polypeptide is named from the end with the free amino group, usually drawn on the left.

PLAN THE SOLUTION

Identify the amino acids involved in the polypeptide. Draw them with the amino groups on the left and then combine them with the elimination of water to form the peptide (amide) links.

SOLVE THE PROBLEM

The amino acids are lysine, alanine, and glycine:

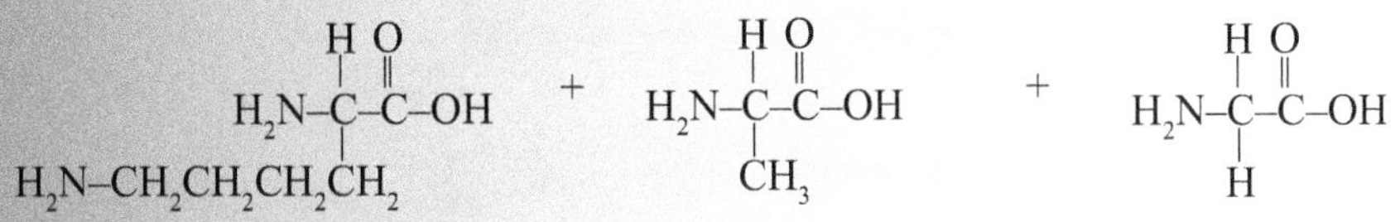

$$H_2N-\overset{\displaystyle \overset{H}{|}}{\underset{\displaystyle \underset{H_2N-CH_2CH_2CH_2CH_2}{|}}{C}}-\overset{\displaystyle \overset{O}{\|}}{C}-OH \quad + \quad H_2N-\overset{\displaystyle \overset{H}{|}}{\underset{\displaystyle \underset{CH_3}{|}}{C}}-\overset{\displaystyle \overset{O}{\|}}{C}-OH \quad + \quad H_2N-\overset{\displaystyle \overset{H}{|}}{\underset{\displaystyle \underset{H}{|}}{C}}-\overset{\displaystyle \overset{O}{\|}}{C}-OH$$

Condensation yields the tripeptide:

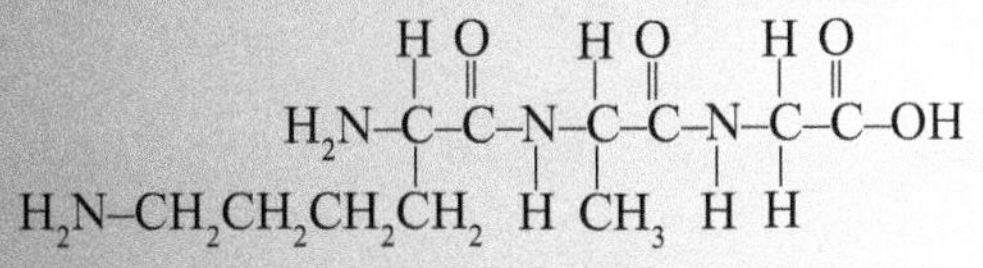

$$H_2N-\overset{\overset{H}{|}}{\underset{\underset{H_2N-CH_2CH_2CH_2CH_2}{|}}{C}}-\overset{\overset{O}{\|}}{C}-\underset{\underset{H}{|}}{N}-\overset{\overset{H}{|}}{\underset{\underset{CH_3}{|}}{C}}-\overset{\overset{O}{\|}}{C}-\underset{\underset{H}{|}}{N}-\overset{\overset{H}{|}}{\underset{\underset{H}{|}}{C}}-\overset{\overset{O}{\|}}{C}-OH$$

The abbreviated name for the tripeptide is Lys-Ala-Gly. The amino group is assumed to be on the left. Sometimes the terminal amino and carboxylic acid groups are added to the sequence: H_2N-Lys-Ala-Gly-CO_2H.

PROBLEM 66.2A

Identify the amino acids in the polypeptide illustrated on the right and write the abbreviated representation:

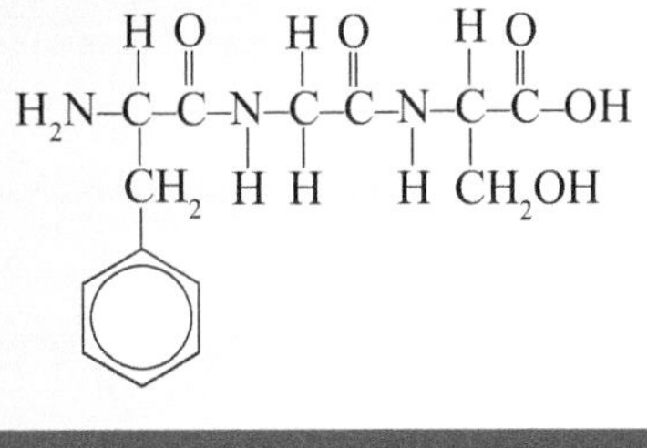

PROBLEM 66.2B

Identify the amino acids in the dipeptide shown and write the abbreviated representation. Draw a circle around the peptide link in this molecule.

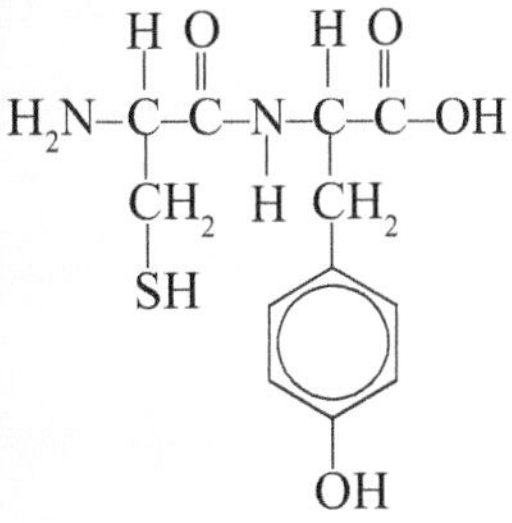

The sequence of amino acids in a polypeptide is called the **primary structure** of the protein. With twenty different amino acids possible in the sequence, the number of possible arrangements is astronomical. In a chain of just four amino acids, there are over 100,000 possible arrangements and typical proteins contain hundreds of amino acids.

The way in which the polypeptide chain is folded or twisted is referred to as the **secondary structure**. Hydrogen bonding between the N—H and C=O groups on adjacent amino acids holds the chain in a particular configuration. The α–helix illustrated in Figure 66.7 is an example of a secondary structure. The diameter of the helix allows the C=O and N—H groups on the amino acids to line up at an appropriate distance for the hydrogen bonding. There are 3.6 amino acids per turn of the helix. Another common configuration for proteins is a β–pleated sheet structure (Figure 66.9). In this secondary structure, hydrogen bonding occurs between different segments of the chain.

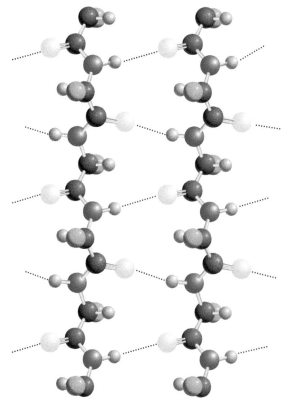

FIGURE 66.9   The β–pleated sheet structure of proteins.
Hydrogen bonding occurs between adjacent segments of the polypeptide chain.

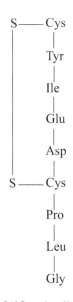

FIGURE 66.10   The disulfide bridge between the cysteine amino acids of the oxytocin polypeptide. The identities of the R groups of the individual amino acids are indicated in the abbreviated primary structure shown.

The overall three-dimensional shape of a protein is called its **tertiary structure**. Other groups on the amino acids play a part in determining the tertiary structure. For example, a —CO_2^- group on one amino acid will attract an —NH_3^+ group on another amino acid. Such an interaction is called a **salt link**. Another interesting interaction occurs between the –SH groups on cysteine amino acids. The two —SH groups react to form a **disulfide bridge**, cross-linking the polypeptide chains. An example of this occurs in the protein oxytocin, which is a hormone that regulates muscle contraction (Figure 66.10).

Hair is composed of a strong fibrous protein called keratin, in which the predominant secondary structure is the α–helix. The tertiary structure involves disulfide bridges between the polypeptide chains. When hair is "permed", a reducing solution (such as thioglycolic acid or glycerol monothioglycolate) is added to break the disulfide bridges. The hair is then curled in the desired fashion and another solution (a mild oxidizing agent such as hydrogen peroxide) is added to reform the disulfide bridges in new positions. The curling tools are then removed leaving the hair with a permanent wave.

The most important interaction, particularly in the aqueous medium of the human body, is hydrogen bonding. Hydrogen bonding not only occurs between the C=O and N—H groups of the peptide links as described earlier, but also between other groups such as —OH and —NH₂ on the amino acids, and between the protein and water. The three-dimensional folding of the protein is organized so that hydrophilic groups are on the outside where they interact with water, and the hydrophobic groups lie on the inside of the structure where they interact through dispersion forces. The four types of interaction important in determining the tertiary structure of proteins are illustrated in Figure 66.11.

Finally, the protein may have a **quaternary structure**. This describes the way in which polypeptide units fit together. Hemoglobin has a quaternary structure composed of four units, one of which is shown in Figure 66.12. Hemoglobin's primary function is to bind oxygen and transport it to where it is needed. Hemoglobin has to the capacity to carry between one and four O_2 molecules and the four units cooperate in binding

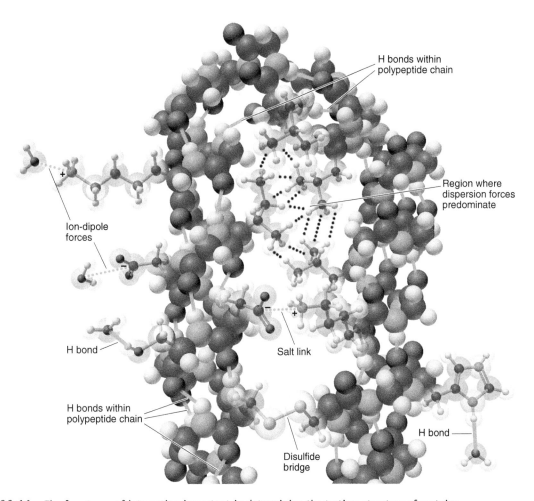

FIGURE 66.11   The four types of interaction important in determining the tertiary structure of proteins.

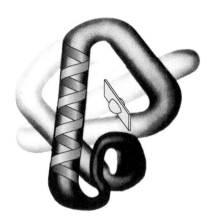

Tertiary structure

FIGURE 66.12   One of the four polypeptide units that makes up the hemoglobin protein.
The α–helices are shown in gray and the heme group is shown in blue.

the oxygen. In the presence of high levels of oxygen, when one unit binds an oxygen molecule, small changes in the conformation of that unit make it easier for the other units to add their oxygen molecules. Equally important, the units cooperate in releasing the oxygen. When oxygen levels are low, the affinity for oxygen drops disproportionately as oxygen is released.

66.3   Nucleic Acids

The ability of biological organisms to reproduce themselves is fascinating. The information necessary for this self-reproduction is stored and transmitted by huge molecules called **nucleic acids**. The organism's genetic information is stored by molecules of deoxyribonucleic acid (**DNA**) found primarily within the nucleus of the cell. The molecules responsible for the transmission of the genetic information are ribonucleic acids (**RNA**). These molecules are smaller and more abundant than DNA and reside mostly outside the nucleus within the cell cytoplasm.

Nucleic acids are polymers of **nucleotides** and each nucleotide is made up of three parts: a nitrogen base, a pentose carbohydrate (sugar), and a phosphate link. The nitrogen bases found in DNA are adenine, guanine, thymine, and cytosine. Thymine is found only in DNA; a fifth nitrogen base, uracil, very similar in structure to thymine, is found only in RNA (Figure 66.13). Adenine and guanine belong to a class of organic molecules called purines and thymine, cytosine, and uracil belong to a class of compounds called pyrimidines.

The sugar component of DNA is deoxyribose, whereas the sugar component of RNA is ribose itself. The difference between the two is an —H in place of an —OH at carbon atom 2′ in the deoxyribose (Figure 66.14).

When adenine condenses with ribose, the product is called adenosine. The general term for the condensation product of one of the five bases with the sugar molecule

The prime is added to the 2′ to indicate a position on the ribose ring and not on the ring of the nitrogen base.

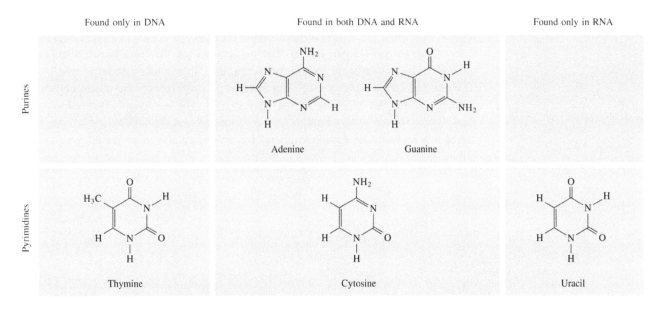

FIGURE 66.13 **The five bases of DNA and RNA.**
Uracil occurs only in RNA and Thymine occurs only in DNA; the molecules differ by one methyl group.

is **nucleoside**. When the nucleoside is phosphorylated to produce the phosphate ester, the product is the nucleotide, the monomer from which the nucleic acids DNA and RNA are made. In the case of the nucleoside made from the adenine base and deoxyribose, the product is the nucleotide adenosine monophosphate (AMP) (Figure 66.15).

The names of the nucleosides are derived as follows:

adenine	adenosine
guanine	guanosine
cytosine	cytidine
thymine	thymidine
uracil	uridine

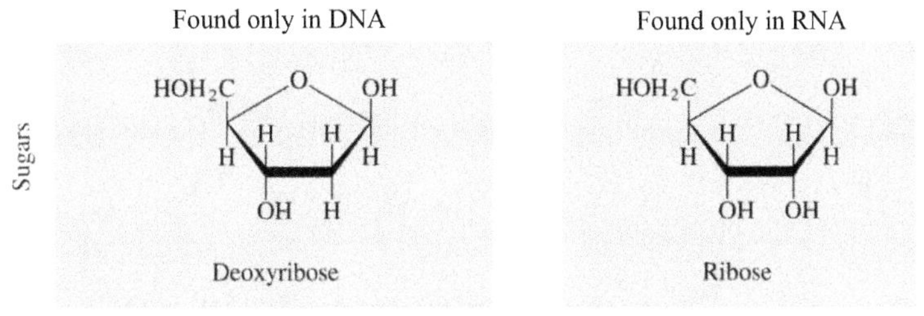

FIGURE 66.14 Ribose, the sugar component of RNA and deoxyribose, the sugar component of DNA.

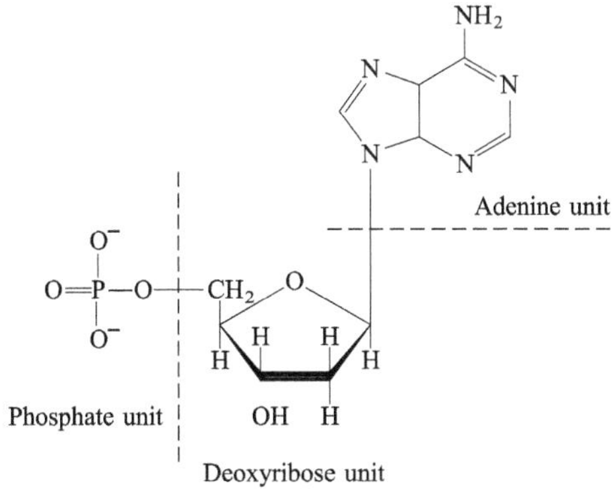

FIGURE 66.15 The three components of the nucleotide adenosine monophosphate.

Alexander Todd (1907–1997) was awarded the 1957 Nobel Prize in Chemistry for the discovery of the basic structure of the polynucleotide chain.

The equal numbers of complementary bases in DNA was discovered by Erwin Chargaff (1905–2002) and are known as Chargaff's Rules.

The nucleotides are linked when the phosphate group on one nucleotide condenses with the 3′–OH group on the sugar molecule of another nucleotide to form a phosphate diester (Figure 66.16). The nucleotides are therefore joined together in nucleic acids by phosphate groups connecting the 5′ carbon of one sugar ring to the 3′ carbon of the next sugar ring. The alternating sugar–phosphate–sugar–phosphate sequence forms the backbone of the nucleic acid. The actual polymerization reaction involves the reaction of nucleoside–5′–triphosphates. Formation of the ester link releases a diphosphate (pyrophosphate) ion and is catalyzed by an enzyme called polymerase.

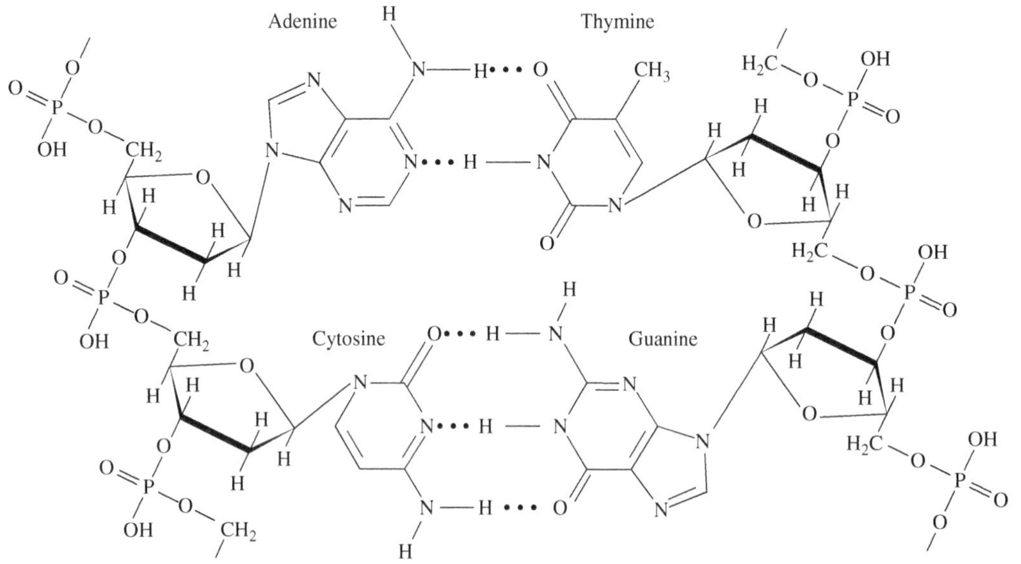

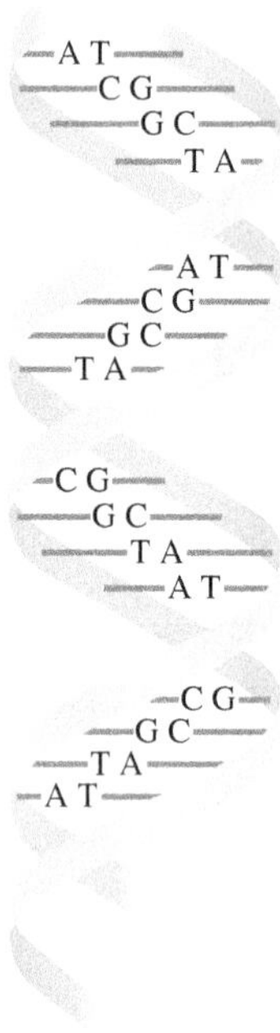

FIGURE 66.16 The linking of the phosphate and sugar groups to form the backbone of the nucleic acids. This example shows just four nucleotides. In human DNA, the number is in the millions.

It is the remarkable ability of the nucleic acids to replicate and pass on genetic information in the synthesis of identical molecules that both puzzled and intrigued scientists for many years. The answer was proposed by James Watson and Francis Crick in 1953. It was known that DNA contains equal numbers of adenine and thymine, and equal numbers of guanine and cytosine. Crick and Watson proposed that these bases were paired by strong hydrogen bonding (Figure 66.17).

Francis Crick, James Watson, and Maurice Wilkins were awarded the 1962 Nobel Prize in Medicine and Physiology for this work.

Using x–ray crystallographic data obtained by Maurice Wilkins and Rosalind Franklin, Watson and Crick proposed that DNA consists of two DNA chains wound together in a double helix, such that bases on each chain were complementary, that is, adenine was always matched with thymine, and cytosine was always matched with guanine (Figure 66.18). Notice how a purine is always matched with a pyrimidine.

Crick and Watson suggested that the double helix might provide a mechanism for replication. When the two strands of DNA are unwound, each strand provides a

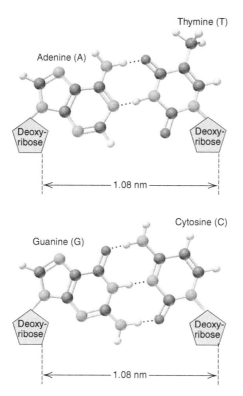

FIGURE 66.17 **Hydrogen bonding between complementary base pairs.**
The distance between the links to the sugar–phosphate backbone is exactly the same for both pairs (108 nm).

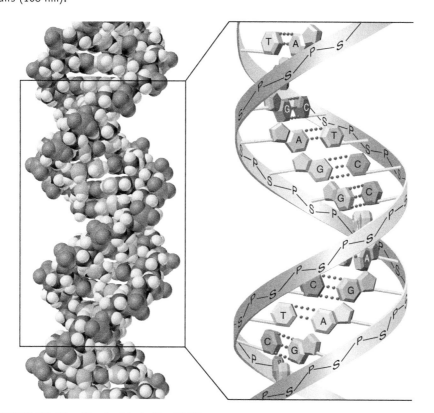

FIGURE 66.18 **The double helix of DNA.**
The nucleotides are linked along the sugar–phosphate backbone. The two strands are held together by hydrogen bonding between the base pairs.

template for the synthesis of a complementary chain. This replication process is cata-lyzed by enzymes and occurs rapidly (Figure 66.19).

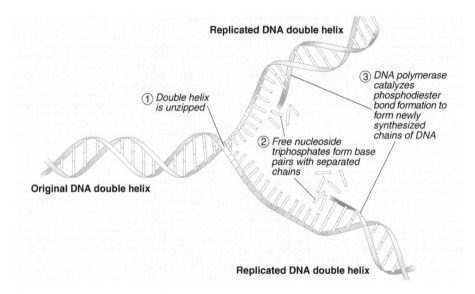

Replicated DNA double helix

① *Double helix is unzipped*

③ *DNA polymerase catalyzes phosphodiester bond formation to form newly synthesized chains of DNA*

② *Free nucleoside triphosphates form base pairs with separated chains*

Original DNA double helix

Replicated DNA double helix

FIGURE 66.19   DNA replication.
As the DNA double helix unwinds, complementary nucleotides link to produce a new partner for each strand. Each new DNA molecule contains one old strand and one new strand and each is identical to the original.

The entire sequence of 3 billion base pairs in the human genome has now been determined. The nucleus of a human cell contains 46 chromosomes, each of which is a DNA molecule. There are approximately 23,000 protein-coding genes in the human genome.

The matching of complementary base pairs also provides the mechanism by which proteins are synthesized. In the first step of the synthesis, referred to as **tran-scription**, a portion of the DNA helix unwinds and the sequence of nucleotides in this segment, called a **gene**, is copied as a complementary sequence to a special molecule of RNA, called **messenger RNA**, or mRNA (Figure 66.20). The matching of the complementary bases is the same as that in the replication of DNA except that uracil is used in place of thymine in the mRNA. Each mRNA molecule contains all the infor-mation necessary to synthesize a particular protein. The mRNA carries the code from the nucleus of the cell (where the DNA is) to the site of protein synthesis at structures called ribosomes.

At the ribosomes, the next step is **translation**. The code, represented by the sequence of bases in the mRNA, is deciphered. Each sequence of three bases on the mRNA, called a **codon**, corresponds to a different amino acid. There are four pos-sible bases, grouped in threes, so there are 4^3, or 64, possible codes (Table 66.2). This is more than enough for the 20 amino acids used in protein synthesis, so some amino acids match more than one codon. For example, the four codes G—G—A, G—G—C, G—G—U, and G—G—G all match the amino acid glycine. Notice how it is the first two letters of the codon that are all the same; this is usually the case when multiple codons match one amino acid. Three of the codons are used to instruct the protein syn-thesis to stop (they have no corresponding amino acid).

The genetic code was deciphered in 1966 by Holley, Khorana, and Nirenberg and they were awarded the 1968 Nobel Prize in Medicine and Physiology.

The amino acids used in the protein synthesis are carried to the site of manufac-ture by other RNA molecules called **transfer RNA**, or tRNA. Each tRNA molecule is a small RNA chain, about 80 nucleotides long, that has the proper sequence of three

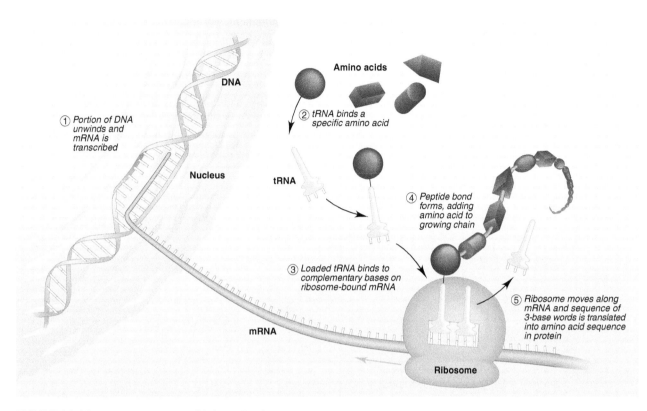

FIGURE 66.20   The transcription of information from DNA to messenger RNA.

TABLE 66.2   A chart of the 64 possible codons and the corresponding amino acids.

First Letter	Second Letter				Third Letter
	U	**C**	**A**	**G**	
U	phenylalanine	serine	tyrosine	cysteine	U
					C
			termination	*termination*	A
				tryptophan	G
C	leucine	proline	histidine	arginine	U
					C
			glutamine		A
					G
A	isoleucine	threonine	asparagine	serine	U
					C
			lysine	arginine	A
	methionine				G
G	valine	alanine	aspartic acid	glycine	U
					C
			glutamic acid		A
					G

It is also the first two letters of the anticodon on tRNA that are more important.

bases, called an **anticodon**, to complement the codon on the mRNA. A particular tRNA molecule always carries the same amino acid. For example, if the tRNA molecule possesses the anticodon C–A–U, it carries the amino acid valine. The sequence C–A–U is the anticodon of G–U–A, which is one of four possible codons for valine.

The addition of amino acids in the synthesis of a protein proceeds at several amino acids per second as the mRNA moves through the ribosome. The appropriate amino acids are added one by one in the protein manufacture, as prescribed by the codons of the mRNA, until the end of the mRNA is reached (Figure 66.21).

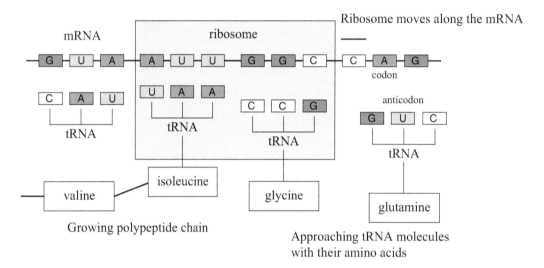

FIGURE 66.21   Protein synthesis directed by a strand of mRNA.

EXAMPLE 66.3   PROTEIN SYNTHESIS

The amino acid sequence in the dipeptide from which aspartame is made is Asp—Phe. One sequence of bases in an mRNA molecule that would direct the synthesis of this dipeptide, ending with a termination codon, is

G—A—C—U—U—U—U—G—A

a. What was the sequence of bases on the DNA that produced this mRNA?

b. What are the anticodons on the two tRNA molecules used to supply the amino acids for the synthesis?

UNDERSTAND THE QUESTION

The DNA provides the template for the mRNA. The sequence of bases on the mRNA is complementary to the sequence on the DNA. The tRNA molecules possess anticodons for the appropriate amino acid. The anticodon is complementary to the codon on the mRNA. Therefore the anticodon of the tRNA matches the sequence of three bases on the DNA, except that uracil is used in place of thymine.

PLAN THE SOLUTION

Split the sequence of bases of the mRNA into the separate codons (groups of three). Identify the complementary sequence that must have been present on the DNA. Then write the anticodons carried by the two tRNA molecules.

SOLVE THE PROBLEM

The three codons of the mRNA are: GAC—UUU—UGA

GAC is the codon for the amino acid aspartic acid.

UUU is the codon for the amino acid phenylalanine.

UGA is a termination codon.

The corresponding complementary sequence is: C—T—G—A—A—A—A—C—T

This is the sequence on the DNA that provided the template for the mRNA.

The two tRNA molecules that carry the amino acids to the site of protein synthesis directed by the mRNA must possess the anticodons:

CUG for aspartate

AAA for phenylalanine

PROBLEM 66.3A

In Problem 66.2 the amino acids in the tripeptide illustrated on the right were identified. Determine a possible sequence of bases on the nucleotides of the mRNA that would direct the synthesis of this tripeptide.

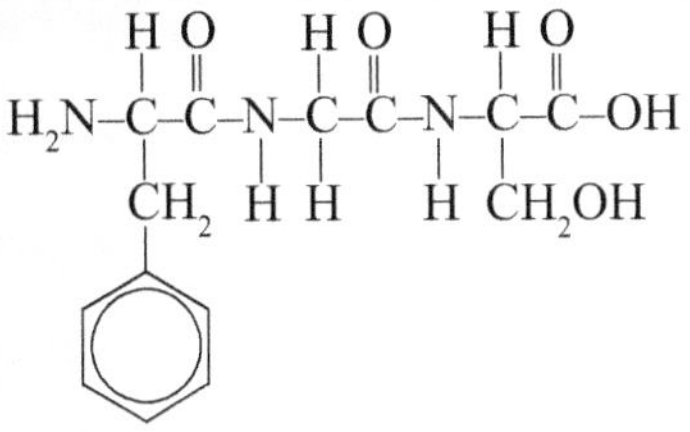

PROBLEM 66.3B

A segment of DNA has the following sequence of nucleotides:

A–A–G–C–A–G–G–T–C–G–T–G

Write the sequence of bases in the mRNA generated when this segment is read and then identify the sequence of four amino acids in the polypeptide synthesized as a result.

66.4   Energy

The biochemical processes occurring all the time within the human body require energy. The average requirement is between 9,000 and 12,000 kJ per day. This energy is derived from food. Food contains many chemicals required for the maintenance of life within the human body—essential minerals and vitamins, proteins, fats and carbohydrates among them. During metabolism, much of the protein, and the fats, and carbohydrates are converted to glucose. It is the combustion of the glucose that provides energy. The products are carbon dioxide and water.

The oxidation of glucose is a complex sequence of steps. The free energy change $\Delta G°$ for the complete oxidation of one mole of glucose is –2880 kJ. Much of the energy produced by this oxidation is stored in molecules such as adenosine triphosphate (ATP). The energy can then be transported by the ATP to sites where the energy is needed. The free energy change for the conversion of ATP to adenosine diphosphate (ADP) is –30.5 kJ. This favorable free energy change means that when the hydrolysis of ATP is coupled with a biochemical process that is not by itself spontaneous, the

You will learn more about the way in which glucose is oxidized in courses in biochemistry.

overall process is spontaneous. For example, energy is required in the synthesis of proteins and the process is powered by the ATP–ADP conversion.

When an ATP molecule is hydrolyzed, a bond between two phosphate groups is broken. This requires energy. However, new bonds are formed between the water participating in the hydrolysis and the two fragments of the hydrolysis and this releases energy. The overall free energy change $\Delta G°$ when ATP is converted to ADP is negative as noted above.

Review Questions

1. Review the carbohydrates and define the terms monosaccharide, disaccharide, and polysaccharide. What is the difference between the two polysaccharides starch and cellulose?

2. What commonly makes an organic compound chiral?

3. What is a protein? Discuss in terms of the primary, secondary, tertiary, and quarternary structure of the protein.

4. What are nucleic acids? Describe their structure and function. Describe the processes of transcription and translation in the transmission of genetic information.

Solutions to Problems

PROBLEM 66.1A

Gulose differs from glucose at positions 3 and 4.

The cyclic structure, derived from that of glucose is therefore:

The structure of the disaccharide derived from two molecules of α–gulose is:

PROBLEM 66.2A

phenylalanine ⟩ glycine ⟩ serine

Abbreviation: Phe–Gly–Ser

PROBLEM 66.3A

Possible codons are: UUU–GGG–UCU

Answers to Review Questions

1. Carbohydrates have the empirical formulas $C_x(H_2O)_y$. The simplest carbohydrates are monosaccharides and, of these, the most important are those containing five carbon atoms (e.g. ribose) or six carbon atoms (e.g. glucose). The glucose molecule is typical; it exists predominantly as a six-membered ring in which one of the atoms in the ring is an oxygen atom. The five carbon atoms of the ring each have a hydrogen atom attached and either a —OH group or a –CH$_2$OH group. Glucose exists as two isomers: α–glucose, in which the —OH group at carbon atom 1 points downward in an axial position, and β–glucose, in which the —OH group points upward in an equatorial position.

   The condensation of two monosaccharides produces a disaccharide with the elimination of a water molecule. An example is sucrose—a disaccharide of glucose and fructose. A polymer of a monosaccharide is called a polysaccharide. There are two main types of polysaccharides: starch, in which the glucose molecules are all linked in the α–position, and cellulose, in which the glucose molecules are all linked in the β–position.

2. The usual reason for chirality in organic compounds is the presence of an asymmetric carbon atom—a carbon atom with four different groups attached in a tetrahedral arrangement. If a molecule contains an asymmetric carbon atom, then it can exist as two stereoisomers—nonsuperimposable mirror images called enantiomers.

3. As mentioned earlier in this unit, proteins perform many functions in the life of an organism. The primary structure of a protein is the sequence of amino acids that makes up the polypeptide chain. The secondary structure is the shape of the chain influenced by hydrogen bonding between the —NH and C=O groups of neighboring amino acids. The tertiary structure is the protein's overall three-dimensional shape influenced by the interaction of different groups present on different amino acids in the chain. The quarternary structure indicates how some proteins cluster to collaborate in their function.

4. The two types of nucleic acids, ribonucleic acids (RNA) and deoxyribonucleic acids (DNA), are polymers of nucleotides. Nucleotides consist of three parts, a sugar, a phosphate group, and a purine or pyrimidine nitrogen base. DNA is a double helix of two strands; each strand is a polymer of nucleotides linked together through the sugar phosphate backbone. The bases on the two strands complement one another and are held together by hydrogen bonding. A section of a DNA strand is called a gene; the gene contains the basic genetic information for the construction of proteins.

   Information is transcribed from the DNA by messenger RNA molecules. The messenger RNA molecules carry the information to the sites of protein synthesis. The code on the mRNA is translated by transfer RNA molecules that carry the appropriate amino acids in sequence for the protein synthesis. An anticodon on the tRNA complements the codon of three bases on the mRNA. Each codon translates to a specific amino acid or to a specific instruction to start or stop the polypeptide synthesis.

End-of-Unit Problems

1. How do the starch amylose and cellulose differ in their structure?

2. Describe how the conformation of the link in a disaccharide depends upon whether the monosaccharide is the α–isomer or the β–isomer.

3. Explain why there are 8 isomers of glucose.

4. Explain why α–glucose and β–glucose cannot be separated in solution.

5. Describe the essential structure of an α–amino acid.

6. Describe the two kinds of nucleic acids. What are the differences between them?

7. By comparing the linear form to that of glucose, draw the cyclic structures of the α–isomer and the β–isomer of D–idose:

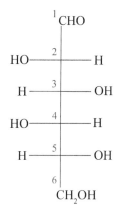

8. By comparing the linear form to that of glucose, draw the cyclic structures of the α–isomer and the β–isomer of D–talose:

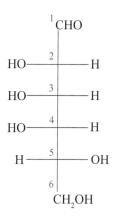

9. What side chains are present on the amino acids:
   a. serine
   b. glycine
   c. cysteine

10. What side chains are present on the amino acids:
    a. valine
    b. alanine
    c. lysine

11. At neutral pH, α–amino acids exist in solution as zwitterions. Draw the zwitterions for the amino acids glycine and valine.

12. Some α–amino acids have side chains that are acidic and some have side chains that are basic. Write the structures of one example of each.

13. Draw the fragment of a polypeptide chain that has the abbreviation Trp—Cys—His.

14. Draw the fragment of a polypeptide chain that has the abbreviation Thr—Tyr—Asn.

15. Identify the amino acids in the polypeptide fragment illustrated on the right and write the abbreviated representation.

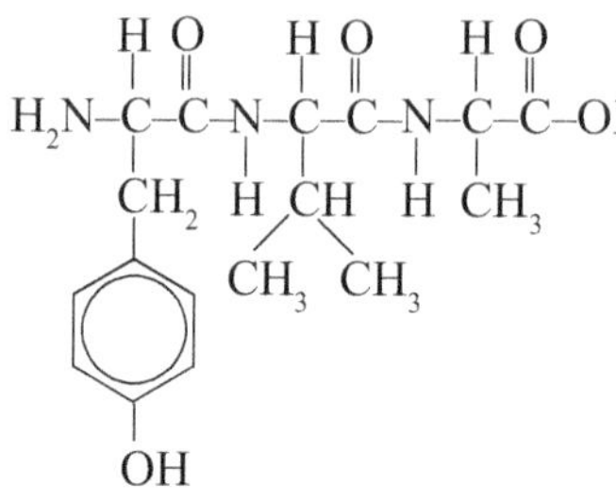

16. Identify the amino acids in the polypeptide fragment illustrated below and write the abbreviated representation.

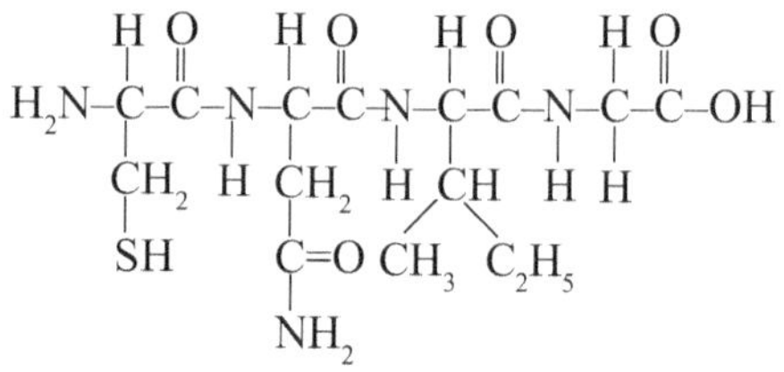

17. How many hydrogen bonds are there between the base pair guanine and cytosine? And how many are there between adenine and thymine? Which would you expect to be the stronger interaction?

18. When a sample of DNA is analyzed, the quantity of adenine present is found to equal the quantity of thymine present. Likewise, the amount of guanine equals the amount of cytosine. However, the relative amounts of adenine and guanine vary. Discuss the significance of these observations.

19. Describe the difference between the base uracil used in RNA and the base thymine used in DNA.

20. Describe the difference between the ribose in RNA and the deoxyribose in DNA.

21. The sequence of bases on one strand of DNA is G—G—T—A—C—T—G—C.

    a. What is the sequence along the complementary strand of the DNA?

    b. What is the sequence of bases in the mRNA molecule transcribed from this segment of DNA?

22. The sequence of bases on one strand of DNA is A—C—T—G—G—T—T—A.

    a. What is the sequence along the complementary strand of the DNA?

    b. What is the sequence of bases in the mRNA molecule transcribed from this segment of DNA?

23. If the sequence of bases along a segment of mRNA is C—C—U—A—G—U—C, what was the sequence of bases on the DNA from which it was transcribed?

24. If the sequence of bases along a segment of mRNA is U—A—C—A—U—C—G, what was the sequence of bases on the DNA from which it was transcribed?

25. a What is the anticodon on the tRNA molecule that complements the codon U—C—U on mRNA?

    b. Which amino acid is carried by the tRNA molecule with this anticodon?

26. a. What is the anticodon on the tRNA molecule that complements the codon A—A—A on mRNA?

    b. Which amino acid is carried by the tRNA molecule with this anticodon?

    Write a possible nucleotide sequence on mRNA that would translate to the amino acid sequence: His—Asp—Lys—Glu—Pro.

    Write a possible nucleotide sequence on mRNA that would translate to the amino acid sequence: Ala—Val—Met—Thr—Ile.

INDEX

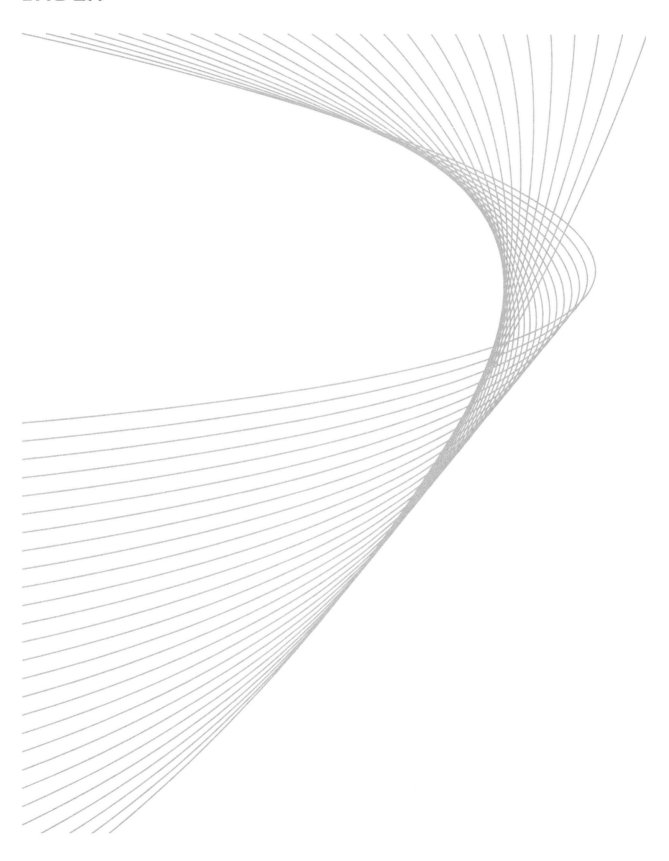